CUMULATIVE PROBABILITIES FOR THE STANDARD NORMAL DISTRIBUTION

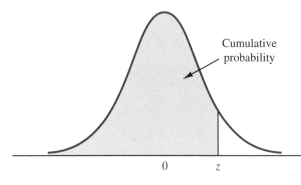

Cumulative probability

Entries in the table give the area under the curve to the left of the z value. For example, for z = 1.25, the cumulative probability is .8944.

z	.00	.01	.02	.03	.04	.05	.06	.07	.08	.09
.0	.5000	.5040	.5080	.5120	.5160	.5199	.5239	.5279	.5319	.5359
.1	.5398	.5438	.5478	.5517	.5557	.5596	.5636	.5675	.5714	.5753
.2	.5793	.5832	.5871	.5910	.5948	.5987	.6026	.6064	.6103	.6141
.3	.6179	.6217	.6255	.6293	.6331	.6368	.6406	.6443	.6480	.6517
.4	.6554	.6591	.6628	.6664	.6700	.6736	.6772	.6808	.6844	.6879
.5	.6915	.6950	.6985	.7019	.7054	.7088	.7123	.7157	.7190	.7224
.6	.7257	.7291	.7324	.7357	.7389	.7422	.7454	.7486	.7517	.7549
.7	.7580	.7611	.7642	.7673	.7704	.7734	.7764	.7794	.7823	.7852
.8	.7881	.7910	.7939	.7967	.7995	.8023	.8051	.8078	.8106	.8133
.9	.8159	.8186	.8212	.8238	.8264	.8289	.8315	.8340	.8365	.8389
1.0	.8413	.8438	.8461	.8485	.8508	.8531	.8554	.8577	.8599	.8621
1.1	.8643	.8665	.8686	.8708	.8729	.8749	.8770	.8790	.8810	.8830
1.2	.8849	.8869	.8888	.8907	.8925	.8944	.8962	.8980	.8997	.9015
1.3	.9032	.9049	.9066	.9082	.9099	.9115	.9131	.9147	.9162	.9177
1.4	.9192	.9207	.9222	.9236	.9251	.9265	.9279	.9292	.9306	.9319
1.5	.9332	.9345	.9357	.9370	.9382	.9394	.9406	.9418	.9429	.9441
1.6	.9452	.9463	.9474	.9484	.9495	.9505	.9515	.9525	.9535	.9545
1.7	.9554	.9564	.9573	.9582	.9591	.9599	.9608	.9616	.9625	.9633
1.8	.9641	.9649	.9656	.9664	.9671	.9678	.9686	.9693	.9699	.9706
1.9	.9713	.9719	.9726	.9732	.9738	.9744	.9750	.9756	.9761	.9767
2.0	.9772	.9778	.9783	.9788	.9793	.9798	.9803	.9808	.9812	.9817
2.1	.9821	.9826	.9830	.9834	.9838	.9842	.9846	.9850	.9854	.9857
2.2	.9861	.9864	.9868	.9871	.9875	.9878	.9881	.9884	.9887	.9890
2.3	.9893	.9896	.9898	.9901	.9904	.9906	.9909	.9911	.9913	.9916
2.4	.9918	.9920	.9922	.9925	.9927	.9929	.9931	.9932	.9934	.9936
2.5	.9938	.9940	.9941	.9943	.9945	.9946	.9948	.9949	.9951	.9952
2.6	.9953	.9955	.9956	.9957	.9959	.9960	.9961	.9962	.9963	.9964
2.7	.9965	.9966	.9967	.9968	.9969	.9970	.9971	.9972	.9973	.9974
2.8	.9974	.9975	.9976	.9977	.9977	.9978	.9979	.9979	.9980	.9981
2.9	.9981	.9982	.9982	.9983	.9984	.9984	.9985	.9985	.9986	.9986
3.0	.9987	.9987	.9987	.9988	.9988	.9989	.9989	.9989	.9990	.9990

Statistics for Business & Economics

Selected Chapters

David R. Anderson | Dennis J. Sweeney | Thomas A.
Williams | Jeffrey D. Camm | James J. Cochran

CENGAGE
Learning·

Australia • Brazil • Japan • Korea • Mexico • Singapore • Spain • United Kingdom • United States

CENGAGE
Learning

Statistics for Business & Economics:
Selected Chapters, Custom Edition

Statistics for Business and Economics, 13th Edition
David R. Anderson, Dennis J. Sweeney, Thomas A. Williams
Jeffrey D. Camm, James J. Cochran

© 2017, 2015 Cengage Learning. All rights reserved.

For product information and technology assistance, contact us at
Cengage Learning Customer & Sales Support, 1-800-354-9706
For permission to use material from this text or product,
submit all requests online at **cengage.com/permissions**
Further permissions questions can be emailed to
permissionrequest@cengage.com

This book contains select works from existing Cengage Learning resources and was produced by Cengage Learning Custom Solutions for collegiate use. As such, those adopting and/or contributing to this work are responsible for editorial content accuracy, continuity and completeness.

Compilation © 2017 Cengage Learning
ISBN: 9781337303521

Cengage Learning

20 Channel Center Street
Boston, MA 02210
USA

Cengage Learning is a leading provider of customized learning solutions with office locations around the globe, including Singapore, the United Kingdom, Australia, Mexico, Brazil, and Japan. Locate your local office at:
www.international.cengage.com/region.

Cengage Learning products are represented in Canada by Nelson Education, Ltd.

For your lifelong learning solutions, visit **www.cengage.com/custom.**

Visit our corporate website at **www.cengage.com.**

Brief Contents

CHAPTER 3

Descriptive Statistics: Numerical Measures

CONTENTS

STATISTICS IN PRACTICE:
SMALL FRY DESIGN

STATISTICS *in* PRACTICE

SMALL FRY DESIGN*
SANTA ANA, CALIFORNIA

Founded in 1997, Small Fry Design is a toy and accessory company that designs and imports products for infants. The company's product line includes teddy bears, mobiles, musical toys, rattles, and security blankets and features high-quality soft toy designs with an emphasis on color, texture, and sound. The products are designed in the United States and manufactured in China.

Small Fry Design uses independent representatives to sell the products to infant furnishing retailers, children's accessory and apparel stores, gift shops, upscale department stores, and major catalog companies. Currently, Small Fry Design products are distributed in more than 1000 retail outlets throughout the United States.

Cash flow management is one of the most critical activities in the day-to-day operation of this company. Ensuring sufficient incoming cash to meet both current and ongoing debt obligations can mean the difference between business success and failure. A critical factor in cash flow management is the analysis and control of accounts receivable. By measuring the average age and dollar value of outstanding invoices, management can predict cash availability and monitor changes in the status of accounts receivable. The company set the following goals: The average age for outstanding invoices should not exceed 45 days, and the dollar value of invoices more than 60 days old should not exceed 5% of the dollar value of all accounts receivable.

In a recent summary of accounts receivable status, the following descriptive statistics were provided for the age of outstanding invoices:

Mean	40 days
Median	35 days
Mode	31 days

Small Fry Design uses descriptive statistics to monitor its accounts receivable and incoming cash flow.

Interpretation of these statistics shows that the mean or average age of an invoice is 40 days. The median shows that half of the invoices remain outstanding 35 days or more. The mode of 31 days, the most frequent invoice age, indicates that the most common length of time an invoice is outstanding is 31 days. The statistical summary also showed that only 3% of the dollar value of all accounts receivable was more than 60 days old. Based on the statistical information, management was satisfied that accounts receivable and incoming cash flow were under control.

In this chapter, you will learn how to compute and interpret some of the statistical measures used by Small Fry Design. In addition to the mean, median, and mode, you will learn about other descriptive statistics such as the range, variance, standard deviation, percentiles, and correlation. These numerical measures will assist in the understanding and interpretation of data.

*The authors are indebted to John A. McCarthy, President of Small Fry Design, for providing this Statistics in Practice.

In Chapter 2 we discussed tabular and graphical presentations used to summarize data. In this chapter, we present several numerical measures that provide additional alternatives for summarizing data.

We start by developing numerical summary measures for data sets consisting of a single variable. When a data set contains more than one variable, the same numerical measures can be computed separately for each variable. However, in the two-variable case, we will also develop measures of the relationship between the variables.

Numerical measures of location, dispersion, shape, and association are introduced. If the measures are computed for data from a sample, they are called **sample statistics**. If the measures are computed for data from a population, they are called **population parameters**. In statistical inference, a sample statistic is referred to as the **point estimator** of the corresponding population parameter. In Chapter 7 we will discuss in more detail the process of point estimation.

In the chapter appendixes we show how Minitab and Excel can be used to compute the numerical measures described in the chapter.

3.1   Measures of Location

Mean

The mean is sometimes referred to as the arithmetic mean.

Perhaps the most important measure of location is the **mean**, or average value, for a variable. The mean provides a measure of central location for the data. If the data are for a sample, the mean is denoted by $\bar{x}$; if the data are for a population, the mean is denoted by the Greek letter μ.

In statistical formulas, it is customary to denote the value of variable x for the first observation by x_1, the value of variable x for the second observation by x_2, and so on. In general, the value of variable x for the ith observation is denoted by x_i. For a sample with n observations, the formula for the sample mean is as follows.

The sample mean $\bar{x}$ is a sample statistic.

SAMPLE MEAN

$$\bar{x} = \frac{\Sigma x_i}{n} \qquad (3.1)$$

In the preceding formula, the numerator is the sum of the values of the n observations. That is,

$$\Sigma x_i = x_1 + x_2 + \cdots + x_n$$

The Greek letter Σ is the summation sign.

To illustrate the computation of a sample mean, let us consider the following class size data for a sample of five college classes.

$$46 \quad 54 \quad 42 \quad 46 \quad 32$$

We use the notation x_1, x_2, x_3, x_4, x_5 to represent the number of students in each of the five classes.

$$x_1 = 46 \qquad x_2 = 54 \qquad x_3 = 42 \qquad x_4 = 46 \qquad x_5 = 32$$

Hence, to compute the sample mean, we can write

$$\bar{x} = \frac{\Sigma x_i}{n} = \frac{x_1 + x_2 + x_3 + x_4 + x_5}{5} = \frac{46 + 54 + 42 + 46 + 32}{5} = 44$$

The sample mean class size is 44 students.

To provide a visual perspective of the mean and to show how it can be influenced by extreme values, consider the dot plot for the class size data shown in Figure 3.1. Treating the horizontal axis used to create the dot plot as a long narrow board in which each of the

FIGURE 3.1   THE MEAN AS THE CENTER OF BALANCE FOR THE DOT PLOT OF THE
              CLASSROOM SIZE DATA

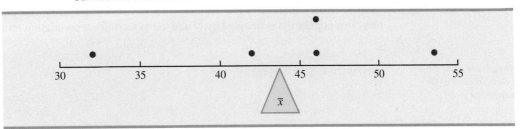

dots has the same fixed weight, the mean is the point at which we would place a fulcrum
or pivot point under the board in order to balance the dot plot. This is the same principle
by which a see-saw on a playground works, the only difference being that the see-saw is
pivoted in the middle so that as one end goes up, the other end goes down. In the dot plot
we are locating the pivot point based upon the location of the dots. Now consider what happens to the balance if we increase the largest value from 54 to 114. We will have to move
the fulcrum under the new dot plot in a positive direction in order to reestablish balance.
To determine how far we would have to shift the fulcrum, we simply compute the sample
mean for the revised class size data.

$$\bar{x} = \frac{\Sigma x_i}{n} = \frac{x_1 + x_2 + x_3 + x_4 + x_5}{5} = \frac{46 + 114 + 42 + 46 + 32}{5} = \frac{280}{5} = 56$$

Thus, the mean for the revised class size data is 56, an increase of 12 students. In other
words, we have to shift the balance point 12 units to the right to establish balance under
the new dot plot.

Another illustration of the computation of a sample mean is given in the following situation. Suppose that a college placement office sent a questionnaire to a sample of business
school graduates requesting information on monthly starting salaries. Table 3.1 shows the
collected data. The mean monthly starting salary for the sample of 12 business college
graduates is computed as

$$\bar{x} = \frac{\Sigma x_i}{n} = \frac{x_1 + x_2 + \cdots + x_{12}}{12}$$

$$= \frac{3850 + 3950 + \cdots + 3880}{12}$$

$$= \frac{47,280}{12} = 3940$$

TABLE 3.1   MONTHLY STARTING SALARIES FOR A SAMPLE OF 12 BUSINESS SCHOOL
             GRADUATES

DATA *file*

2012StartSalary

Graduate	Monthly Starting Salary ($)	Graduate	Monthly Starting Salary ($)
1	3850	7	3890
2	3950	8	4130
3	4050	9	3940
4	3880	10	4325
5	3755	11	3920
6	3710	12	3880

Equation (3.1) shows how the mean is computed for a sample with n observations. The formula for computing the mean of a population remains the same, but we use different notation to indicate that we are working with the entire population. The number of observations in a population is denoted by N and the symbol for a population mean is μ.

The sample mean $\bar{x}$ is a point estimator of the population mean μ.

POPULATION MEAN

$$\mu = \frac{\Sigma x_i}{N}$$

(3.2)

Weighted Mean

In the formulas for the sample mean and population mean, each x_i is given equal importance or weight. For instance, the formula for the sample mean can be written as follows:

$$\bar{x} = \frac{\Sigma x_i}{n} = \frac{1}{n}\left(\Sigma x_i\right) = \frac{1}{n}(x_1 + x_2 + \cdots + x_n) = \frac{1}{n}(x_1) + \frac{1}{n}(x_2) + \cdots + \frac{1}{n}(x_n)$$

This shows that each observation in the sample is given a weight of $1/n$. Although this practice is most common, in some instances the mean is computed by giving each observation a weight that reflects its relative importance. A mean computed in this manner is referred to as a **weighted mean**. The weighted mean is computed as follows:

WEIGHTED MEAN

$$\bar{x} = \frac{\Sigma w_i x_i}{\Sigma w_i}$$

(3.3)

where

$$w_i = \text{weight for observation } i$$

When the data are from a sample, equation (3.3) provides the weighted sample mean. If the data are from a population, μ replaces $\bar{x}$ and equation (3.3) provides the weighted population mean.

As an example of the need for a weighted mean, consider the following sample of five purchases of a raw material over the past three months.

Purchase	Cost per Pound ($)	Number of Pounds
1	3.00	1200
2	3.40	500
3	2.80	2750
4	2.90	1000
5	3.25	800

Note that the cost per pound varies from $2.80 to $3.40, and the quantity purchased varies from 500 to 2750 pounds. Suppose that a manager wanted to know the mean cost per pound of the raw material. Because the quantities ordered vary, we must use the formula for a weighted mean. The five cost-per-pound data values are $x_1 = 3.00$, $x_2 = 3.40$, $x_3 = 2.80$, $x_4 = 2.90$, and $x_5 = 3.25$. The weighted mean cost per pound is found by weighting each cost by its corresponding quantity. For this example, the weights are $w_1 = 1200$, $w_2 = 500$, $w_3 = 2750$, $w_4 = 1000$, and $w_5 = 800$. Based on equation (3.3), the weighted mean is calculated as follows:

$$\bar{x} = \frac{1200(3.00) + 500(3.40) + 2750(2.80) + 1000(2.90) + 800(3.25)}{1200 + 500 + 2750 + 1000 + 800}$$

$$= \frac{18,500}{6250} = 2.96$$

Thus, the weighted mean computation shows that the mean cost per pound for the raw material is $2.96. Note that using equation (3.1) rather than the weighted mean formula in equation (3.3) would provide misleading results. In this case, the sample mean of the five cost-per-pound values is $(3.00 + 3.40 + 2.80 + 2.90 + 3.25)/5 = 15.35/5 = \$3.07$, which overstates the actual mean cost per pound purchased.

The choice of weights for a particular weighted mean computation depends upon the application. An example that is well known to college students is the computation of a grade point average (GPA). In this computation, the data values generally used are 4 for an A grade, 3 for a B grade, 2 for a C grade, 1 for a D grade, and 0 for an F grade. The weights are the number of credit hours earned for each grade. Exercise 16 at the end of this section provides an example of this weighted mean computation. In other weighted mean computations, quantities such as pounds, dollars, or volume are frequently used as weights. In any case, when observations vary in importance, the analyst must choose the weight that best reflects the importance of each observation in the determination of the mean.

Median

The **median** is another measure of central location. The median is the value in the middle when the data are arranged in ascending order (smallest value to largest value). With an odd number of observations, the median is the middle value. An even number of observations has no single middle value. In this case, we follow convention and define the median as the average of the values for the middle two observations. For convenience the definition of the median is restated as follows.

MEDIAN

Arrange the data in ascending order (smallest value to largest value).

(a) For an odd number of observations, the median is the middle value.
(b) For an even number of observations, the median is the average of the two middle values.

Let us apply this definition to compute the median class size for the sample of five college classes. Arranging the data in ascending order provides the following list.

32   42   46   46   54

Because $n = 5$ is odd, the median is the middle value. Thus the median class size is 46 students. Even though this data set contains two observations with values of 46, each observation is treated separately when we arrange the data in ascending order.

Suppose we also compute the median starting salary for the 12 business college graduates in Table 3.1. We first arrange the data in ascending order.

3710 3755 3850 3880 3880 3890 3920 3940 3950 4050 4130 4325

Middle Two Values

Because $n = 12$ is even, we identify the middle two values: 3890 and 3920. The median is the average of these values.

$$\text{Median} = \frac{3890 + 3920}{2} = 3905$$

The procedure we used to compute the median depends upon whether there is an odd number of observations or an even number of observations. Let us now describe a more conceptual and visual approach using the monthly starting salary for the 12 business college graduates. As before, we begin by arranging the data in ascending order.

3710 3755 3850 3880 3880 3890 3920 3940 3950 4050 4130 4325

Once the data are in ascending order, we trim pairs of extreme high and low values until no further pairs of values can be trimmed without completely eliminating all the data. For instance, after trimming the lowest observation (3710) and the highest observation (4325) we obtain a new data set with 10 observations.

3710 3755 3850 3880 3880 3890 3920 3940 3950 4050 4130 4325

We then trim the next lowest remaining value (3755) and the next highest remaining value (4130) to produce a new data set with eight observations.

3710 3755 3850 3880 3880 3890 3920 3940 3950 4050 4130 4325

Continuing this process, we obtain the following results.

3710 3755 3850 3880 3880 3890 3920 3940 3950 4050 4130 4325
3710 3755 3850 3880 3880 3890 3920 3940 3950 4050 4130 4325
3710 3755 3850 3880 3880 3890 3920 3940 3950 4050 4130 4325

At this point no further trimming is possible without eliminating all the data. So, the median is just the average of the remaining two values. When there is an even number of observations, the trimming process will always result in two remaining values, and the average of these values will be the median. When there is an odd number of observations, the trimming process will always result in one final value, and this value will be the median. Thus, this method works whether the number of observations is odd or even.

The median is the measure of location most often reported for annual income and property value data because a few extremely large incomes or property values can inflate the mean. In such cases, the median is the preferred measure of central location.

Although the mean is the more commonly used measure of central location, in some situations the median is preferred. The mean is influenced by extremely small and large data values. For instance, suppose that the highest paid graduate (see Table 3.1) had a starting salary of $10,000 per month (maybe the individual's family owns the company). If we change the highest monthly starting salary in Table 3.1 from $4325 to $10,000 and recompute the mean, the sample mean changes from $3940 to $4413. The median of $3905, however, is unchanged, because $3890 and $3920 are still the middle two values. With the extremely high starting salary included, the median provides a better measure of central location than the mean. We can generalize to say that whenever a data set contains extreme values, the median is often the preferred measure of central location.

Geometric Mean

The **geometric mean** is a measure of location that is calculated by finding the nth root of the product of n values. The general formula for the geometric mean, denoted $\bar{x}_g$, follows.

GEOMETRIC MEAN

$$\bar{x}_g = \sqrt[n]{(x_1)(x_2)\cdots(x_n)} = [(x_1)(x_2)\cdots(x_n)]^{1/n} \qquad (3.4)$$

The geometric mean is often used in analyzing growth rates in financial data. In these types of situations the arithmetic mean or average value will provide misleading results.

To illustrate the use of the geometric mean, consider Table 3.2, which shows the percentage annual returns, or growth rates, for a mutual fund over the past 10 years. Suppose we want to compute how much $100 invested in the fund at the beginning of year 1 would be worth at the end of year 10. Let's start by computing the balance in the fund at the end of year 1. Because the percentage annual return for year 1 was −22.1%, the balance in the fund at the end of year 1 would be

$$\$100 - .221(\$100) = \$100(1 - .221) = \$100(.779) = \$77.90$$

The growth factor for each year is 1 plus .01 times the percentage return. A growth factor less than 1 indicates negative growth, while a growth factor greater than 1 indicates positive growth. The growth factor cannot be less than zero.

Note that .779 is identified as the growth factor for year 1 in Table 3.2. This result shows that we can compute the balance at the end of year 1 by multiplying the value invested in the fund at the beginning of year 1 times the growth factor for year 1.

The balance in the fund at the end of year 1, $77.90, now becomes the beginning balance in year 2. So, with a percentage annual return for year 2 of 28.7%, the balance at the end of year 2 would be

$$\$77.90 + .287(\$77.90) = \$77.90(1 + .287) = \$77.90(1.287) = \$100.2573$$

Note that 1.287 is the growth factor for year 2. And, by substituting $100(.779) for $77.90 we see that the balance in the fund at the end of year 2 is

$$\$100(.779)(1.287) = \$100.2573$$

In other words, the balance at the end of year 2 is just the initial investment at the beginning of year 1 times the product of the first two growth factors. This result can be generalized to

TABLE 3.2   PERCENTAGE ANNUAL RETURNS AND GROWTH FACTORS FOR THE MUTUAL FUND DATA

Year	Return (%)	Growth Factor
1	−22.1	0.779
2	28.7	1.287
3	10.9	1.109
4	4.9	1.049
5	15.8	1.158
6	5.5	1.055
7	−37.0	0.630
8	26.5	1.265
9	15.1	1.151
10	2.1	1.021

show that the balance at the end of year 10 is the initial investment times the product of all 10 growth factors.

$$\$100[(.779)(1.287)(1.109)(1.049)(1.158)(1.055)(.630)(1.265)(1.151)(1.021)] =$$

$$\$100(1.334493) = \$133.4493$$

The nth root can be computed using most calculators or by using the POWER function in Excel. For instance, using Excel, the 10th root of 1.334493 = POWER (1.334493, 1/10) or 1.029275.

So, a $100 investment in the fund at the beginning of year 1 would be worth $133.4493 at the end of year 10. Note that the product of the 10 growth factors is 1.334493. Thus, we can compute the balance at the end of year 10 for any amount of money invested at the beginning of year 1 by multiplying the value of the initial investment times 1.334493. For instance, an initial investment of $2500 at the beginning of year 1 would be worth $2500(1.334493) or approximately $3336 at the end of year 10.

But, what was the mean percentage annual return or mean rate of growth for this investment over the 10-year period? Let us see how the geometric mean of the 10 growth factors can be used to answer to this question. Because the product of the 10 growth factors is 1.334493, the geometric mean is the 10th root of 1.334493 or

$$\bar{x}_g = \sqrt[10]{1.334493} = 1.029275$$

The geometric mean tells us that annual returns grew at an average annual rate of $(1.029275 - 1)100\%$ or 2.9275%. In other words, with an average annual growth rate of 2.9275%, a $100 investment in the fund at the beginning of year 1 would grow to $\$100(1.029275)^{10} = \$133.4493$ at the end of 10 years.

It is important to understand that the arithmetic mean of the percentage annual returns does not provide the mean annual growth rate for this investment. The sum of the 10 annual percentage returns in Table 3.2 is 50.4. Thus, the arithmetic mean of the 10 percentage annual returns is $50.4/10 = 5.04\%$. A broker might try to convince you to invest in this fund by stating that the mean annual percentage return was 5.04%. Such a statement is not only misleading, it is inaccurate. A mean annual percentage return of 5.04% corresponds to an average growth factor of 1.0504. So, if the average growth factor were really 1.0504, $100 invested in the fund at the beginning of year 1 would have grown to $\$100(1.0504)^{10} = \$163.51$ at the end of 10 years. But, using the 10 annual percentage returns in Table 3.2, we showed that an initial $100 investment is worth $133.45 at the end of 10 years. The broker's claim that the mean annual percentage return is 5.04% grossly overstates the true growth for this mutual fund. The problem is that the sample mean is only appropriate for an additive process. For a multiplicative process, such as applications involving growth rates, the geometric mean is the appropriate measure of location.

While the applications of the geometric mean to problems in finance, investments, and banking are particularly common, the geometric mean should be applied any time you want to determine the mean rate of change over several successive periods. Other common applications include changes in populations of species, crop yields, pollution levels, and birth and death rates. Also note that the geometric mean can be applied to changes that occur over any number of successive periods of any length. In addition to annual changes, the geometric mean is often applied to find the mean rate of change over quarters, months, weeks, and even days.

Mode

Another measure of location is the **mode**. The mode is defined as follows.

MODE

The mode is the value that occurs with greatest frequency.

To illustrate the identification of the mode, consider the sample of five class sizes. The only value that occurs more than once is 46. Because this value, occurring with a frequency of 2, has the greatest frequency, it is the mode. As another illustration, consider the sample of starting salaries for the business school graduates. The only monthly starting salary that occurs more than once is $3880. Because this value has the greatest frequency, it is the mode.

Situations can arise for which the greatest frequency occurs at two or more different values. In these instances more than one mode exists. If the data contain exactly two modes, we say that the data are *bimodal.* If data contain more than two modes, we say that the data are *multimodal.* In multimodal cases the mode is almost never reported because listing three or more modes would not be particularly helpful in describing a location for the data.

Percentiles

A **percentile** provides information about how the data are spread over the interval from the smallest value to the largest value. For a data set containing n observations, the ***p*th percentile** divides the data into two parts: approximately $p\%$ of the observations are less than the pth percentile, and approximately $(100 - p)\%$ of the observations are greater than the pth percentile.

Colleges and universities frequently report admission test scores in terms of percentiles. For instance, suppose an applicant obtains a score of 630 on the math portion of an admission test. How this applicant performed in relation to others taking the same test may not be readily apparent from this score. However, if the score of 630 corresponds to the 82nd percentile, we know that approximately that 82% of the applicants scored lower than this individual and approximately 18% of the applicants scored higher than this individual.

To calculate the pth percentile for a data set containing n observations, we must first arrange the data in ascending order (smallest value to largest value). The smallest value is in position 1, the next smallest value is in position 2, and so on. The location of the pth percentile, denoted L_p, is computed using the following equation:

Several procedures can be used to compute the location of the pth percentile using sample data. All provide similar values, especially for large data sets. The procedure we show here is the procedure used by Excel's PERCENTILE.EXC function as well as several other statistical software packages.

LOCATION OF THE *P*TH PERCENTILE

$$L_p = \frac{p}{100}(n + 1) \tag{3.5}$$

Once we find the position of the value of the pth percentile, we have the information we need to calculate the pth percentile.

To illustrate the computation of the pth percentile, let us compute the 80th percentile for the starting salary data in Table 3.1. We begin by arranging the sample of 12 starting salaries in ascending order.

3710	3755	3850	3880	3880	3890	3920	3940	3950	4050	4130	4325
Position 1	2	3	4	5	6	7	8	9	10	11	12

The position of each observation in the sorted data is shown directly below its value. For instance, the smallest value (3710) is in position 1, the next smallest value (3755) is in position 2, and so on. Using equation (3.5) with $p = 80$ and $n = 12$, the location of the 80th percentile is

$$L_{80} = \frac{p}{100}(n + 1) = \left(\frac{80}{100} \right)(12 + 1) = 10.4$$

The interpretation of $L_{80} = 10.4$ is that the 80th percentile is 40% of the way between the value in position 10 and the value in position 11. In other words, the 80th percentile is the value in position 10 (4050) plus .4 times the difference between the value in position 11 (4130) and the value in position 10 (4050). Thus, the 80th percentile is

$$\text{80th percentile} = 4050 + .4(4130 - 4050) = 4050 + .4(80) = 4082$$

Let us now compute the 50th percentile for the starting salary data. With $p = 50$ and $n = 12$, the location of the 50th percentile is

$$L_{50} = \frac{p}{100}(n + 1) = \left(\frac{50}{100}\right)(12 + 1) = 6.5$$

With $L_{50} = 6.5$, we see that the 50th percentile is 50% of the way between the value in position 6 (3890) and the value in position 7 (3920). Thus, the 50th percentile is

50th percentile $= 3890 + .5(3920 - 3890) = 3890 + .5(30) = 3905$

Note that the *50th percentile is also the median.*

Quartiles

Quartiles are just specific percentiles; thus, the steps for computing percentiles can be applied directly in the computation of quartiles.

It is often desirable to divide a data set into four parts, with each part containing approximately one-fourth, or 25%, of the observations. These division points are referred to as the **quartiles** and are defined as follows.

Q_1 = first quartile, or 25th percentile

Q_2 = second quartile, or 50th percentile (also the median)

Q_3 = third quartile, or 75th percentile

Because quartiles are specific percentiles, the procedure for computing percentiles can be used to compute the quartiles.

To illustrate the computation of the quartiles for a data set consisting of n observations, we will compute the quartiles for the starting salary data in Table 3.1. Previously we showed that the 50th percentile for the starting salary data is 3905; thus, the second quartile (median) is $Q_2 = 3905$. To compute the first and third quartiles, we must find the 25th and 75th percentiles. The calculations follow.

For Q_1,

$$L_{25} = \frac{p}{100}(n + 1) = \left(\frac{25}{100}\right)(12 + 1) = 3.25$$

The first quartile, or 25th percentile, is .25 of the way between the value in position 3 (3850) and the value in position 4 (3880). Thus,

$Q_1 = 3850 + .25(3880 - 3850) = 3850 + .25(30) = 3857.5$

For Q_3,

$$L_{75} = \frac{p}{100}(n + 1) = \left(\frac{75}{100}\right)(12 + 1) = 9.75$$

The third quartile, or 75th percentile, is .75 of the way between the value in position 9 (3950) and the value in position 10 (4050). Thus,

$Q_3 = 3950 + .75(4050 - 3950) = 3950 + .75(100) = 4025$

The quartiles divide the starting salary data into four parts, with each part containing 25% of the observations.

25% of the data		25% of the data		25% of the data		25% of the data	

3710   3755   3850 | 3880   3880   3890 | 3920   3940   3950 | 4050   4130   4325

$Q_1 = 3857.5$ $Q_2 = 3905$ $Q_3 = 4025$
                                    (Median)

We defined the quartiles as the 25th, 50th, and 75th percentiles and then we computed the quartiles in the same way as percentiles. However, other conventions are sometimes used to compute quartiles, and the actual values reported for quartiles may vary slightly depending on the convention used. Nevertheless, the objective of all procedures for computing quartiles is to divide the data into four parts that contain equal numbers of observations.

NOTES AND COMMENTS

1. It is better to use the median than the mean as a measure of central location when a data set contains extreme values. Another measure that is sometimes used when extreme values are present is the trimmed mean. The trimmed mean is obtained by deleting a percentage of the smallest and largest values from a data set and then computing the mean of the remaining values. For example, the 5% trimmed mean is obtained by removing the smallest 5% and the largest 5% of the data values and then computing the mean of the remaining values. Using the sample with $n = 12$ starting salaries, $0.05(12) = 0.6$. Rounding this value to 1 indicates that the 5% trimmed mean is obtained by removing the smallest data value and the largest data value and then computing the mean of the remaining 10 values. For the starting salary data, the 5% trimmed mean is 3924.50.

2. Other commonly used percentiles are the quintiles (the 20th, 40th, 60th, and 80th percentiles) and the deciles (the 10th, 20th, 30th, 40th, 50th, 60th, 70th, 80th, and 90th percentiles).

Exercises

Methods

1. Consider a sample with data values of 10, 20, 12, 17, and 16. Compute the mean and median.

2. Consider a sample with data values of 10, 20, 21, 17, 16, and 12. Compute the mean and median.

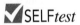 SELF*test*

3. Consider the following data and corresponding weights.

x_i	Weight (w_i)
3.2	6
2.0	3
2.5	2
5.0	8

   a. Compute the weighted mean.
   b. Compute the sample mean of the four data values without weighting. Note the difference in the results provided by the two computations.

4. Consider the following data.

Period	Rate of Return (%)
1	−6.0
2	−8.0
3	−4.0
4	2.0
5	5.4

What is the mean growth rate over these five periods?

 SELF*test*

5. Consider a sample with data values of 27, 25, 20, 15, 30, 34, 28, and 25. Compute the 20th, 25th, 65th, and 75th percentiles.

6. Consider a sample with data values of 53, 55, 70, 58, 64, 57, 53, 69, 57, 68, and 53. Compute the mean, median, and mode.

Applications

7. The average number of minutes Americans commute to work is 27.7 minutes (*Sterling's Best Places*, April 13, 2012). The average commute time in minutes for 48 cities are as follows:

CommuteTime

Albuquerque	23.3	Jacksonville	26.2	Phoenix	28.3
Atlanta	28.3	Kansas City	23.4	Pittsburgh	25.0
Austin	24.6	Las Vegas	28.4	Portland	26.4
Baltimore	32.1	Little Rock	20.1	Providence	23.6
Boston	31.7	Los Angeles	32.2	Richmond	23.4
Charlotte	25.8	Louisville	21.4	Sacramento	25.8
Chicago	38.1	Memphis	23.8	Salt Lake City	20.2
Cincinnati	24.9	Miami	30.7	San Antonio	26.1
Cleveland	26.8	Milwaukee	24.8	San Diego	24.8
Columbus	23.4	Minneapolis	23.6	San Francisco	32.6
Dallas	28.5	Nashville	25.3	San Jose	28.5
Denver	28.1	New Orleans	31.7	Seattle	27.3
Detroit	29.3	New York	43.8	St. Louis	26.8
El Paso	24.4	Oklahoma City	22.0	Tucson	24.0
Fresno	23.0	Orlando	27.1	Tulsa	20.1
Indianapolis	24.8	Philadelphia	34.2	Washington, D.C.	32.8

   a. What is the mean commute time for these 48 cities?
   b. Compute the median commute time.
   c. Compute the mode.
   d. Compute the third quartile.

8. *The Wall Street Journal* reported that the median salary for middle-level manager jobs was approximately $85,000 (*The Wall Street Journal*, August 6, 2013). Suppose that an independent study of middle-level managers employed at companies located in Atlanta, Georgia, was conducted to compare the salaries of managers working at firms in Atlanta to the national average. The following data show the salary, in thousands of dollars, for a sample of 15 middle-level managers.

   108   83   106   73   53   85   80   63   67   75   124   55   93   118   77

   a. Compute the median salary for the sample of 15 middle-level managers. How does the median for this group compare to the median reported by *The Wall Street Journal*?
   b. Compute the mean annual salary and discuss how and why it differs from the median computed in part (a).
   c. Compute the first and third quartiles.

AdvertisingSpend

9. Which companies spend the most money on advertising? *Business Insider* maintains a list of the top-spending companies. In 2014, Procter & Gamble spent more than any other company, a whopping $5 billion. In second place was Comcast, which spent $3.08 billion (*Business Insider* website, December 2014). The top 12 companies and the amount each spent on advertising in billions of dollars are as follows.

Company	Advertising ($billions)	Company	Advertising ($billions)
Procter & Gamble	$5.00	American Express	$2.19
Comcast	3.08	General Motors	2.15
AT&T	2.91	Toyota	2.09
Ford	2.56	Fiat Chrysler	1.97
Verizon	2.44	Walt Disney Company	1.96
L'Oreal	2.34	J.P Morgan	1.88

a. What is the mean amount spent on advertising?
b. What is the median amount spent on advertising?
c. What are the first and third quartiles?

JacketRatings

10. Over a nine-month period, OutdoorGearLab tested hardshell jackets designed for ice climbing, mountaineering, and backpacking. Based on the breathability, durability, versatility, features, mobility, and weight of each jacket, an overall rating ranging from 0 (lowest) to 100 (highest) was assigned to each jacket tested. The following data show the results for 20 top-of-the-line jackets (OutdoorGearLab website, February 27, 2013).

42	66	67	71	78	62	61	76	71	67
61	64	61	54	83	63	68	69	81	53

a. Compute the mean, median, and mode.
b. Compute the first and third quartiles.
c. Compute and interpret the 90th percentile.

11. According to the National Education Association (NEA), teachers generally spend more than 40 hours each week working on instructional duties (NEA website, April 2012). The following data show the number of hours worked per week for a sample of 13 high school science teachers and a sample of 11 high school English teachers.

High School Science Teachers: 53 56 54 54 55 58 49 61 54 54 52 53 54

High School English Teachers: 52 47 50 46 47 48 49 46 55 44 47

a. What is the median number of hours worked per week for the sample of 13 high school science teachers?
b. What is the median number of hours worked per week for the sample of 11 high school English teachers?
c. Which group has the higher median number of hours worked per week? What is the difference between the median number of hours worked per week?

BigBangTheory

12. *The Big Bang Theory*, a situation comedy featuring Johnny Galecki, Jim Parsons, and Kaley Cuoco-Sweeting, is one of the most watched programs on network television. The first two episodes for the 2011–2012 season premiered on September 22, 2011; the first episode attracted 14.1 million viewers and the second episode attracted 14.7 million viewers. The following table shows the number of viewers in millions for the first 21 episodes of the 2011–2012 season (*The Big Bang Theory* website, April 17, 2012).

Air Date	Viewers (millions)	Air Date	Viewers (millions)
September 22, 2011	14.1	January 12, 2012	16.1
September 22, 2011	14.7	January 19, 2012	15.8
September 29, 2011	14.6	January 26, 2012	16.1
October 6, 2011	13.6	February 2, 2012	16.5
October 13, 2011	13.6	February 9, 2012	16.2
October 20, 2011	14.9	February 16, 2012	15.7
October 27, 2011	14.5	February 23, 2012	16.2
November 3, 2011	16.0	March 8, 2012	15.0
November 10, 2011	15.9	March 29, 2012	14.0
November 17, 2011	15.1	April 5, 2012	13.3
December 8, 2011	14.0		

a. Compute the minimum and maximum number of viewers.
b. Compute the mean, median, and mode.
c. Compute the first and third quartiles.
d. Has viewership grown or declined over the 2011–2012 season? Discuss.

13. In automobile mileage and gasoline-consumption testing, 13 automobiles were road tested for 300 miles in both city and highway driving conditions. The following data were recorded for miles-per-gallon performance.

City: 16.2 16.7 15.9 14.4 13.2 15.3 16.8 16.0 16.1 15.3 15.2 15.3 16.2
Highway: 19.4 20.6 18.3 18.6 19.2 17.4 17.2 18.6 19.0 21.1 19.4 18.5 18.7

Use the mean, median, and mode to make a statement about the difference in performance for city and highway driving.

StateUnemp

14. The data contained in the file named StateUnemp show the unemployment rate in March 2011 and the unemployment rate in March 2012 for every state and the District of Columbia (Bureau of Labor Statistics website, April 20, 2012). To compare unemployment rates in March 2011 with unemployment rates in March 2012, compute the first quartile, the median, and the third quartile for the March 2011 unemployment data and the March 2012 unemployment data. What do these statistics suggest about the change in unemployment rates across the states?

15. Martinez Auto Supplies has retail stores located in eight cities in California. The price they charge for a particular product in each city varies because of differing competitive conditions. For instance, the price they charge for a case of a popular brand of motor oil in each city follows. Also shown are the number of cases that Martinez Auto sold last quarter in each city.

City	Price ($)	Sales (cases)
Bakersfield	34.99	501
Los Angeles	38.99	1425
Modesto	36.00	294
Oakland	33.59	882
Sacramento	40.99	715
San Diego	38.59	1088
San Francisco	39.59	1644
San Jose	37.99	819

Compute the average sales price per case for this product during the last quarter.

16. The grade point average for college students is based on a weighted mean computation. For most colleges, the grades are given the following data values: A (4), B (3), C (2), D (1), and F (0). After 60 credit hours of course work, a student at State University earned 9 credit hours of A, 15 credit hours of B, 33 credit hours of C, and 3 credit hours of D.
    a. Compute the student's grade point average.
    b. Students at State University must maintain a 2.5 grade point average for their first 60 credit hours of course work in order to be admitted to the business college. Will this student be admitted?

17. The following table shows the total return and the number of funds for four categories of mutual funds.

Type of Fund	Number of Funds	Total Return (%)
Domestic Equity	9191	4.65
International Equity	2621	18.15
Specialty Stock	1419	11.36
Hybrid	2900	6.75

a. Using the number of funds as weights, compute the weighted average total return for these mutual funds.
b. Is there any difficulty associated with using the "number of funds" as the weights in computing the weighted average total return in part (a)? Discuss. What else might be used for weights?
c. Suppose you invested $10,000 in this group of mutual funds and diversified the investment by placing $2000 in Domestic Equity funds, $4000 in International Equity funds, $3000 in Specialty Stock funds, and $1000 in Hybrid funds. What is the expected return on the portfolio?

18. Based on a survey of master's programs in business administration, magazines such as *U.S. News & World Report* rank U.S. business schools. These types of rankings are based in part on surveys of business school deans and corporate recruiters. Each survey respondent is asked to rate the overall academic quality of the master's program on a scale from 1 "marginal" to 5 "outstanding." Use the sample of responses shown below to compute the weighted mean score for the business school deans and the corporate recruiters. Discuss.

Quality Assessment	Business School Deans	Corporate Recruiters
5	44	31
4	66	34
3	60	43
2	10	12
1	0	0

19. Annual revenue for Corning Supplies grew by 5.5% in 2010, 1.1% in 2011, −3.5% in 2012, −1.1% in 2013, and 1.8% in 2014. What is the mean growth annual rate over this period?

20. Suppose that at the beginning of 2004 you invested $10,000 in the Stivers mutual fund and $5000 in the Trippi mutual fund. The value of each investment at the end of each subsequent year is provided in the table below. Which mutual fund performed better?

Year	Stivers	Trippi
2004	11,000	5,600
2005	12,000	6,300
2006	13,000	6,900
2007	14,000	7,600
2008	15,000	8,500
2009	16,000	9,200
2010	17,000	9,900
2011	18,000	10,600

21. If an asset declines in value from $5000 to $3500 over nine years, what is the mean annual growth rate in the asset's value over these nine years?

22. The current value of a company is $25 million. If the value of the company six year ago was $10 million, what is the company's mean annual growth rate over the past six years?

3.2 Measures of Variability

In addition to measures of location, it is often desirable to consider measures of variability, or dispersion. For example, suppose that you are a purchasing agent for a large manufacturing firm and that you regularly place orders with two different suppliers. After several months of operation, you find that the mean number of days required to fill orders is 10 days for both of the suppliers. The histograms summarizing the number of working days required to fill orders from the suppliers are shown in Figure 3.2. Although the mean number of days is 10 for both suppliers, do the two suppliers demonstrate the same degree of reliability in terms of making deliveries on schedule? Note the dispersion, or variability, in delivery times indicated by the histograms. Which supplier would you prefer?

The variability in the delivery time creates uncertainty for production scheduling. Methods in this section help measure and understand variability.

For most firms, receiving materials and supplies on schedule is important. The 7- or 8-day deliveries shown for J.C. Clark Distributors might be viewed favorably; however, a few of the slow 13- to 15-day deliveries could be disastrous in terms of keeping a workforce busy and production on schedule. This example illustrates a situation in which the variability in the delivery times may be an overriding consideration in selecting a supplier. For most purchasing agents, the lower variability shown for Dawson Supply, Inc., would make Dawson the preferred supplier.

We turn now to a discussion of some commonly used measures of variability.

Range

The simplest measure of variability is the **range**.

> RANGE
>
> $$\text{Range} = \text{Largest value} - \text{Smallest value}$$

Let us refer to the data on starting salaries for business school graduates in Table 3.1. The largest starting salary is 4325 and the smallest is 3710. The range is $4325 - 3710 = 615$.

FIGURE 3.2   HISTORICAL DATA SHOWING THE NUMBER OF DAYS REQUIRED TO FILL ORDERS

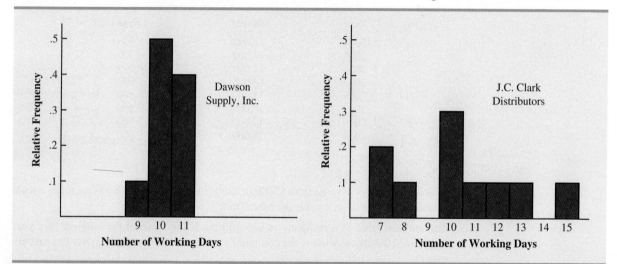

Although the range is the easiest of the measures of variability to compute, it is seldom used as the only measure. The reason is that the range is based on only two of the observations and thus is highly influenced by extreme values. Suppose the highest paid graduate received a starting salary of $10,000 per month. In this case, the range would be $10,000 - 3710 = 6290$ rather than 615. This large value for the range would not be especially descriptive of the variability in the data because 11 of the 12 starting salaries are closely grouped between 3710 and 4130.

Interquartile Range

A measure of variability that overcomes the dependency on extreme values is the **interquartile range (IQR)**. This measure of variability is the difference between the third quartile, Q_3, and the first quartile, Q_1. In other words, the interquartile range is the range for the middle 50% of the data.

INTERQUARTILE RANGE

$$IQR = Q_3 - Q_1 \qquad (3.6)$$

For the data on monthly starting salaries, the quartiles are $Q_3 = 4000$ and $Q_1 = 3865$. Thus, the interquartile range is $4000 - 3865 = 135$.

Variance

The **variance** is a measure of variability that utilizes all the data. The variance is based on the difference between the value of each observation (x_i) and the mean. The difference between each x_i and the mean ($\bar{x}$ for a sample, μ for a population) is called a *deviation about the mean.* For a sample, a deviation about the mean is written ($x_i - \bar{x}$); for a population, it is written ($x_i - \mu$). In the computation of the variance, the deviations about the mean are *squared.*

If the data are for a population, the average of the squared deviations is called the *population variance.* The population variance is denoted by the Greek symbol σ^2. For a population of N observations and with μ denoting the population mean, the definition of the population variance is as follows.

POPULATION VARIANCE

$$\sigma^2 = \frac{\Sigma(x_i - \mu)^2}{N} \qquad (3.7)$$

In most statistical applications, the data being analyzed are for a sample. When we compute a sample variance, we are often interested in using it to estimate the population variance σ^2. Although a detailed explanation is beyond the scope of this text, it can be shown that if the sum of the squared deviations about the sample mean is divided by $n - 1$, and not n, the resulting sample variance provides an unbiased estimate of the population variance. For this reason, the *sample variance,* denoted by s^2, is defined as follows.

The sample variance s^2 is a point estimator of the population variance σ^2.

SAMPLE VARIANCE

$$s^2 = \frac{\Sigma(x_i - \bar{x})^2}{n - 1} \qquad (3.8)$$

TABLE 3.3   COMPUTATION OF DEVIATIONS AND SQUARED DEVIATIONS ABOUT THE MEAN FOR THE CLASS SIZE DATA

Number of Students in Class (x_i)	Mean Class Size ($\bar{x}$)	Deviation About the Mean ($x_i - \bar{x}$)	Squared Deviation About the Mean ($x_i - \bar{x})^2$
46	44	2	4
54	44	10	100
42	44	−2	4
46	44	2	4
32	44	−12	144
		0	256
		$\Sigma(x_i - \bar{x})$	$\Sigma(x_i - \bar{x})^2$

To illustrate the computation of the sample variance, we will use the data on class size for the sample of five college classes as presented in Section 3.1. A summary of the data, including the computation of the deviations about the mean and the squared deviations about the mean, is shown in Table 3.3. The sum of squared deviations about the mean is $\Sigma(x_i - \bar{x})^2 = 256$. Hence, with $n - 1 = 4$, the sample variance is

$$s^2 = \frac{\Sigma(x_i - \bar{x})^2}{n - 1} = \frac{256}{4} = 64$$

Before moving on, let us note that the units associated with the sample variance often cause confusion. Because the values being summed in the variance calculation, $(x_i - \bar{x})^2$, are squared, the units associated with the sample variance are also *squared*. For instance, the sample variance for the class size data is $s^2 = 64$ (students)^2. The squared units associated with variance make it difficult to develop an intuitive understanding and interpretation of the numerical value of the variance. We recommend that you think of the variance as a measure useful in comparing the amount of variability for two or more variables. In a comparison of the variables, the one with the largest variance shows the most variability. Further interpretation of the value of the variance may not be necessary.

The variance is useful in comparing the variability of two or more variables.

As another illustration of computing a sample variance, consider the starting salaries listed in Table 3.1 for the 12 business school graduates. In Section 3.1, we showed that the sample mean starting salary was 3940. The computation of the sample variance ($s^2 = 27,440.91$) is shown in Table 3.4.

In Tables 3.3 and 3.4 we show both the sum of the deviations about the mean and the sum of the squared deviations about the mean. For any data set, the sum of the deviations about the mean will *always equal zero*. Note that in Tables 3.3 and 3.4, $\Sigma(x_i - \bar{x}) = 0$. The positive deviations and negative deviations cancel each other, causing the sum of the deviations about the mean to equal zero.

Standard Deviation

The **standard deviation** is defined to be the positive square root of the variance. Following the notation we adopted for a sample variance and a population variance, we use s to denote the sample standard deviation and σ to denote the population standard deviation. The standard deviation is derived from the variance in the following way.

TABLE 3.4 COMPUTATION OF THE SAMPLE VARIANCE FOR THE STARTING SALARY DATA

Monthly Salary (x_i)	Sample Mean $(\bar{x})$	Deviation About the Mean $(x_i - \bar{x})$	Squared Deviation About the Mean $(x_i - \bar{x})^2$
3850	3940	−90	8100
3950	3940	10	100
4050	3940	110	12,100
3880	3940	−60	3600
3755	3940	−185	34,225
3710	3940	−230	52,900
3890	3940	−50	2500
4130	3940	190	36,100
3940	3940	0	0
4325	3940	385	148,225
3920	3940	−20	400
3880	3940	−60	3600
		0	301,850
		$\Sigma(x_i - \bar{x})$	$\Sigma(x_i - \bar{x})^2$

Using equation (3.8),

$$s^2 = \frac{\Sigma(x_i - \bar{x})^2}{n - 1} = \frac{301,850}{11} = 27{,}440.91$$

STANDARD DEVIATION

The sample standard deviation s is a point estimator of the population standard deviation σ.

$$\text{Sample standard deviation} = s = \sqrt{s^2} \qquad (3.9)$$

$$\text{Population standard deviation} = \sigma = \sqrt{\sigma^2} \qquad (3.10)$$

Recall that the sample variance for the sample of class sizes in five college classes is $s^2 = 64$. Thus, the sample standard deviation is $s = \sqrt{64} = 8$. For the data on starting salaries, the sample standard deviation is $s = \sqrt{27{,}440.91} = 165.65$.

The standard deviation is easier to interpret than the variance because the standard deviation is measured in the same units as the data.

What is gained by converting the variance to its corresponding standard deviation? Recall that the units associated with the variance are squared. For example, the sample variance for the starting salary data of business school graduates is $s^2 = 27{,}440.91$ (dollars)^2. Because the standard deviation is the square root of the variance, the units of the variance, dollars squared, are converted to dollars in the standard deviation. Thus, the standard deviation of the starting salary data is $165.65. In other words, the standard deviation is measured in the same units as the original data. For this reason the standard deviation is more easily compared to the mean and other statistics that are measured in the same units as the original data.

Coefficient of Variation

The coefficient of variation is a relative measure of variability; it measures the standard deviation relative to the mean.

In some situations we may be interested in a descriptive statistic that indicates how large the standard deviation is relative to the mean. This measure is called the **coefficient of variation** and is usually expressed as a percentage.

COEFFICIENT OF VARIATION

$$\left(\frac{\text{Standard deviation}}{\text{Mean}} \times 100 \right)\% \qquad (3.11)$$

For the class size data, we found a sample mean of 44 and a sample standard deviation of 8. The coefficient of variation is $[(8/44) \times 100]\% = 18.2\%$. In words, the coefficient of variation tells us that the sample standard deviation is 18.2% of the value of the sample mean. For the starting salary data with a sample mean of 3940 and a sample standard deviation of 165.65, the coefficient of variation, $[(165.65/3940) \times 100]\% = 4.2\%$, tells us the sample standard deviation is only 4.2% of the value of the sample mean. In general, the coefficient of variation is a useful statistic for comparing the variability of variables that have different standard deviations and different means.

NOTES AND COMMENTS

1. Statistical software packages and spreadsheets can be used to develop the descriptive statistics presented in this chapter. After the data are entered into a worksheet, a few simple commands can be used to generate the desired output. In two chapter-ending appendixes we show how Minitab and Excel can be used to develop descriptive statistics.

2. The standard deviation is a commonly used measure of the risk associated with investing in stock and stock funds (*Morningstar* website, July 21, 2012). It provides a measure of how monthly returns fluctuate around the long-run average return.

3. Rounding the value of the sample mean $\bar{x}$ and the values of the squared deviations $(x_i - \bar{x})^2$ may introduce errors when a calculator is used in the computation of the variance and standard deviation. To reduce rounding errors, we recommend carrying at least six significant digits during intermediate calculations. The resulting variance or standard deviation can then be rounded to fewer digits.

4. An alternative formula for the computation of the sample variance is

$$s^2 = \frac{\Sigma x_i^2 - n\bar{x}^2}{n - 1}$$

where $\Sigma x_i^2 = x_1^2 + x_2^2 + \cdots + x_n^2$.

5. The mean absolute error (MAE) is another measure of variability that is computed by summing the absolute values of the deviations of the observations about the mean and dividing this sum by the number of observations. For a sample of size n, the MAE is computed as follows:

$$\text{MAE} = \frac{\Sigma |x_i - \bar{x}|}{n}$$

For the class size data presented in Section 3.1, $\bar{x} = 44$, $\Sigma |x_i - \bar{x}| = 28$, and the MAE $= 28/5 = 5.6$. You can learn more about the MAE and other measures of variability in Chapter 17.

Exercises

Methods

23. Consider a sample with data values of 10, 20, 12, 17, and 16. Compute the range and interquartile range.

24. Consider a sample with data values of 10, 20, 12, 17, and 16. Compute the variance and standard deviation.

 SELF*test*   25. Consider a sample with data values of 27, 25, 20, 15, 30, 34, 28, and 25. Compute the range, interquartile range, variance, and standard deviation.

Applications

 SELF*test*   26. Data collected by the Oil Price Information Service from more than 90,000 gasoline and convenience stores throughout the U.S. showed that the average price for a gallon of unleaded gasoline was $3.28 (MSN Auto website, February 2, 2014). The following data show the price per gallon ($) for a sample of 20 gasoline and convenience stores located in San Francisco.

DATA *file*

SFGasPrices

3.59	3.59	4.79	3.56	3.55	3.71	3.65	3.60	3.75	3.56
3.57	3.59	3.55	3.99	4.15	3.66	3.63	3.73	3.61	3.57

    a. Use the sample data to estimate the mean price for a gallon of unleaded gasoline in San Francisco.

    b. Compute the sample standard deviation.

    c. Compare the mean price per gallon for the sample data to the national average price. What conclusions can you draw about the cost living in San Francisco?

27. The results of a search to find the least expensive round-trip flights to Atlanta and Salt Lake City from 14 major U.S. cities are shown in the following table. The departure date was June 20, 2012, and the return date was June 27, 2012.

Flights

Departure City	Round-Trip Cost ($)	
	Atlanta	Salt Lake City
Cincinnati	340.10	570.10
New York	321.60	354.60
Chicago	291.60	465.60
Denver	339.60	219.60
Los Angeles	359.60	311.60
Seattle	384.60	297.60
Detroit	309.60	471.60
Philadelphia	415.60	618.40
Washington, D.C.	293.60	513.60
Miami	249.60	523.20
San Francisco	539.60	381.60
Las Vegas	455.60	159.60
Phoenix	359.60	267.60
Dallas	333.90	458.60

    a. Compute the mean price for a round-trip flight into Atlanta and the mean price for a round-trip flight into Salt Lake City. Is Atlanta less expensive to fly into than Salt Lake City? If so, what could explain this difference?

    b. Compute the range, variance, and standard deviation for the two samples. What does this information tell you about the prices for flights into these two cities?

28. The Australian Open is the first of the four Grand Slam professional tennis events held each year. Victoria Azarenka beat Maria Sharapova to win the 2012 Australian Open women's title (*Washington Post,* January 27, 2012). During the tournament Ms. Azarenka's serve speed reached 178 kilometers per hour. A list of the 20 Women's Singles serve speed leaders for the 2012 Australian Open is provided below.

AustralianOpen

Player	Serve Speed (km/h)	Player	Serve Speed (km/h)
S. Williams	191	G. Arn	179
S. Lisicki	190	V. Azarenka	178
M. Keys	187	A. Ivanovic	178
L. Hradecka	187	P. Kvitova	178
J. Gajdosova	187	M. Krajicek	178
J. Hampton	181	V. Dushevina	178
B. Mattek-Sands	181	S. Stosur	178
F. Schiavone	179	S. Cirstea	177
P. Parmentier	179	M. Barthel	177
N. Petrova	179	P. Ormaechea	177

    a. Compute the mean, variance, and standard deviation for the serve speeds.

    b. A similar sample of the 20 Women's Singles serve speed leaders for the 2011 Wimbledon tournament showed a sample mean serve speed of 182.5 kilometers per hour. The variance and standard deviation were 33.3 and 5.77, respectively. Discuss any difference between the serve speeds in the Australian Open and the Wimbledon women's tournaments.

29. The *Los Angeles Times* regularly reports the air quality index for various areas of Southern California. A sample of air quality index values for Pomona provided the following data: 28, 42, 58, 48, 45, 55, 60, 49, and 50.
   a. Compute the range and interquartile range.
   b. Compute the sample variance and sample standard deviation.
   c. A sample of air quality index readings for Anaheim provided a sample mean of 48.5, a sample variance of 136, and a sample standard deviation of 11.66. What comparisons can you make between the air quality in Pomona and that in Anaheim on the basis of these descriptive statistics?

30. The following data were used to construct the histograms of the number of days required to fill orders for Dawson Supply, Inc., and J.C. Clark Distributors (see Figure 3.2).

   Dawson Supply Days for Delivery: 11   10   9   10   11   11   10   11   10   10
   Clark Distributors Days for Delivery: 8   10   13   7   10   11   10   7   15   12

   Use the range and standard deviation to support the previous observation that Dawson Supply provides the more consistent and reliable delivery times.

31. The results of Accounting Principals' latest Workonomix survey indicate the average American worker spends $1092 on coffee annually (*The Consumerist,* January 20, 2012). To determine if there are any differences in coffee expenditures by age group, samples of 10 consumers were selected for three age groups (18–34, 35–44, and 45 and Older). The dollar amount each consumer in the sample spent last year on coffee is provided below.

Coffee

18–34	35–44	45 and Older
1355	969	1135
115	434	956
1456	1792	400
2045	1500	1374
1621	1277	1244
994	1056	825
1937	1922	763
1200	1350	1192
1567	1586	1305
1390	1415	1510

   a. Compute the mean, variance, and standard deviation for the each of these three samples.
   b. What observations can be made based on these data?

Advertising

32. *Advertising Age* annually compiles a list of the 100 companies that spend the most on advertising. Consumer-goods company Procter & Gamble has often topped the list, spending billions of dollars annually (*Advertising Age* website, March 12, 2013). Consider the data found in the file Advertising. It contains annual advertising expenditures for a sample of 20 companies in the automotive sector and 20 companies in the department store sector.
   a. What is the mean advertising spent for each sector?
   b. What is the standard deviation for each sector?
   c. What is the range of advertising spent for each sector?
   d. What is the interquartile range for each sector?
   e. Based on this sample and your answers to parts (a) to (d), comment on any differences in the advertising spending in the automotive companies versus the department store companies.

33. Scores turned in by an amateur golfer at the Bonita Fairways Golf Course in Bonita Springs, Florida, during 2011 and 2012 are as follows:

   2011 Season: 74   78   79   77   75   73   75   77
   2012 Season: 71   70   75   77   85   80   71   79

a. Use the mean and standard deviation to evaluate the golfer's performance over the two-year period.

b. What is the primary difference in performance between 2011 and 2012? What improvement, if any, can be seen in the 2012 scores?

34. The following times were recorded by the quarter-mile and mile runners of a university track team (times are in minutes).

Quarter-Mile Times:	.92	.98	1.04	.90	.99
Mile Times:	4.52	4.35	4.60	4.70	4.50

After viewing this sample of running times, one of the coaches commented that the quarter-milers turned in the more consistent times. Use the standard deviation and the coefficient of variation to summarize the variability in the data. Does the use of the coefficient of variation indicate that the coach's statement should be qualified?

Measures of Distribution Shape, Relative Location, and Detecting Outliers

We have described several measures of location and variability for data. In addition, it is often important to have a measure of the shape of a distribution. In Chapter 2 we noted that a histogram provides a graphical display showing the shape of a distribution. An important numerical measure of the shape of a distribution is called **skewness**.

Distribution Shape

Figure 3.3 shows four histograms constructed from relative frequency distributions. The histograms in Panels A and B are moderately skewed. The one in Panel A is skewed to the left; its skewness is $-.85$. The histogram in Panel B is skewed to the right; its skewness is $+.85$. The histogram in Panel C is symmetric; its skewness is zero. The histogram in Panel D is highly skewed to the right; its skewness is 1.62. The formula used to compute skewness is somewhat complex.[1] However, the skewness can easily be computed using statistical software. For data skewed to the left, the skewness is negative; for data skewed to the right, the skewness is positive. If the data are symmetric, the skewness is zero.

For a symmetric distribution, the mean and the median are equal. When the data are positively skewed, the mean will usually be greater than the median; when the data are negatively skewed, the mean will usually be less than the median. The data used to construct the histogram in Panel D are customer purchases at a women's apparel store. The mean purchase amount is $77.60 and the median purchase amount is $59.70. The relatively few large purchase amounts tend to increase the mean, while the median remains unaffected by the large purchase amounts. The median provides the preferred measure of location when the data are highly skewed.

z-Scores

In addition to measures of location, variability, and shape, we are also interested in the relative location of values within a data set. Measures of relative location help us determine how far a particular value is from the mean.

---

[1] The formula for the skewness of sample data:

$$\text{Skewness} = \frac{n}{(n-1)(n-2)} \Sigma \left(\frac{x_i - \bar{x}}{s} \right)^3$$

FIGURE 3.3   HISTOGRAMS SHOWING THE SKEWNESS FOR FOUR DISTRIBUTIONS

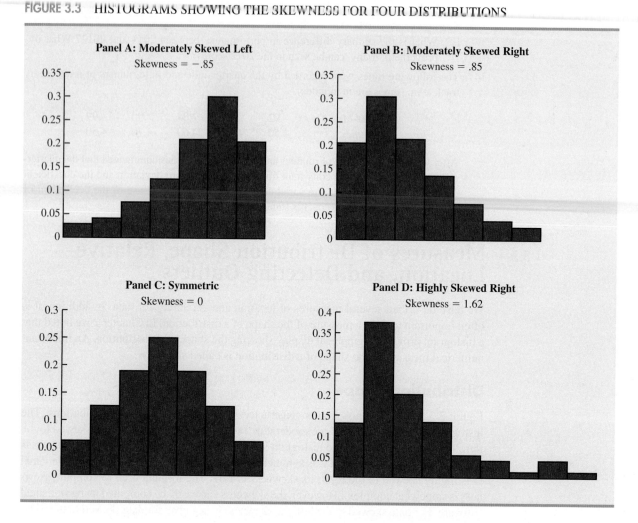

By using both the mean and standard deviation, we can determine the relative location of any observation. Suppose we have a sample of n observations, with the values denoted by $x_1, x_2, \ldots, x_n$. In addition, assume that the sample mean, $\bar{x}$, and the sample standard deviation, s, are already computed. Associated with each value, x_i, is another value called its **z-score**. Equation (3.12) shows how the z-score is computed for each x_i.

z-SCORE

$$z_i = \frac{x_i - \bar{x}}{s} \tag{3.12}$$

where

z_i = the z-score for x_i
$\bar{x}$ = the sample mean
s = the sample standard deviation

TABLE 3.5 z-SCORES FOR THE CLASS SIZE DATA

Number of Students in Class (x_i)	Deviation About the Mean ($x_i - \bar{x}$)	z-Score $\left(\dfrac{x_i - \bar{x}}{s}\right)$
46	2	2/8 = .25
54	10	10/8 = 1.25
42	−2	−2/8 = −.25
46	2	2/8 = .25
32	−12	−12/8 = −1.50

The z-score is often called the *standardized value*. The z-score, z_i, can be interpreted as the *number of standard deviations x_i is from the mean $\bar{x}$*. For example, $z_1 = 1.2$ would indicate that x_1 is 1.2 standard deviations greater than the sample mean. Similarly, $z_2 = −.5$ would indicate that x_2 is .5, or 1/2, standard deviation less than the sample mean. A z-score greater than zero occurs for observations with a value greater than the mean, and a z-score less than zero occurs for observations with a value less than the mean. A z-score of zero indicates that the value of the observation is equal to the mean.

The z-score for any observation can be interpreted as a measure of the relative location of the observation in a data set. Thus, observations in two different data sets with the same z-score can be said to have the same relative location in terms of being the same number of standard deviations from the mean.

The process of converting a value for a variable to a z-score is often referred to as a z transformation.

The z-scores for the class size data from Section 3.1 are computed in Table 3.5. Recall the previously computed sample mean, $\bar{x} = 44$, and sample standard deviation, $s = 8$. The z-score of −1.50 for the fifth observation shows it is farthest from the mean; it is 1.50 standard deviations below the mean. Figure 3.4 provides a dot plot of the class size data with a graphical representation of the associated z-scores on the axis below.

Chebyshev's Theorem

Chebyshev's theorem enables us to make statements about the proportion of data values that must be within a specified number of standard deviations of the mean.

FIGURE 3.4 DOT PLOT SHOWING CLASS SIZE DATA AND z-SCORES

CHEBYSHEV'S THEOREM

At least $(1 - 1/z^2)$ of the data values must be within z standard deviations of the mean, where z is any value greater than 1.

Some of the implications of this theorem, with $z = 2, 3,$ and 4 standard deviations, follow.

- At least .75, or 75%, of the data values must be within $z = 2$ standard deviations of the mean.
- At least .89, or 89%, of the data values must be within $z = 3$ standard deviations of the mean.
- At least .94, or 94%, of the data values must be within $z = 4$ standard deviations of the mean.

For an example using Chebyshev's theorem, suppose that the midterm test scores for 100 students in a college business statistics course had a mean of 70 and a standard deviation of 5. How many students had test scores between 60 and 80? How many students had test scores between 58 and 82?

For the test scores between 60 and 80, we note that 60 is two standard deviations below the mean and 80 is two standard deviations above the mean. Using Chebyshev's theorem, we see that at least .75, or at least 75%, of the observations must have values within two standard deviations of the mean. Thus, at least 75% of the students must have scored between 60 and 80.

Chebyshev's theorem requires $z > 1$; but z need not be an integer.

For the test scores between 58 and 82, we see that $(58 - 70)/5 = -2.4$ indicates 58 is 2.4 standard deviations below the mean and that $(82 - 70)/5 = +2.4$ indicates 82 is 2.4 standard deviations above the mean. Applying Chebyshev's theorem with $z = 2.4$, we have

$$\left(1 - \frac{1}{z^2}\right) = \left(1 - \frac{1}{(2.4)^2}\right) = .826$$

At least 82.6% of the students must have test scores between 58 and 82.

Empirical Rule

The empirical rule is based on the normal probability distribution, which will be discussed in Chapter 6. The normal distribution is used extensively throughout the text.

One of the advantages of Chebyshev's theorem is that it applies to any data set regardless of the shape of the distribution of the data. Indeed, it could be used with any of the distributions in Figure 3.3. In many practical applications, however, data sets exhibit a symmetric mound-shaped or bell-shaped distribution like the one shown in blue in Figure 3.5. When the data are believed to approximate this distribution, the **empirical rule** can be used to determine the percentage of data values that must be within a specified number of standard deviations of the mean.

EMPIRICAL RULE

For data having a bell-shaped distribution:

- Approximately 68% of the data values will be within one standard deviation of the mean.
- Approximately 95% of the data values will be within two standard deviations of the mean.
- Almost all of the data values will be within three standard deviations of the mean.

FIGURE 3.5   A BELL-SHAPED DISTRIBUTION OF DETERGENT CARTON WEIGHTS
WITH PERCENTAGE OF DATA VALUES WITHIN 1, 2, AND 3 STANDARD
DEVIATIONS

For example, liquid detergent cartons are filled automatically on a production line. Filling weights frequently have a bell-shaped distribution. If the mean filling weight is 16 ounces and the standard deviation is .25 ounces, we can use the empirical rule to draw the following conclusions.

- Approximately 68% of the filled cartons will have weights between 15.75 and 16.25 ounces (within one standard deviation of the mean).
- Approximately 95% of the filled cartons will have weights between 15.50 and 16.50 ounces (within two standard deviations of the mean).
- Almost all filled cartons will have weights between 15.25 and 16.75 ounces (within three standard deviations of the mean).

Use Figure 3.5 to help you answer these four questions.

Can we use this information to say anything about how many filled cartons will:

- weigh between 16 and 16.25 ounces?
- weigh between 15.50 and 16 ounces?
- weigh less than 15.50 ounces?
- weigh between 15.50 and 16.25 ounces?

If we recognize that the normal distribution is symmetric about its mean, we can answer each of the questions in the previous list, and we will be able to determine the following:

- Since the percentage of filled cartons that will weigh between 15.75 and 16.25 is approximately 68% and the mean 16 is at the midpoint between 15.75 and 16.25, the percentage of filled cartons that will weigh between 16 and 16.25 ounces is approximately (68%)/2 or approximately 34%.

- Since the percentage of filled cartons that will weigh between 15.50 and 16.50 is approximately 95% and the mean 16 is at the midpoint between 15.50 and 16.50, the percentage of filled cartons that will weigh between 15.50 and 16 ounces is approximately (95%)/2 or approximately 47.5%.
- We just determined that the percentage of filled cartons that will weigh between 15.50 and 16 ounces is approximately 47.5%. Since the distribution is symmetric about its mean, we also know that 50% of the filled cartons will weigh below 16 ounces. Therefore, the percentage of filled cartons with weights less than 15.50 ounces is approximately 50% – 47.5% or approximately 2.5%.
- We just determined that approximately 47.5% of the filled cartons will weigh between 15.50 and 16 ounces, and we earlier determined that approximately 34% of the filled cartons will weigh between 16 and 16.25 ounces. Therefore, the percentage of filled cartons that will weigh between 15.50 and 16.25 ounces is approximately 47.5% + 34% or approximately 81.5%.

In Chapter 6 we will learn to work with noninteger values of z to answer a much broader range of these types of questions.

Detecting Outliers

Sometimes a data set will have one or more observations with unusually large or unusually small values. These extreme values are called **outliers**. Experienced statisticians take steps to identify outliers and then review each one carefully. An outlier may be a data value that has been incorrectly recorded. If so, it can be corrected before further analysis. An outlier may also be from an observation that was incorrectly included in the data set; if so, it can be removed. Finally, an outlier may be an unusual data value that has been recorded correctly and belongs in the data set. In such cases it should remain.

It is a good idea to check for outliers before making decisions based on data analysis. Errors are often made in recording data and entering data into the computer. Outliers should not necessarily be deleted, but their accuracy and appropriateness should be verified.

Standardized values (z-scores) can be used to identify outliers. Recall that the empirical rule allows us to conclude that for data with a bell-shaped distribution, almost all the data values will be within three standard deviations of the mean. Hence, in using z-scores to identify outliers, we recommend treating any data value with a z-score less than -3 or greater than $+3$ as an outlier. Such data values can then be reviewed for accuracy and to determine whether they belong in the data set.

Refer to the z-scores for the class size data in Table 3.5. The z-score of -1.50 shows the fifth class size is farthest from the mean. However, this standardized value is well within the -3 to $+3$ guideline for outliers. Thus, the z-scores do not indicate that outliers are present in the class size data.

Another approach to identifying outliers is based upon the values of the first and third quartiles (Q_1 and Q_3) and the interquartile range (IQR). Using this method, we first compute the following lower and upper limits:

The approach that uses the first and third quartiles and the IQR to identify outliers does not necessarily provide the same results as the approach based upon a z-score less than −3 or greater than +3. Either or both procedures may be used.

$$\text{Lower Limit} = Q_1 - 1.5(\text{IQR})$$
$$\text{Upper Limit} = Q_3 + 1.5(\text{IQR})$$

An observation is classified as an outlier if its value is less than the lower limit or greater than the upper limit. For the monthly starting salary data shown in Table 3.1, $Q_1 = 3857.5$, $Q_3 = 4025$, IQR = 167.5, and the lower and upper limits are

$$\text{Lower Limit} = Q_1 - 1.5(\text{IQR}) = 3857.5 - 1.5(167.5) = 3606.25$$
$$\text{Upper Limit} = Q_3 + 1.5(\text{IQR}) = 4025 + 1.5(167.5) = 4276.25$$

Looking at the data in Table 3.1, we see that there are no observations with a starting salary less than the lower limit of 3606.25. But, there is one starting salary, 4325, that is greater than the upper limit of 4276.25. Thus, 4325 is considered to be an outlier using this alternate approach to identifying outliers.

NOTES AND COMMENTS

1. Chebyshev's theorem is applicable for any data set and can be used to state the minimum number of data values that will be within a certain number of standard deviations of the mean. If the data are known to be approximately bell-shaped, more can be said. For instance, the empirical rule allows us to say that *approximately* 95% of the data values will be within two standard deviations of the mean; Chebyshev's theorem allows us to conclude only that at least 75% of the data values will be in that interval.

2. Before analyzing a data set, statisticians usually make a variety of checks to ensure the validity of data. In a large study it is not uncommon for errors to be made in recording data values or in entering the values into a computer. Identifying outliers is one tool used to check the validity of the data.

Exercises

Methods

35. Consider a sample with data values of 10, 20, 12, 17, and 16. Compute the z-score for each of the five observations.

36. Consider a sample with a mean of 500 and a standard deviation of 100. What are the z-scores for the following data values: 520, 650, 500, 450, and 280?

 SELF*test*

37. Consider a sample with a mean of 30 and a standard deviation of 5. Use Chebyshev's theorem to determine the percentage of the data within each of the following ranges:
    a.   20 to 40
    b.   15 to 45
    c.   22 to 38
    d.   18 to 42
    e.   12 to 48

38. Suppose the data have a bell-shaped distribution with a mean of 30 and a standard deviation of 5. Use the empirical rule to determine the percentage of data within each of the following ranges:
    a.   20 to 40
    b.   15 to 45
    c.   25 to 35

Applications

SELF*test*

39. The results of a national survey showed that on average, adults sleep 6.9 hours per night. Suppose that the standard deviation is 1.2 hours.
    a.   Use Chebyshev's theorem to calculate the percentage of individuals who sleep between 4.5 and 9.3 hours.
    b.   Use Chebyshev's theorem to calculate the percentage of individuals who sleep between 3.9 and 9.9 hours.

c. Assume that the number of hours of sleep follows a bell-shaped distribution. Use the empirical rule to calculate the percentage of individuals who sleep between 4.5 and 9.3 hours per day. How does this result compare to the value that you obtained using Chebyshev's theorem in part (a)?

40. The Energy Information Administration reported that the mean retail price per gallon of regular grade gasoline was $3.43 (Energy Information Administration, July 2012). Suppose that the standard deviation was $.10 and that the retail price per gallon has a bell-shaped distribution.
    a. What percentage of regular grade gasoline sold between $3.33 and $3.53 per gallon?
    b. What percentage of regular grade gasoline sold between $3.33 and $3.63 per gallon?
    c. What percentage of regular grade gasoline sold for more than $3.63 per gallon?

41. The Graduate Management Admission Test (GMAT) is a standardized exam used by many universities as part of the assessment for admission to graduate study in business. The average GMAT score is 547 (*Magoosh* website, January 5, 2015). Assume that GMAT scores are bell-shaped with a standard deviation of 100.
    a. What percentage of GMAT scores are 647 or higher?
    b. What percentage of GMAT scores are 747 or higher?
    c. What percentage of GMAT scores are between 447 and 547?
    d. What percentage of GMAT scores are between 347 and 647?

42. Many families in California are using backyard structures for home offices, art studios, and hobby areas as well as for additional storage. Suppose that the mean price for a customized wooden, shingled backyard structure is $3100. Assume that the standard deviation is $1200.
    a. What is the z-score for a backyard structure costing $2300?
    b. What is the z-score for a backyard structure costing $4900?
    c. Interpret the z-scores in parts (a) and (b). Comment on whether either should be considered an outlier.
    d. If the cost for a backyard shed-office combination built in Albany, California, is $13,000, should this structure be considered an outlier? Explain.

43. According to a *Los Angeles Times* study of more than 1 million medical dispatches from 2007 to 2012, the 911 response time for medical aid varies dramatically across Los Angeles (*LA Times* website, November 2012). Under national standards adopted by the Los Angeles Fire Department, rescuers are supposed to arrive within six minutes to almost all medical emergencies. But the *Times* analysis found that in affluent hillside communities stretching from Griffith Park to Pacific Palisades, firefighters failed to hit that mark nearly 85% of the time.

    The following data show the response times, in minutes, for 10 emergency calls in the Griffith Park neighborhood.

    11.8   10.3   10.7   10.6   11.5   8.3   10.5   10.9   10.7   11.2

    Based on this sample of ten response times, compute the descriptive statistics in parts (a) and (b) and then answer the questions in parts (c) and (d):
    a. Mean, median, and mode
    b. Range and standard deviation
    c. Should the response time of 8.3 minutes be considered an outlier in comparison to the other response times?
    d. Do the response times indicate that the city is meeting the national standards? Should the city consider making changes to its response strategies? Would adding more stations to areas in the city be a practical solution? Discuss.

44. A sample of 10 NCAA college basketball game scores provided the following data.

DATA *file*

NCAA

Winning Team	Points	Losing Team	Points	Winning Margin
Arizona	90	Oregon	66	24
Duke	85	Georgetown	66	19
Florida State	75	Wake Forest	70	5
Kansas	78	Colorado	57	21
Kentucky	71	Notre Dame	63	8
Louisville	65	Tennessee	62	3
Oklahoma State	72	Texas	66	6
Purdue	76	Michigan State	70	6
Stanford	77	Southern Cal	67	10
Wisconsin	76	Illinois	56	20

a. Compute the mean and standard deviation for the points scored by the winning team.

b. Assume that the points scored by the winning teams for all NCAA games follow a bell-shaped distribution. Using the mean and standard deviation found in part (a), estimate the percentage of all NCAA games in which the winning team scores 84 or more points. Estimate the percentage of NCAA games in which the winning team scores more than 90 points.

c. Compute the mean and standard deviation for the winning margin. Do the data contain outliers? Explain.

45. *The Wall Street Journal* reported that Walmart Stores Inc. is planning to lay off 2300 employees at its Sam's Club warehouse unit. Approximately half of the layoffs will be hourly employees (*The Wall Street Journal*, January 25–26, 2014). Suppose the following data represent the percentage of hourly employees laid off for 15 Sam's Club stores.

55 56 44 43 44 56 60 62 57 45 36 38 50 69 65

a. Compute the mean and median percentage of hourly employees being laid off at these stores.

b. Compute the first and third quartiles.

c. Compute the range and interquartile range.

d. Compute the variance and standard deviation.

e. Do the data contain any outliers?

f. Based on the sample data, does it appear that Walmart is meeting its goal for reducing the number of hourly employees?

(3.4) Five-Number Summaries and Box Plots

Summary statistics and easy-to-draw graphs based on summary statistics can be used to quickly summarize large quantities of data. In this section we show how five-number summaries and box plots can be developed to identify several characteristics of a data set.

Five-Number Summary

In a **five-number summary**, five numbers are used to summarize the data:

1. Smallest value
2. First quartile (Q_1)
3. Median (Q_2)
4. Third quartile (Q_3)
5. Largest value

To illustrate the development of a five-number summary, we will use the monthly starting salary data shown in Table 3.1. Arranging the data in ascending order, we obtain the following results.

3710 3755 3850 3880 3880 3890 3920 3940 3950 4050 4130 4325

The smallest value is 3710 and the largest value is 4325. We showed how to compute the quartiles ($Q_1 = 3857.5$; $Q_2 = 3905$; and $Q_3 = 4025$) in Section 3.1. Thus, the five-number summary for the monthly starting salary data is

3710   3857.5   3905   4025   4325

The five-number summary indicates that the starting salaries in the sample are between 3710 and 4325 and that the median or middle value is 3905; and, the first and third quartiles show that approximately 50% of the starting salaries are between 3857.5 and 4025.

Box Plot

A box plot is a graphical display of data based on a five-number summary. A key to the development of a box plot is the computation of the interquartile range, IQR $= Q_3 - Q_1$. Figure 3.6 shows a box plot for the monthly starting salary data. The steps used to construct the box plot follow.

Box plots provide another way to identify outliers. But they do not necessarily identify the same values as those with a z-score less than –3 or greater than +3. Either or both procedures may be used.

1. A box is drawn with the ends of the box located at the first and third quartiles. For the salary data, $Q_1 = 3857.5$ and $Q_2 = 4025$. This box contains the middle 50% of the data.
2. A vertical line is drawn in the box at the location of the median (3905 for the salary data).
3. By using the interquartile range, IQR $= Q_3 - Q_1$, *limits* are located at 1.5(IQR) below Q_1 and 1.5(IQR) above Q_3. For the salary data, IQR $= Q_3 - Q_1 = 4025 - 3857.5 = 167.5$. Thus, the limits are $3857.5 - 1.5(167.5) = 3606.25$ and $4025 + 1.5(167.5) = 4276.25$. Data outside these limits are considered *outliers*.
4. The horizontal lines extending from each end of the box in Figure 3.6 are called *whiskers*. The whiskers are drawn from the ends of the box to the smallest and largest values *inside* the *limits* computed in step 3. Thus, the whiskers end at salary values of 3710 and 4130.
5. Finally, the location of each outlier is shown with a small asterisk. In Figure 3.6 we see one outlier, 4325.

FIGURE 3.6   BOX PLOT OF THE MONTHLY STARTING SALARY DATA WITH LINES SHOWING THE LOWER AND UPPER LIMITS

FIGURE 3.7   BOX PLOT OF THE MONTHLY STARTING SALARY DATA

In Figure 3.6 we included lines showing the location of the upper and lower limits. These lines were drawn to show how the limits are computed and where they are located. Although the limits are always computed, generally they are not drawn on the box plots. Figure 3.7 shows the usual appearance of a box plot for the starting salary data.

Comparative Analysis Using Box Plots

Box plots can also be used to provide a graphical summary of two or more groups and facilitate visual comparisons among the groups. For example, suppose the placement office decided to conduct a follow-up study to compare monthly starting salaries by the graduate's major: accounting, finance, information systems, management, and marketing. The major and starting salary data for a new sample of 111 recent business school graduates are shown in the data set named 2012MajorSalary, and Figure 3.8 shows the box plots corresponding to each major. Note that major is shown on the horizontal axis, and each box plot is shown vertically above the corresponding major. Displaying box plots in this manner is an excellent graphical technique for making comparisons among two or more groups.

What interpretations can you make from the box plots in Figure 3.8? Specifically, we note the following:

DATA *file*

2012MajorSalary

- The higher salaries are in accounting; the lower salaries are in management and marketing.

FIGURE 3.8   MINITAB BOX PLOTS OF MONTHLY STARTING SALARY BY MAJOR

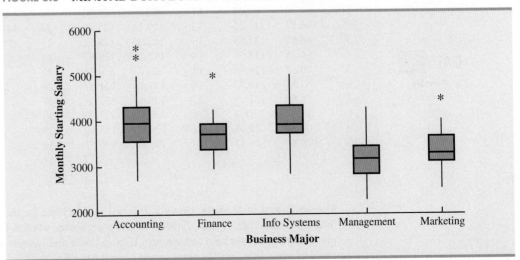

- Based on the medians, accounting and information systems have similar and higher median salaries. Finance is next, with management and marketing showing lower median salaries.
- High salary outliers exist for accounting, finance, and marketing majors.

Can you think of additional interpretations based on these box plots?

NOTES AND COMMENTS

In Appendix 3.1, we show how to construct a box plot for the starting salary data using Minitab.   The box plot obtained looks just like the one in Figure 3.7, but turned on its side.

Exercises

Methods

46. Consider a sample with data values of 27, 25, 20, 15, 30, 34, 28, and 25. Provide the five-number summary for the data.

47. Show the box plot for the data in exercise 46.

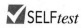 SELF*test*

48. Show the five-number summary and the box plot for the following data: 5, 15, 18, 10, 8, 12, 16, 10, 6.

49. A data set has a first quartile of 42 and a third quartile of 50. Compute the lower and upper limits for the corresponding box plot. Should a data value of 65 be considered an outlier?

Applications

50. Naples, Florida, hosts a half-marathon (13.1-mile race) in January each year. The event attracts top runners from throughout the United States as well as from around the world. In January 2009, 22 men and 31 women entered the 19–24 age class. Finish times in minutes are as follows (*Naples Daily News*, January 19, 2009). Times are shown in order of finish.

 DATA *file*

Runners

Finish	Men	Women	Finish	Men	Women	Finish	Men	Women
1	65.30	109.03	11	109.05	123.88	21	143.83	136.75
2	66.27	111.22	12	110.23	125.78	22	148.70	138.20
3	66.52	111.65	13	112.90	129.52	23		139.00
4	66.85	111.93	14	113.52	129.87	24		147.18
5	70.87	114.38	15	120.95	130.72	25		147.35
6	87.18	118.33	16	127.98	131.67	26		147.50
7	96.45	121.25	17	128.40	132.03	27		147.75
8	98.52	122.08	18	130.90	133.20	28		153.88
9	100.52	122.48	19	131.80	133.50	29		154.83
10	108.18	122.62	20	138.63	136.57	30		189.27
						31		189.28

a. George Towett of Marietta, Georgia, finished in first place for the men and Lauren Wald of Gainesville, Florida, finished in first place for the women. Compare the first-place finish times for men and women. If the 53 men and women runners had competed as one group, in what place would Lauren have finished?

b.   What is the median time for men and women runners? Compare men and women runners based on their median times.
c.   Provide a five-number summary for both the men and the women.
d.   Are there outliers in either group?
e.   Show the box plots for the two groups. Did men or women have the most variation in finish times? Explain.

 SELF*test*

51.   Annual sales, in millions of dollars, for 21 pharmaceutical companies follow.

8408	1374	1872	8879	2459	11413
608	14138	6452	1850	2818	1356
10498	7478	4019	4341	739	2127
3653	5794	8305			

a.   Provide a five-number summary.
b.   Compute the lower and upper limits.
c.   Do the data contain any outliers?
d.   Johnson & Johnson's sales are the largest on the list at $14,138 million. Suppose a data entry error (a transposition) had been made and the sales had been entered as $41,138 million. Would the method of detecting outliers in part (c) identify this problem and allow for correction of the data entry error?
e.   Show a box plot.

52.   *Consumer Reports* provided overall customer satisfaction scores for AT&T, Sprint, T-Mobile, and Verizon cell-phone services in major metropolitan areas throughout the United States. The rating for each service reflects the overall customer satisfaction considering a variety of factors such as cost, connectivity problems, dropped calls, static interference, and customer support. A satisfaction scale from 0 to 100 was used with 0 indicating completely dissatisfied and 100 indicating completely satisfied. The ratings for the four cell-phone services in 20 metropolitan areas are as shown (*Consumer Reports,* January 2009).

CellService

Metropolitan Area	AT&T	Sprint	T-Mobile	Verizon
Atlanta	70	66	71	79
Boston	69	64	74	76
Chicago	71	65	70	77
Dallas	75	65	74	78
Denver	71	67	73	77
Detroit	73	65	77	79
Jacksonville	73	64	75	81
Las Vegas	72	68	74	81
Los Angeles	66	65	68	78
Miami	68	69	73	80
Minneapolis	68	66	75	77
Philadelphia	72	66	71	78
Phoenix	68	66	76	81
San Antonio	75	65	75	80
San Diego	69	68	72	79
San Francisco	66	69	73	75
Seattle	68	67	74	77
St. Louis	74	66	74	79
Tampa	73	63	73	79
Washington	72	68	71	76

a.   Consider T-Mobile first. What is the median rating?
b.   Develop a five-number summary for the T-Mobile service.
c.   Are there outliers for T-Mobile? Explain.

d. Repeat parts (b) and (c) for the other three cell-phone services.

e. Show the box plots for the four cell-phone services on one graph. Discuss what a comparison of the box plots tells about the four services. Which service did *Consumer Reports* recommend as being best in terms of overall customer satisfaction?

AdmiredCompanies

53. *Fortune* magazine's list of the world's most admired companies for 2014 is provided in the data contained in the DATAfile named AdmiredCompanies (*Fortune*, March 17, 2014). The data in the column labelled Return shows the one-year total return (%) for the top ranked 50 companies. For the same time period the S&P average return was 18.4%.

a. Compute the median return for the top ranked 50 companies.

b. What percentage of the top-ranked 50 companies had a one-year return greater than the S&P average return?

c. Develop the five-number summary for the data.

d. Are there any outliers?

e. Develop a box plot for the one-year total return.

BorderCrossings

54. The Bureau of Transportation Statistics keeps track of all border crossings through ports of entry along the U.S.-Canadian and U.S.-Mexican borders. The data contained in the DATAfile named BorderCrossings show the most recently published figures for the number of personal vehicle crossings (rounded to the nearest 1000) at the 50 busiest ports of entry during the month of August (U.S. Department of Transportation website, February 28, 2013).

a. What are the mean and median number of crossings for these ports of entry?

b. What are the first and third quartiles?

c. Provide a five-number summary.

d. Do the data contain any outliers? Show a box plot.

3.5 Measures of Association Between Two Variables

Thus far we have examined numerical methods used to summarize the data for *one variable at a time*. Often a manager or decision maker is interested in the *relationship between two variables*. In this section we present covariance and correlation as descriptive measures of the relationship between two variables.

We begin by reconsidering the application concerning a stereo and sound equipment store in San Francisco as presented in Section 2.4. The store's manager wants to determine the relationship between the number of weekend television commercials shown and the sales at the store during the following week. Sample data with sales expressed in hundreds of dollars are provided in Table 3.6. It shows 10 observations ($n = 10$), one for each week. The scatter diagram in Figure 3.9 shows a positive relationship, with higher sales (y) associated with a greater number of commercials (x). In fact, the scatter diagram suggests that a straight line could be used as an approximation of the relationship. In the following discussion, we introduce **covariance** as a descriptive measure of the linear association between two variables.

Covariance

For a sample of size n with the observations (x_1, y_1), (x_2, y_2), and so on, the sample covariance is defined as follows:

SAMPLE COVARIANCE

$$s_{xy} = \frac{\Sigma(x_i - \bar{x})(y_i - \bar{y})}{n - 1} \qquad (3.13)$$

This formula pairs each x_i with a y_i. We then sum the products obtained by multiplying the deviation of each x_i from its sample mean $\bar{x}$ by the deviation of the corresponding y_i from its sample mean $\bar{y}$; this sum is then divided by $n - 1$.

To measure the strength of the linear relationship between the number of commercials x and the sales volume y in the stereo and sound equipment store problem, we use equation (3.13) to compute the sample covariance. The calculations in Table 3.7 show the computation of

TABLE 3.6 SAMPLE DATA FOR THE STEREO AND SOUND EQUIPMENT STORE

Week	Number of Commercials x	Sales Volume (\$100s) y
1	2	50
2	5	57
3	1	41
4	3	54
5	4	54
6	1	38
7	5	63
8	3	48
9	4	59
10	2	46

DATA *file*

Stereo

FIGURE 3.9 SCATTER DIAGRAM FOR THE STEREO AND SOUND EQUIPMENT STORE

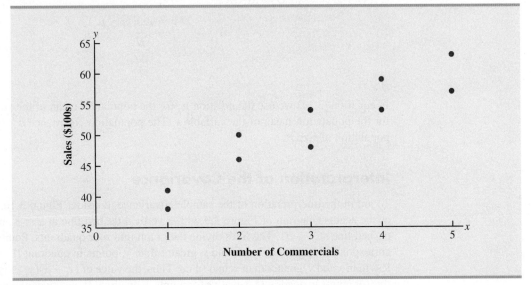

TABLE 3.7   CALCULATIONS FOR THE SAMPLE COVARIANCE

x_i	y_i	$x_i - \bar{x}$	$y_i - \bar{y}$	$(x_i - \bar{x})(y_i - \bar{y})$
2	50	−1	−1	1
5	57	2	6	12
1	41	−2	−10	20
3	54	0	3	0
4	54	1	3	3
1	38	−2	−13	26
5	63	2	12	24
3	48	0	−3	0
4	59	1	8	8
2	46	−1	−5	5
Totals 30	510	0	0	99

$$s_{xy} = \frac{\Sigma(x_i - \bar{x})(y_i - \bar{y})}{n - 1} = \frac{99}{10 - 1} = 11$$

$\Sigma(x_i - \bar{x})(y_i - \bar{y})$. Note that $\bar{x} = 30/10 = 3$ and $\bar{y} = 510/10 = 51$. Using equation (3.13), we obtain a sample covariance of

$$s_{xy} = \frac{\Sigma(x_i - \bar{x})(y_i - \bar{y})}{n - 1} = \frac{99}{9} = 11$$

The formula for computing the covariance of a population of size N is similar to equation (3.13), but we use different notation to indicate that we are working with the entire population.

POPULATION COVARIANCE

$$\sigma_{xy} = \frac{\Sigma(x_i - \mu_x)(y_i - \mu_y)}{N} \qquad \textbf{(3.14)}$$

In equation (3.14) we use the notation μ_x for the population mean of the variable x and μ_y for the population mean of the variable y. The population covariance σ_{xy} is defined for a population of size N.

Interpretation of the Covariance

To aid in the interpretation of the sample covariance, consider Figure 3.10. It is the same as the scatter diagram of Figure 3.9 with a vertical dashed line at $\bar{x} = 3$ and a horizontal dashed line at $\bar{y} = 51$. The lines divide the graph into four quadrants. Points in quadrant I correspond to x_i greater than $\bar{x}$ and y_i greater than $\bar{y}$, points in quadrant II correspond to x_i less than $\bar{x}$ and y_i greater than $\bar{y}$, and so on. Thus, the value of $(x_i - \bar{x})(y_i - \bar{y})$ must be positive for points in quadrant I, negative for points in quadrant II, positive for points in quadrant III, and negative for points in quadrant IV.

FIGURE 3.10 PARTITIONED SCATTER DIAGRAM FOR THE STEREO AND SOUND
EQUIPMENT STORE

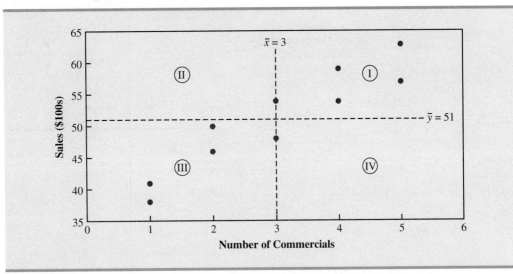

The covariance is a measure of the linear association between two variables.

If the value of s_{xy} is positive, the points with the greatest influence on s_{xy} must be in quadrants I and III. Hence, a positive value for s_{xy} indicates a positive linear association between x and y; that is, as the value of x increases, the value of y increases. If the value of s_{xy} is negative, however, the points with the greatest influence on s_{xy} are in quadrants II and IV. Hence, a negative value for s_{xy} indicates a negative linear association between x and y; that is, as the value of x increases, the value of y decreases. Finally, if the points are evenly distributed across all four quadrants, the value of s_{xy} will be close to zero, indicating no linear association between x and y. Figure 3.11 shows the values of s_{xy} that can be expected with three different types of scatter diagrams.

Referring again to Figure 3.10, we see that the scatter diagram for the stereo and sound equipment store follows the pattern in the top panel of Figure 3.11. As we should expect, the value of the sample covariance indicates a positive linear relationship with $s_{xy} = 11$.

From the preceding discussion, it might appear that a large positive value for the covariance indicates a strong positive linear relationship and that a large negative value indicates a strong negative linear relationship. However, one problem with using covariance as a measure of the strength of the linear relationship is that the value of the covariance depends on the units of measurement for x and y. For example, suppose we are interested in the relationship between height x and weight y for individuals. Clearly the strength of the relationship should be the same whether we measure height in feet or inches. Measuring the height in inches, however, gives us much larger numerical values for $(x_i - \bar{x})$ than when we measure height in feet. Thus, with height measured in inches, we would obtain a larger value for the numerator $\Sigma(x_i - \bar{x})(y_i - \bar{y})$ in equation (3.13)— and hence a larger covariance—when in fact the relationship does not change. A measure of the relationship between two variables that is not affected by the units of measurement for x and y is the **correlation coefficient**.

Correlation Coefficient

For sample data, the Pearson product moment correlation coefficient is defined as follows.

FIGURE 3.11   INTERPRETATION OF SAMPLE COVARIANCE

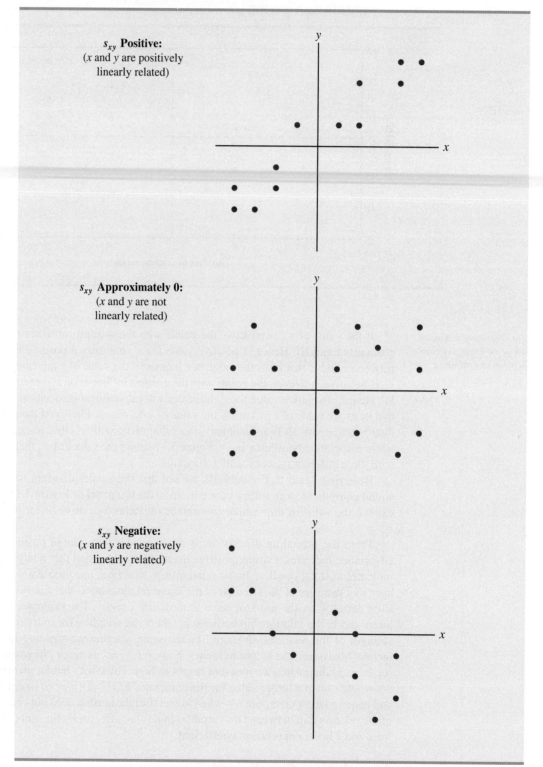

PEARSON PRODUCT MOMENT CORRELATION COEFFICIENT: SAMPLE DATA

$$r_{xy} = \frac{s_{xy}}{s_x s_y} \qquad (3.15)$$

where

r_{xy} = sample correlation coefficient
s_{xy} = sample covariance
s_x = sample standard deviation of x
s_y = sample standard deviation of y

Equation (3.15) shows that the Pearson product moment correlation coefficient for sample data (commonly referred to more simply as the *sample correlation coefficient*) is computed by dividing the sample covariance by the product of the sample standard deviation of x and the sample standard deviation of y.

Let us now compute the sample correlation coefficient for the stereo and sound equipment store. Using the data in Table 3.6, we can compute the sample standard deviations for the two variables:

$$s_x = \sqrt{\frac{\Sigma(x_i - \bar{x})^2}{n - 1}} = \sqrt{\frac{20}{9}} = 1.49$$

$$s_y = \sqrt{\frac{\Sigma(y_i - \bar{y})^2}{n - 1}} = \sqrt{\frac{566}{9}} = 7.93$$

Now, because $s_{xy} = 11$, the sample correlation coefficient equals

$$r_{xy} = \frac{s_{xy}}{s_x s_y} = \frac{11}{(1.49)(7.93)} = .93$$

The formula for computing the correlation coefficient for a population, denoted by the Greek letter ρ_{xy} (rho, pronounced "row"), follows.

PEARSON PRODUCT MOMENT CORRELATION COEFFICIENT: POPULATION DATA

$$\rho_{xy} = \frac{\sigma_{xy}}{\sigma_x \sigma_y} \qquad (3.16)$$

where

ρ_{xy} = population correlation coefficient
σ_{xy} = population covariance
σ_x = population standard deviation for x
σ_y = population standard deviation for y

The sample correlation coefficient r_{xy} is a point estimator of the population correlation coefficient ρ_{xy}.

The sample correlation coefficient r_{xy} provides an estimate of the population correlation coefficient ρ_{xy}.

FIGURE 3.12   SCATTER DIAGRAM DEPICTING A PERFECT POSITIVE LINEAR RELATIONSHIP

Interpretation of the Correlation Coefficient

First let us consider a simple example that illustrates the concept of a perfect positive linear relationship. The scatter diagram in Figure 3.12 depicts the relationship between x and y based on the following sample data.

x_i	y_i
5	10
10	30
15	50

The straight line drawn through each of the three points shows a perfect linear relationship between x and y. In order to apply equation (3.15) to compute the sample correlation we must first compute s_{xy}, s_x, and s_y. Some of the computations are shown in Table 3.8. Using the results in this table, we find

$$s_{xy} = \frac{\Sigma(x_i - \bar{x})(y_i - \bar{y})}{n - 1} = \frac{200}{2} = 100$$

$$s_x = \sqrt{\frac{\Sigma(x_i - \bar{x})^2}{n - 1}} = \sqrt{\frac{50}{2}} = 5$$

$$s_y = \sqrt{\frac{\Sigma(y_i - \bar{y})^2}{n - 1}} = \sqrt{\frac{800}{2}} = 20$$

$$r_{xy} = \frac{s_{xy}}{s_x s_y} = \frac{100}{5(20)} = 1$$

Thus, we see that the value of the sample correlation coefficient is 1.

TABLE 3.8 COMPUTATIONS USED IN CALCULATING THE SAMPLE CORRELATION COEFFICIENT

	x_i	y_i	$x_i - \bar{x}$	$(x_i - \bar{x})^2$	$y_i - \bar{y}$	$(y_i - \bar{y})^2$	$(x_i - \bar{x})(y_i - \bar{y})$
	5	10	−5	25	−20	400	100
	10	30	0	0	0	0	0
	15	50	5	25	20	400	100
Totals	30	90	0	50	0	800	200

$$\bar{x} = 10 \quad \bar{y} = 30$$

The correlation coefficient ranges from −1 to +1. Values close to −1 or +1 indicate a strong linear relationship. The closer the correlation is to zero, the weaker the relationship.

In general, it can be shown that if all the points in a data set fall on a positively-sloped straight line, the value of the sample correlation coefficient is +1; that is, a sample correlation coefficient of +1 corresponds to a perfect positive linear relationship between x and y. Moreover, if the points in the data set fall on a straight line having negative slope, the value of the sample correlation coefficient is −1; that is, a sample correlation coefficient of −1 corresponds to a perfect negative linear relationship between x and y.

Let us now suppose that a certain data set indicates a positive linear relationship between x and y but that the relationship is not perfect. The value of r_{xy} will be less than 1, indicating that the points in the scatter diagram are not all on a straight line. As the points deviate more and more from a perfect positive linear relationship, the value of r_{xy} becomes smaller and smaller. A value of r_{xy} equal to zero indicates no linear relationship between x and y, and values of r_{xy} near zero indicate a weak linear relationship.

For the data involving the stereo and sound equipment store, $r_{xy} = .93$. Therefore, we conclude that a strong positive linear relationship occurs between the number of commercials and sales. More specifically, an increase in the number of commercials is associated with an increase in sales.

In closing, we note that correlation provides a measure of linear association and not necessarily causation. A high correlation between two variables does not mean that changes in one variable will cause changes in the other variable. For example, we may find that the quality rating and the typical meal price of restaurants are positively correlated. However, simply increasing the meal price at a restaurant will not cause the quality rating to increase.

NOTES AND COMMENTS

1. Because the correlation coefficient measures only the strength of the linear relationship between two quantitative variables, it is possible for the correlation coefficient to be near zero, suggesting no linear relationship, when the relationship between the two variables is nonlinear. For example, the following scatter diagram shows the relationship between the amount spent by a small retail store for environmental control (heating and cooling) and the daily high outside temperature over 100 days.

The sample correlation coefficient for these data is $r_{xy} = -.007$ and indicates there is no linear relationship between the two variables. However, the scatter diagram provides strong visual evidence of a nonlinear relationship. That is, we can see that as the daily high outside temperature increases, the money spent on environmental control first decreases as less heating is required and then increases as greater cooling is required.

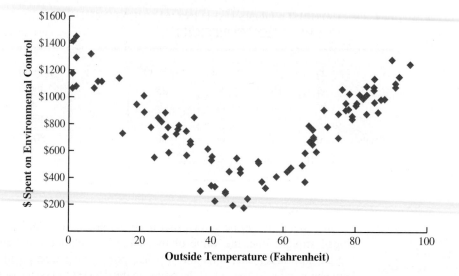

2. While the correlation coefficient is useful in assessing the relationship between two quantitative variables, other measures—such as the Spearman rank-correlation coefficient—can be used to assess a relationship between two variables when at least one of the variables is nominal or ordinal. We discuss the use of the Spearman rank-correlation coefficient in Chapter 18.

Exercises

Methods

55. Five observations taken for two variables follow.

x_i	4	6	11	3	16
y_i	50	50	40	60	30

   a. Develop a scatter diagram with x on the horizontal axis.
   b. What does the scatter diagram developed in part (a) indicate about the relationship between the two variables?
   c. Compute and interpret the sample covariance.
   d. Compute and interpret the sample correlation coefficient.

56. Five observations taken for two variables follow.

x_i	6	11	15	21	27
y_i	6	9	6	17	12

   a. Develop a scatter diagram for these data.
   b. What does the scatter diagram indicate about a relationship between x and y?
   c. Compute and interpret the sample covariance.
   d. Compute and interpret the sample correlation coefficient.

Applications

57. Ten major college football bowl games were played in January 2010, with the University of Alabama beating the University of Texas 37 to 21 to become the national champion of college football. The results of the 10 bowl games follow (*USA Today*, January 8, 2010).

Bowl Game	Score	Predicted Point Margin	Actual Point Margin
Outback	Auburn 38 Northwestern 35	5	3
Gator	Florida State 33 West Virginia 21	1	12
Capital One	Penn State 19 LSU 17	3	2
Rose	Ohio State 26 Oregon 17	−2	9
Sugar	Florida 51 Cincinnati 24	14	27
Cotton	Mississippi State 21 Oklahoma State 7	3	14
Alamo	Texas Tech 41 Michigan State 31	9	10
Fiesta	Boise State 17 TCU 10	−4	7
Orange	Iowa 24 Georgia Tech 14	−3	10
Championship	Alabama 37 Texas 21	4	16

DATA *file*
BowlGames

The predicted winning point margin was based on Las Vegas betting odds approximately one week before the bowl games were played. For example, Auburn was predicted to beat Northwestern in the Outback Bowl by five points. The actual winning point margin for Auburn was three points. A negative predicted winning point margin means that the team that won the bowl game was an underdog and expected to lose. For example, in the Rose Bowl, Ohio State was a two-point underdog to Oregon and ended up winning by nine points.

a. Develop a scatter diagram with predicted point margin on the horizontal axis.
b. What is the relationship between predicted and actual point margins?
c. Compute and interpret the sample covariance.
d. Compute the sample correlation coefficient. What does this value indicate about the relationship between the Las Vegas predicted point margin and the actual point margin in college football bowl games?

58. A department of transportation's study on driving speed and miles per gallon for midsize automobiles resulted in the following data:

Speed (Miles per Hour)	30	50	40	55	30	25	60	25	50	55
Miles per Gallon	28	25	25	23	30	32	21	35	26	25

Compute and interpret the sample correlation coefficient.

DATA *file*
SmokeDetectors

59. Over the past 40 years, the percentage of homes in the United States with smoke detectors has risen steadily and has plateaued at about 96% (*National Fire Protection Association* website, January, 2015). With this increase in the use of home smoke detectors, what has happened to the death rate from home fires? The DATAfile *SmokeDetectors* contains 17 years of data on the estimated percentage of homes with smoke detectors and the estimated home fire deaths per million of population.

a. Do you expect a positive or negative relationship between smoke detector use and deaths from home fires? Why or why not?
b. Compute and report the correlation coefficient. Is there a positive or negative correlation between smoke detector use and deaths from home fires? Comment.
c. Show a scatter plot of the death rate per million of population and the percentage of homes with smoke detectors.

DATA *file*
Russell

60. The Russell 1000 is a stock market index consisting of the largest U.S. companies. The Dow Jones Industrial Average is based on 30 large companies. The DATAfile Russell gives the annual percentage returns for each of these stock indexes for the years 1988 to 2012 (1stock1 website).

a. Plot these percentage returns using a scatter plot.
b. Compute the sample mean and standard deviation for each index.

c. Compute the sample correlation.

d. Discuss similarities and differences in these two indexes.

BestPrivateColleges

61. A random sample of 30 colleges from Kiplinger's list of the best values in private college provided the data shown in the DATAfile named BestPrivateColleges (Kiplinger, October 2013). The variable named Admit Rate (%) shows the percentage of students that applied to the college and were admitted, and the variable named 4-yr Grad. Rate (%) shows the percentage of students that were admitted and graduated in four years.

a. Develop a scatter diagram with Admit Rate (%) as the independent variable. What does the scatter diagram indicate about the relationship between the two variables?

b. Compute the sample correlation coefficient. What does the value of the sample correlation coefficient indicate about the relationship between the Admit Rate (%) and the 4-yr Grad. Rate (%)?

3.6   Data Dashboards: Adding Numerical Measures to Improve Effectiveness

In Section 2.5 we provided an introduction to data visualization, a term used to describe the use of graphical displays to summarize and present information about a data set. The goal of data visualization is to communicate key information about the data as effectively and clearly as possible. One of the most widely used data visualization tools is a data dashboard, a set of visual displays that organizes and presents information that is used to monitor the performance of a company or organization in a manner that is easy to read, understand, and interpret. In this section we extend the discussion of data dashboards to show how the addition of numerical measures can improve the overall effectiveness of the display.

The addition of numerical measures, such as the mean and standard deviation of key performance indicators (KPIs) to a data dashboard is critical because numerical measures often provide benchmarks or goals by which KPIs are evaluated. In addition, graphical displays that include numerical measures as components of the display are also frequently included in data dashboards. We must keep in mind that the purpose of a data dashboard is to provide information on the KPIs in a manner that is easy to read, understand, and interpret. Adding numerical measures and graphs that utilize numerical measures can help us accomplish these objectives.

To illustrate the use of numerical measures in a data dashboard, recall the Grogan Oil Company application that we used in Section 2.5 to introduce the concept of a data dashboard. Grogan Oil has offices located in three Texas cities: Austin (its headquarters), Houston, and Dallas. Grogan's Information Technology (IT) call center, located in the Austin office, handles calls regarding computer-related problems (software, Internet, and email) from employees in the three offices. Figure 3.13 shows the data dashboard that Grogan developed to monitor the performance of the call center. The key components of this dashboard are as follows:

- The stacked bar chart in the upper left corner of the dashboard shows the call volume for each type of problem (software, Internet, or email) over time.
- The pie chart in the upper right corner of the dashboard shows the percentage of time that call center employees spent on each type of problem or not working on a call (idle).
- For each unresolved case that was received more than 15 minutes ago, the bar chart shown in the middle left portion of the dashboard shows the length of time that each of these cases has been unresolved.
- The bar chart in the middle right portion of the dashboard shows the call volume by office (Houston, Dallas, Austin) for each type of problem.

FIGURE 3.13   INITIAL GROGAN OIL INFORMATION TECHNOLOGY CALL CENTER DATA DASHBOARD

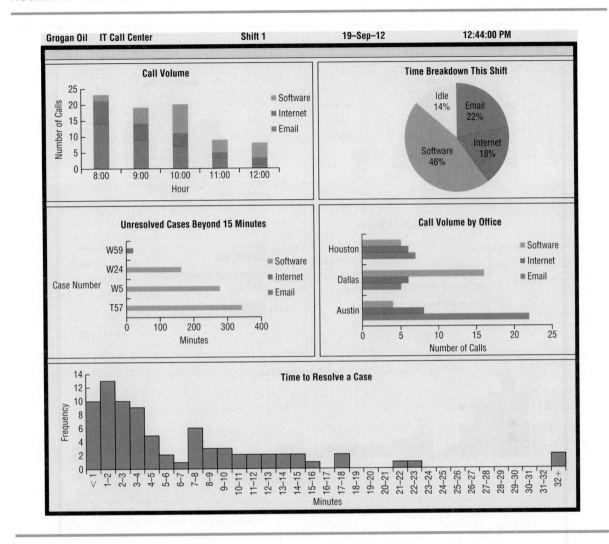

- The histogram at the bottom of the dashboard shows the distribution of the time to resolve a case for all resolved cases for the current shift.

In order to gain additional insight into the performance of the call center, Grogan's IT manager has decided to expand the current dashboard by adding box plots for the time required to resolve calls received for each type of problem (email, Internet, and software). In addition, a graph showing the time to resolve individual cases has been added in the lower left portion of the dashboard. Finally, the IT manager added a display of summary statistics for each type of problem and summary statistics for each of the first few hours of the shift. The updated dashboard is shown in Figure 3.14.

The IT call center has set a target performance level or benchmark of 10 minutes for the mean time to resolve a case. Furthermore, the center has decided it is undesirable for the time to resolve a case to exceed 15 minutes. To reflect these benchmarks, a black horizontal line at the mean target value of 10 minutes and a red horizontal line at the maximum acceptable level of 15 minutes have been added to both the graph showing the time to resolve cases and the box plots of the time required to resolve calls received for each type of problem.

FIGURE 3.14   UPDATED GROGAN OIL INFORMATION TECHNOLOGY CALL CENTER DATA
DASHBOARD

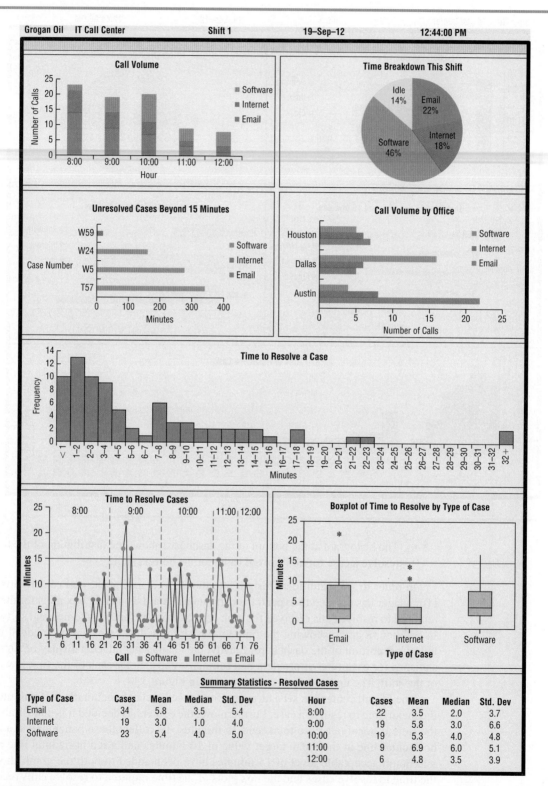

The summary statistics in the dashboard in Figure 3.21 show that the mean time to resolve an email case is 5.8 minutes, the mean time to resolve an Internet case is 3.0 minutes, and the mean time to resolve a software case is 5.4 minutes. Thus, the mean time to resolve each type of case is better than the target mean (10 minutes).

Reviewing the box plots, we see that the box associated with the email cases is "larger" than the boxes associated with the other two types of cases. The summary statistics also show that the standard deviation of the time to resolve email cases is larger than the standard deviations of the times to resolve the other types of cases. This leads us to take a closer look at the email cases in the two new graphs. The box plot for the email cases has a whisker that extends beyond 15 minutes and an outlier well beyond 15 minutes. The graph of the time to resolve individual cases (in the lower left position of the dashboard) shows that this is because of two calls on email cases during the 9:00 hour that took longer than the target maximum time (15 minutes) to resolve. This analysis may lead the IT call center manager to further investigate why resolution times are more variable for email cases than for Internet or software cases. Based on this analysis, the IT manager may also decide to investigate the circumstances that led to inordinately long resolution times for the two email cases that took longer than 15 minutes to resolve.

The graph of the time to resolve individual cases shows that most calls received during the first hour of the shift were resolved relatively quickly; the graph also shows that the time to resolve cases increased gradually throughout the morning. This could be due to a tendency for complex problems to arise later in the shift or possibly to the backlog of calls that accumulates over time. Although the summary statistics suggest that cases submitted during the 9:00 hour take the longest to resolve, the graph of time to resolve individual cases shows that two time-consuming email cases and one time-consuming software case were reported during that hour, and this may explain why the mean time to resolve cases during the 9:00 hour is larger than during any other hour of the shift. Overall, reported cases have generally been resolved in 15 minutes or less during this shift.

Drilling down refers to functionality in interactive data dashboards that allows the user to access information and analyses at an increasingly detailed level.

Dashboards such as the Grogan Oil data dashboard are often interactive. For instance, when a manager uses a mouse or a touch screen monitor to position the cursor over the display or point to something on the display, additional information, such as the time to resolve the problem, the time the call was received, and the individual and/or the location that reported the problem, may appear. Clicking on the individual item may also take the user to a new level of analysis at the individual case level.

Summary

In this chapter we introduced several descriptive statistics that can be used to summarize the location, variability, and shape of a data distribution. Unlike the tabular and graphical displays introduced in Chapter 2, the measures introduced in this chapter summarize the data in terms of numerical values. When the numerical values obtained are for a sample, they are called sample statistics. When the numerical values obtained are for a population, they are called population parameters. Some of the notation used for sample statistics and population parameters follow.

In statistical inference, a sample statistic is referred to as a point estimator of the population parameter.

	Sample Statistic	Population Parameter
Mean	$\bar{x}$	μ
Variance	s^2	σ^2
Standard deviation	s	σ
Covariance	s_{xy}	σ_{xy}
Correlation	r_{xy}	ρ_{xy}

As measures of location, we defined the mean, median, mode, weighted mean, geometric mean, percentiles, and quartiles. Next, we presented the range, interquartile range, variance, standard deviation, and coefficient of variation as measures of variability or dispersion. Our primary measure of the shape of a data distribution was the skewness. Negative values of skewness indicate a data distribution skewed to the left, and positive values of skewness indicate a data distribution skewed to the right. We then described how the mean and standard deviation could be used, applying Chebyshev's theorem and the empirical rule, to provide more information about the distribution of data and to identify outliers.

In Section 3.4 we showed how to develop a five-number summary and a box plot to provide simultaneous information about the location, variability, and shape of the distribution. In Section 3.5 we introduced covariance and the correlation coefficient as measures of association between two variables. In the final section, we showed how adding numerical measures can improve the effectiveness of data dashboards.

The descriptive statistics we discussed can be developed using statistical software packages and spreadsheets. In the chapter-ending appendixes we show how to use Minitab and Excel to develop the descriptive statistics introduced in this chapter.

Glossary

Box plot A graphical summary of data based on a five-number summary.

Chebyshev's theorem A theorem that can be used to make statements about the proportion of data values that must be within a specified number of standard deviations of the mean.

Coefficient of variation A measure of relative variability computed by dividing the standard deviation by the mean and multiplying by 100.

Correlation coefficient A measure of linear association between two variables that takes on values between -1 and $+1$. Values near $+1$ indicate a strong positive linear relationship; values near -1 indicate a strong negative linear relationship; and values near zero indicate the lack of a linear relationship.

Covariance A measure of linear association between two variables. Positive values indicate a positive relationship; negative values indicate a negative relationship.

Empirical rule A rule that can be used to compute the percentage of data values that must be within one, two, and three standard deviations of the mean for data that exhibit a bell-shaped distribution.

Five-number summary A technique that uses five numbers to summarize the data: smallest value, first quartile, median, third quartile, and largest value.

Geometric mean A measure of location that is calculated by finding the nth root of the product of n values.

Interquartile range (IQR) A measure of variability, defined to be the difference between the third and first quartiles.

Mean A measure of central location computed by summing the data values and dividing by the number of observations.

Median A measure of central location provided by the value in the middle when the data are arranged in ascending order.

Mode A measure of location, defined as the value that occurs with greatest frequency.

Outlier An unusually small or unusually large data value.

Percentile A value such that at least p percent of the observations are less than or equal to this value and at least $(100 - p)$ percent of the observations are greater than or equal to this value. The 50th percentile is the median.

Point estimator A sample statistic, such as $\bar{x}$, s^2, and s, used to estimate the corresponding population parameter.

Population parameter A numerical value used as a summary measure for a population (e.g., the population mean, μ, the population variance, σ^2, and the population standard deviation, σ).

Quartiles The 25th, 50th, and 75th percentiles, referred to as the first quartile, the second quartile (median), and third quartile, respectively. The quartiles can be used to divide a data set into four parts, with each part containing approximately 25% of the data.

Range A measure of variability, defined to be the largest value minus the smallest value.

Sample statistic A numerical value used as a summary measure for a sample (e.g., the sample mean, $\bar{x}$, the sample variance, s^2, and the sample standard deviation, s).

Skewness A measure of the shape of a data distribution. Data skewed to the left result in negative skewness; a symmetric data distribution results in zero skewness; and data skewed to the right result in positive skewness.

Standard deviation A measure of variability computed by taking the positive square root of the variance.

Variance A measure of variability based on the squared deviations of the data values about the mean.

Weighted mean The mean obtained by assigning each observation a weight that reflects its importance.

z-score A value computed by dividing the deviation about the mean ($x_i - \bar{x}$) by the standard deviation s. A z-score is referred to as a standardized value and denotes the number of standard deviations x_i is from the mean.

Key Formulas

Sample Mean

$$\bar{x} = \frac{\Sigma x_i}{n} \tag{3.1}$$

Population Mean

$$\mu = \frac{\Sigma x_i}{N} \tag{3.2}$$

Weighted Mean

$$\bar{x} = \frac{\Sigma w_i x_i}{\Sigma w_i} \tag{3.3}$$

Geometric Mean

$$\bar{x}_g = \sqrt[n]{(x_1)(x_2) \cdots (x_n)} = [(x_1)(x_2) \cdots (x_n)]^{1/n} \tag{3.4}$$

Location of the pth Percentile

$$L_p = \frac{p}{100}(n + 1) \tag{3.5}$$

Interquartile Range

$$IQR = Q_3 - Q_1 \tag{3.6}$$

Population Variance

$$\sigma^2 = \frac{\Sigma(x_i - \mu)^2}{N} \tag{3.7}$$

Sample Variance

$$s^2 = \frac{\Sigma(x_i - \bar{x})^2}{n - 1} \tag{3.8}$$

Standard Deviation

$$\text{Sample standard deviation} = s = \sqrt{s^2} \tag{3.9}$$

$$\text{Population standard deviation} = \sigma = \sqrt{\sigma^2} \tag{3.10}$$

Coefficient of Variation

$$\left(\frac{\text{Standard deviation}}{\text{Mean}} \times 100 \right)\% \tag{3.11}$$

z-Score

$$z_i = \frac{x_i - \bar{x}}{s} \tag{3.12}$$

Sample Covariance

$$s_{xy} = \frac{\Sigma(x_i - \bar{x})(y_i - \bar{y})}{n - 1} \tag{3.13}$$

Population Covariance

$$\sigma_{xy} = \frac{\Sigma(x_i - \mu_x)(y_i - \mu_y)}{N} \tag{3.14}$$

Pearson Product Moment Correlation Coefficient: Sample Data

$$r_{xy} = \frac{s_{xy}}{s_x s_y} \tag{3.15}$$

Pearson Product Moment Correlation Coefficient: Population Data

$$\rho_{xy} = \frac{\sigma_{xy}}{\sigma_x \sigma_y} \tag{3.16}$$

Supplementary Exercises

62. The average number of times Americans dine out in a week fell from 4.0 in 2008 to 3.8 in 2012 (Zagat.com, April, 2012). The number of times a sample of 20 families dined out last week provides the following data.

6	1	5	3	7	3	0	3	1	3
4	1	2	4	1	0	5	6	3	1

   a. Compute the mean and median.
   b. Compute the first and third quartiles.
   c. Compute the range and interquartile range.
   d. Compute the variance and standard deviation.
   e. The skewness measure for these data is 0.34. Comment on the shape of this distribution. Is it the shape you would expect? Why or why not?
   f. Do the data contain outliers?

Coaches

63. *USA Today* reports that NCAA colleges and universities are paying higher salaries to a newly recruited football coach compared to what they paid their previous football coach. (*USA Today*, February 12, 2013). The annual base salaries for the previous head football coach and the new head football coach at 23 schools are given in the DATAfile Coaches.
   a. Determine the median annual salary for a previous head football coach and a new head football coach.
   b. Compute the range for salaries for both previous and new head football coaches.
   c. Compute the standard deviation for salaries for both previous and new head football coaches.
   d. Based on your answers to (a) to (c), comment on any differences between the annual base salary a school pays a new head football coach compared to what it paid its previous head football coach.

64. The average waiting time for a patient at an El Paso physician's office is just over 29 minutes, well above the national average of 21 minutes. In fact, El Paso has the longest physician's office waiting times in the United States (*El Paso Times,* January 8, 2012). In order to address the issue of long patient wait times, some physician's offices are using wait tracking systems to notify patients of expected wait times. Patients can adjust their arrival times based on this information and spend less time in waiting rooms. The following data show wait times (minutes) for a sample of patients at offices that do not have an office tracking system and wait times for a sample of patients at offices with an office tracking system.

WaitTracking

Without Wait Tracking System	With Wait Tracking System
24	31
67	11
17	14
20	18
31	12
44	37
12	9
23	13
16	12
37	15

a. What are the mean and median patient wait times for offices with a wait tracking system? What are the mean and median patient wait times for offices without a wait tracking system?

b. What are the variance and standard deviation of patient wait times for offices with a wait tracking system? What are the variance and standard deviation of patient wait times for visits to offices without a wait tracking system?

c. Do offices with a wait tracking system have shorter patient wait times than offices without a wait tracking system? Explain.

d. Considering only offices without a wait tracking system, what is the z-score for the tenth patient in the sample?

e. Considering only offices with a wait tracking system, what is the z-score for the sixth patient in the sample? How does this z-score compare with the z-score you calculated for part (d)?

f. Based on z-scores, do the data for offices without a wait tracking system contain any outliers? Based on z-scores, do the data for offices with a wait tracking system contain any outliers?

DATA *file*
Sleep

65. U.S. companies lose $63.2 billion per year from workers with insomnia. Workers lose an average of 7.8 days of productivity per year due to lack of sleep (*Wall Street Journal*, January 23, 2013). The following data show the number of hours of sleep attained during a recent night for a sample of 20 workers.

6	5	10	5	6	9	9	5	9	5
8	7	8	6	9	8	9	6	10	8

a. What is the mean number of hours of sleep for this sample?
b. What is the variance? Standard deviation?

DATA *file*
Smartphone

66. A study of smartphone users shows that 68% of smartphone use occurs at home and a user spends an average of 410 minutes per month using a smartphone to interact with other people (*Harvard Business Review*, January–February 2013). Consider the following data indicating the number of minutes in a month spent interacting with others via a smartphone for a sample of 50 smartphone users.

353	458	404	394	416
437	430	369	448	430
431	469	446	387	445
354	468	422	402	360
444	424	441	357	435
461	407	470	413	351
464	374	417	460	352
445	387	468	368	430
384	367	436	390	464
405	372	401	388	367

a. What is the mean number of minutes spent interacting with others for this sample? How does it compare to the mean reported in the study?
b. What is the standard deviation for this sample?
c. Are there any outliers in this sample?

67. Public transportation and the automobile are two methods an employee can use to get to work each day. Samples of times recorded for each method are shown. Times are in minutes.

Public Transportation:	28	29	32	37	33	25	29	32	41	34
Automobile:		29	31	33	32	34	30	31	32	35	33

a. Compute the sample mean time to get to work for each method.
b. Compute the sample standard deviation for each method.
c. On the basis of your results from parts (a) and (b), which method of transportation should be preferred? Explain.
d. Develop a box plot for each method. Does a comparison of the box plots support your conclusion in part (c)?

68. In 2007 the *New York Times* reported that the median annual household income in the United States was $55,500 (*New York Times* website, August, 21, 2013). Answer the following questions based on the following sample of 14 household incomes for 2013 ($1000s).

49.4	52.4	53.4	51.3	52.1	48.7	52.1
52.2	64.5	51.6	46.5	52.9	52.5	51.2

a. What is the median household income for the sample data for 2013?
b. Based on the sample data, estimate the percentage change in the median household income from 2007 to 2013.
c. Compute the first and third quartiles.
d. Provide a five-number summary.
e. Using the z-score approach, do the data contain any outliers? Does the approach that uses the values of the first and third quartiles and the interquartile range to detect outliers provide the same results?

69. The data contained in the DATAfile named FoodIndustry show the company/chain name, the average sales per store ($1000s), and the food segment industry for 47 restaurant chains (*Quick Service Restaurant Magazine* website, August 2013).

FoodIndustry

a. What was the mean U.S. sales per store for the 47 restaurant chains?
b. What are the first and third quartiles? What is your interpretation of the quartiles?
c. Show a box plot for the level of sales and discuss if there are any outliers in terms of sales that would skew the results.
d. Develop a frequency distribution showing the average sales per store for each segment. Comment on the results obtained.

70. *Travel + Leisure* magazine provides an annual list of the 500 best hotels in the world. The magazine provides a rating for each hotel along with a brief description that includes the size of the hotel, amenities, and the cost per night for a double room. A sample of 12 of the top-rated hotels in the United States follows.

DATA *file*

Travel

Hotel	Location	Rooms	Cost/Night
Boulders Resort & Spa	Phoenix, AZ	220	499
Disney's Wilderness Lodge	Orlando, FL	727	340
Four Seasons Hotel Beverly Hills	Los Angeles, CA	285	585
Four Seasons Hotel	Boston, MA	273	495
Hay-Adams	Washington, DC	145	495
Inn on Biltmore Estate	Asheville, NC	213	279
Loews Ventana Canyon Resort	Phoenix, AZ	398	279
Mauna Lani Bay Hotel	Island of Hawaii	343	455
Montage Laguna Beach	Laguna Beach, CA	250	595
Sofitel Water Tower	Chicago, IL	414	367
St. Regis Monarch Beach	Dana Point, CA	400	675
The Broadmoor	Colorado Springs, CO	700	420

a. What is the mean number of rooms?
b. What is the mean cost per night for a double room?

c. Develop a scatter diagram with the number of rooms on the horizontal axis and the cost per night on the vertical axis. Does there appear to be a relationship between the number of rooms and the cost per night? Discuss.

d. What is the sample correlation coefficient? What does it tell you about the relationship between the number of rooms and the cost per night for a double room? Does this appear reasonable? Discuss.

71. The 32 teams in the National Football League (NFL) are worth, on average, $1.17 billion, 5% more than last year. The following data show the annual revenue ($ millions) and the estimated team value ($ millions) for the 32 NFL teams (*Forbes* website, February 28, 2014).

DATA *file*

NFLTeamValue

Team	Revenue ($ millions)	Current Value ($ millions)
Arizona Cardinals	253	961
Atlanta Falcons	252	933
Baltimore Ravens	292	1227
Buffalo Bills	256	870
Carolina Panthers	271	1057
Chicago Bears	298	1252
Cincinnati Bengals	250	924
Cleveland Browns	264	1005
Dallas Cowboys	539	2300
Denver Broncos	283	1161
Detroit Lions	248	900
Green Bay Packers	282	1183
Houston Texans	320	1450
Indianapolis Colts	276	1200
Jacksonville Jaguars	260	840
Kansas City Chiefs	245	1009
Miami Dolphins	268	1074
Minnesota Vikings	234	1007
New England Patriots	408	1800
New Orleans Saints	276	1004
New York Giants	338	1550
New York Jets	321	1380
Oakland Raiders	229	825
Philadelphia Eagles	306	1314
Pittsburgh Steelers	266	1118
San Diego Chargers	250	949
San Francisco 49ers	255	1224
Seattle Seahawks	270	1081
St. Louis Rams	239	875
Tampa Bay Buccaneers	267	1067
Tennessee Titans	270	1055
Washington Redskins	381	1700

a. Develop a scatter diagram with Revenue on the horizontal axis and Value on the vertical axis. Does there appear that there is any relationship between the two variables?

b. What is the sample correlation coefficient? What can you say about the strength of the relationship between Revenue and Value?

72. Does a major league baseball team's record during spring training indicate how the team will play during the regular season? Over a six-year period, the correlation coefficient between a team's winning percentage in spring training and its winning percentage in the regular season is .18. Shown are the winning percentages for the 14 American League teams during a previous season.

Team	Spring Training	Regular Season	Team	Spring Training	Regular Season
Baltimore Orioles	.407	.422	Minnesota Twins	.500	.540
Boston Red Sox	.429	.586	New York Yankees	.577	.549
Chicago White Sox	.417	.546	Oakland A's	.692	.466
Cleveland Indians	.569	.500	Seattle Mariners	.500	.377
Detroit Tigers	.569	.457	Tampa Bay Rays	.731	.599
Kansas City Royals	.533	.463	Texas Rangers	.643	.488
Los Angeles Angels	.724	.617	Toronto Blue Jays	.448	.531

DATA *file*

SpringTraining

a. What is the correlation coefficient between the spring training and the regular season winning percentages?

b. What is your conclusion about a team's record during spring training indicating how the team will play during the regular season? What are some of the reasons why this occurs? Discuss.

73. The days to maturity for a sample of five money market funds are shown here. The dollar amounts invested in the funds are provided. Use the weighted mean to determine the mean number of days to maturity for dollars invested in these five money market funds.

Days to Maturity	Dollar Value ($millions)
20	20
12	30
7	10
5	15
6	10

74. Automobiles traveling on a road with a posted speed limit of 55 miles per hour are checked for speed by a state police radar system. Following is a frequency distribution of speeds.

Speed (miles per hour)	Frequency
45–49	10
50–54	40
55–59	150
60–64	175
65–69	75
70–74	15
75–79	10
Total	475

a. What is the mean speed of the automobiles traveling on this road?

b. Compute the variance and the standard deviation.

75. The Panama Railroad Company was established in 1850 to construct a railroad across the isthmus that would allow fast and easy access between the Atlantic and Pacific Oceans. The following table (*The Big Ditch*, Mauer and Yu, 2011) provides annual returns for Panama Railroad stock from 1853 through 1880.

Year	Return on Panama Railroad Company Stock (%)
1853	−1
1854	−9
1855	19
1856	2
1857	3
1858	36
1859	21
1860	16
1861	−5
1862	43
1863	44
1864	48
1865	7
1866	11
1867	23
1868	20
1869	−11
1870	−51
1871	−42
1872	39
1873	42
1874	12
1875	26
1876	9
1877	−6
1878	25
1879	31
1880	30

DATA *file*

PanamaRailroad

a. Create a graph of the annual returns on the stock. The New York Stock Exchange earned an annual average return of 8.4% from 1853 through 1880. Can you tell from the graph if the Panama Railroad Company stock outperformed the New York Stock Exchange?

b. Calculate the mean annual return on Panama Railroad Company stock from 1853 through 1880. Did the stock outperform the New York Stock Exchange over the same period?

Case Problem 1   Pelican Stores

Pelican Stores, a division of National Clothing, is a chain of women's apparel stores operating throughout the country. The chain recently ran a promotion in which discount coupons were sent to customers of other National Clothing stores. Data collected for a sample of 100 in-store credit card transactions at Pelican Stores during one day while the promotion was running are contained in the file named PelicanStores. Table 3.9 shows a portion of the data set. The proprietary card method of payment refers to charges made using a National Clothing charge card. Customers who made a purchase using a discount coupon are referred to as promotional customers and customers who made a purchase but did not use a discount coupon are referred to as regular customers. Because the promotional coupons were not sent to regular Pelican Stores customers, management considers the sales made to people presenting the promotional coupons as sales it would not otherwise make. Of course, Pelican also hopes that the promotional customers will continue to shop at its stores.

TABLE 3.9   SAMPLE OF 100 CREDIT CARD PURCHASES AT PELICAN STORES

Customer	Type of Customer	Items	Net Sales	Method of Payment	Gender	Marital Status	Age
1	Regular	1	39.50	Discover	Male	Married	32
2	Promotional	1	102.40	Proprietary Card	Female	Married	36
3	Regular	1	22.50	Proprietary Card	Female	Married	32
4	Promotional	5	100.40	Proprietary Card	Female	Married	28
5	Regular	2	54.00	MasterCard	Female	Married	34
6	Regular	1	44.50	MasterCard	Female	Married	44
7	Promotional	2	78.00	Proprietary Card	Female	Married	30
8	Regular	1	22.50	Visa	Female	Married	40
9	Promotional	2	56.52	Proprietary Card	Female	Married	46
10	Regular	1	44.50	Proprietary Card	Female	Married	36
.	.	.	.	.	.	.	.
96	Regular	1	39.50	MasterCard	Female	Married	44
97	Promotional	9	253.00	Proprietary Card	Female	Married	30
98	Promotional	10	287.59	Proprietary Card	Female	Married	52
99	Promotional	2	47.60	Proprietary Card	Female	Married	30
100	Promotional	1	28.44	Proprietary Card	Female	Married	44

DATA *file*

PelicanStores

Most of the variables shown in Table 3.9 are self-explanatory, but two of the variables require some clarification.

Items   The total number of items purchased
Net Sales   The total amount ($) charged to the credit card

Pelican's management would like to use this sample data to learn about its customer base and to evaluate the promotion involving discount coupons.

Managerial Report

Use the methods of descriptive statistics presented in this chapter to summarize the data and comment on your findings. At a minimum, your report should include the following:

1. Descriptive statistics on net sales and descriptive statistics on net sales by various classifications of customers.
2. Descriptive statistics concerning the relationship between age and net sales.

Case Problem 2   Motion Picture Industry

The motion picture industry is a competitive business. More than 50 studios produce several hundred new motion pictures each year, and the financial success of the motion pictures varies considerably. The opening weekend gross sales, the total gross sales, the number of theaters the movie was shown in, and the number of weeks the motion picture was in release are common variables used to measure the success of a motion picture. Data on the top 100 grossing motion pictures released in 2011 (Box Office Mojo website, March 17, 2012) are contained in a file named 2011Movies. Table 3.10 shows the data for the first 10 motion pictures in this file. Note that some movies, such as *War Horse,* were released late in 2011 and continued to run in 2012.

TABLE 3.10   PERFORMANCE DATA FOR 10 MOTION PICTURES

Motion Picture	Opening Gross Sales ($millions)	Total Gross Sales ($millions)	Number of Theaters	Weeks in Release
Harry Potter and the Deathly Hallows Part 2	169.19	381.01	4375	19
Transformers: Dark of the Moon	97.85	352.39	4088	15
The Twilight Saga: Breaking Dawn Part 1	138.12	281.29	4066	14
The Hangover Part II	85.95	254.46	3675	16
Pirates of the Caribbean: On Stranger Tides	90.15	241.07	4164	19
Fast Five	86.20	209.84	3793	15
Mission: Impossible—Ghost Protocol	12.79	208.55	3555	13
Cars 2	66.14	191.45	4115	25
Sherlock Holmes: A Game of Shadows	39.64	186.59	3703	13
Thor	65.72	181.03	3963	16

Managerial Report

Use the numerical methods of descriptive statistics presented in this chapter to learn how these variables contribute to the success of a motion picture. Include the following in your report:

1. Descriptive statistics for each of the four variables along with a discussion of what the descriptive statistics tell us about the motion picture industry.
2. What motion pictures, if any, should be considered high-performance outliers? Explain.
3. Descriptive statistics showing the relationship between total gross sales and each of the other variables. Discuss.

Case Problem 3   Business Schools of Asia–Pacific

The pursuit of a higher education degree in business is now international. A survey shows that more and more Asians choose the master of business administration (MBA) degree route to corporate success. As a result, the number of applicants for MBA courses at Asia-Pacific schools continues to increase.

Across the region, thousands of Asians show an increasing willingness to temporarily shelve their careers and spend two years in pursuit of a theoretical business qualification. Courses in these schools are notoriously tough and include economics, banking, marketing, behavioral sciences, labor relations, decision making, strategic thinking, business law, and more. The data set in Table 3.11 shows some of the characteristics of the leading Asia-Pacific business schools.

Managerial Report

Use the methods of descriptive statistics to summarize the data in Table 3.11. Discuss your findings.

1. Include a summary for each variable in the data set. Make comments and interpretations based on maximums and minimums, as well as the appropriate means and proportions. What new insights do these descriptive statistics provide concerning Asia-Pacific business schools?

TABLE 3.11 DATA FOR 25 ASIA-PACIFIC BUSINESS SCHOOLS

Business School	Full-Time Enrollment	Students per Faculty	Local Tuition ($)	Foreign Tuition ($)	Age	%Foreign	GMAT	English Test	Work Experience	Starting Salary ($)
Melbourne Business School	200	5	24,420	29,600	28	47	Yes	No	Yes	71,400
University of New South Wales (Sydney)	228	4	19,993	32,582	29	28	Yes	No	Yes	65,200
Indian Institute of Management (Ahmedabad)	392	5	4,300	4,300	22	0	No	No	No	7,100
Chinese University of Hong Kong	90	5	11,140	11,140	29	10	Yes	No	No	31,000
International University of Japan (Niigata)	126	4	33,060	33,060	28	60	Yes	Yes	No	87,000
Asian Institute of Management (Manila)	389	5	7,562	9,000	25	50	Yes	No	Yes	22,800
Indian Institute of Management (Bangalore)	380	5	3,935	16,000	23	1	Yes	No	No	7,500
National University of Singapore	147	6	6,146	7,170	29	51	Yes	Yes	Yes	43,300
Indian Institute of Management (Calcutta)	463	8	2,880	16,000	23	0	No	No	No	7,400
Australian National University (Canberra)	42	2	20,300	20,300	30	80	Yes	Yes	Yes	46,600
Nanyang Technological University (Singapore)	50	5	8,500	8,500	32	20	Yes	No	Yes	49,300
University of Queensland (Brisbane)	138	17	16,000	22,800	32	26	No	No	Yes	49,600
Hong Kong University of Science and Technology	60	2	11,513	11,513	26	37	Yes	No	Yes	34,000
Macquarie Graduate School of Management (Sydney)	12	8	17,172	19,778	34	27	No	No	Yes	60,100
Chulalongkorn University (Bangkok)	200	7	17,355	17,355	25	6	Yes	No	Yes	17,600
Monash Mt. Eliza Business School (Melbourne)	350	13	16,200	22,500	30	30	Yes	Yes	Yes	52,500
Asian Institute of Management (Bangkok)	300	10	18,200	18,200	29	90	No	Yes	Yes	25,000
University of Adelaide	20	19	16,426	23,100	30	10	No	No	Yes	66,000
Massey University (Palmerston North, New Zealand)	30	15	13,106	21,625	37	35	No	Yes	Yes	41,400
Royal Melbourne Institute of Technology Business Graduate School	30	7	13,880	17,765	32	30	No	Yes	Yes	48,900
Jamnalal Bajaj Institute of Management Studies (Mumbai)	240	9	1,000	1,000	24	0	No	No	Yes	7,000
Curtin Institute of Technology (Perth)	98	15	9,475	19,097	29	43	Yes	No	Yes	55,000
Lahore University of Management Sciences	70	14	11,250	26,300	23	2.5	No	No	No	7,500
Universiti Sains Malaysia (Penang)	30	5	2,260	2,260	32	15	No	Yes	Yes	16,000
De La Salle University (Manila)	44	17	3,300	3,600	28	3.5	Yes	No	Yes	13,100

2. Summarize the data to compare the following:
   a. Any difference between local and foreign tuition costs.
   b. Any difference between mean starting salaries for schools requiring and not requiring work experience.
   c. Any difference between starting salaries for schools requiring and not requiring English tests.
3. Do starting salaries appear to be related to tuition?
4. Present any additional graphical and numerical summaries that will be beneficial in communicating the data in Table 3.11 to others.

Case Problem 4   Heavenly Chocolates Website Transactions

Heavenly Chocolates manufactures and sells quality chocolate products at its plant and retail store located in Saratoga Springs, New York. Two years ago the company developed a website and began selling its products over the Internet. Website sales have exceeded the company's expectations, and management is now considering strategies to increase sales even further. To learn more about the website customers, a sample of 50 Heavenly Chocolate transactions was selected from the previous month's sales. Data showing the day of the week each transaction was made, the type of browser the customer used, the time spent on the website, the number of website pages viewed, and the amount spent by each of the 50 customers are contained in the file named Shoppers. A portion of the data are shown in Table 3.12.

Heavenly Chocolates would like to use the sample data to determine if online shoppers who spend more time and view more pages also spend more money during their visit to the website. The company would also like to investigate the effect that the day of the week and the type of browser have on sales.

Managerial Report

Use the methods of descriptive statistics to learn about the customers who visit the Heavenly Chocolates website. Include the following in your report.

1. Graphical and numerical summaries for the length of time the shopper spends on the website, the number of pages viewed, and the mean amount spent per transaction.

DATA *file*

Shoppers

TABLE 3.12   A SAMPLE OF 50 HEAVENLY CHOCOLATES WEBSITE TRANSACTIONS

Customer	Day	Browser	Time (min)	Pages Viewed	Amount Spent ($)
1	Mon	Internet Explorer	12.0	4	54.52
2	Wed	Other	19.5	6	94.90
3	Mon	Internet Explorer	8.5	4	26.68
4	Tue	Firefox	11.4	2	44.73
5	Wed	Internet Explorer	11.3	4	66.27
6	Sat	Firefox	10.5	6	67.80
7	Sun	Internet Explorer	11.4	2	36.04
.	.	.	.	.	.
.	.	.	.	.	.
.	.	.	.	.	.
48	Fri	Internet Explorer	9.7	5	103.15
49	Mon	Other	7.3	6	52.15
50	Fri	Internet Explorer	13.4	3	98.75

Discuss what you learn about Heavenly Cholcolates' online shoppers from these numerical summaries.

2. Summarize the frequency, the total dollars spent, and the mean amount spent per transaction for each day of week. What observations can you make about Heavenly Chocolates' business based on the day of the week? Discuss.

3. Summarize the frequency, the total dollars spent, and the mean amount spent per transaction for each type of browser. What observations can you make about Heavenly Chocolate's business based on the type of browser? Discuss.

4. Develop a scatter diagram and compute the sample correlation coefficient to explore the relationship between the time spent on the website and the dollar amount spent. Use the horizontal axis for the time spent on the website. Discuss.

5. Develop a scatter diagram and compute the sample correlation coefficient to explore the relationship between the number of website pages viewed and the amount spent. Use the horizontal axis for the number of website pages viewed. Discuss.

6. Develop a scatter diagram and compute the sample correlation coefficient to explore the relationship between the time spent on the website and the number of pages viewed. Use the horizontal axis to represent the number of pages viewed. Discuss.

Case Problem 5   African Elephant Populations

Although millions of elephants once roamed across Africa, by the mid-1980s elephant populations in African nations had been devastated by poaching. Elephants are important to African ecosystems. In tropical forests, elephants create clearings in the canopy that encourage new tree growth. In savannas, elephants reduce bush cover to create an environment that is favorable to browsing and grazing animals. In addition, the seeds of many plant species depend on passing through an elephant's digestive tract before germination.

The status of the elephant now varies greatly across the continent. In some nations, strong measures have been taken to effectively protect elephant populations; for example, Kenya has destroyed over five tons of elephant ivory confiscated from poachers in an attempt to deter the growth of illegal ivory trade (Associated Press, July 20, 2011). In other nations the elephant populations remain in danger due to poaching for meat and ivory, loss of habitat, and conflict with humans. Table 3.13 shows elephant populations for several African nations in 1979, 1989, and 2007 (ElephantDatabase.org website, December 15, 2014).

The David Sheldrick Wildlife Trust was established in 1977 to honor the memory of naturalist David Leslie William Sheldrick, who founded Warden of Tsavo East National Park in Kenya and headed the Planning Unit of the Wildlife Conservation and Management Department in that country. Management of the Sheldrick Trust would like to know what these data indicate about elephant populations in various African countries since 1979.

Managerial Report

Use methods of descriptive statistics to summarize the data and comment on changes in elephant populations in African nations since 1979. At a minimum your report should include the following.

1. The mean annual change in elephant population for each country in the 10 years from 1979 to 1989, and a discussion of which countries saw the largest changes in elephant population over this 10-year period.

2. The mean annual change in elephant population for each country from 1989 to 2007, and a discussion of which countries saw the largest changes in elephant population over this 18-year period.

TABLE 3.13   ELEPHANT POPULATIONS FOR SEVERAL AFRICAN NATIONS IN 1979, 1989, AND 2007

Country	1979 Elephant Population	1989 Elephant Population	2007 Elephant Population	2012 Elephant Population
Angola	12,400	12,400	2,530	2,530
Botswana	20,000	51,000	175,487	175,454
Cameroon	16,200	21,200	15,387	14,049
Cen African Rep	63,000	19,000	3,334	2,285
Chad	15,000	3,100	6,435	3,004
Congo	10,800	70,000	22,102	49,248
Dem Rep of Congo	377,700	85,000	23,714	13,674
Gabon	13,400	76,000	70,637	77,252
Kenya	65,000	19,000	31,636	36,260
Mozambique	54,800	18,600	26,088	26,513
Somalia	24,300	6,000	70	70
Tanzania	316,300	80,000	167,003	117,456
Zambia	150,000	41,000	29,231	21,589
Zimbabwe	30,000	43,000	99,107	100,291

The heading "Elephant Population" spans the four population columns.

DATA *file*

2012African Eliphants

3. The mean annual change in elephant population for each country from 2007 to 2012, and a discussion of which countries saw the largest changes in elephant population over this 5-year period.

4. A comparison of your results from parts 1, 2, and 3, and a discussion of the conclusions you can draw from this comparison.

Appendix 3.1   Descriptive Statistics Using Minitab

In this appendix, we describe how Minitab can be used to compute a variety of descriptive statistics and display box plots. We then show how Minitab can be used to obtain covariance and correlation measures for two variables.

Descriptive Statistics

DATA *file*

2012StartSalary

Table 3.1 provided the starting salaries for 12 business school graduates. These data are in column C2 of the file 2012StartSalary. The following steps can be used to generate descriptive statistics for the starting salary data.

Step 1. Select the **Stat** menu
Step 2. Choose **Basic Statistics**
Step 3. Choose **Display Descriptive Statistics**
Step 4. When the Display Descriptive Statistics dialog box appears:
         Enter C2 in the **Variables** box
         Click **OK**

Figure 3.15 shows the descriptive statistics obtained using Minitab. Definitions of the headings follow.

N	number of data values	Minimum	minimum data value
N*	number of missing data values	Q1	first quartile
Mean	mean	Median	median
SE Mean	standard error of mean	Q3	third quartile
StDev	standard deviation	Maximum	maximum data value

FIGURE 3.15   DESCRIPTIVE STATISTICS PROVIDED BY MINITAB

N	N*	Mean	SEMean	StDev
12	0	3940.0	47.8	165.7
Minimum	Q1	Median	Q3	Maximum
3710.0	3857.5	3905.0	4025.0	4325.0

The label SE Mean refers to the *standard error of the mean*. It is computed by dividing the standard deviation by the square root of N. The interpretation and use of this measure are discussed in Chapter 7 when we introduce the topics of sampling and sampling distributions.

The 10 descriptive statistics shown in Figure 3.15 are the default descriptive statistics selected automatically by Minitab. These descriptive statistics are of interest to the majority of users. However, Minitab provides 15 additional descriptive statistics that may be selected depending upon the preferences of the user. The variance, coefficient of variation, range, interquartile range, mode, and skewness are among the additional descriptive statistics available. To select one or more of these additional descriptive statistics, modify step 4 as follows.

Step 4. When the Display Descriptive Statistics dialog box appears:
      Enter C2 in the **Variables** box
      Click **Statistics**
      Select the **descriptive statistics** you wish to obtain or
          choose **All** to obtain all 25 descriptive statistics
      Click **OK**
      Click **OK**

Box Plot

The following steps use the file 2012StartSalary to generate the box plot for the starting salary data.

Step 1. Select the **Graph** menu
Step 2. Choose **Boxplot**
Step 3. Under the heading **OneY** select **Simple** and click **OK**
Step 4. When the Boxplot: One Y, Simple dialog box appears:
      Enter C2 in the **Graph variables** box
      Click **OK**

Covariance and Correlation

Stereo

Table 3.6 provided the number of commercials and the sales volume for a stereo and sound equipment store. These data are available in the file Stereo, with the number of commercials in column C2 and the sales volume in column C3. The following steps show how Minitab can be used to compute the covariance for the two variables.

Step 1. Select the **Stat** menu
Step 2. Choose **Basic Statistics**
Step 3. Choose **Covariance**
Step 4. When the Covariance dialog box appears:
      Enter C2 C3 in the **Variables** box
      Click **OK**

To obtain the correlation coefficient for the number of commercials and the sales volume, only one change is necessary in the preceding procedure. In step 3, choose the **Correlation** option.

Appendix 3.2 Descriptive Statistics Using Excel

Excel can be used to generate the descriptive statistics discussed in this chapter. We show how Excel can be used to generate several measures of location and variability for a single variable and to generate the covariance and correlation coefficient as measures of association between two variables.

Using Excel Functions

DATA *file*

2012StartSalary

Excel provides functions for computing the mean, median, mode, sample variance, and sample standard deviation. We illustrate the use of these Excel functions by computing the mean, median, mode, sample variance, and sample standard deviation for the starting salary data in Table 3.1. Refer to Figure 3.16 as we describe the steps involved. The data are entered in column B.

FIGURE 3.16   USING EXCEL FUNCTIONS FOR COMPUTING THE MEAN, MEDIAN, MODE, VARIANCE, AND STANDARD DEVIATION

	A	B	C	D	E
1	Graduate	Starting Salary		Mean	=AVERAGE(B2:B13)
2	1	3850		Median	=MEDIAN(B2:B13)
3	2	3950		Mode	=MODE.SNGL(B2:B13)
4	3	4050		Variance	=VAR.S(B2:B13)
5	4	3880		Standard Deviation	=STDEV.S(B2:B13)
6	5	3755			
7	6	3710			
8	7	3890			
9	8	4130			
10	9	3940			
11	10	4325			
12	11	3920			
13	12	3880			

	A	B	C	D	E
1	Graduate	Starting Salary		Mean	3940
2	1	3850		Median	3905
3	2	3950		Mode	3880
4	3	4050		Variance	27440.91
5	4	3880		Standard Deviation	165.65
6	5	3755			
7	6	3710			
8	7	3890			
9	8	4130			
10	9	3940			
11	10	4325			
12	11	3920			
13	12	3880			

Stereo

To find the variance, standard deviation, and covariance for population data, follow the same steps but use the VAR.P, STDEV.P, and COV.P functions.

*If the **Analysis** tab doesn't appear on your ribbon or if the **Data Analysis** option doesn't appear in the **Data Analysis** tab, you need to activate the **Data Analysis ToolPak** by following these three steps:*

1. *Click the **File** tab, then click **Options**, and then click the **Add-Ins** category.*
2. *In the **Manage** box, click **Excel Add-ins**, and then click **Go**. The **Add-Ins** dialog box will then appear.*
3. *In the **Add-Ins available** box, select the check box next to the **Data Analysis ToolPak** add-in and click **OK**.*

*The **Analysis** tab will now be available with the **Data Analysis** option.*

Excel's AVERAGE function can be used to compute the mean by entering the following formula into cell E1:

$$=AVERAGE(B2:B13)$$

Similarly, the formulas =MEDIAN(B2:B13), =MODE.SNGL(B2:B13), =VAR.S(B2:B13), and =STDEV.S(B2:B13) are entered into cells E2:E5, respectively, to compute the median, mode, variance, and standard deviation for this sample. The worksheet in the foreground shows that the values computed using the Excel functions are the same as we computed earlier in the chapter.

Excel also provides functions that can be used to compute the sample covariance and the sample correlation coefficient. We show here how these functions can be used to compute the sample covariance and the sample correlation coefficient for the stereo and sound equipment store data in Table 3.6. Refer to Figure 3.17 as we present the steps involved.

Excel's sample covariance function, COVARIANCE.S, can be used to compute the sample covariance by entering the following formula into cell F1:

$$=COVARIANCE.S(B2:B11,C2:C11)$$

Similarly, the formula =CORREL(B2:B11,C2:C11) is entered into cell F2 to compute the sample correlation coefficient. The worksheet in the foreground shows the values computed using the Excel functions. Note that the value of the sample covariance (11) is the same as computed using equation (3.13). And the value of the sample correlation coefficient (.93) is the same as computed using equation (3.15).

Using Excel's Descriptive Statistics Tool

As we already demonstrated, Excel provides statistical functions to compute descriptive statistics for a data set. These functions can be used to compute one statistic at a time (e.g., mean, variance, etc.). Excel also provides a variety of Data Analysis Tools. One of these tools, called Descriptive Statistics, allows the user to compute a variety of descriptive statistics at once. We show here how it can be used to compute descriptive statistics for the starting salary data in Table 3.1.

FIGURE 3.17   USING EXCEL FUNCTIONS FOR COMPUTING THE COVARIANCE AND CORRELATION

	A	B	C	D	E	F	G
1	Week	Commercials	Sales Volume		Sample Covariance	=COVARIANCE.S(B2:B11,C2:C11)	
2	1	2	50		Sample Correlation	=CORREL(B2:B11,C2:C11)	
3	2	5	57				
4	3	1	41				
5	4	3	54				
6	5	4	54				
7	6	1	38				
8	7	5	63				
9	8	3	48				
10	9	4	59				
11	10	2	46				
12							

	A	B	C	D	E	F	G
1	Week	Commercials	Sales Volume		Sample Covariance	11	
2	1	2	50		Sample Correlation	0.9305	
3	2	5	57				
4	3	1	41				
5	4	3	54				
6	5	4	54				
7	6	1	38				
8	7	5	63				
9	8	3	48				
10	9	4	59				
11	10	2	46				
12							

FIGURE 3.18   EXCEL'S DESCRIPTIVE STATISTICS TOOL OUTPUT

	A	B	C	D	E
1	Graduate	Starting Salary		*Starting Salary*	
2	1	3850			
3	2	3950		Mean	3940
4	3	4050		Standard Error	47.82
5	4	3880		Median	3905
6	5	3755		Mode	3880
7	6	3710		Standard Deviation	165.65
8	7	3890		Sample Variance	27440.91
9	8	4130		Kurtosis	1.72
10	9	3940		Skewness	1.09
11	10	4325		Range	615
12	11	3920		Minimum	3710
13	12	3880		Maximum	4325
14				Sum	47280
15				Count	12

DATA *file*

2012StartSalary

Step 1. Click the **Data** tab on the Ribbon

Step 2. In the **Analysis** group, click **Data Analysis**

Step 3. When the Data Analysis dialog box appears:

  Choose **Descriptive Statistics**

  Click **OK**

Step 4. When the Descriptive Statistics dialog box appears:

  Enter B1:B13 in the **Input Range** box

  Select **Grouped By Columns**

  Select **Labels in First Row**

  Select **Output Range**

  Enter D1 in the **Output Range** box (to identify the upper left-hand corner of the section of the worksheet where the descriptive statistics will appear)

  Select **Summary statistics**

  Click **OK**

Cells D1:E15 of Figure 3.18 show the descriptive statistics provided by Excel. The boldface entries are the descriptive statistics we covered in this chapter. The descriptive statistics that are not boldface are either covered subsequently in the text or discussed in more advanced texts.

CHAPTER 4

Introduction to Probability

CONTENTS

STATISTICS *in* PRACTICE

NATIONAL AERONAUTICS AND SPACE ADMINISTRATION*
WASHINGTON, D.C.

The National Aeronautics and Space Administration (NASA) is the agency of the United States government that is responsible for the U.S. civilian space program and aeronautics and aerospace research. NASA is best known for its manned space exploration; its mission statement is to "pioneer the future in space exploration, scientific discovery and aeronautics research." NASA, with its 18,800 employees, is currently working on the design of a new Space Launch System that will take the astronauts farther into space than ever before and provide the cornerstone for future human space exploration.

Although NASA's primary mission is space exploration, its expertise has been called upon to assist countries and organizations throughout the world. In one such situation, the San José copper and gold mine in Copiapó, Chile, caved in, trapping 33 men more than 2000 feet underground. While it was important to bring the men safely to the surface as quickly as possible, it was imperative that the rescue effort be carefully designed and implemented to save as many miners as possible. The Chilean government asked NASA to provide assistance in developing a rescue method. In response, NASA sent a four-person team consisting of an engineer, two physicians, and a psychologist with expertise in vehicle design and issues of long-term confinement.

The probability of success and failure of various rescue methods was prominent in the thoughts of everyone involved. Since there were no historical data available that applied to this unique rescue situation, NASA scientists developed subjective probability estimates

---

*The authors are indebted to Dr. Michael Duncan and Clinton Cragg at NASA for providing this Statistics in Practice.

NASA scientists based probabilities on similar circumstances experienced during space flights.

for the success and failure of various rescue methods based on similar circumstances experienced by astronauts returning from short- and long-term space missions. The probability estimates provided by NASA guided officials in the selection of a rescue method and provided insight as to how the miners would survive the ascent in a rescue cage.

The rescue method designed by the Chilean officials in consultation with the NASA team resulted in the construction of 13-foot-long, 924-pound steel rescue capsule that would be used to bring up the miners one at a time. All miners were rescued, with the last miner emerging 68 days after the cave-in occurred.

In this chapter you will learn about probability as well as how to compute and interpret probabilities for a variety of situations. In addition to subjective probabilities, you will learn about classical and relative frequency methods for assigning probabilities. The basic relationships of probability, conditional probability, and Bayes' theorem will be covered.

Managers often base their decisions on an analysis of uncertainties such as the following:

1. What are the chances that sales will decrease if we increase prices?
2. What is the likelihood a new assembly method will increase productivity?
3. How likely is it that the project will be finished on time?
4. What is the chance that a new investment will be profitable?

Some of the earliest work on probability originated in a series of letters between Pierre de Fermat and Blaise Pascal in the 1650s.

Probability is a numerical measure of the likelihood that an event will occur. Thus, probabilities can be used as measures of the degree of uncertainty associated with the four

FIGURE 4.1   PROBABILITY AS A NUMERICAL MEASURE OF THE LIKELIHOOD
OF AN EVENT OCCURRING

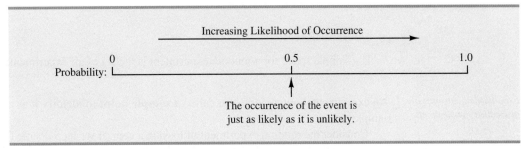

events previously listed. If probabilities are available, we can determine the likelihood of each event occurring.

Probability values are always assigned on a scale from 0 to 1. A probability near zero indicates an event is unlikely to occur; a probability near 1 indicates an event is almost certain to occur. Other probabilities between 0 and 1 represent degrees of likelihood that an event will occur. For example, if we consider the event "rain tomorrow," we understand that when the weather report indicates "a near-zero probability of rain," it means almost no chance of rain. However, if a .90 probability of rain is reported, we know that rain is likely to occur. A .50 probability indicates that rain is just as likely to occur as not. Figure 4.1 depicts the view of probability as a numerical measure of the likelihood of an event occurring.

4.1 Random Experiments, Counting Rules, and Assigning Probabilities

In discussing probability, we deal with experiments that have the following characteristics:

1. The experimental outcomes are well defined, and in many cases can even be listed prior to conducting the experiment.
2. On any single repetition or *trial* of the experiment, one and only one of the possible experimental outcomes will occur.
3. The experimental outcome that occurs on any trial is determined solely by chance.

We refer to these types of experiments as **random experiments**.

> RANDOM EXPERIMENT
>
> A random experiment is a process that generates well-defined experimental outcomes. On any single repetition or trial, the outcome that occurs is determined completely by chance.

To illustrate the key features associated with a random experiment, consider the process of tossing a coin. Referring to one face of the coin as the head and to the other face as the tail, after tossing the coin the upward face will be either a head or a tail. Thus, there are two possible experimental outcomes: head or tail. On an any single repetition or *trial* of this experiment, only one of the two possible experimental outcomes will occur; in other words, each time we toss the coin we will either observe a head or a tail. And, the outcome that occurs on any trial is determined solely by chance or random variability. As a result, the process of tossing a coin is considered a random experiment.

By specifying all the possible experimental outcomes, we identify the **sample space** for a random experiment.

SAMPLE SPACE

The sample space for a random experiment is the set of all experimental outcomes.

Experimental outcomes are also called sample points.

An experimental outcome is also called a **sample point** to identify it as an element of the sample space.

Consider the random experiment of tossing a coin. If we let S denote the sample space, we can use the following notation to describe the sample space.

$$S = \{\text{Head, Tail}\}$$

The random experiment of tossing a coin has two experimental outcomes (sample points). As an illustration of a random experiment with more than two experimental outcomes, consider the process of rolling a die. The possible experimental outcomes, defined as the number of dots appearing on the face of the die, are the six sample points in the sample space for this random experiment,

$$S = \{1, 2, 3, 4, 5, 6\}$$

Counting Rules, Combinations, and Permutations

Being able to identify and count the experimental outcomes is a necessary step in assigning probabilities. We now discuss three useful counting rules.

Multiple-step experiments The first counting rule applies to **multiple-step experiments**. Consider the experiment of tossing two coins. Let the experimental outcomes be defined in terms of the pattern of heads and tails appearing on the upward faces of the two coins. How many experimental outcomes are possible for this experiment? The experiment of tossing two coins can be thought of as a two-step experiment in which step 1 is the tossing of the first coin and step 2 is the tossing of the second coin. If we use H to denote a head and T to denote a tail, (H, H) indicates the experimental outcome with a head on the first coin and a head on the second coin. Continuing this notation, we can describe the sample space (S) for this coin-tossing experiment as follows:

$$S = \{(H, H), (H, T), (T, H), (T, T)\}$$

Thus, we see that four experimental outcomes are possible. In this case, we can easily list all the experimental outcomes.

The counting rule for multiple-step experiments makes it possible to determine the number of experimental outcomes without listing them.

COUNTING RULE FOR MULTIPLE-STEP EXPERIMENTS

If an experiment can be described as a sequence of k steps with n_1 possible outcomes on the first step, n_2 possible outcomes on the second step, and so on, then the total number of experimental outcomes is given by $(n_1)(n_2) \cdots (n_k)$.

Viewing the experiment of tossing two coins as a sequence of first tossing one coin ($n_1 = 2$) and then tossing the other coin ($n_2 = 2$), we can see from the counting rule that $(2)(2) = 4$ distinct experimental outcomes are possible. As shown, they are $S = \{(H, H),$

FIGURE 4.2   TREE DIAGRAM FOR THE EXPERIMENT OF TOSSING TWO COINS

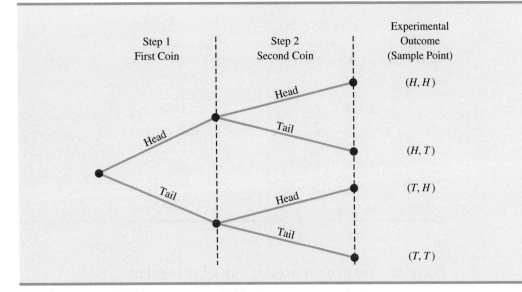

(H, T), (T, H), (T, T)}. The number of experimental outcomes in an experiment involving tossing six coins is $(2)(2)(2)(2)(2)(2) = 64$.

Without the tree diagram, one might think only three experimental outcomes are possible for two tosses of a coin: 0 heads, 1 head, and 2 heads.

A **tree diagram** is a graphical representation that helps in visualizing a multiple-step experiment. Figure 4.2 shows a tree diagram for the experiment of tossing two coins. The sequence of steps moves from left to right through the tree. Step 1 corresponds to tossing the first coin, and step 2 corresponds to tossing the second coin. For each step, the two possible outcomes are head or tail. Note that for each possible outcome at step 1 two branches correspond to the two possible outcomes at step 2. Each of the points on the right end of the tree corresponds to an experimental outcome. Each path through the tree from the leftmost node to one of the nodes at the right side of the tree corresponds to a unique sequence of outcomes.

Let us now see how the counting rule for multiple-step experiments can be used in the analysis of a capacity expansion project for the Kentucky Power & Light Company (KP&L). KP&L is starting a project designed to increase the generating capacity of one of its plants in northern Kentucky. The project is divided into two sequential stages or steps: stage 1 (design) and stage 2 (construction). Even though each stage will be scheduled and controlled as closely as possible, management cannot predict beforehand the exact time required to complete each stage of the project. An analysis of similar construction projects revealed possible completion times for the design stage of 2, 3, or 4 months and possible completion times for the construction stage of 6, 7, or 8 months. In addition, because of the critical need for additional electrical power, management set a goal of 10 months for the completion of the entire project.

Because this project has three possible completion times for the design stage (step 1) and three possible completion times for the construction stage (step 2), the counting rule for multiple-step experiments can be applied here to determine a total of $(3)(3) = 9$ experimental outcomes. To describe the experimental outcomes, we use a two-number notation; for instance, $(2, 6)$ indicates that the design stage is completed in 2 months and the construction stage is completed in 6 months. This experimental outcome results in a total of $2 + 6 = 8$ months to complete the entire project. Table 4.1 summarizes the nine experimental outcomes for the KP&L problem. The tree diagram in Figure 4.3 shows how the nine outcomes (sample points) occur.

The counting rule and tree diagram help the project manager identify the experimental outcomes and determine the possible project completion times. From the information in

TABLE 4.1   EXPERIMENTAL OUTCOMES (SAMPLE POINTS) FOR THE KP&L PROJECT

Completion Time (months)			
Stage 1 Design	Stage 2 Construction	Notation for Experimental Outcome	Total Project Completion Time (months)
2	6	(2, 6)	8
2	7	(2, 7)	9
2	8	(2, 8)	10
3	6	(3, 6)	9
3	7	(3, 7)	10
3	8	(3, 8)	11
4	6	(4, 6)	10
4	7	(4, 7)	11
4	8	(4, 8)	12

FIGURE 4.3   TREE DIAGRAM FOR THE KP&L PROJECT

Figure 4.3, we see that the project will be completed in 8 to 12 months, with six of the nine experimental outcomes providing the desired completion time of 10 months or less. Even though identifying the experimental outcomes may be helpful, we need to consider how probability values can be assigned to the experimental outcomes before making an assessment of the probability that the project will be completed within the desired 10 months.

Combinations   A second useful counting rule allows one to count the number of experimental outcomes when the experiment involves selecting n objects from a set of N objects. It is called the counting rule for **combinations**.

COUNTING RULE FOR COMBINATIONS

The number of combinations of N objects taken n at a time is

$$C_n^N = \binom{N}{n} = \frac{N!}{n!(N-n)!} \tag{4.1}$$

where
$$N! = N(N-1)(N-2)\cdots(2)(1)$$
$$n! = n(n-1)(n-2)\cdots(2)(1)$$

and, by definition,
$$0! = 1$$

In sampling from a finite population of size N, the counting rule for combinations is used to find the number of different samples of size n that can be selected.

The notation ! means *factorial;* for example, 5 factorial is $5! = (5)(4)(3)(2)(1) = 120$.

As an illustration of the counting rule for combinations, consider a quality control procedure in which an inspector randomly selects two of five parts to test for defects. In a group of five parts, how many combinations of two parts can be selected? The counting rule in equation (4.1) shows that with $N = 5$ and $n = 2$, we have

$$C_2^5 = \binom{5}{2} = \frac{5!}{2!(5-2)!} = \frac{(5)(4)(3)(2)(1)}{(2)(1)(3)(2)(1)} = \frac{120}{12} = 10$$

Thus, 10 outcomes are possible for the experiment of randomly selecting two parts from a group of five. If we label the five parts as A, B, C, D, and E, the 10 combinations or experimental outcomes can be identified as AB, AC, AD, AE, BC, BD, BE, CD, CE, and DE.

As another example, consider that the Florida lottery system uses the random selection of 6 integers from a group of 53 to determine the weekly winner. The counting rule for combinations, equation (4.1), can be used to determine the number of ways 6 different integers can be selected from a group of 53.

$$\binom{53}{6} = \frac{53!}{6!(53-6)!} = \frac{53!}{6!47!} = \frac{(53)(52)(51)(50)(49)(48)}{(6)(5)(4)(3)(2)(1)} = 22,957,480$$

The counting rule for combinations shows that the chance of winning the lottery is very unlikely.

The counting rule for combinations tells us that almost 23 million experimental outcomes are possible in the lottery drawing. An individual who buys a lottery ticket has 1 chance in 22,957,480 of winning.

Permutations   A third counting rule that is sometimes useful is the counting rule for **permutations**. It allows one to compute the number of experimental outcomes when n objects are to be selected from a set of N objects where the order of selection is important. The same n objects selected in a different order are considered a different experimental outcome.

COUNTING RULE FOR PERMUTATIONS

The number of permutations of N objects taken n at a time is given by

$$P_n^N = n!\binom{N}{n} = \frac{N!}{(N-n)!} \tag{4.2}$$

The counting rule for permutations closely relates to the one for combinations; however, an experiment results in more permutations than combinations for the same number of objects because every selection of n objects can be ordered in $n!$ different ways.

As an example, consider again the quality control process in which an inspector selects two of five parts to inspect for defects. How many permutations may be selected? The counting rule in equation (4.2) shows that with $N = 5$ and $n = 2$, we have

$$P_2^5 = \frac{5!}{(5-2)!} = \frac{5!}{3!} = \frac{(5)(4)(3)(2)(1)}{(3)(2)(1)} = \frac{120}{6} = 20$$

Thus, 20 outcomes are possible for the experiment of randomly selecting two parts from a group of five when the order of selection must be taken into account. If we label the parts A, B, C, D, and E, the 20 permutations are AB, BA, AC, CA, AD, DA, AE, EA, BC, CB, BD, DB, BE, EB, CD, DC, CE, EC, DE, and ED.

Assigning Probabilities

Now let us see how probabilities can be assigned to experimental outcomes. The three approaches most frequently used are the classical, relative frequency, and subjective methods. Regardless of the method used, two **basic requirements for assigning probabilities** must be met.

BASIC REQUIREMENTS FOR ASSIGNING PROBABILITIES

1. The probability assigned to each experimental outcome must be between 0 and 1, inclusively. If we let E_i denote the ith experimental outcome and $P(E_i)$ its probability, then this requirement can be written as

$$0 \leq P(E_i) \leq 1 \text{ for all } i \tag{4.3}$$

2. The sum of the probabilities for all the experimental outcomes must equal 1.0. For n experimental outcomes, this requirement can be written as

$$P(E_1) + P(E_2) + \cdots + P(E_n) = 1 \tag{4.4}$$

The **classical method** of assigning probabilities is appropriate when all the experimental outcomes are equally likely. If n experimental outcomes are possible, a probability of $1/n$ is assigned to each experimental outcome. When using this approach, the two basic requirements for assigning probabilities are automatically satisfied.

For an example, consider the experiment of tossing a fair coin; the two experimental outcomes—head and tail—are equally likely. Because one of the two equally likely outcomes is a head, the probability of observing a head is 1/2, or .50. Similarly, the probability of observing a tail is also 1/2, or .50.

As another example, consider the experiment of rolling a die. It would seem reasonable to conclude that the six possible outcomes are equally likely, and hence each outcome is assigned a probability of 1/6. If $P(1)$ denotes the probability that one dot appears on the upward face of the die, then $P(1) = 1/6$. Similarly, $P(2) = 1/6$, $P(3) = 1/6$, $P(4) = 1/6$, $P(5) = 1/6$, and $P(6) = 1/6$. Note that these probabilities satisfy the two basic requirements of equations (4.3) and (4.4) because each of the probabilities is greater than or equal to zero and they sum to 1.0.

The **relative frequency method** of assigning probabilities is appropriate when data are available to estimate the proportion of the time the experimental outcome will occur if the experiment is repeated a large number of times. As an example, consider a study of waiting times in the X-ray department for a local hospital. A clerk recorded the number of patients waiting for service at 9:00 A.M. on 20 successive days and obtained the following results.

Number Waiting	Number of Days Outcome Occurred
0	2
1	5
2	6
3	4
4	3
Total	20

These data show that on 2 of the 20 days, zero patients were waiting for service; on 5 of the days, one patient was waiting for service; and so on. Using the relative frequency method, we would assign a probability of 2/20 = .10 to the experimental outcome of zero patients waiting for service, 5/20 = .25 to the experimental outcome of one patient waiting, 6/20 = .30 to two patients waiting, 4/20 = .20 to three patients waiting, and 3/20 = .15 to four patients waiting. As with the classical method, using the relative frequency method automatically satisfies the two basic requirements of equations (4.3) and (4.4).

The **subjective method** of assigning probabilities is most appropriate when one cannot realistically assume that the experimental outcomes are equally likely and when little relevant data are available. When the subjective method is used to assign probabilities to the experimental outcomes, we may use any information available, such as our experience or intuition. After considering all available information, a probability value that expresses our *degree of belief* (on a scale from 0 to 1) that the experimental outcome will occur is specified. Because subjective probability expresses a person's degree of belief, it is personal. Using the subjective method, different people can be expected to assign different probabilities to the same experimental outcome.

The subjective method requires extra care to ensure that the two basic requirements of equations (4.3) and (4.4) are satisfied. Regardless of a person's degree of belief, the probability value assigned to each experimental outcome must be between 0 and 1, inclusive, and the sum of all the probabilities for the experimental outcomes must equal 1.0.

Consider the case in which Tom and Judy Elsbernd make an offer to purchase a house. Two outcomes are possible:

$$E_1 = \text{their offer is accepted}$$
$$E_2 = \text{their offer is rejected}$$

Judy believes that the probability their offer will be accepted is .8; thus, Judy would set $P(E_1) = .8$ and $P(E_2) = .2$. Tom, however, believes that the probability that their offer will be accepted is .6; hence, Tom would set $P(E_1) = .6$ and $P(E_2) = .4$. Note that Tom's probability estimate for E_1 reflects a greater pessimism that their offer will be accepted.

Bayes' theorem (see Section 4.5) provides a means for combining subjectively determined prior probabilities with probabilities obtained by other means to obtain revised, or posterior, probabilities.

Both Judy and Tom assigned probabilities that satisfy the two basic requirements. The fact that their probability estimates are different emphasizes the personal nature of the subjective method.

Even in business situations where either the classical or the relative frequency approach can be applied, managers may want to provide subjective probability estimates. In such cases, the best probability estimates often are obtained by combining the estimates from the classical or relative frequency approach with subjective probability estimates.

Probabilities for the KP&L Project

To perform further analysis on the KP&L project, we must develop probabilities for each of the nine experimental outcomes listed in Table 4.1. On the basis of experience and judgment, management concluded that the experimental outcomes were not equally likely. Hence, the classical method of assigning probabilities could not be used. Management then decided to conduct a study of the completion times for similar projects undertaken by KP&L over the past three years. The results of a study of 40 similar projects are summarized in Table 4.2.

After reviewing the results of the study, management decided to employ the relative frequency method of assigning probabilities. Management could have provided subjective probability estimates but felt that the current project was quite similar to the 40 previous projects. Thus, the relative frequency method was judged best.

In using the data in Table 4.2 to compute probabilities, we note that outcome (2, 6)— stage 1 completed in 2 months and stage 2 completed in 6 months—occurred six times in the 40 projects. We can use the relative frequency method to assign a probability of $6/40 = .15$ to this outcome. Similarly, outcome (2, 7) also occurred in six of the 40 projects, providing a $6/40 = .15$ probability. Continuing in this manner, we obtain the probability assignments for the sample points of the KP&L project shown in Table 4.3. Note that $P(2, 6)$ represents the probability of the sample point (2, 6), $P(2, 7)$ represents the probability of the sample point (2, 7), and so on.

TABLE 4.2   COMPLETION RESULTS FOR 40 KP&L PROJECTS

Completion Time (months)			Number of Past Projects Having These Completion Times
Stage 1 Design	Stage 2 Construction	Sample Point	
2	6	(2, 6)	6
2	7	(2, 7)	6
2	8	(2, 8)	2
3	6	(3, 6)	4
3	7	(3, 7)	8
3	8	(3, 8)	2
4	6	(4, 6)	2
4	7	(4, 7)	4
4	8	(4, 8)	6
		Total	40

TABLE 4.3   PROBABILITY ASSIGNMENTS FOR THE KP&L PROJECT BASED ON THE RELATIVE FREQUENCY METHOD

Sample Point	Project Completion Time	Probability of Sample Point
(2, 6)	8 months	$P(2, 6) = 6/40 = $ .15
(2, 7)	9 months	$P(2, 7) = 6/40 = $ .15
(2, 8)	10 months	$P(2, 8) = 2/40 = $ .05
(3, 6)	9 months	$P(3, 6) = 4/40 = $ .10
(3, 7)	10 months	$P(3, 7) = 8/40 = $ .20
(3, 8)	11 months	$P(3, 8) = 2/40 = $ .05
(4, 6)	10 months	$P(4, 6) = 2/40 = $ .05
(4, 7)	11 months	$P(4, 7) = 4/40 = $ .10
(4, 8)	12 months	$P(4, 8) = 6/40 = $ .15
		Total 1.00

NOTES AND COMMENTS

1. In statistics, the notion of an experiment differs somewhat from the notion of an experiment in the physical sciences. In the physical sciences, researchers usually conduct an experiment in a laboratory or a controlled environment in order to learn about cause and effect. In statistical experiments, probability determines outcomes. Even though the experiment is repeated in exactly the same way, an entirely different outcome may occur. Because of this influence of probability on the outcome, the experiments of statistics are sometimes called *random experiments*.

2. When drawing a random sample without replacement from a population of size N, the counting rule for combinations is used to find the number of different samples of size n that can be selected.

Exercises

Methods

1. An experiment has three steps with three outcomes possible for the first step, two outcomes possible for the second step, and four outcomes possible for the third step. How many experimental outcomes exist for the entire experiment?

SELF*test*

2. How many ways can three items be selected from a group of six items? Use the letters A, B, C, D, E, and F to identify the items, and list each of the different combinations of three items.

3. How many permutations of three items can be selected from a group of six? Use the letters A, B, C, D, E, and F to identify the items, and list each of the permutations of items B, D, and F.

4. Consider the experiment of tossing a coin three times.
   a. Develop a tree diagram for the experiment.
   b. List the experimental outcomes.
   c. What is the probability for each experimental outcome?

5. Suppose an experiment has five equally likely outcomes: E_1, E_2, E_3, E_4, E_5. Assign probabilities to each outcome and show that the requirements in equations (4.3) and (4.4) are satisfied. What method did you use?

SELF*test*

6. An experiment with three outcomes has been repeated 50 times, and it was learned that E_1 occurred 20 times, E_2 occurred 13 times, and E_3 occurred 17 times. Assign probabilities to the outcomes. What method did you use?

7. A decision maker subjectively assigned the following probabilities to the four outcomes of an experiment: $P(E_1) = .10$, $P(E_2) = .15$, $P(E_3) = .40$, and $P(E_4) = .20$. Are these probability assignments valid? Explain.

Applications

8. In the city of Milford, applications for zoning changes go through a two-step process: a review by the planning commission and a final decision by the city council. At step 1 the planning commission reviews the zoning change request and makes a positive or negative recommendation concerning the change. At step 2 the city council reviews the planning commission's recommendation and then votes to approve or to disapprove the zoning change. Suppose the developer of an apartment complex submits an application for a zoning change. Consider the application process as an experiment.
    a. How many sample points are there for this experiment? List the sample points.
    b. Construct a tree diagram for the experiment.

SELF*test*

9. Simple random sampling uses a sample of size *n* from a population of size *N* to obtain data that can be used to make inferences about the characteristics of a population. Suppose that, from a population of 50 bank accounts, we want to take a random sample of four accounts in order to learn about the population. How many different random samples of four accounts are possible?

SELF*test*

10. The following table shows the percentage of on-time arrivals, the number of mishandled baggage reports per 1000 passengers, and the number of customer complaints per 1000 passengers for 10 airlines (*Forbes* website, February, 2014).

Airline	On-Time Arrivals (%)	Mishandled Baggage per 1000 Passengers	Customer Complaints per 1000 Passengers
Virgin America	83.5	0.87	1.50
JetBlue	79.1	1.88	0.79
AirTran Airways	87.1	1.58	0.91
Delta Air Lines	86.5	2.10	0.73
Alaska Airlines	87.5	2.93	0.51
Frontier Airlines	77.9	2.22	1.05
Southwest Airlines	83.1	3.08	0.25
US Airways	85.9	2.14	1.74
American Airlines	76.9	2.92	1.80
United Airlines	77.4	3.87	4.24

a. If you randomly choose a Delta Air Lines flight, what is the probability that this individual flight has an on-time arrival?
b. If you randomly choose one of the 10 airlines for a follow-up study on airline quality ratings, what is the probability that you will choose an airline with less than two mishandled baggage reports per 1000 passengers?
c. If you randomly choose 1 of the 10 airlines for a follow-up study on airline quality ratings, what is the probability that you will choose an airline with more than one customer complaint per 1000 passengers?
d. What is the probability that a randomly selected AirTran Airways flight will not arrive on time?

11. The National Occupant Protection Use Survey (NOPUS) was conducted to provide probability-based data on motorcycle helmet use in the United States. The survey was conducted by sending observers to randomly selected roadway sites where they collected data on motorcycle helmet use, including the number of motorcyclists wearing a Department of Transportation (DOT)-compliant helmet (National Highway Traffic Safety Administration website, January 7, 2010). Sample data consistent with the most recent NOPUS are shown below.

	Type of Helmet	
Region	**DOT-Compliant**	**Noncompliant**
Northeast	96	62
Midwest	86	43
South	92	49
West	76	16
Total	350	170

    a. Use the sample data to compute an estimate of the probability that a motorcyclist wears a DOT-compliant helmet.

    b. The probability that a motorcyclist wore a DOT-compliant helmet five years ago was .48, and last year this probability was .63. Would the National Highway Traffic Safety Administration be pleased with the most recent survey results?

    c. What is the probability of DOT-compliant helmet use by region of the country? What region has the highest probability of DOT-compliant helmet use?

12. The Powerball lottery is played twice each week in 31 states, the District of Columbia, and the Virgin Islands. To play Powerball, a participant must purchase a $2 ticket, select five numbers from the digits 1 through 59, and then select a Powerball number from the digits 1 through 35. To determine the winning numbers for each game, lottery officials draw 5 white balls out a drum of 59 white balls numbered 1 through 59 and 1 red ball out of a drum of 35 red balls numbered 1 through 35. To win the Powerball jackpot, a participant's numbers must match the numbers on the 5 white balls in any order and must also match the number on the red Powerball. The numbers 5–16–22–23–29 with a Powerball number of 6 provided the record jackpot of $580 million (Powerball website, November 29, 2012).

    a. How many Powerball lottery outcomes are possible? (*Hint:* Consider this a two-step random experiment. Select the 5 white ball numbers and then select the 1 red Powerball number.)

    b. What is the probability that a $2 lottery ticket wins the Powerball lottery?

13. A company that manufactures toothpaste is studying five different package designs. Assuming that one design is just as likely to be selected by a consumer as any other design, what selection probability would you assign to each of the package designs? In an actual experiment, 100 consumers were asked to pick the design they preferred. The following data were obtained. Do the data confirm the belief that one design is just as likely to be selected as another? Explain.

Design	Number of Times Preferred
1	5
2	15
3	30
4	40
5	10

4.2   Events and Their Probabilities

In the introduction to this chapter we used the term *event* much as it would be used in everyday language. Then, in Section 4.1 we introduced the concept of an experiment and its associated experimental outcomes or sample points. Sample points and events provide the foundation for the study of probability. As a result, we must now introduce the formal definition of an **event** as it relates to sample points. Doing so will provide the basis for determining the probability of an event.

EVENT

An event is a collection of sample points.

For an example, let us return to the KP&L project and assume that the project manager is interested in the event that the entire project can be completed in 10 months or less. Referring to Table 4.3, we see that six sample points—(2, 6), (2, 7), (2, 8), (3, 6), (3, 7), and (4, 6)—provide a project completion time of 10 months or less. Let C denote the event that the project is completed in 10 months or less; we write

$$C = \{(2, 6), (2, 7), (2, 8), (3, 6), (3, 7), (4, 6)\}$$

Event C is said to occur if *any one* of these six sample points appears as the experimental outcome.

Other events that might be of interest to KP&L management include the following.

L = The event that the project is completed in *less* than 10 months
M = The event that the project is completed in *more* than 10 months

Using the information in Table 4.3, we see that these events consist of the following sample points.

$$L = \{(2, 6), (2, 7), (3, 6)\}$$
$$M = \{(3, 8), (4, 7), (4, 8)\}$$

A variety of additional events can be defined for the KP&L project, but in each case the event must be identified as a collection of sample points for the experiment.

Given the probabilities of the sample points shown in Table 4.3, we can use the following definition to compute the probability of any event that KP&L management might want to consider.

PROBABILITY OF AN EVENT

The probability of any event is equal to the sum of the probabilities of the sample points in the event.

Using this definition, we calculate the probability of a particular event by adding the probabilities of the sample points (experimental outcomes) that make up the event. We can now compute the probability that the project will take 10 months or less to complete. Because this event is given by $C = \{(2, 6), (2, 7), (2, 8), (3, 6), (3, 7), (4, 6)\}$, the probability of event C, denoted $P(C)$, is given by

$$P(C) = P(2, 6) + P(2, 7) + P(2, 8) + P(3, 6) + P(3, 7) + P(4, 6)$$

Refer to the sample point probabilities in Table 4.3; we have

$$P(C) = .15 + .15 + .05 + .10 + .20 + .05 = .70$$

Similarly, because the event that the project is completed in less than 10 months is given by $L = \{(2, 6), (2, 7), (3, 6)\}$, the probability of this event is given by

$$P(L) = P(2, 6) + P(2, 7) + P(3, 6)$$
$$= .15 + .15 + .10 = .40$$

Finally, for the event that the project is completed in more than 10 months, we have $M = \{(3, 8), (4, 7), (4, 8)\}$ and thus

$$P(M) = P(3, 8) + P(4, 7) + P(4, 8)$$
$$= .05 + .10 + .15 = .30$$

Using these probability results, we can now tell KP&L management that there is a .70 probability that the project will be completed in 10 months or less, a .40 probability that the project will be completed in less than 10 months, and a .30 probability that the project will be completed in more than 10 months. This procedure of computing event probabilities can be repeated for any event of interest to the KP&L management.

Any time that we can identify all the sample points of an experiment and assign probabilities to each, we can compute the probability of an event using the definition. However, in many experiments the large number of sample points makes the identification of the sample points, as well as the determination of their associated probabilities, extremely cumbersome, if not impossible. In the remaining sections of this chapter, we present some basic probability relationships that can be used to compute the probability of an event without knowledge of all the sample point probabilities.

NOTES AND COMMENTS

1. The sample space, S, is an event. Because it contains all the experimental outcomes, it has a probability of 1; that is, $P(S) = 1$.
2. When the classical method is used to assign probabilities, the assumption is that the experimental outcomes are equally likely. In such cases, the probability of an event can be computed by counting the number of experimental outcomes in the event and dividing the result by the total number of experimental outcomes.

Exercises

Methods

14. An experiment has four equally likely outcomes: E_1, E_2, E_3, and E_4.
    a. What is the probability that E_2 occurs?
    b. What is the probability that any two of the outcomes occur (e.g., E_1 or E_3)?
    c. What is the probability that any three of the outcomes occur (e.g., E_1 or E_2 or E_4)?

☑ SELF*test* 15. Consider the experiment of selecting a playing card from a deck of 52 playing cards. Each card corresponds to a sample point with a 1/52 probability.
    a. List the sample points in the event an ace is selected.
    b. List the sample points in the event a club is selected.
    c. List the sample points in the event a face card (jack, queen, or king) is selected.
    d. Find the probabilities associated with each of the events in parts (a), (b), and (c).

16. Consider the experiment of rolling a pair of dice. Suppose that we are interested in the sum of the face values showing on the dice.
    a. How many sample points are possible? (*Hint:* Use the counting rule for multiple-step experiments.)
    b. List the sample points.
    c. What is the probability of obtaining a value of 7?
    d. What is the probability of obtaining a value of 9 or greater?
    e. Because each roll has six possible even values (2, 4, 6, 8, 10, and 12) and only five possible odd values (3, 5, 7, 9, and 11), the dice should show even values more often than odd values. Do you agree with this statement? Explain.
    f. What method did you use to assign the probabilities requested?

Applications

 SELF*test*

17. Refer to the KP&L sample points and sample point probabilities in Tables 4.2 and 4.3.
    a. The design stage (stage 1) will run over budget if it takes 4 months to complete. List the sample points in the event the design stage is over budget.
    b. What is the probability that the design stage is over budget?
    c. The construction stage (stage 2) will run over budget if it takes 8 months to complete. List the sample points in the event the construction stage is over budget.
    d. What is the probability that the construction stage is over budget?
    e. What is the probability that both stages are over budget?

18. *Fortune* magazine publishes an annual list of the 500 largest companies in the United States. The corporate headquarters for the 500 companies are located in 38 different states. The following table shows the 8 states with the largest number of *Fortune* 500 companies (*Money*/CNN website, May, 2012).

State	Number of Companies	State	Number of Companies
California	53	Ohio	28
Illinois	32	Pennsylvania	23
New Jersey	21	Texas	52
New York	50	Virginia	24

Suppose one of the 500 companies is selected at random for a follow-up questionnaire.
    a. What is the probability that the company selected has its corporate headquarters in California?
    b. What is the probability that the company selected has its corporate headquarters in California, New York, or Texas?
    c. What is the probability that the company selected has its corporate headquarters in one of the 8 states listed above?

19. Do you think global warming will have an impact on you during your lifetime? A CBS News/*New York Times* poll of 1000 adults in the United States asked this question (CBS News website, December, 2014). Consider the responses by age groups shown below.

Response	Age 18–29	Age 30+
Yes	134	293
No	131	432
Unsure	2	8

    a. What is the probability that a respondent 18–29 years of age thinks that global warming will not pose a serious threat during his/her lifetime?
    b. What is the probability that a respondent 30+ years of age thinks that global warming will not pose a serious threat during his/her lifetime?
    c. For a randomly selected respondent, what is the probability that a respondent answers yes?
    d. Based on the survey results, does there appear to be a difference between ages 18–29 and 30+ regarding concern over global warming?

20. Junior Achievement USA and the Allstate Foundation surveyed teenagers aged 14 to 18 and asked at what age they think that they will become financially independent (*USA Today*, April 30, 2012). The responses of 944 teenagers who answered this survey question are as follows.

Age Financially Independent	Number of Responses
16 to 20	191
21 to 24	467
25 to 27	244
28 or older	42

Consider the experiment of randomly selecting a teenager from the population of teenagers aged 14 to 18.
   a. Compute the probability of being financially independent for each of the four age categories.
   b. What is the probability of being financially independent before the age of 25?
   c. What is the probability of being financially independent after the age of 24?
   d. Do the probabilities suggest that the teenagers may be somewhat unrealistic in their expectations about when they will become financially independent?

21. Data on U.S. work-related fatalities by cause follow (*The World Almanac*, 2012).

Cause of Fatality	Number of Fatalities
Transportation incidents	1795
Assaults and violent acts	837
Contact with objects and equipment	741
Falls	645
Exposure to harmful substances or environments	404
Fires and explosions	113

Assume that a fatality will be randomly chosen from this population.
   a. What is the probability the fatality resulted from a fall?
   b. What is the probability the fatality resulted from a transportation incident?
   c. What cause of fatality is least likely to occur? What is the probability the fatality resulted from this cause?

4.3   Some Basic Relationships of Probability

Complement of an Event

Given an event A, the **complement of** A is defined to be the event consisting of all sample points that are *not* in A. The complement of A is denoted by A^c. Figure 4.4 is a diagram, known as a **Venn diagram**, which illustrates the concept of a complement. The rectangular area represents the sample space for the experiment and as such contains all possible sample points. The circle represents event A and contains only the sample points that belong to A. The shaded region of the rectangle contains all sample points not in event A and is by definition the complement of A.

In any probability application, either event A or its complement A^c must occur. Therefore, we have

$$P(A) + P(A^c) = 1$$

FIGURE 4.4   COMPLEMENT OF EVENT A IS SHADED

Solving for $P(A)$, we obtain the following result.

COMPUTING PROBABILITY USING THE COMPLEMENT

$$P(A) = 1 - P(A^c) \qquad \text{(4.5)}$$

Equation (4.5) shows that the probability of an event A can be computed easily if the probability of its complement, $P(A^c)$, is known.

As an example, consider the case of a sales manager who, after reviewing sales reports, states that 80% of new customer contacts result in no sale. By allowing A to denote the event of a sale and A^c to denote the event of no sale, the manager is stating that $P(A^c) = .80$. Using equation (4.5), we see that

$$P(A) = 1 - P(A^c) = 1 - .80 = .20$$

We can conclude that a new customer contact has a .20 probability of resulting in a sale.

In another example, a purchasing agent states a .90 probability that a supplier will send a shipment that is free of defective parts. Using the complement, we can conclude that there is a $1 - .90 = .10$ probability that the shipment will contain defective parts.

Addition Law

The addition law is helpful when we are interested in knowing the probability that at least one of two events occurs. That is, with events A and B we are interested in knowing the probability that event A or event B or both occur.

Before we present the addition law, we need to discuss two concepts related to the combination of events: the *union* of events and the *intersection* of events. Given two events A and B, the **union of A and B** is defined as follows.

UNION OF TWO EVENTS

The *union* of A and B is the event containing *all* sample points belonging to A *or B or both*. The union is denoted by $A \cup B$.

The Venn diagram in Figure 4.5 depicts the union of events A and B. Note that the two circles contain all the sample points in event A as well as all the sample points in event B.

FIGURE 4.5   UNION OF EVENTS *A* AND *B* IS SHADED

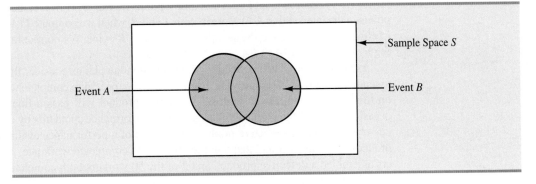

The fact that the circles overlap indicates that some sample points are contained in both *A* and *B*.

The definition of the **intersection of *A* and *B*** follows.

INTERSECTION OF TWO EVENTS

Given two events *A* and *B*, the *intersection* of *A* and *B* is the event containing the sample points belonging to *both A and B*. The intersection is denoted by $A \cap B$.

The Venn diagram depicting the intersection of events *A* and *B* is shown in Figure 4.6. The area where the two circles overlap is the intersection; it contains the sample points that are in both *A* and *B*.

Let us now continue with a discussion of the addition law. The **addition law** provides a way to compute the probability that event *A* or event *B* or both occur. In other words, the addition law is used to compute the probability of the union of two events. The addition law is written as follows.

ADDITION LAW

$$P(A \cup B) = P(A) + P(B) - P(A \cap B) \qquad \textbf{(4.6)}$$

FIGURE 4.6   INTERSECTION OF EVENTS *A* AND *B* IS SHADED

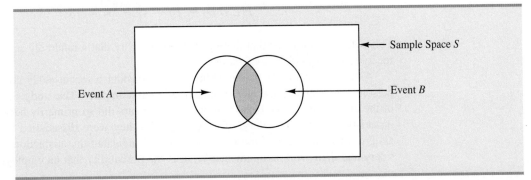

To understand the addition law intuitively, note that the first two terms in the addition law, $P(A) + P(B)$, account for all the sample points in $A \cup B$. However, because the sample points in the intersection $A \cap B$ are in both A and B, when we compute $P(A) + P(B)$, we are in effect counting each of the sample points in $A \cap B$ twice. We correct for this overcounting by subtracting $P(A \cap B)$.

As an example of an application of the addition law, let us consider the case of a small assembly plant with 50 employees. Each worker is expected to complete work assignments on time and in such a way that the assembled product will pass a final inspection. On occasion, some of the workers fail to meet the performance standards by completing work late or assembling a defective product. At the end of a performance evaluation period, the production manager found that 5 of the 50 workers completed work late, 6 of the 50 workers assembled a defective product, and 2 of the 50 workers both completed work late *and* assembled a defective product.

Let

$$L = \text{the event that the work is completed late}$$
$$D = \text{the event that the assembled product is defective}$$

The relative frequency information leads to the following probabilities.

$$P(L) = \frac{5}{50} = .10$$

$$P(D) = \frac{6}{50} = .12$$

$$P(L \cap D) = \frac{2}{50} = .04$$

After reviewing the performance data, the production manager decided to assign a poor performance rating to any employee whose work was either late or defective; thus the event of interest is $L \cup D$. What is the probability that the production manager assigned an employee a poor performance rating?

Note that the probability question is about the union of two events. Specifically, we want to know $P(L \cup D)$. Using equation (4.6), we have

$$P(L \cup D) = P(L) + P(D) - P(L \cap D)$$

Knowing values for the three probabilities on the right side of this expression, we can write

$$P(L \cup D) = .10 + .12 - .04 = .18$$

This calculation tells us that there is a .18 probability that a randomly selected employee received a poor performance rating.

As another example of the addition law, consider a recent study conducted by the personnel manager of a major computer software company. The study showed that 30% of the employees who left the firm within two years did so primarily because they were dissatisfied with their salary, 20% left because they were dissatisfied with their work assignments, and 12% of the former employees indicated dissatisfaction with *both* their salary and their work assignments. What is the probability that an employee who leaves within two years does so because of dissatisfaction with salary, dissatisfaction with the work assignment, or both?

Let

$$S = \text{the event that the employee leaves because of salary}$$
$$W = \text{the event that the employee leaves because of work assignment}$$

We have $P(S) = .30$, $P(W) = .20$, and $P(S \cap W) = .12$. Using equation (4.6), the addition law, we have

$$P(S \cup W) = P(S) + P(W) - P(S \cap W) = .30 + .20 - .12 = .38.$$

We find a .38 probability that an employee leaves for salary or work assignment reasons.

Before we conclude our discussion of the addition law, let us consider a special case that arises for **mutually exclusive events.**

MUTUALLY EXCLUSIVE EVENTS

Two events are said to be mutually exclusive if the events have no sample points in common.

Events A and B are mutually exclusive if, when one event occurs, the other cannot occur. Thus, a requirement for A and B to be mutually exclusive is that their intersection must contain no sample points. The Venn diagram depicting two mutually exclusive events A and B is shown in Figure 4.7. In this case $P(A \cap B) = 0$ and the addition law can be written as follows.

ADDITION LAW FOR MUTUALLY EXCLUSIVE EVENTS
$$P(A \cup B) = P(A) + P(B)$$

FIGURE 4.7   MUTUALLY EXCLUSIVE EVENTS

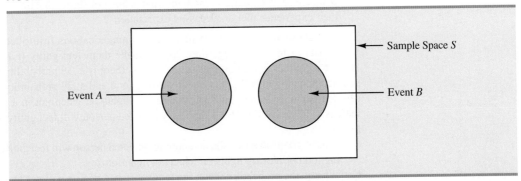

Exercises

Methods

22. Suppose that we have a sample space with five equally likely experimental outcomes: E_1, E_2, E_3, E_4, E_5. Let

$$A = \{E_1, E_2\}$$
$$B = \{E_3, E_4\}$$
$$C = \{E_2, E_3, E_5\}$$

a. Find $P(A)$, $P(B)$, and $P(C)$.
b. Find $P(A \cup B)$. Are A and B mutually exclusive?
c. Find A^c, C^c, $P(A^c)$, and $P(C^c)$.
d. Find $A \cup B^c$ and $P(A \cup B^c)$.
e. Find $P(B \cup C)$.

✓**SELF**test 23. Suppose that we have a sample space $S = \{E_1, E_2, E_3, E_4, E_5, E_6, E_7\}$, where $E_1, E_2, \ldots,$ E_7 denote the sample points. The following probability assignments apply: $P(E_1) = .05$, $P(E_2) = .20$, $P(E_3) = .20$, $P(E_4) = .25$, $P(E_5) = .15$, $P(E_6) = .10$, and $P(E_7) = .05$. Let

$$A = \{E_1, E_4, E_6\}$$
$$B = \{E_2, E_4, E_7\}$$
$$C = \{E_2, E_3, E_5, E_7\}$$

a. Find $P(A)$, $P(B)$, and $P(C)$.
b. Find $A \cup B$ and $P(A \cup B)$.
c. Find $A \cap B$ and $P(A \cap B)$.
d. Are events A and C mutually exclusive?
e. Find B^c and $P(B^c)$.

Applications

24. Clarkson University surveyed alumni to learn more about what they think of Clarkson. One part of the survey asked respondents to indicate whether their overall experience at Clarkson fell short of expectations, met expectations, or surpassed expectations. The results showed that 4% of the respondents did not provide a response, 26% said that their experience fell short of expectations, and 65% of the respondents said that their experience met expectations.
a. If we chose an alumnus at random, what is the probability that the alumnus would say their experience *surpassed* expectations?
b. If we chose an alumnus at random, what is the probability that the alumnus would say their experience met or surpassed expectations?

25. The Eco Pulse survey from the marketing communications firm Shelton Group asked individuals to indicate things they do that make them feel guilty (*Los Angeles Times*, August 15, 2012). Based on the survey results, there is a .39 probability that a randomly selected person will feel guilty about wasting food and a .27 probability that a randomly selected person will feel guilty about leaving lights on when not in a room. Moreover, there is a .12 probability that a randomly selected person will feel guilty for both of these reasons.
a. What is the probability that a randomly selected person will feel guilty for either wasting food or leaving lights on when not in a room?
b. What is the probability that a randomly selected person will not feel guilty for either of these reasons?

26. Information about mutual funds provided by Morningstar includes the type of mutual fund (Domestic Equity, International Equity, or Fixed Income) and the Morningstar rating for the fund. The rating is expressed from 1-star (lowest rating) to 5-star (highest rating). Suppose a sample of 25 mutual funds provided the following counts:

- Sixteen mutual funds were Domestic Equity funds.
- Thirteen mutual funds were rated 3-star or less.
- Seven of the Domestic Equity funds were rated 4-star.
- Two of the Domestic Equity funds were rated 5-star.

Assume that one of these 25 mutual funds will be randomly selected in order to learn more about the mutual fund and its investment strategy.

a. What is the probability of selecting a Domestic Equity fund?
b. What is the probability of selecting a fund with a 4-star or 5-star rating?
c. What is the probability of selecting a fund that is both a Domestic Equity fund *and* a fund with a 4-star or 5-star rating?
d. What is the probability of selecting a fund that is a Domestic Equity fund *or* a fund with a 4-star or 5-star rating?

27. What NCAA college basketball conferences have the higher probability of having a team play in college basketball's national championship game? Over the last 20 years, the Atlantic Coast Conference (ACC) ranks first by having a team in the championship game 10 times. The Southeastern Conference (SEC) ranks second by having a team in the championship game 8 times. However, these two conferences have both had teams in the championship game only one time, when Arkansas (SEC) beat Duke (ACC) 76–70 in 1994 (NCAA website, April 2009). Use these data to estimate the following probabilities.

a. What is the probability the ACC will have a team in the championship game?
b. What is the probability the SEC will have team in the championship game?
c. What is the probability the ACC and SEC will both have teams in the championship game?
d. What is the probability at least one team from these two conferences will be in the championship game? That is, what is the probability a team from the ACC or SEC will play in the championship game?
e. What is the probability that the championship game will not a have team from one of these two conferences?

✓SELF*test*

28. A survey of magazine subscribers showed that 45.8% rented a car during the past 12 months for business reasons, 54% rented a car during the past 12 months for personal reasons, and 30% rented a car during the past 12 months for both business and personal reasons.

a. What is the probability that a subscriber rented a car during the past 12 months for business or personal reasons?
b. What is the probability that a subscriber did not rent a car during the past 12 months for either business or personal reasons?

29. High school seniors with strong academic records apply to the nation's most selective colleges in greater numbers each year. Because the number of slots remains relatively stable, some colleges reject more early applicants. Suppose that for a recent admissions class, an Ivy League college received 2851 applications for early admission. Of this group, it admitted 1033 students early, rejected 854 outright, and deferred 964 to the regular admission pool for further consideration. In the past, this school has admitted 18% of the deferred early admission applicants during the regular admission process. Counting the students admitted early and the students admitted during the regular admission process, the total class size was 2375. Let E, R, and D represent the events that a student who applies for early admission is admitted early, rejected outright, or deferred to the regular admissions pool.

a. Use the data to estimate $P(E)$, $P(R)$, and $P(D)$.
b. Are events E and D mutually exclusive? Find $P(E \cap D)$.

c. For the 2375 students who were admitted, what is the probability that a randomly selected student was accepted during early admission?

d. Suppose a student applies for early admission. What is the probability that the student will be admitted for early admission or be deferred and later admitted during the regular admission process?

4.4   Conditional Probability

Often, the probability of an event is influenced by whether a related event already occurred. Suppose we have an event A with probability $P(A)$. If we obtain new information and learn that a related event, denoted by B, already occurred, we will want to take advantage of this information by calculating a new probability for event A. This new probability of event A is called a **conditional probability** and is written $P(A \mid B)$. We use the notation $\mid$ to indicate that we are considering the probability of event A *given* the condition that event B has occurred. Hence, the notation $P(A \mid B)$ reads "the probability of A given B."

As an illustration of the application of conditional probability, consider the situation of the promotion status of male and female officers of a major metropolitan police force in the eastern United States. The police force consists of 1200 officers, 960 men and 240 women. Over the past two years, 324 officers on the police force received promotions. The specific breakdown of promotions for male and female officers is shown in Table 4.4.

After reviewing the promotion record, a committee of female officers raised a discrimination case on the basis that 288 male officers had received promotions, but only 36 female officers had received promotions. The police administration argued that the relatively low number of promotions for female officers was due not to discrimination, but to the fact that relatively few females are members of the police force. Let us show how conditional probability could be used to analyze the discrimination charge.

Let

$$M = \text{event an officer is a man}$$
$$W = \text{event an officer is a woman}$$
$$A = \text{event an officer is promoted}$$
$$A^c = \text{event an officer is not promoted}$$

Dividing the data values in Table 4.4 by the total of 1200 officers enables us to summarize the available information with the following probability values.

$$P(M \cap A) = 288/1200 = .24 \text{ probability that a randomly selected officer is a man } and \text{ is promoted}$$

$$P(M \cap A^c) = 672/1200 = .56 \text{ probability that a randomly selected officer is a man } and \text{ is not promoted}$$

TABLE 4.4   PROMOTION STATUS OF POLICE OFFICERS OVER THE PAST TWO YEARS

	Men	Women	Total
Promoted	288	36	324
Not Promoted	672	204	876
Total	960	240	1200

TABLE 4.5   JOINT PROBABILITY TABLE FOR PROMOTIONS

Joint probabilities appear in the body of the table.	Men (*M*)	Women (*W*)	Total
Promoted (*A*)	.24	.03	.27
Not Promoted (*A^c*)	.56	.17	.73
Total	.80	.20	1.00

Marginal probabilities appear in the margins of the table.

$$P(W \cap A) = 36/1200 = .03 \text{ probability that a randomly selected officer is a woman } and \text{ is promoted}$$

$$P(W \cap A^c) = 204/1200 = .17 \text{ probability that a randomly selected officer is a woman } and \text{ is not promoted}$$

Because each of these values gives the probability of the intersection of two events, the probabilities are called **joint probabilities**. Table 4.5, which provides a summary of the probability information for the police officer promotion situation, is referred to as a *joint probability table*.

The values in the margins of the joint probability table provide the probabilities of each event separately. That is, $P(M) = .80$, $P(W) = .20$, $P(A) = .27$, and $P(A^c) = .73$. These probabilities are referred to as **marginal probabilities** because of their location in the margins of the joint probability table. We note that the marginal probabilities are found by summing the joint probabilities in the corresponding row or column of the joint probability table. For instance, the marginal probability of being promoted is $P(A) = P(M \cap A) + P(W \cap A) = .24 + .03 = .27$. From the marginal probabilities, we see that 80% of the force is male, 20% of the force is female, 27% of all officers received promotions, and 73% were not promoted.

Let us begin the conditional probability analysis by computing the probability that an officer is promoted given that the officer is a man. In conditional probability notation, we are attempting to determine $P(A \mid M)$. To calculate $P(A \mid M)$, we first realize that this notation simply means that we are considering the probability of the event *A* (promotion) given that the condition designated as event *M* (the officer is a man) is known to exist. Thus $P(A \mid M)$ tells us that we are now concerned only with the promotion status of the 960 male officers. Because 288 of the 960 male officers received promotions, the probability of being promoted given that the officer is a man is 288/960 = .30. In other words, given that an officer is a man, that officer had a 30% chance of receiving a promotion over the past two years.

This procedure was easy to apply because the values in Table 4.4 show the number of officers in each category. We now want to demonstrate how conditional probabilities such as $P(A \mid M)$ can be computed directly from related event probabilities rather than the frequency data of Table 4.4.

We have shown that $P(A \mid M) = 288/960 = .30$. Let us now divide both the numerator and denominator of this fraction by 1200, the total number of officers in the study.

$$P(A \mid M) = \frac{288}{960} = \frac{288/1200}{960/1200} = \frac{.24}{.80} = .30$$

We now see that the conditional probability $P(A \mid M)$ can be computed as .24/.80. Refer to the joint probability table (Table 4.5). Note in particular that .24 is the joint probability of *A* and *M*; that is, $P(A \cap M) = .24$. Also note that .80 is the marginal probability that a randomly selected officer is a man; that is, $P(M) = .80$. Thus, the conditional probability $P(A \mid M)$ can be computed as the ratio of the joint probability $P(A \cap M)$ to the marginal probability $P(M)$.

$$P(A \mid M) = \frac{P(A \cap M)}{P(M)} = \frac{.24}{.80} = .30$$

The fact that conditional probabilities can be computed as the ratio of a joint probability to a marginal probability provides the following general formula for conditional probability calculations for two events A and B.

CONDITIONAL PROBABILITY

$$P(A \mid B) = \frac{P(A \cap B)}{P(B)} \qquad (4.7)$$

or

$$P(B \mid A) = \frac{P(A \cap B)}{P(A)} \qquad (4.8)$$

The Venn diagram in Figure 4.8 is helpful in obtaining an intuitive understanding of conditional probability. The circle on the right shows that event B has occurred; the portion of the circle that overlaps with event A denotes the event $(A \cap B)$. We know that once event B has occurred, the only way that we can also observe event A is for the event $(A \cap B)$ to occur. Thus, the ratio $P(A \cap B)/P(B)$ provides the conditional probability that we will observe event A given that event B has already occurred.

Let us return to the issue of discrimination against the female officers. The marginal probability in row 1 of Table 4.5 shows that the probability of promotion of an officer is $P(A) = .27$ (regardless of whether that officer is male or female). However, the critical issue in the discrimination case involves the two conditional probabilities $P(A \mid M)$ and $P(A \mid W)$. That is, what is the probability of a promotion *given* that the officer is a man, and what is the probability of a promotion *given* that the officer is a woman? If these two probabilities are equal, a discrimination argument has no basis because the chances of a promotion are the same for male and female officers. However, a difference in the two conditional probabilities will support the position that male and female officers are treated differently in promotion decisions.

FIGURE 4.8   CONDITIONAL PROBABILITY $P(A \mid B) = P(A \cap B)/P(B)$

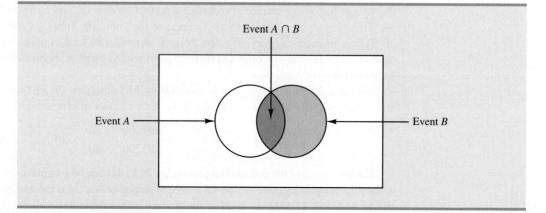

We already determined that $P(A \mid M) = .30$. Let us now use the probability values in Table 4.5 and the basic relationship of conditional probability in equation (4.7) to compute the probability that an officer is promoted given that the officer is a woman; that is, $P(A \mid W)$. Using equation (4.7), with W replacing B, we obtain

$$P(A \mid W) = \frac{P(A \cap W)}{P(W)} = \frac{.03}{.20} = .15$$

What conclusion do you draw? The probability of a promotion given that the officer is a man is .30, twice the .15 probability of a promotion given that the officer is a woman. Although the use of conditional probability does not in itself prove that discrimination exists in this case, the conditional probability values support the argument presented by the female officers.

Independent Events

In the preceding illustration, $P(A) = .27$, $P(A \mid M) = .30$, and $P(A \mid W) = .15$. We see that the probability of a promotion (event A) is affected or influenced by whether the officer is a man or a woman. Particularly, because $P(A \mid M) \neq P(A)$, we would say that events A and M are dependent events. That is, the probability of event A (promotion) is altered or affected by knowing that event M (the officer is a man) exists. Similarly, with $P(A \mid W) \neq P(A)$, we would say that events A and W are *dependent events*. However, if the probability of event A is not changed by the existence of event M—that is, $P(A \mid M) = P(A)$—we would say that events A and M are **independent events**. This situation leads to the following definition of the independence of two events.

INDEPENDENT EVENTS

Two events A and B are independent if

$$P(A \mid B) = P(A) \tag{4.9}$$

or

$$P(B \mid A) = P(B) \tag{4.10}$$

Otherwise, the events are dependent.

Multiplication Law

Whereas the addition law of probability is used to compute the probability of a union of two events, the multiplication law is used to compute the probability of the intersection of two events. The multiplication law is based on the definition of conditional probability. Using equations (4.7) and (4.8) and solving for $P(A \cap B)$, we obtain the **multiplication law**.

MULTIPLICATION LAW

$$P(A \cap B) = P(B)P(A \mid B) \tag{4.11}$$

or

$$P(A \cap B) = P(A)P(B \mid A) \tag{4.12}$$

To illustrate the use of the multiplication law, consider a newspaper circulation department where it is known that 84% of the households in a particular neighborhood subscribe to the daily edition of the paper. If we let D denote the event that a household subscribes to the daily edition, $P(D) = .84$. In addition, it is known that the probability that a household that already holds a daily subscription also subscribes to the Sunday edition (event S) is .75; that is, $P(S \mid D) = .75$. What is the probability that a household subscribes to both the Sunday and daily editions of the newspaper? Using the multiplication law, we compute the desired $P(S \cap D)$ as

$$P(S \cap D) = P(D)P(S \mid D) = .84(.75) = .63$$

We now know that 63% of the households subscribe to both the Sunday and daily editions.

Before concluding this section, let us consider the special case of the multiplication law when the events involved are independent. Recall that events A and B are independent whenever $P(A \mid B) = P(A)$ or $P(B \mid A) = P(B)$. Hence, using equations (4.11) and (4.12) for the special case of independent events, we obtain the following multiplication law.

MULTIPLICATION LAW FOR INDEPENDENT EVENTS

$$P(A \cap B) = P(A)P(B) \qquad\qquad (4.13)$$

To compute the probability of the intersection of two independent events, we simply multiply the corresponding probabilities. Note that the multiplication law for independent events provides another way to determine whether A and B are independent. That is, if $P(A \cap B) = P(A)P(B)$, then A and B are independent; if $P(A \cap B) \neq P(A)P(B)$, then A and B are dependent.

As an application of the multiplication law for independent events, consider the situation of a service station manager who knows from past experience that 80% of the customers use a credit card when they purchase gasoline. What is the probability that the next two customers purchasing gasoline will each use a credit card? If we let

A = the event that the first customer uses a credit card

B = the event that the second customer uses a credit card

then the event of interest is $A \cap B$. Given no other information, we can reasonably assume that A and B are independent events. Thus,

$$P(A \cap B) = P(A)P(B) = (.80)(.80) = .64$$

To summarize this section, we note that our interest in conditional probability is motivated by the fact that events are often related. In such cases, we say the events are dependent and the conditional probability formulas in equations (4.7) and (4.8) must be used to compute the event probabilities. If two events are not related, they are independent; in this case neither event's probability is affected by whether the other event occurred.

NOTES AND COMMENTS

Do not confuse the notion of mutually exclusive events with that of independent events. Two events with nonzero probabilities cannot be both mutually exclusive and independent. If one mutually exclusive event is known to occur, the other cannot occur; thus, the probability of the other event occurring is reduced to zero. They are therefore dependent.

Exercises

Methods

SELF*test*

30. Suppose that we have two events, A and B, with $P(A) = .50$, $P(B) = .60$, and $P(A \cap B) = .40$.
    a. Find $P(A \mid B)$.
    b. Find $P(B \mid A)$.
    c. Are A and B independent? Why or why not?

31. Assume that we have two events, A and B, that are mutually exclusive. Assume further that we know $P(A) = .30$ and $P(B) = .40$.
    a. What is $P(A \cap B)$?
    b. What is $P(A \mid B)$?
    c. A student in statistics argues that the concepts of mutually exclusive events and independent events are really the same, and that if events are mutually exclusive they must be independent. Do you agree with this statement? Use the probability information in this problem to justify your answer.
    d. What general conclusion would you make about mutually exclusive and independent events given the results of this problem?

Applications

32. The automobile industry sold 657,000 vehicles in the United States during January 2009 (*The Wall Street Journal,* February 4, 2009). This volume was down 37% from January 2008 as economic conditions continued to decline. The Big Three U.S. automakers—General Motors, Ford, and Chrysler—sold 280,500 vehicles, down 48% from January 2008. A summary of sales by automobile manufacturer and type of vehicle sold is shown in the following table. Data are in thousands of vehicles. The non-U.S. manufacturers are led by Toyota, Honda, and Nissan. The category Light Truck includes pickup, minivan, SUV, and crossover models.

		Type of Vehicle	
		Car	**Light Truck**
Manufacturer	**U.S.**	87.4	193.1
	Non-U.S.	228.5	148.0

    a. Develop a joint probability table for these data and use the table to answer the remaining questions.
    b. What are the marginal probabilities? What do they tell you about the probabilities associated with the manufacturer and the type of vehicle sold?
    c. If a vehicle was manufactured by one of the U.S. automakers, what is the probability that the vehicle was a car? What is the probability it was a light truck?
    d. If a vehicle was not manufactured by one of the U.S. automakers, what is the probability that the vehicle was a car? What is the probability it was a light truck?
    e. If the vehicle was a light truck, what is the probability that it was manufactured by one of the U.S. automakers?
    f. What does the probability information tell you about sales?

SELF*test*

33. Students taking the Graduate Management Admissions Test (GMAT) were asked about their undergraduate major and intent to pursue their MBA as a full-time or part-time student. A summary of their responses follows.

		Undergraduate Major			
		Business	**Engineering**	**Other**	**Totals**
Intended	**Full-Time**	352	197	251	800
Enrollment	**Part-Time**	150	161	194	505
Status	**Totals**	502	358	445	1305

    a. Develop a joint probability table for these data.
    b. Use the marginal probabilities of undergraduate major (business, engineering, or other) to comment on which undergraduate major produces the most potential MBA students.

    c.   If a student intends to attend classes full-time in pursuit of an MBA degree, what is the probability that the student was an undergraduate engineering major?

    d.   If a student was an undergraduate business major, what is the probability that the student intends to attend classes full-time in pursuit of an MBA degree?

    e.   Let A denote the event that the student intends to attend classes full-time in pursuit of an MBA degree, and let B denote the event that the student was an undergraduate business major. Are events A and B independent? Justify your answer.

34.   The Bureau of Transportation Statistics reports on-time performance for airlines at major U.S. airports. JetBlue, United, and US Airways share terminal C at Boston's Logan Airport. The percentage of on-time flights reported for August 2012 was 76.8% for JetBlue, 71.5% for United, and 82.2% for US Airways (Bureau of Transportation Statistics website, October 2012). Assume that 30% of the flights arriving at terminal C are JetBlue flights, 32% are United flights, and 38% are US Airways flights.

    a.   Develop a joint probability table with three rows (the airlines) and two columns (on-time and late).

    b.   An announcement is made that Flight 1382 will be arriving at gate 20 of terminal C. What is the probability that Flight 1382 will arrive on time?

    c.   What is the most likely airline for Flight 1382? What is the probability that Flight 1382 is by this airline?

    d.   Suppose that an announcement is made saying that Flight 1382 will now be arriving late. What is the most likely airline for this flight? What is the probability that Flight 1382 is by this airline?

35.   To better understand how husbands and wives feel about their finances, *Money Magazine* conducted a national poll of 1010 married adults age 25 and older with household incomes of $50,000 or more (*Money Magazine* website, December 14, 2014). Consider the following example set of responses to the question, "Who is better at getting deals?"

	Who Is Better?		
Respondent	I Am	My Spouse	We Are Equal
Husband	278	127	102
Wife	290	111	102

    a.   Develop a joint probability table and use it to answer the following questions.

    b.   Construct the marginal probabilities for Who Is Better (I Am, My Spouse, We Are Equal). Comment.

    c.   Given that the respondent is a husband, what is the probability that he feels he is better at getting deals than his wife?

    d.   Given that the respondent is a wife, what is the probability that she feels she is better at getting deals than her husband?

    e.   Given a response "My spouse" is better at getting deals, what is the probability that the response came from a husband?

    f.   Given a response "We are equal," what is the probability that the response came from a husband? What is the probability that the response came from a wife?

36.   Jamal Crawford of the National Basketball Association's Portland Trail Blazers is the best free-throw shooter on the team, making 93% of his shots (ESPN website, April 5, 2012). Assume that late in a basketball game, Jamal Crawford is fouled and is awarded two shots.

    a.   What is the probability that he will make both shots?

    b.   What is the probability that he will make at least one shot?

    c.   What is the probability that he will miss both shots?

    d.   Late in a basketball game, a team often intentionally fouls an opposing player in order to stop the game clock. The usual strategy is to intentionally foul the other team's worst free-throw shooter. Assume that the Portland Trail Blazers' center makes 58% of his free-throw shots. Calculate the probabilities for the center as shown in parts (a), (b), and (c), and show that intentionally fouling the Portland Trail Blazers' center is a better strategy than intentionally fouling Jamal Crawford. Assume as in parts (a), (b), and (c) that two shots will be awarded.

37. A joint survey by *Parade* magazine and Yahoo! found that 59% of American workers say that if they could do it all over again, they would choose a different career (*USA Today*, September 24, 2012). The survey also found that 33% of American workers say they plan to retire early and 67% say they plan to wait and retire at age 65 or older. Assume that the following joint probability table applies.

		Retire Early		
		Yes	**No**	
Career	**Same**	.20	.21	.41
	Different	.13	.46	.59
		.33	.67	

    a.   What is the probability a worker would select the same career?

    b.   What is the probability a worker who would select the same career plans to retire early?

    c.   What is the probability a worker who would select a different career plans to retire early?

    d.   What do the conditional probabilities in parts (b) and (c) suggest about the reasons workers say they would select the same career?

38. The Institute for Higher Education Policy, a Washington, D.C.-based research firm, studied the payback of student loans for 1.8 million college students who had student loans that began to become due six years ago (*The Wall Street Journal*, November 27, 2012). The study found that 50% of the student loans were being paid back in a satisfactory fashion, whereas 50% of the student loans were delinquent. The following joint probability table shows the probabilities of the student loan status and whether or not the student had received a college degree.

		College Degree		
		Yes	**No**	
Loan	**Satisfactory**	.26	.24	.50
Status	**Delinquent**	.16	.34	.50
		.42	.58	

    a.   What is the probability that a student with a student loan had received a college degree?

    b.   What is the probability that a student with a student loan had not received a college degree?

    c.   Given the student had received a college degree, what is the probability that the student has a delinquent loan?

    d.   Given the student had not received a college degree, what is the probability that the student has a delinquent loan?

    e.   What is the impact of dropping out of college without a degree for students who have a student loan?

4.5   Bayes' Theorem

In the discussion of conditional probability, we indicated that revising probabilities when new information is obtained is an important phase of probability analysis. Often, we begin the analysis with initial or **prior probability** estimates for specific events of interest. Then, from sources such as a sample, a special report, or a product test, we obtain additional information about the events. Given this new information, we update the prior probability values by calculating revised probabilities, referred to as **posterior probabilities. Bayes' theorem** provides a means for making these probability calculations. The steps in this probability revision process are shown in Figure 4.9.

As an application of Bayes' theorem, consider a manufacturing firm that receives shipments of parts from two different suppliers. Let A_1 denote the event that a part is from supplier 1 and A_2 denote the event that a part is from supplier 2. Currently, 65% of the parts purchased by the company are from supplier 1 and the remaining 35% are from supplier 2. Hence, if a part is selected at random, we would assign the prior probabilities $P(A_1) = .65$ and $P(A_2) = .35$.

The quality of the purchased parts varies with the source of supply. Historical data suggest that the quality ratings of the two suppliers are as shown in Table 4.6. If we let G denote the event that a part is good and B denote the event that a part is bad, the information in Table 4.6 provides the following conditional probability values.

$$P(G \mid A_1) = .98 \quad P(B \mid A_1) = .02$$
$$P(G \mid A_2) = .95 \quad P(B \mid A_2) = .05$$

The tree diagram in Figure 4.10 depicts the process of the firm receiving a part from one of the two suppliers and then discovering that the part is good or bad as a two-step experiment. We see that four experimental outcomes are possible; two correspond to the part being good and two correspond to the part being bad.

Each of the experimental outcomes is the intersection of two events, so we can use the multiplication rule to compute the probabilities. For instance,

$$P(A_1, G) = P(A_1 \cap G) = P(A_1)P(G \mid A_1)$$

FIGURE 4.9   PROBABILITY REVISION USING BAYES' THEOREM

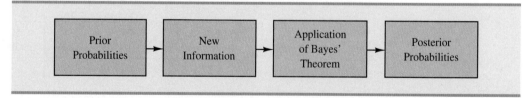

TABLE 4.6   HISTORICAL QUALITY LEVELS OF TWO SUPPLIERS

	Percentage Good Parts	Percentage Bad Parts
Supplier 1	98	2
Supplier 2	95	5

FIGURE 4.10 TREE DIAGRAM FOR TWO-SUPPLIER EXAMPLE

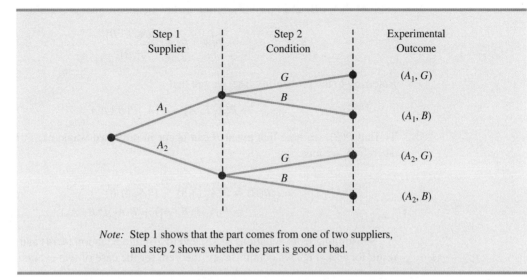

Note: Step 1 shows that the part comes from one of two suppliers, and step 2 shows whether the part is good or bad.

The process of computing these joint probabilities can be depicted in what is called a probability tree (see Figure 4.11). From left to right through the tree, the probabilities for each branch at step 1 are prior probabilities and the probabilities for each branch at step 2 are conditional probabilities. To find the probabilities of each experimental outcome, we simply multiply the probabilities on the branches leading to the outcome. Each of these joint probabilities is shown in Figure 4.11 along with the known probabilities for each branch.

Suppose now that the parts from the two suppliers are used in the firm's manufacturing process and that a machine breaks down because it attempts to process a bad part. Given the information that the part is bad, what is the probability that it came from supplier 1 and what is the probability that it came from supplier 2? With the information in the probability tree (Figure 4.11), Bayes' theorem can be used to answer these questions.

FIGURE 4.11 PROBABILITY TREE FOR TWO-SUPPLIER EXAMPLE

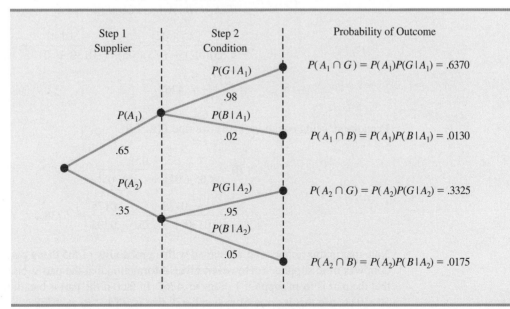

Letting B denote the event that the part is bad, we are looking for the posterior probabilities $P(A_1 \mid B)$ and $P(A_2 \mid B)$. From the law of conditional probability, we know that

$$P(A_1 \mid B) = \frac{P(A_1 \cap B)}{P(B)} \qquad (4.14)$$

Referring to the probability tree, we see that

$$P(A_1 \cap B) = P(A_1)P(B \mid A_1) \qquad (4.15)$$

To find $P(B)$, we note that event B can occur in only two ways: $(A_1 \cap B)$ and $(A_2 \cap B)$. Therefore, we have

$$\begin{aligned} P(B) &= P(A_1 \cap B) + P(A_2 \cap B) \\ &= P(A_1)P(B \mid A_1) + P(A_2)P(B \mid A_2) \end{aligned} \qquad (4.16)$$

Substituting from equations (4.15) and (4.16) into equation (4.14) and writing a similar result for $P(A_2 \mid B)$, we obtain Bayes' theorem for the case of two events.

The Reverend Thomas Bayes (1702–1761), a Presbyterian minister, is credited with the original work leading to the version of Bayes' theorem in use today.

BAYES' THEOREM (TWO-EVENT CASE)

$$P(A_1 \mid B) = \frac{P(A_1)P(B \mid A_1)}{P(A_1)P(B \mid A_1) + P(A_2)P(B \mid A_2)} \qquad (4.17)$$

$$P(A_2 \mid B) = \frac{P(A_2)P(B \mid A_2)}{P(A_1)P(B \mid A_1) + P(A_2)P(B \mid A_2)} \qquad (4.18)$$

Using equation (4.17) and the probability values provided in the example, we have

$$P(A_1 \mid B) = \frac{P(A_1)P(B \mid A_1)}{P(A_1)P(B \mid A_1) + P(A_2)P(B \mid A_2)}$$

$$= \frac{(.65)(.02)}{(.65)(.02) + (.35)(.05)} = \frac{.0130}{.0130 + .0175}$$

$$= \frac{.0130}{.0305} = .4262$$

In addition, using equation (4.18), we find $P(A_2 \mid B)$.

$$P(A_2 \mid B) = \frac{(.35)(.05)}{(.65)(.02) + (.35)(.05)}$$

$$= \frac{.0175}{.0130 + .0175} = \frac{.0175}{.0305} = .5738$$

Note that in this application we started with a probability of .65 that a part selected at random was from supplier 1. However, given information that the part is bad, the probability that the part is from supplier 1 drops to .4262. In fact, if the part is bad, it has better than a 50–50 chance that it came from supplier 2; that is, $P(A_2 \mid B) = .5738$.

Bayes' theorem is applicable when the events for which we want to compute posterior probabilities are mutually exclusive and their union is the entire sample space.[1] For the case of n mutually exclusive events $A_1, A_2, \ldots, A_n$, whose union is the entire sample space, Bayes' theorem can be used to compute any posterior probability $P(A_i \mid B)$ as shown here.

BAYES' THEOREM

$$P(A_i \mid B) = \frac{P(A_i)P(B \mid A_i)}{P(A_1)P(B \mid A_1) + P(A_2)P(B \mid A_2) + \cdots + P(A_n)P(B \mid A_n)} \qquad (4.19)$$

With prior probabilities $P(A_1), P(A_2), \ldots, P(A_n)$ and the appropriate conditional probabilities $P(B \mid A_1), P(B \mid A_2), \ldots, P(B \mid A_n)$, equation (4.19) can be used to compute the posterior probability of the events $A_1, A_2, \ldots, A_n$.

Tabular Approach

A tabular approach is helpful in conducting the Bayes' theorem calculations. Such an approach is shown in Table 4.7 for the parts supplier problem. The computations shown there are done in the following steps.

Step 1. Prepare the following three columns:

Column 1—The mutually exclusive events A_i for which posterior probabilities are desired

Column 2—The prior probabilities $P(A_i)$ for the events

Column 3—The conditional probabilities $P(B \mid A_i)$ of the new information B given each event

Step 2. In column 4, compute the joint probabilities $P(A_i \cap B)$ for each event and the new information B by using the multiplication law. These joint probabilities are found by multiplying the prior probabilities in column 2 by the corresponding conditional probabilities in column 3; that is, $P(A_i \cap B) = P(A_i)P(B \mid A_i)$.

Step 3. Sum the joint probabilities in column 4. The sum is the probability of the new information, $P(B)$. Thus we see in Table 4.7 that there is a .0130 probability that the part came from supplier 1 and is bad and a .0175 probability that the part came from supplier 2 and is bad. Because these are the only two ways in which a bad part can be obtained, the sum .0130 + .0175 shows an overall

TABLE 4.7 TABULAR APPROACH TO BAYES' THEOREM CALCULATIONS FOR THE TWO-SUPPLIER PROBLEM

(1) Events A_i	(2) Prior Probabilities $P(A_i)$	(3) Conditional Probabilities $P(B \mid A_i)$	(4) Joint Probabilities $P(A_i \cap B)$	(5) Posterior Probabilities $P(A_i \mid B)$
A_1	.65	.02	.0130	.0130/.0305 = .4262
A_2	.35	.05	.0175	.0175/.0305 = .5738
	1.00		$P(B) = .0305$	1.0000

---

[1] If the union of events is the entire sample space, the events are said to be collectively exhaustive.

probability of .0305 of finding a bad part from the combined shipments of the two suppliers.

Step 4. In column 5, compute the posterior probabilities using the basic relationship of conditional probability.

$$P(A_i \mid B) = \frac{P(A_i \cap B)}{P(B)}$$

Note that the joint probabilities $P(A_i \cap B)$ are in column 4 and the probability $P(B)$ is the sum of column 4.

NOTES AND COMMENTS

1. Bayes' theorem is used extensively in decision analysis. The prior probabilities are often subjective estimates provided by a decision maker. Sample information is obtained and posterior probabilities are computed for use in choosing the best decision.

2. An event and its complement are mutually exclusive, and their union is the entire sample space. Thus, Bayes' theorem is always applicable for computing posterior probabilities of an event and its complement.

Exercises

Methods

SELFtest

39. The prior probabilities for events A_1 and A_2 are $P(A_1) = .40$ and $P(A_2) = .60$. It is also known that $P(A_1 \cap A_2) = 0$. Suppose $P(B \mid A_1) = .20$ and $P(B \mid A_2) = .05$.
   a. Are A_1 and A_2 mutually exclusive? Explain.
   b. Compute $P(A_1 \cap B)$ and $P(A_2 \cap B)$.
   c. Compute $P(B)$.
   d. Apply Bayes' theorem to compute $P(A_1 \mid B)$ and $P(A_2 \mid B)$.

40. The prior probabilities for events A_1, A_2, and A_3 are $P(A_1) = .20$, $P(A_2) = .50$, and $P(A_3) = .30$. The conditional probabilities of event B given A_1, A_2, and A_3 are $P(B \mid A_1) = .50$, $P(B \mid A_2) = .40$, and $P(B \mid A_3) = .30$.
   a. Compute $P(B \cap A_1)$, $P(B \cap A_2)$, and $P(B \cap A_3)$.
   b. Apply Bayes' theorem, equation (4.19), to compute the posterior probability $P(A_2 \mid B)$.
   c. Use the tabular approach to applying Bayes' theorem to compute $P(A_1 \mid B)$, $P(A_2 \mid B)$, and $P(A_3 \mid B)$.

Applications

41. A consulting firm submitted a bid for a large research project. The firm's management initially felt they had a 50–50 chance of getting the project. However, the agency to which the bid was submitted subsequently requested additional information on the bid. Past experience indicates that for 75% of the successful bids and 40% of the unsuccessful bids the agency requested additional information.
   a. What is the prior probability of the bid being successful (that is, prior to the request for additional information)?

b.   What is the conditional probability of a request for additional information given that the bid will ultimately be successful?

c.   Compute the posterior probability that the bid will be successful given a request for additional information.

 SELF*test*

42.   A local bank reviewed its credit card policy with the intention of recalling some of its credit cards. In the past approximately 5% of cardholders defaulted, leaving the bank unable to collect the outstanding balance. Hence, management established a prior probability of .05 that any particular cardholder will default. The bank also found that the probability of missing a monthly payment is .20 for customers who do not default. Of course, the probability of missing a monthly payment for those who default is 1.

a.   Given that a customer missed one or more monthly payments, compute the posterior probability that the customer will default.

b.   The bank would like to recall its card if the probability that a customer will default is greater than .20. Should the bank recall its card if the customer misses a monthly payment? Why or why not?

43.   In August 2012, tropical storm Isaac formed in the Caribbean and was headed for the Gulf of Mexico. There was an initial probability of .69 that Isaac would become a hurricane by the time it reached the Gulf of Mexico (National Hurricane Center website, August 21, 2012).

a.   What was the probability that Isaac would not become a hurricane but remain a tropical storm when it reached the Gulf of Mexico?

b.   Two days later, the National Hurricane Center projected the path of Isaac would pass directly over Cuba before reaching the Gulf of Mexico. How did passing over Cuba alter the probability that Isaac would become a hurricane by the time it reached the Gulf of Mexico? Use the following probabilities to answer this question. Hurricanes that reach the Gulf of Mexico have a .08 probability of having passed over Cuba. Tropical storms that reach the Gulf of Mexico have a .20 probability of having passed over Cuba.

c.   What happens to the probability of becoming a hurricane when a tropical storm passes over a landmass such as Cuba?

44.   ParFore created a website to market golf equipment and golf apparel. Management would like a special pop-up offer to appear for female website visitors and a different special pop-up offer to appear for male website visitors. From a sample of past website visitors, ParFore's management learned that 60% of the visitors are male and 40% are female.

a.   What is the probability that a current visitor to the website is female?

b.   Suppose 30% of ParFore's female visitors previously visited the Dillard's Department Store website and 10% of ParFore's male visitors previously visited the Dillard's Department Store website. If the current visitor to ParFore's website previously visited the Dillard's website, what is the revised probability that the current visitor is female? Should the ParFore's website display the special offer that appeals to female visitors or the special offer that appeals to male visitors?

45.   The percentage of adult users of the Internet who use Facebook has increased over time (*Pew Research Internet Project*, 2013). Of adult Internet users age 18–49, 81% use Facebook. Of adult Internet users age 50 and older, 54% use Facebook. Assume that 52% of adult Internet users are age 18–49.

a.   What is the probability that a randomly selected adult user of the Internet is age 50 or older?

b.   Given that an adult Internet user uses Facebook, what is the probability that he/she is age 18–49?

Summary

In this chapter we introduced basic probability concepts and illustrated how probability analysis can be used to provide helpful information for decision making. We described how probability can be interpreted as a numerical measure of the likelihood that an event will occur. In addition, we saw that the probability of an event can be computed either by summing the probabilities of the experimental outcomes (sample points) comprising the event or by using the relationships established by the addition, conditional probability, and multiplication laws of probability. For cases in which additional information is available, we showed how Bayes' theorem can be used to obtain revised or posterior probabilities.

Glossary

Addition law A probability law used to compute the probability of the union of two events. It is $P(A \cup B) = P(A) + P(B) - P(A \cap B)$. For mutually exclusive events, $P(A \cap B) = 0$; in this case the addition law reduces to $P(A \cup B) = P(A) + P(B)$.

Basic requirements for assigning probabilities Two requirements that restrict the manner in which probability assignments can be made: (1) for each experimental outcome E_i we must have $0 \le P(E_i) \le 1$; (2) considering all experimental outcomes, we must have $P(E_1) + P(E_2) + \cdots + P(E_n) = 1.0$.

Bayes' theorem A method used to compute posterior probabilities.

Classical method A method of assigning probabilities that is appropriate when all the experimental outcomes are equally likely.

Combination In an experiment we may be interested in determining the number of ways n objects may be selected from among N objects without regard to the *order in which the n objects are selected*. Each selection of n objects is called a combination and the total number of combinations of N objects taken n at a time is $C_n^N = \binom{N}{n} = \dfrac{N!}{n!(N-n)!}$ for $n = 0, 1, 2, \ldots, N$.

Complement of A The event consisting of all sample points that are not in A.

Conditional probability The probability of an event given that another event already occurred. The conditional probability of A given B is $P(A \mid B) = P(A \cap B)/P(B)$.

Event A collection of sample points.

Experiment A process that generates well-defined outcomes.

Independent events Two events A and B where $P(A \mid B) = P(A)$ or $P(B \mid A) = P(B)$; that is, the events have no influence on each other.

Intersection of A and B The event containing the sample points belonging to both A and B. The intersection is denoted $A \cap B$.

Joint probability The probability of two events both occurring; that is, the probability of the intersection of two events.

Marginal probability The values in the margins of a joint probability table that provide the probabilities of each event separately.

Multiple-step experiment An experiment that can be described as a sequence of steps. If a multiple-step experiment has k steps with n_1 possible outcomes on the first step, n_2 possible outcomes on the second step, and so on, the total number of experimental outcomes is given by $(n_1)(n_2) \cdots (n_k)$.

Multiplication law A probability law used to compute the probability of the intersection of two events. It is $P(A \cap B) = P(B)P(A \mid B)$ or $P(A \cap B) = P(A)P(B \mid A)$. For independent events it reduces to $P(A \cap B) = P(A)P(B)$.

Mutually exclusive events Events that have no sample points in common; that is, $A \cap B$ is empty and $P(A \cap B) = 0$.

Permutation In an experiment we may be interested in determining the number of ways n objects may be selected from among N objects when the *order in which the n objects are selected* is important. Each ordering of n objects is called a permutation and the total number of permutations of N objects taken n at a time is $P_n^N = n!\binom{N}{n} = \dfrac{N!}{(N-n)!}$ for $n = 0, 1, 2, \ldots, N$.

Posterior probabilities Revised probabilities of events based on additional information.

Prior probabilities Initial estimates of the probabilities of events.

Probability A numerical measure of the likelihood that an event will occur.

Relative frequency method A method of assigning probabilities that is appropriate when data are available to estimate the proportion of the time the experimental outcome will occur if the experiment is repeated a large number of times.

Sample point An element of the sample space. A sample point represents an experimental outcome.

Sample space The set of all experimental outcomes.

Subjective method A method of assigning probabilities on the basis of judgment.

Tree diagram A graphical representation that helps in visualizing a multiple-step experiment.

Union of A and B The event containing all sample points belonging to A or B or both. The union is denoted $A \cup B$.

Venn diagram A graphical representation for showing symbolically the sample space and operations involving events in which the sample space is represented by a rectangle and events are represented as circles within the sample space.

Key Formulas

Counting Rule for Combinations

$$C_n^N = \binom{N}{n} = \frac{N!}{n!(N-n)!}$$

(4.1)

Counting Rule for Permutations

$$P_n^N = n!\binom{N}{n} = \frac{N!}{(N-n)!}$$

(4.2)

Computing Probability Using the Complement

$$P(A) = 1 - P(A^c)$$

(4.5)

Addition Law

$$P(A \cup B) = P(A) + P(B) - P(A \cap B)$$

(4.6)

Conditional Probability

$$P(A \mid B) = \frac{P(A \cap B)}{P(B)}$$

(4.7)

$$P(B \mid A) = \frac{P(A \cap B)}{P(A)}$$

(4.8)

Multiplication Law

$$P(A \cap B) = P(B)P(A \mid B)$$

(4.11)

$$P(A \cap B) = P(A)P(B \mid A)$$

(4.12)

Multiplication Law for Independent Events

$$P(A \cap B) = P(A)P(B) \qquad (4.13)$$

Bayes' Theorem

$$P(A_i \mid B) = \frac{P(A_i)P(B \mid A_i)}{P(A_1)P(B \mid A_1) + P(A_2)P(B \mid A_2) + \cdots + P(A_n)P(B \mid A_n)} \qquad (4.19)$$

Supplementary Exercises

46. A survey of adults aged 18 and older conducted by Princess Cruises asked how many days into your vacation does it take until you feel truly relaxed (*USA Today*, August 24, 2011). The responses were as follows: 422—a day or less; 181—2 days; 80—3 days; 121—4 or more days; and 201—never feel relaxed.
    a. How many adults participated in the Princess Cruises survey?
    b. What response has the highest probability? What is the probability of this response?
    c. What is the probability a respondent never feels truly relaxed on a vacation?
    d. What is the probability it takes a respondent 2 or more days to feel truly relaxed?

47. A financial manager made two new investments—one in the oil industry and one in municipal bonds. After a one-year period, each of the investments will be classified as either successful or unsuccessful. Consider the making of the two investments as a random experiment.
    a. How many sample points exist for this experiment?
    b. Show a tree diagram and list the sample points.
    c. Let O = the event that the oil industry investment is successful and M = the event that the municipal bond investment is successful. List the sample points in O and in M.
    d. List the sample points in the union of the events $(O \cup M)$.
    e. List the sample points in the intersection of the events $(O \cap M)$.
    f. Are events O and M mutually exclusive? Explain.

48. Forty-three percent of Americans use social media and other websites to voice their opinions about television programs (*The Huffington Post,* November 23, 2011). Below are the results of a survey of 1400 individuals who were asked if they use social media and other websites to voice their opinions about television programs.

	Uses Social Media and Other Websites to Voice Opinions About Television Programs	Doesn't Use Social Media and Other Websites to Voice Opinions About Television Programs
Female	395	291
Male	323	355

    a. What is the probability a respondent is female?
    b. What is the conditional probability a respondent uses social media and other websites to voice opinions about television programs given the respondent is female?
    c. Let F denote the event that the respondent is female and A denote the event that the respondent uses social media and other websites to voice opinions about television programs. Are events F and A independent?

49. A study of 31,000 hospital admissions in New York State found that 4% of the admissions led to treatment-caused injuries. One-seventh of these treatment-caused injuries resulted in death, and one-fourth were caused by negligence. Malpractice claims were filed in one out of 7.5 cases involving negligence, and payments were made in one out of every two claims.
    a. What is the probability a person admitted to the hospital will suffer a treatment-caused injury due to negligence?

    b.   What is the probability a person admitted to the hospital will die from a treatment-caused injury?

    c.   In the case of a negligent treatment-caused injury, what is the probability a malpractice claim will be paid?

50. A telephone survey to determine viewer response to a new television show obtained the following data.

Rating	Frequency
Poor	4
Below average	8
Average	11
Above average	14
Excellent	13

    a.   What is the probability that a randomly selected viewer will rate the new show as average or better?

    b.   What is the probability that a randomly selected viewer will rate the new show below average or worse?

51. The U.S. Census Bureau serves as the leading source of quantitative data about the nation's people and economy. The following crosstabulation shows the number of households (1000s) and the household income by the highest level of education for the head of household (U.S. Census Bureau website, 2013). Only households in which the head has a high school diploma or more are included.

Highest Level of Education	Household Income				
	Under $25,000	$25,000 to $49,999	$50,000 to $99,999	$100,000 and Over	Total
High school graduate	9880	9970	9441	3482	32,773
Bachelor's degree	2484	4164	7666	7817	22,131
Master's degree	685	1205	3019	4094	9003
Doctoral degree	79	160	422	1076	1737
Total	13,128	15,499	20,548	16,469	65,644

    a.   Develop a joint probability table.

    b.   What is the probability of the head of one of these households having a master's degree or more education?

    c.   What is the probability of a household headed by someone with a high school diploma earning $100,000 or more?

    d.   What is the probability of one of these households having an income below $25,000?

    e.   What is the probability of a household headed by someone with a bachelor's degree earning less than $25,000?

    f.   Is household income independent of educational level?

52. An MBA new-matriculants survey provided the following data for 2018 students.

		Applied to More Than One School	
		Yes	No
Age Group	23 and under	207	201
	24–26	299	379
	27–30	185	268
	31–35	66	193
	36 and over	51	169

   a. For a randomly selected MBA student, prepare a joint probability table for the experiment consisting of observing the student's age and whether the student applied to one or more schools.
   b. What is the probability that a randomly selected applicant is 23 or under?
   c. What is the probability that a randomly selected applicant is older than 26?
   d. What is the probability that a randomly selected applicant applied to more than one school?

53. Refer again to the data from the MBA new-matriculants survey in exercise 52.
   a. Given that a person applied to more than one school, what is the probability that the person is 24–26 years old?
   b. Given that a person is in the 36-and-over age group, what is the probability that the person applied to more than one school?
   c. What is the probability that a person is 24–26 years old or applied to more than one school?
   d. Suppose a person is known to have applied to only one school. What is the probability that the person is 31 or more years old?
   e. Is the number of schools applied to independent of age? Explain.

54. In February 2012, the Pew Internet & American Life project conducted a survey that included several questions about how Internet users feel about search engines and other websites collecting information about them and using this information either to shape search results or target advertising to them (Pew Research Center, March 9, 2012). In one question, participants were asked, "If a search engine kept track of what you search for, and then used that information to personalize your future search results, how would you feel about that?" Respondents could indicate either "Would *not* be okay with it because you feel it is an invasion of your privacy" or "Would be *okay* with it, even if it means they are gathering information about you." Frequencies of responses by age group are summarized in the following table.

Age	Not Okay	Okay
18–29	.1485	.0604
30–49	.2273	.0907
50+	.4008	.0723

   a. What is the probability a survey respondent will say she or he is *not okay* with this practice?
   b. Given a respondent is 30–49 years old, what is the probability the respondent will say she or he is *okay* with this practice?
   c. Given a respondent says she or he is *not okay* with this practice, what is the probability the respondent is 50+ years old?
   d. Is the attitude about this practice independent of the age of the respondent? Why or why not?
   e. Do attitudes toward this practice for respondents who are 18–29 years old and respondents who are 50+ years old differ?

55. A large consumer goods company ran a television advertisement for one of its soap products. On the basis of a survey that was conducted, probabilities were assigned to the following events.

B = individual purchased the product

S = individual recalls seeing the advertisement

$B \cap S$ = individual purchased the product and recalls seeing the advertisement

The probabilities assigned were $P(B) = .20$, $P(S) = .40$, and $P(B \cap S) = .12$.

   a. What is the probability of an individual's purchasing the product given that the individual recalls seeing the advertisement? Does seeing the advertisement increase the probability that the individual will purchase the product? As a decision maker, would you recommend continuing the advertisement (assuming that the cost is reasonable)?

b. Assume that individuals who do not purchase the company's soap product buy from its competitors. What would be your estimate of the company's market share? Would you expect that continuing the advertisement will increase the company's market share? Why or why not?

c. The company also tested another advertisement and assigned it values of $P(S) = .30$ and $P(B \cap S) = .10$. What is $P(B \mid S)$ for this other advertisement? Which advertisement seems to have had the bigger effect on customer purchases?

56. Cooper Realty is a small real estate company located in Albany, New York, specializing primarily in residential listings. They recently became interested in determining the likelihood of one of their listings being sold within a certain number of days. An analysis of company sales of 800 homes in previous years produced the following data.

		Days Listed Until Sold			
		Under 30	31–90	Over 90	Total
Initial Asking Price	Under $150,000	50	40	10	100
	$150,000–$199,999	20	150	80	250
	$200,000–$250,000	20	280	100	400
	Over $250,000	10	30	10	50
	Total	100	500	200	800

a. If A is defined as the event that a home is listed for more than 90 days before being sold, estimate the probability of A.

b. If B is defined as the event that the initial asking price is under $150,000, estimate the probability of B.

c. What is the probability of $A \cap B$?

d. Assuming that a contract was just signed to list a home with an initial asking price of less than $150,000, what is the probability that the home will take Cooper Realty more than 90 days to sell?

e. Are events A and B independent?

57. A company studied the number of lost-time accidents occurring at its Brownsville, Texas, plant. Historical records show that 6% of the employees suffered lost-time accidents last year. Management believes that a special safety program will reduce such accidents to 5% during the current year. In addition, it estimates that 15% of employees who had lost-time accidents last year will experience a lost-time accident during the current year.

a. What percentage of the employees will experience lost-time accidents in both years?

b. What percentage of the employees will suffer at least one lost-time accident over the two-year period?

58. According to the Open Doors Report, 9.5% of all full-time U.S. undergraduate students study abroad (Institute of International Education, November 14, 2011). Assume that 60% of the undergraduate students who study abroad are female and that 49% of the undergraduate students who do not study abroad are female.

a. Given a female undergraduate student, what is the probability that she studies abroad?

b. Given a male undergraduate student, what is the probability that he studies abroad?

c. What is the overall percentage of full-time female undergraduate students? What is the overall percentage of full-time male undergraduate students?

59. An oil company purchased an option on land in Alaska. Preliminary geologic studies assigned the following prior probabilities.

$$P(\text{high-quality oil}) = .50$$
$$P(\text{medium-quality oil}) = .20$$
$$P(\text{no oil}) = .30$$

a. What is the probability of finding oil?
b. After 200 feet of drilling on the first well, a soil test is taken. The probabilities of finding the particular type of soil identified by the test follow.

$$P(\text{soil} \mid \text{high-quality oil}) = .20$$
$$P(\text{soil} \mid \text{medium-quality oil}) = .80$$
$$P(\text{soil} \mid \text{no oil}) = .20$$

How should the firm interpret the soil test? What are the revised probabilities, and what is the new probability of finding oil?

60. The five most common words appearing in spam emails are *shipping!, today!, here!, available,* and *fingertips!* (Andy Greenberg, "The Most Common Words In Spam Email," *Forbes* website, March 17, 2010). Many spam filters separate spam from ham (email not considered to be spam) through application of Bayes' theorem. Suppose that for one email account, 1 in every 10 messages is spam and the proportions of spam messages that have the five most common words in spam email are given below.

shipping!	.051
today!	.045
here!	.034
available	.014
fingertips!	.014

Also suppose that the proportions of ham messages that have these words are

shipping!	.0015
today!	.0022
here!	.0022
available	.0041
fingertips!	.0011

a. If a message includes the word *shipping!,* what is the probability the message is spam? If a message includes the word *shipping!,* what is the probability the message is ham? Should messages that include the word *shipping!* be flagged as spam?
b. If a message includes the word *today!,* what is the probability the message is spam? If a message includes the word *here!,* what is the probability the message is spam? Which of these two words is a stronger indicator that a message is spam? Why?
c. If a message includes the word *available,* what is the probability the message is spam? If a message includes the word *fingertips!,* what is the probability the message is spam? Which of these two words is a stronger indicator that a message is spam? Why?
d. What insights do the results of parts (b) and (c) yield about what enables a spam filter that uses Bayes' theorem to work effectively?

Case Problem   Hamilton County Judges

Hamilton County judges try thousands of cases per year. In an overwhelming majority of the cases disposed, the verdict stands as rendered. However, some cases are appealed, and of those appealed, some of the cases are reversed. Kristen DelGuzzi of *The Cincinnati Enquirer* conducted a study of cases handled by Hamilton County judges over a three-year period. Shown in Table 4.8 are the results for 182,908 cases handled (disposed) by 38 judges

TABLE 4.8   TOTAL CASES DISPOSED, APPEALED, AND REVERSED IN HAMILTON COUNTY COURTS

Judge

Common Pleas Court			
Judge	**Total Cases Disposed**	**Appealed Cases**	**Reversed Cases**
Fred Cartolano	3037	137	12
Thomas Crush	3372	119	10
Patrick Dinkelacker	1258	44	8
Timothy Hogan	1954	60	7
Robert Kraft	3138	127	7
William Mathews	2264	91	18
William Morrissey	3032	121	22
Norbert Nadel	2959	131	20
Arthur Ney, Jr.	3219	125	14
Richard Niehaus	3353	137	16
Thomas Nurre	3000	121	6
John O'Connor	2969	129	12
Robert Ruehlman	3205	145	18
J. Howard Sundermann	955	60	10
Ann Marie Tracey	3141	127	13
Ralph Winkler	3089	88	6
Total	43,945	1762	199

Domestic Relations Court			
Judge	**Total Cases Disposed**	**Appealed Cases**	**Reversed Cases**
Penelope Cunningham	2729	7	1
Patrick Dinkelacker	6001	19	4
Deborah Gaines	8799	48	9
Ronald Panioto	12,970	32	3
Total	30,499	106	17

Municipal Court			
Judge	**Total Cases Disposed**	**Appealed Cases**	**Reversed Cases**
Mike Allen	6149	43	4
Nadine Allen	7812	34	6
Timothy Black	7954	41	6
David Davis	7736	43	5
Leslie Isaiah Gaines	5282	35	13
Karla Grady	5253	6	0
Deidra Hair	2532	5	0
Dennis Helmick	7900	29	5
Timothy Hogan	2308	13	2
James Patrick Kenney	2798	6	1
Joseph Luebbers	4698	25	8
William Mallory	8277	38	9
Melba Marsh	8219	34	7
Beth Mattingly	2971	13	1
Albert Mestemaker	4975	28	9
Mark Painter	2239	7	3
Jack Rosen	7790	41	13
Mark Schweikert	5403	33	6
David Stockdale	5371	22	4
John A. West	2797	4	2
Total	108,464	500	104

in Common Pleas Court, Domestic Relations Court, and Municipal Court. Two of the judges (Dinkelacker and Hogan) did not serve in the same court for the entire three-year period.

The purpose of the newspaper's study was to evaluate the performance of the judges. Appeals are often the result of mistakes made by judges, and the newspaper wanted to know which judges were doing a good job and which were making too many mistakes. You are called in to assist in the data analysis. Use your knowledge of probability and conditional probability to help with the ranking of the judges. You also may be able to analyze the likelihood of appeal and reversal for cases handled by different courts.

Managerial Report

Prepare a report with your rankings of the judges. Also, include an analysis of the likelihood of appeal and case reversal in the three courts. At a minimum, your report should include the following:

1. The probability of cases being appealed and reversed in the three different courts.
2. The probability of a case being appealed for each judge.
3. The probability of a case being reversed for each judge.
4. The probability of reversal given an appeal for each judge.
5. Rank the judges within each court. State the criteria you used and provide a rationale for your choice.

CHAPTER 6

Continuous Probability Distributions

CONTENTS

STATISTICS IN PRACTICE:
PROCTER & GAMBLE

PROCTER & GAMBLE*
CINCINNATI, OHIO

Procter & Gamble (P&G) produces and markets such products as detergents, disposable diapers, over-the-counter pharmaceuticals, dentifrices, bar soaps, mouthwashes, and paper towels. Worldwide, it has the leading brand in more categories than any other consumer products company. Since its merger with Gillette, P&G also produces and markets razors, blades, and many other personal care products.

As a leader in the application of statistical methods in decision making, P&G employs people with diverse academic backgrounds: engineering, statistics, operations research, and business. The major quantitative technologies for which these people provide support are probabilistic decision and risk analysis, advanced simulation, quality improvement, and quantitative methods (e.g., linear programming, regression analysis, probability analysis).

The Industrial Chemicals Division of P&G is a major supplier of fatty alcohols derived from natural substances such as coconut oil and from petroleum-based derivatives. The division wanted to know the economic risks and opportunities of expanding its fatty-alcohol production facilities, so it called in P&G's experts in probabilistic decision and risk analysis to help. After structuring and modeling the problem, they determined that the key to profitability was the cost difference between the petroleum- and coconut-based raw materials. Future costs were unknown, but the analysts were able to approximate them with the following continuous random variables.

x = the coconut oil price per pound of fatty alcohol

and

y = the petroleum raw material price per pound of fatty alcohol

Because the key to profitability was the difference between these two random variables, a third random variable, $d = x - y$, was used in the analysis. Experts were interviewed to determine the probability distributions for x and y. In turn, this information was used to develop a probability distribution for the difference in prices d. This continuous probability distribution showed

John Sommers II/Reuters

Procter & Gamble is a leader in the application of statistical methods in decision making.

a .90 probability that the price difference would be \$.0655 or less and a .50 probability that the price difference would be \$.035 or less. In addition, there was only a .10 probability that the price difference would be \$.0045 or less.[†]

The Industrial Chemicals Division thought that being able to quantify the impact of raw material price differences was key to reaching a consensus. The probabilities obtained were used in a sensitivity analysis of the raw material price difference. The analysis yielded sufficient insight to form the basis for a recommendation to management.

The use of continuous random variables and their probability distributions was helpful to P&G in analyzing the economic risks associated with its fatty-alcohol production. In this chapter, you will gain an understanding of continuous random variables and their probability distributions, including one of the most important probability distributions in statistics, the normal distribution.

---

*The authors are indebted to Joel Kahn of Procter & Gamble for providing this Statistics in Practice.

[†]The price differences stated here have been modified to protect proprietary data.

In the preceding chapter we discussed discrete random variables and their probability distributions. In this chapter we turn to the study of continuous random variables. Specifically, we discuss three continuous probability distributions: the uniform, the normal, and the exponential.

A fundamental difference separates discrete and continuous random variables in terms of how probabilities are computed. For a discrete random variable, the probability function $f(x)$ provides the probability that the random variable assumes a particular value. With continuous random variables, the counterpart of the probability function is the **probability density function**, also denoted by $f(x)$. The difference is that the probability density function does not directly provide probabilities. However, the area under the graph of $f(x)$ corresponding to a given interval does provide the probability that the continuous random variable x assumes a value in that interval. So when we compute probabilities for continuous random variables we are computing the probability that the random variable assumes any value in an interval.

Because the area under the graph of $f(x)$ at any particular point is zero, one of the implications of the definition of probability for continuous random variables is that the probability of any particular value of the random variable is zero. In Section 6.1 we demonstrate these concepts for a continuous random variable that has a uniform distribution.

Much of the chapter is devoted to describing and showing applications of the normal distribution. The normal distribution is of major importance because of its wide applicability and its extensive use in statistical inference. The chapter closes with a discussion of the exponential distribution. The exponential distribution is useful in applications involving such factors as waiting times and service times.

(6.1) Uniform Probability Distribution

Consider the random variable x representing the flight time of an airplane traveling from Chicago to New York. Suppose the flight time can be any value in the interval from 120 minutes to 140 minutes. Because the random variable x can assume any value in that interval, x is a continuous rather than a discrete random variable. Let us assume that sufficient actual flight data are available to conclude that the probability of a flight time within any 1-minute interval is the same as the probability of a flight time within any other 1-minute interval contained in the larger interval from 120 to 140 minutes. With every 1-minute interval being equally likely, the random variable x is said to have a **uniform probability distribution**. The probability density function, which defines the uniform distribution for the flight-time random variable, is

Whenever the probability is proportional to the length of the interval, the random variable is uniformly distributed.

$$f(x) = \begin{cases} 1/20 & \text{for } 120 \leq x \leq 140 \\ 0 & \text{elsewhere} \end{cases}$$

Figure 6.1 is a graph of this probability density function. In general, the uniform probability density function for a random variable x is defined by the following formula.

UNIFORM PROBABILITY DENSITY FUNCTION

$$f(x) = \begin{cases} \dfrac{1}{b - a} & \text{for } a \leq x \leq b \\ 0 & \text{elsewhere} \end{cases} \tag{6.1}$$

For the flight-time random variable, $a = 120$ and $b = 140$.

FIGURE 6.1   UNIFORM PROBABILITY DISTRIBUTION FOR FLIGHT TIME

As noted in the introduction, for a continuous random variable, we consider probability only in terms of the likelihood that a random variable assumes a value within a specified interval. In the flight time example, an acceptable probability question is: What is the probability that the flight time is between 120 and 130 minutes? That is, what is $P(120 \leq x \leq 130)$? Because the flight time must be between 120 and 140 minutes and because the probability is described as being uniform over this interval, we feel comfortable saying $P(120 \leq x \leq 130) = .50$. In the following subsection we show that this probability can be computed as the area under the graph of $f(x)$ from 120 to 130 (see Figure 6.2).

Area as a Measure of Probability

Let us make an observation about the graph in Figure 6.2. Consider the area under the graph of $f(x)$ in the interval from 120 to 130. The area is rectangular, and the area of a rectangle is simply the width multiplied by the height. With the width of the interval equal to $130 - 120 = 10$ and the height equal to the value of the probability density function $f(x) = 1/20$, we have area = width × height = $10(1/20) = 10/20 = .50$.

FIGURE 6.2   AREA PROVIDES PROBABILITY OF A FLIGHT TIME BETWEEN
                 120 AND 130 MINUTES

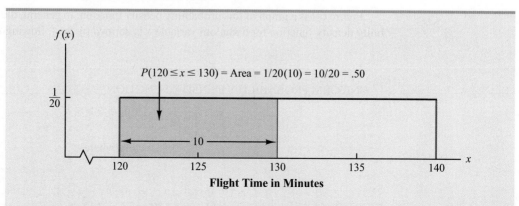

What observation can you make about the area under the graph of $f(x)$ and probability? They are identical! Indeed, this observation is valid for all continuous random variables. Once a probability density function $f(x)$ is identified, the probability that x takes a value between some lower value x_1 and some higher value x_2 can be found by computing the area under the graph of $f(x)$ over the interval from x_1 to x_2.

Given the uniform distribution for flight time and using the interpretation of area as probability, we can answer any number of probability questions about flight times. For example, what is the probability of a flight time between 128 and 136 minutes? The width of the interval is $136 - 128 = 8$. With the uniform height of $f(x) = 1/20$, we see that $P(128 \leq x \leq 136) = 8(1/20) = .40$.

Note that $P(120 \leq x \leq 140) = 20(1/20) = 1$; that is, the total area under the graph of $f(x)$ is equal to 1. This property holds for all continuous probability distributions and is the analog of the condition that the sum of the probabilities must equal 1 for a discrete probability function. For a continuous probability density function, we must also require that $f(x) \geq 0$ for all values of x. This requirement is the analog of the requirement that $f(x) \geq 0$ for discrete probability functions.

Two major differences stand out between the treatment of continuous random variables and the treatment of their discrete counterparts.

1. We no longer talk about the probability of the random variable assuming a particular value. Instead, we talk about the probability of the random variable assuming a value within some given interval.

To see that the probability of any single point is 0, refer to Figure 6.2 and compute the probability of a single point, say, $x = 125$. $P(x = 125) = P(125 \leq x \leq 125) = 0(1/20) = 0$.

2. The probability of a continuous random variable assuming a value within some given interval from x_1 to x_2 is defined to be the area under the graph of the probability density function between x_1 and x_2. Because a single point is an interval of zero width, this implies that the probability of a continuous random variable assuming any particular value exactly is zero. It also means that the probability of a continuous random variable assuming a value in any interval is the same whether or not the endpoints are included.

The calculation of the expected value and variance for a continuous random variable is analogous to that for a discrete random variable. However, because the computational procedure involves integral calculus, we leave the derivation of the appropriate formulas to more advanced texts.

For the uniform continuous probability distribution introduced in this section, the formulas for the expected value and variance are

$$E(x) = \frac{a + b}{2}$$

$$Var(x) = \frac{(b - a)^2}{12}$$

In these formulas, a is the smallest value and b is the largest value that the random variable may assume.

Applying these formulas to the uniform distribution for flight times from Chicago to New York, we obtain

$$E(x) = \frac{(120 + 140)}{2} = 130$$

$$Var(x) = \frac{(140 - 120)^2}{12} = 33.33$$

The standard deviation of flight times can be found by taking the square root of the variance. Thus, $\sigma = 5.77$ minutes.

NOTES AND COMMENTS

To see more clearly why the height of a probability density function is not a probability, think about a random variable with the following uniform probability distribution.

$$f(x) = \begin{cases} 2 & \text{for } 0 \leq x \leq .5 \\ 0 & \text{elsewhere} \end{cases}$$

The height of the probability density function, $f(x)$, is 2 for values of x between 0 and .5. However, we know probabilities can never be greater than 1. Thus, we see that $f(x)$ cannot be interpreted as the probability of x.

Exercises

Methods

☑ SELF*test*

1. The random variable x is known to be uniformly distributed between 1.0 and 1.5.
   a. Show the graph of the probability density function.
   b. Compute $P(x = 1.25)$.
   c. Compute $P(1.0 \leq x \leq 1.25)$.
   d. Compute $P(1.20 < x < 1.5)$.

2. The random variable x is known to be uniformly distributed between 10 and 20.
   a. Show the graph of the probability density function.
   b. Compute $P(x < 15)$.
   c. Compute $P(12 \leq x \leq 18)$.
   d. Compute $E(x)$.
   e. Compute $Var(x)$.

Applications

3. Delta Airlines quotes a flight time of 2 hours, 5 minutes for its flights from Cincinnati to Tampa. Suppose we believe that actual flight times are uniformly distributed between 2 hours and 2 hours, 20 minutes.
   a. Show the graph of the probability density function for flight time.
   b. What is the probability that the flight will be no more than 5 minutes late?
   c. What is the probability that the flight will be more than 10 minutes late?
   d. What is the expected flight time?

☑ SELF*test*

4. Most computer languages include a function that can be used to generate random numbers. In Excel, the RAND function can be used to generate random numbers between 0 and 1. If we let x denote a random number generated using RAND, then x is a continuous random variable with the following probability density function.

$$f(x) = \begin{cases} 1 & \text{for } 0 \leq x \leq 1 \\ 0 & \text{elsewhere} \end{cases}$$

   a. Graph the probability density function.
   b. What is the probability of generating a random number between .25 and .75?
   c. What is the probability of generating a random number with a value less than or equal to .30?
   d. What is the probability of generating a random number with a value greater than .60?
   e. Generate 50 random numbers by entering =RAND() into 50 cells of an Excel worksheet.
   f. Compute the mean and standard deviation for the random numbers in part (e).

5. In October 2012, Apple introduced a much smaller variant of the Apple iPad, known as the iPad Mini. Weighing less than 11 ounces, it was about 50% lighter than the standard iPad. Battery tests for the iPad Mini showed a mean life of 10.25 hours (*The Wall Street Journal*, October 31, 2012). Assume that battery life of the iPad Mini is uniformly distributed between 8.5 and 12 hours.

    a. Give a mathematical expression for the probability density function of battery life.
    b. What is the probability that the battery life for an iPad Mini will be 10 hours or less?
    c. What is the probability that the battery life for an iPad Mini will be at least 11 hours?
    d. What is the probability that the battery life for an iPad Mini will be between 9.5 and 11.5 hours?
    e. In a shipment of 100 iPad Minis, how many should have a battery life of at least 9 hours?

6. A Gallup Daily Tracking Survey found that the mean daily discretionary spending by Americans earning over $90,000 per year was $136 per day (*USA Today*, July 30, 2012). The discretionary spending excluded home purchases, vehicle purchases, and regular monthly bills. Let x = the discretionary spending per day and assume that a uniform probability density function applies with $f(x) = .00625$ for $a \leq x \leq b$.

    a. Find the values of a and b for the probability density function.
    b. What is the probability that consumers in this group have daily discretionary spending between $100 and $200?
    c. What is the probability that consumers in this group have daily discretionary spending of $150 or more?
    d. What is the probability that consumers in this group have daily discretionary spending of $80 or less?

7. Suppose we are interested in bidding on a piece of land and we know one other bidder is interested.[1] The seller announced that the highest bid in excess of $10,000 will be accepted. Assume that the competitor's bid x is a random variable that is uniformly distributed between $10,000 and $15,000.

    a. Suppose you bid $12,000. What is the probability that your bid will be accepted?
    b. Suppose you bid $14,000. What is the probability that your bid will be accepted?
    c. What amount should you bid to maximize the probability that you get the property?
    d. Suppose you know someone who is willing to pay you $16,000 for the property. Would you consider bidding less than the amount in part (c)? Why or why not?

6.2 Normal Probability Distribution

Abraham de Moivre, a French mathematician, published The Doctrine of Chances *in 1733. He derived the normal distribution.*

The most important probability distribution for describing a continuous random variable is the **normal probability distribution**. The normal distribution has been used in a wide variety of practical applications in which the random variables are heights and weights of people, test scores, scientific measurements, amounts of rainfall, and other similar values. It is also widely used in statistical inference, which is the major topic of the remainder of this book. In such applications, the normal distribution provides a description of the likely results obtained through sampling.

Normal Curve

The form, or shape, of the normal distribution is illustrated by the bell-shaped normal curve in Figure 6.3. The probability density function that defines the bell-shaped curve of the normal distribution follows.

---

[1]This exercise is based on a problem suggested to us by Professor Roger Myerson of Northwestern University.

FIGURE 6.3   BELL-SHAPED CURVE FOR THE NORMAL DISTRIBUTION

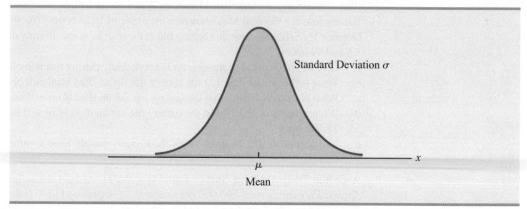

NORMAL PROBABILITY DENSITY FUNCTION

$$f(x) = \frac{1}{\sigma\sqrt{2\pi}} e^{-\frac{1}{2}\left(\frac{x-\mu}{\sigma}\right)^2}$$ (6.2)

where

μ = mean

σ = standard deviation

π = 3.14159

e = 2.71828

We make several observations about the characteristics of the normal distribution.

The normal curve has two parameters, μ and σ. They determine the location and shape of the normal distribution.

1. The entire family of normal distributions is differentiated by two parameters: the mean μ and the standard deviation σ.
2. The highest point on the normal curve is at the mean, which is also the median and mode of the distribution.
3. The mean of the distribution can be any numerical value: negative, zero, or positive. Three normal distributions with the same standard deviation but three different means (-10, 0, and 20) are shown here.

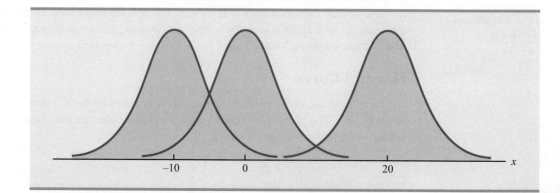

4. The normal distribution is symmetric, with the shape of the normal curve to the left of the mean a mirror image of the shape of the normal curve to the right of the mean. The tails of the normal curve extend to infinity in both directions and theoretically never touch the horizontal axis. Because it is symmetric, the normal distribution is not skewed; its skewness measure is zero.

5. The standard deviation determines how flat and wide the normal curve is. Larger values of the standard deviation result in wider, flatter curves, showing more variability in the data. Two normal distributions with the same mean but with different standard deviations are shown here.

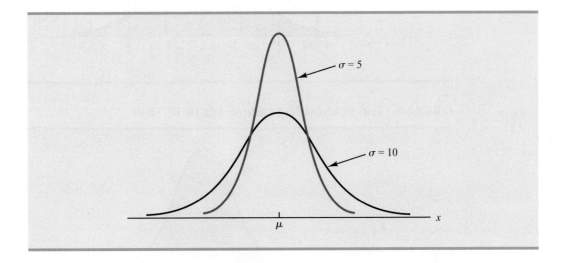

6. Probabilities for the normal random variable are given by areas under the normal curve. The total area under the curve for the normal distribution is 1. Because the distribution is symmetric, the area under the curve to the left of the mean is .50 and the area under the curve to the right of the mean is .50.

7. The percentage of values in some commonly used intervals are

    a. 68.3% of the values of a normal random variable are within plus or minus one standard deviation of its mean.

These percentages are the basis for the empirical rule introduced in Section 3.3.

    b. 95.4% of the values of a normal random variable are within plus or minus two standard deviations of its mean.

    c. 99.7% of the values of a normal random variable are within plus or minus three standard deviations of its mean.

    Figure 6.4 shows properties (a), (b), and (c) graphically.

Standard Normal Probability Distribution

A random variable that has a normal distribution with a mean of zero and a standard deviation of one is said to have a **standard normal probability distribution**. The letter z is commonly used to designate this particular normal random variable. Figure 6.5 is the graph of the standard normal distribution. It has the same general appearance as other normal distributions, but with the special properties of $\mu = 0$ and $\sigma = 1$.

FIGURE 6.4   AREAS UNDER THE CURVE FOR ANY NORMAL DISTRIBUTION

FIGURE 6.5   THE STANDARD NORMAL DISTRIBUTION

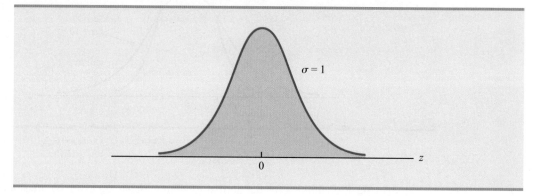

Because $\mu = 0$ and $\sigma = 1$, the formula for the standard normal probability density function is a simpler version of equation (6.2).

STANDARD NORMAL DENSITY FUNCTION

$$f(z) = \frac{1}{\sqrt{2\pi}} e^{-\frac{z^2}{2}}$$

For the normal probability density function, the height of the normal curve varies and more advanced mathematics is required to compute the areas that represent probability.

As with other continuous random variables, probability calculations with any normal distribution are made by computing areas under the graph of the probability density function. Thus, to find the probability that a normal random variable is within any specific interval, we must compute the area under the normal curve over that interval.

For the standard normal distribution, areas under the normal curve have been computed and are available in tables that can be used to compute probabilities. Such a table appears on the two pages inside the front cover of the text. The table on the left-hand page contains areas, or cumulative probabilities, for z values less than or equal to the mean of zero. The table on the right-hand page contains areas, or cumulative probabilities, for z values greater than or equal to the mean of zero.

The three types of probabilities we need to compute include (1) the probability that the standard normal random variable z will be less than or equal to a given value; (2) the probability that z will be between two given values; and (3) the probability that z will be greater than or equal to a given value. To see how the cumulative probability table for the standard normal distribution can be used to compute these three types of probabilities, let us consider some examples.

Because the standard normal random variable is continuous, $P(z \leq 1.00) = P(z < 1.00)$.

We start by showing how to compute the probability that z is less than or equal to 1.00; that is, $P(z \leq 1.00)$. This cumulative probability is the area under the normal curve to the left of $z = 1.00$ in the following graph.

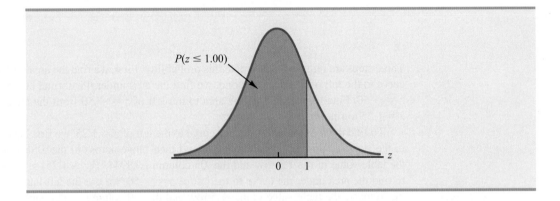

Refer to the right-hand page of the standard normal probability table inside the front cover of the text. The cumulative probability corresponding to $z = 1.00$ is the table value located at the intersection of the row labeled 1.0 and the column labeled .00. First we find 1.0 in the left column of the table and then find .00 in the top row of the table. By looking in the body of the table, we find that the 1.0 row and the .00 column intersect at the value of .8413; thus, $P(z \leq 1.00) = .8413$. The following excerpt from the probability table shows these steps.

z	.00	.01	.02
.			
.			
.			
.9	.8159	.8186	.8212
1.0	.8413	.8438	.8461
1.1	.8643	.8665	.8686
1.2	.8849	.8869	.8888
.			
.			
.			

$P(z \leq 1.00)$

To illustrate the second type of probability calculation we show how to compute the probability that z is in the interval between $-.50$ and 1.25; that is, $P(-.50 \leq z \leq 1.25)$. The following graph shows this area, or probability.

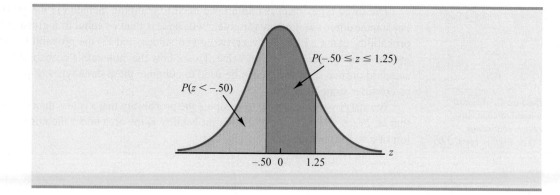

Three steps are required to compute this probability. First, we find the area under the normal curve to the left of $z = 1.25$. Second, we find the area under the normal curve to the left of $z = -.50$. Finally, we subtract the area to the left of $z = -.50$ from the area to the left of $z = 1.25$ to find $P(-.50 \leq z \leq 1.25)$.

To find the area under the normal curve to the left of $z = 1.25$, we first locate the 1.2 row in the standard normal probability table and then move across to the .05 column. Because the table value in the 1.2 row and the .05 column is .8944, $P(z \leq 1.25) = .8944$. Similarly, to find the area under the curve to the left of $z = -.50$, we use the left-hand page of the table to locate the table value in the $-.5$ row and the .00 column; with a table value of .3085, $P(z \leq -.50) = .3085$. Thus, $P(-.50 \leq z \leq 1.25) = P(z \leq 1.25) - P(z \leq -.50) = .8944 - .3085 = .5859$.

Let us consider another example of computing the probability that z is in the interval between two given values. Often it is of interest to compute the probability that a normal random variable assumes a value within a certain number of standard deviations of the mean. Suppose we want to compute the probability that the standard normal random variable is within one standard deviation of the mean; that is, $P(-1.00 \leq z \leq 1.00)$. To compute this probability we must find the area under the curve between -1.00 and 1.00. Earlier we found that $P(z \leq 1.00) = .8413$. Referring again to the table inside the front cover of the book, we find that the area under the curve to the left of $z = -1.00$ is .1587, so $P(z \leq -1.00) = .1587$. Therefore, $P(-1.00 \leq z \leq 1.00) = P(z \leq 1.00) - P(z \leq -1.00) = .8413 - .1587 = .6826$. This probability is shown graphically in the following figure.

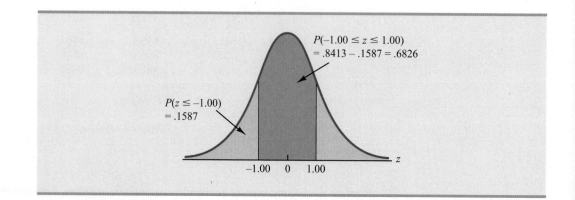

To illustrate how to make the third type of probability computation, suppose we want to compute the probability of obtaining a z value of at least 1.58; that is, $P(z \geq 1.58)$. The value in the $z = 1.5$ row and the .08 column of the cumulative normal table is .9429; thus, $P(z < 1.58) = .9429$. However, because the total area under the normal curve is 1, $P(z \geq 1.58) = 1 - .9429 = .0571$. This probability is shown in the following figure.

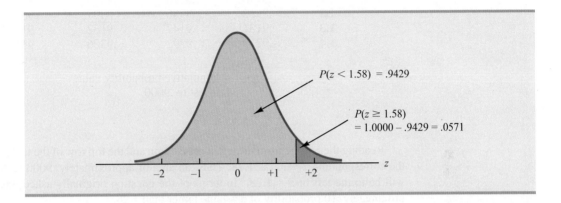

In the preceding illustrations, we showed how to compute probabilities given specified z values. In some situations, we are given a probability and are interested in working backward to find the corresponding z value. Suppose we want to find a z value such that the probability of obtaining a larger z value is .10. The following figure shows this situation graphically.

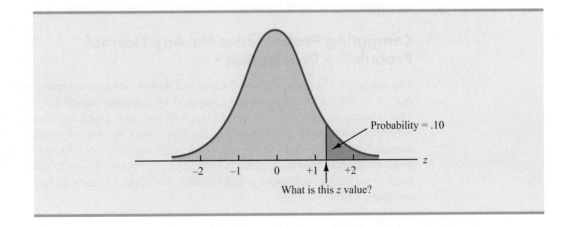

Given a probability, we can use the standard normal table in an inverse fashion to find the corresponding z value.

This problem is the inverse of those in the preceding examples. Previously, we specified the z value of interest and then found the corresponding probability, or area. In this example, we are given the probability, or area, and asked to find the corresponding z value. To do so, we use the standard normal probability table somewhat differently.

Recall that the standard normal probability table gives the area under the curve to the left of a particular z value. We have been given the information that the area in the upper tail of the curve is .10. Hence, the area under the curve to the left of the unknown z value must equal .9000. Scanning the body of the table, we find .8997 is the cumulative probability value closest to .9000. The section of the table providing this result follows.

z	.06	.07	.08	.09
.				
.				
.				
1.0	.8554	.8577	.8599	.8621
1.1	.8770	.8790	.8810	.8830
1.2	.8962	.8980	.8997	.9015
1.3	.9131	.9147	.9162	.9177
1.4	.9279	.9292	.9306	.9319
.				
.				
.				

Cumulative probability value
closest to .9000

Reading the z value from the left-most column and the top row of the table, we find that the corresponding z value is 1.28. Thus, an area of approximately .9000 (actually .8997) will be to the left of $z = 1.28$.[2] In terms of the question originally asked, there is an approximately .10 probability of a z value larger than 1.28.

The examples illustrate that the table of cumulative probabilities for the standard normal probability distribution can be used to find probabilities associated with values of the standard normal random variable z. Two types of questions can be asked. The first type of question specifies a value, or values, for z and asks us to use the table to determine the corresponding areas or probabilities. The second type of question provides an area, or probability, and asks us to use the table to determine the corresponding z value. Thus, we need to be flexible in using the standard normal probability table to answer the desired probability question. In most cases, sketching a graph of the standard normal probability distribution and shading the appropriate area will help to visualize the situation and aid in determining the correct answer.

Computing Probabilities for Any Normal Probability Distribution

The reason for discussing the standard normal distribution so extensively is that probabilities for all normal distributions are computed by using the standard normal distribution. That is, when we have a normal distribution with any mean μ and any standard deviation σ, we answer probability questions about the distribution by first converting to the standard normal distribution. Then we can use the standard normal probability table and the appropriate z values to find the desired probabilities. The formula used to convert any normal random variable x with mean μ and standard deviation σ to the standard normal random variable z follows.

The formula for the standard normal random variable is similar to the formula we introduced in Chapter 3 for computing z-scores for a data set.

CONVERTING TO THE STANDARD NORMAL RANDOM VARIABLE

$$z = \frac{x - \mu}{\sigma} \qquad (6.3)$$

[2] We could use interpolation in the body of the table to get a better approximation of the z value that corresponds to an area of .9000. Doing so to provide one more decimal place of accuracy would yield a z value of 1.282. However, in most practical situations, sufficient accuracy is obtained by simply using the table value closest to the desired probability.

A value of x equal to its mean μ results in $z = (\mu - \mu)/\sigma = 0$. Thus, we see that a value of x equal to its mean μ corresponds to $z = 0$. Now suppose that x is one standard deviation above its mean; that is, $x = \mu + \sigma$. Applying equation (6.3), we see that the corresponding z value is $z = [(\mu + \sigma) - \mu]/\sigma = \sigma/\sigma = 1$. Thus, an x value that is one standard deviation above its mean corresponds to $z = 1$. In other words, *we can interpret z as the number of standard deviations that the normal random variable x is from its mean μ.*

To see how this conversion enables us to compute probabilities for any normal distribution, suppose we have a normal distribution with $\mu = 10$ and $\sigma = 2$. What is the probability that the random variable x is between 10 and 14? Using equation (6.3), we see that at $x = 10$, $z = (x - \mu)/\sigma = (10 - 10)/2 = 0$ and that at $x = 14$, $z = (14 - 10)/2 = 4/2 = 2$. Thus, the answer to our question about the probability of x being between 10 and 14 is given by the equivalent probability that z is between 0 and 2 for the standard normal distribution. In other words, the probability that we are seeking is the probability that the random variable x is between its mean and two standard deviations above the mean. Using $z = 2.00$ and the standard normal probability table inside the front cover of the text, we see that $P(z \leq 2) = .9772$. Because $P(z \leq 0) = .5000$, we can compute $P(.00 \leq z \leq 2.00) = P(z \leq 2) - P(z \leq 0) = .9772 - .5000 = .4772$. Hence the probability that x is between 10 and 14 is .4772.

Grear Tire Company Problem

We turn now to an application of the normal probability distribution. Suppose the Grear Tire Company developed a new steel-belted radial tire to be sold through a national chain of discount stores. Because the tire is a new product, Grear's managers believe that the mileage guarantee offered with the tire will be an important factor in the acceptance of the product. Before finalizing the tire mileage guarantee policy, Grear's managers want probability information about $x =$ number of miles the tires will last.

From actual road tests with the tires, Grear's engineering group estimated that the mean tire mileage is $\mu = 36,500$ miles and that the standard deviation is $\sigma = 5000$. In addition, the data collected indicate that a normal distribution is a reasonable assumption. What percentage of the tires can be expected to last more than 40,000 miles? In other words, what is the probability that the tire mileage, x, will exceed 40,000? This question can be answered by finding the area of the darkly shaded region in Figure 6.6.

FIGURE 6.6 GREAR TIRE COMPANY MILEAGE DISTRIBUTION

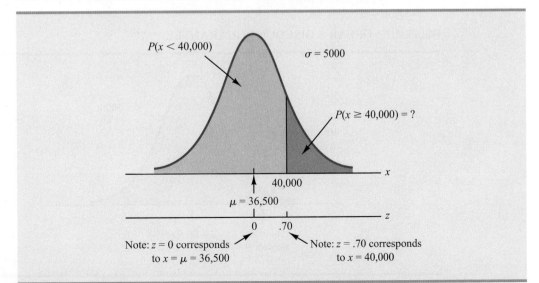

At $x = 40{,}000$, we have

$$z = \frac{x - \mu}{\sigma} = \frac{40{,}000 - 36{,}500}{5000} = \frac{3500}{5000} = .70$$

Refer now to the bottom of Figure 6.6. We see that a value of $x = 40{,}000$ on the Grear Tire normal distribution corresponds to a value of $z = .70$ on the standard normal distribution. Using the standard normal probability table, we see that the area under the standard normal curve to the left of $z = .70$ is .7580. Thus, $1.000 - .7580 = .2420$ is the probability that z will exceed .70 and hence x will exceed 40,000. We can conclude that about 24.2% of the tires will exceed 40,000 in mileage.

Let us now assume that Grear is considering a guarantee that will provide a discount on replacement tires if the original tires do not provide the guaranteed mileage. What should the guarantee mileage be if Grear wants no more than 10% of the tires to be eligible for the discount guarantee? This question is interpreted graphically in Figure 6.7.

According to Figure 6.7, the area under the curve to the left of the unknown guarantee mileage must be .10. So, we must first find the z value that cuts off an area of .10 in the left tail of a standard normal distribution. Using the standard normal probability table, we see that $z = -1.28$ cuts off an area of .10 in the lower tail. Hence, $z = -1.28$ is the value of the standard normal random variable corresponding to the desired mileage guarantee on the Grear Tire normal distribution. To find the value of x corresponding to $z = -1.28$, we have

The guarantee mileage we need to find is 1.28 standard deviations below the mean. Thus, $x = \mu - 1.28\sigma$.

$$z = \frac{x - \mu}{\sigma} = -1.28$$

$$x - \mu = -1.28\sigma$$

$$x = \mu - 1.28\sigma$$

With $\mu = 36{,}500$ and $\sigma = 5000$,

$$x = 36{,}500 - 1.28(5000) = 30{,}100$$

Thus, a guarantee of 30,100 miles will meet the requirement that approximately 10% of the tires will be eligible for the guarantee. Perhaps, with this information, the firm will set its tire mileage guarantee at 30,000 miles.

With the guarantee set at 30,000 miles, the actual percentage eligible for the guarantee will be 9.68%.

Again, we see the important role that probability distributions play in providing decision-making information. Namely, once a probability distribution is established for a

FIGURE 6.7   GREAR'S DISCOUNT GUARANTEE

particular application, it can be used to obtain probability information about the problem. Probability does not make a decision recommendation directly, but it provides information that helps the decision maker better understand the risks and uncertainties associated with the problem. Ultimately, this information may assist the decision maker in reaching a good decision.

Exercises

Methods

8. Using Figure 6.4 as a guide, sketch a normal curve for a random variable x that has a mean of $\mu = 100$ and a standard deviation of $\sigma = 10$. Label the horizontal axis with values of 70, 80, 90, 100, 110, 120, and 130.

9. A random variable is normally distributed with a mean of $\mu = 50$ and a standard deviation of $\sigma = 5$.
   a. Sketch a normal curve for the probability density function. Label the horizontal axis with values of 35, 40, 45, 50, 55, 60, and 65. Figure 6.4 shows that the normal curve almost touches the horizontal axis at three standard deviations below and at three standard deviations above the mean (in this case at 35 and 65).
   b. What is the probability the random variable will assume a value between 45 and 55?
   c. What is the probability the random variable will assume a value between 40 and 60?

10. Draw a graph for the standard normal distribution. Label the horizontal axis at values of $-3, -2, -1, 0, 1, 2,$ and 3. Then use the table of probabilities for the standard normal distribution inside the front cover of the text to compute the following probabilities.
   a. $P(z \le 1.5)$
   b. $P(z \le 1)$
   c. $P(1 \le z \le 1.5)$
   d. $P(0 < z < 2.5)$

11. Given that z is a standard normal random variable, compute the following probabilities.
   a. $P(z \le -1.0)$
   b. $P(z \ge -1)$
   c. $P(z \ge -1.5)$
   d. $P(-2.5 \le z)$
   e. $P(-3 < z \le 0)$

12. Given that z is a standard normal random variable, compute the following probabilities.
   a. $P(0 \le z \le .83)$
   b. $P(-1.57 \le z \le 0)$
   c. $P(z > .44)$
   d. $P(z \ge -.23)$
   e. $P(z < 1.20)$
   f. $P(z \le -.71)$

SELFtest

13. Given that z is a standard normal random variable, compute the following probabilities.
   a. $P(-1.98 \le z \le .49)$
   b. $P(.52 \le z \le 1.22)$
   c. $P(-1.75 \le z \le -1.04)$

14. Given that z is a standard normal random variable, find z for each situation.
   a. The area to the left of z is .9750.
   b. The area between 0 and z is .4750.
   c. The area to the left of z is .7291.
   d. The area to the right of z is .1314.
   e. The area to the left of z is .6700.
   f. The area to the right of z is .3300.

✓SELF*test*   15.   Given that z is a standard normal random variable, find z for each situation.
   a.   The area to the left of z is .2119.
   b.   The area between $-z$ and z is .9030.
   c.   The area between $-z$ and z is .2052.
   d.   The area to the left of z is .9948.
   e.   The area to the right of z is .6915.

   16.   Given that z is a standard normal random variable, find z for each situation.
   a.   The area to the right of z is .01.
   b.   The area to the right of z is .025.
   c.   The area to the right of z is .05.
   d.   The area to the right of z is .10.

Applications

   17.   The mean cost of domestic airfares in the United States rose to an all-time high of $385 per ticket (Bureau of Transportation Statistics website, November 2, 2012). Airfares were based on the total ticket value, which consisted of the price charged by the airlines plus any additional taxes and fees. Assume domestic airfares are normally distributed with a standard deviation of $110.
   a.   What is the probability that a domestic airfare is $550 or more?
   b.   What is the probability that a domestic airfare is $250 or less?
   c.   What is the probability that a domestic airfare is between $300 and $500?
   d.   What is the cost for the 3% highest domestic airfares?

✓SELF*test*   18.   The average return for large-cap domestic stock funds over the three years 2009–2011 was 14.4% (*AAII Journal*, February, 2012). Assume the three-year returns were normally distributed across funds with a standard deviation of 4.4%.
   a.   What is the probability an individual large-cap domestic stock fund had a three-year return of at least 20%?
   b.   What is the probability an individual large-cap domestic stock fund had a three-year return of 10% or less?
   c.   How big does the return have to be to put a domestic stock fund in the top 10% for the three-year period?

   19.   Automobile repair costs continue to rise with the average cost now at $367 per repair (*U.S. News & World Report* website, January 5, 2015). Assume that the cost for an automobile repair is normally distributed with a standard deviation of $88. Answer the following questions about the cost of automobile repairs.
   a.   What is the probability that the cost will be more than $450?
   b.   What is the probability that the cost will be less than $250?
   c.   What is the probability that the cost will be between $250 and $450?
   d.   If the cost for your car repair is in the lower 5% of automobile repair charges, what is your cost?

   20.   The average price for a gallon of gasoline in the United States is $3.73 and in Russia it is $3.40 (*Bloomberg Businessweek*, March 5–March 11, 2012). Assume these averages are the population means in the two countries and that the probability distributions are normally distributed with a standard deviation of $.25 in the United States and a standard deviation of $.20 in Russia.
   a.   What is the probability that a randomly selected gas station in the United States charges less than $3.50 per gallon?
   b.   What percentage of the gas stations in Russia charge less than $3.50 per gallon?
   c.   What is the probability that a randomly selected gas station in Russia charged more than the mean price in the United States?

21. A person must score in the upper 2% of the population on an IQ test to qualify for membership in Mensa, the international high-IQ society. If IQ scores are normally distributed with a mean of 100 and a standard deviation of 15, what score must a person have to qualify for Mensa?

22. Television viewing reached a new high when the Nielsen Company reported a mean daily viewing time of 8.35 hours per household (*USA Today,* November 11, 2009). Use a normal probability distribution with a standard deviation of 2.5 hours to answer the following questions about daily television viewing per household.
    a. What is the probability that a household views television between 5 and 10 hours a day?
    b. How many hours of television viewing must a household have in order to be in the top 3% of all television viewing households?
    c. What is the probability that a household views television more than 3 hours a day?

23. The time needed to complete a final examination in a particular college course is normally distributed with a mean of 80 minutes and a standard deviation of 10 minutes. Answer the following questions.
    a. What is the probability of completing the exam in one hour or less?
    b. What is the probability that a student will complete the exam in more than 60 minutes but less than 75 minutes?
    c. Assume that the class has 60 students and that the examination period is 90 minutes in length. How many students do you expect will be unable to complete the exam in the allotted time?

24. The American Automobile Association (AAA) reported that families planning to travel over the Labor Day weekend would spend an average of $749 (The Associated Press, August 12, 2012). Assume that the amount spent is normally distributed with a standard deviation of $225.
    a. What is the probability of family expenses for the weekend being less that $400?
    b. What is the probability of family expenses for the weekend being $800 or more?
    c. What is the probability that family expenses for the weekend will be between $500 and $1000?
    d. What would the Labor Day weekend expenses have to be for the 5% of the families with the most expensive travel plans?

25. New York City is the most expensive city in the United States for lodging. The mean hotel room rate is $204 per night (*USA Today,* April 30, 2012). Assume that room rates are normally distributed with a standard deviation of $55.
    a. What is the probability that a hotel room costs $225 or more per night?
    b. What is the probability that a hotel room costs less than $140 per night?
    c. What is the probability that a hotel room costs between $200 and $300 per night?
    d. What is the cost of the 20% most expensive hotel rooms in New York City?

6.3 Normal Approximation of Binomial Probabilities

In Section 5.5 we presented the discrete binomial distribution. Recall that a binomial experiment consists of a sequence of n identical independent trials with each trial having two possible outcomes, a success or a failure. The probability of a success on a trial is the same for all trials and is denoted by p. The binomial random variable is the number of successes in the n trials, and probability questions pertain to the probability of x successes in the n trials.

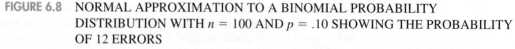

FIGURE 6.8   NORMAL APPROXIMATION TO A BINOMIAL PROBABILITY
DISTRIBUTION WITH $n = 100$ AND $p = .10$ SHOWING THE PROBABILITY
OF 12 ERRORS

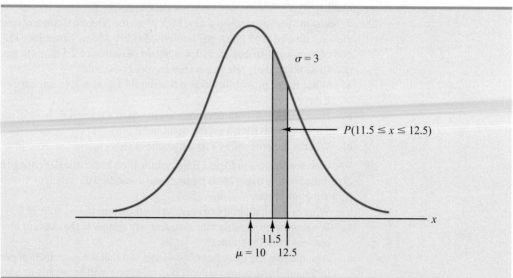

When the number of trials becomes large, evaluating the binomial probability function by hand or with a calculator is difficult. In cases where $np \geq 5$, and $n(1 - p) \geq 5$, the normal distribution provides an easy-to-use approximation of binomial probabilities. When using the normal approximation to the binomial, we set $\mu = np$ and $\sigma = \sqrt{np(1 - p)}$ in the definition of the normal curve.

Let us illustrate the normal approximation to the binomial by supposing that a particular company has a history of making errors in 10% of its invoices. A sample of 100 invoices has been taken, and we want to compute the probability that 12 invoices contain errors. That is, we want to find the binomial probability of 12 successes in 100 trials. In applying the normal approximation in this case, we set $\mu = np = (100)(.1) = 10$ and $\sigma = \sqrt{np(1 - p)} = \sqrt{(100)(.1)(.9)} = 3$. A normal distribution with $\mu = 10$ and $\sigma = 3$ is shown in Figure 6.8.

Recall that, with a continuous probability distribution, probabilities are computed as areas under the probability density function. As a result, the probability of any single value for the random variable is zero. Thus to approximate the binomial probability of 12 successes, we compute the area under the corresponding normal curve between 11.5 and 12.5. The .5 that we add and subtract from 12 is called a **continuity correction factor**. It is introduced because a continuous distribution is being used to approximate a discrete distribution. Thus, $P(x = 12)$ for the *discrete* binomial distribution is approximated by $P(11.5 \leq x \leq 12.5)$ for the *continuous* normal distribution.

Converting to the standard normal distribution to compute $P(11.5 \leq x \leq 12.5)$, we have

$$z = \frac{x - \mu}{\sigma} = \frac{12.5 - 10.0}{3} = .83 \qquad \text{at } x = 12.5$$

and

$$z = \frac{x - \mu}{\sigma} = \frac{11.5 - 10.0}{3} = .50 \qquad \text{at } x = 11.5$$

FIGURE 6.9   NORMAL APPROXIMATION TO A BINOMIAL PROBABILITY
DISTRIBUTION WITH $n = 100$ AND $p = .10$ SHOWING THE PROBABILITY
OF 13 OR FEWER ERRORS

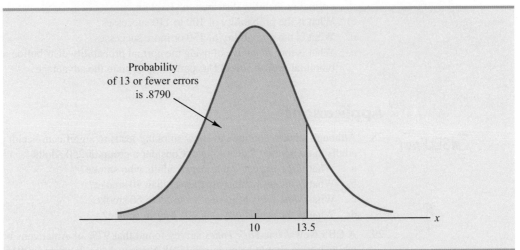

Using the standard normal probability table, we find that the area under the curve (in Figure 6.8) to the left of 12.5 is .7967. Similarly, the area under the curve to the left of 11.5 is .6915. Therefore, the area between 11.5 and 12.5 is $.7967 - .6915 = .1052$. The normal approximation to the probability of 12 successes in 100 trials is .1052.

For another illustration, suppose we want to compute the probability of 13 or fewer errors in the sample of 100 invoices. Figure 6.9 shows the area under the normal curve that approximates this probability. Note that the use of the continuity correction factor results in the value of 13.5 being used to compute the desired probability. The z value corresponding to $x = 13.5$ is

$$z = \frac{13.5 - 10.0}{3.0} = 1.17$$

The standard normal probability table shows that the area under the standard normal curve to the left of $z = 1.17$ is .8790. The area under the normal curve approximating the probability of 13 or fewer errors is given by the shaded portion of the graph in Figure 6.9.

Exercises

Methods

26. A binomial probability distribution has $p = .20$ and $n = 100$.
     a. What are the mean and standard deviation?
     b. Is this situation one in which binomial probabilities can be approximated by the normal probability distribution? Explain.
     c. What is the probability of exactly 24 successes?
     d. What is the probability of 18 to 22 successes?
     e. What is the probability of 15 or fewer successes?

27. Assume a binomial probability distribution has $p = .60$ and $n = 200$.
    a. What are the mean and standard deviation?
    b. Is this situation one in which binomial probabilities can be approximated by the normal probability distribution? Explain.
    c. What is the probability of 100 to 110 successes?
    d. What is the probability of 130 or more successes?
    e. What is the advantage of using the normal probability distribution to approximate the binomial probabilities? Use part (d) to explain the advantage.

Applications

☑SELF*test*

28. Although studies continue to show smoking leads to significant health problems, 20% of adults in the United States smoke. Consider a group of 250 adults.
    a. What is the expected number of adults who smoke?
    b. What is the probability that fewer than 40 smoke?
    c. What is the probability that from 55 to 60 smoke?
    d. What is the probability that 70 or more smoke?

29. A CBS News/*New York Times* survey found that 97% of Americans believe that texting while driving should be outlawed (CBS News website, January 5, 2015).
    a. For a sample of 10 Americans, what is the probability that at least 8 say that they believe texting while driving should be outlawed? Use the binomial distribution probability function discussed in Section 5.5 to answer this question.
    b. For a sample of 100 Americans, what is the probability that at least 95 say that they believe texting while driving should be outlawed? Use the normal approximation of the binomial distribution to answer this question.
    c. As the number of trials in a binomial distribution application becomes large, what is the advantage of using the normal approximation of the binomial distribution to compute probabilities?
    d. When the number of trials for a binominal distribution application becomes large, would developers of statistical software packages prefer to use the binomial distribution probability function shown in Section 5.5 or the normal approximation of the binomial distribution discussed in Section 6.3? Explain.

30. Playing video and computer games is very popular. Over 70% of households play such games. Of those individuals who play video and computer games, 18% are under 18 years old, 53% are 18–59 years old, and 29% are over 59 years old (*The Wall Street Journal,* March 6, 2012).
    a. For a sample of 800 people who play these games, how many would you expect to be under 18 years of age?
    b. For a sample of 600 people who play these games, what is the probability that fewer than 100 will be under 18 years of age?
    c. For a sample of 800 people who play these games, what is the probability that 200 or more will be over 59 years of age?

31. The *Bank of America Trends in Consumer Mobility Report* indicates that in a typical day, 51% of users of mobile phones use their phone at least once per hour, 26% use their phone a few times per day, 8% use their phone morning and evening, and 13% hardly ever use their phones. The remaining 2% indicated that they did not know how often they used their mobile phone (*USA Today*, July 7, 2014). Consider a sample of 150 mobile phone users.
    a. What is the probability that at least 70 use their phone at least once per hour?
    b. What is the probability that at least 75 but less than 80 use their phone at least once per hour?
    c. What is the probability that less than 5 of the 150 phone users do not know how often they use their phone?

6.4 Exponential Probability Distribution

The **exponential probability distribution** may be used for random variables such as the time between arrivals at a car wash, the time required to load a truck, the distance between major defects in a highway, and so on. The exponential probability density function follows.

EXPONENTIAL PROBABILITY DENSITY FUNCTION

$$f(x) = \frac{1}{\mu} e^{-x/\mu} \qquad \text{for } x \geq 0 \qquad\qquad \textbf{(6.4)}$$

where μ = expected value or mean

As an example of the exponential distribution, suppose that x represents the loading time for a truck at the Schips loading dock and follows such a distribution. If the mean, or average, loading time is 15 minutes ($\mu = 15$), the appropriate probability density function for x is

$$f(x) = \frac{1}{15} e^{-x/15}$$

Figure 6.10 is the graph of this probability density function.

Computing Probabilities for the Exponential Distribution

In waiting line applications, the exponential distribution is often used for service time.

As with any continuous probability distribution, the area under the curve corresponding to an interval provides the probability that the random variable assumes a value in that interval. In the Schips loading dock example, the probability that loading a truck will take 6 minutes or less, $P(x \leq 6)$, is defined to be the area under the curve in Figure 6.10 from $x = 0$ to $x = 6$. Similarly, the probability that the loading time will be 18 minutes or less, $P(x \leq 18)$, is the area under the curve from $x = 0$ to $x = 18$. Note also that the probability that the loading time will be between 6 minutes and 18 minutes, $P(6 \leq x \leq 18)$, is given by the area under the curve from $x = 6$ to $x = 18$.

FIGURE 6.10   EXPONENTIAL DISTRIBUTION FOR THE SCHIPS LOADING DOCK EXAMPLE

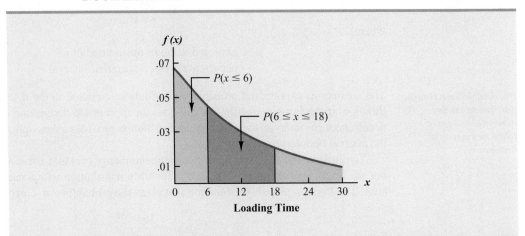

To compute exponential probabilities such as those just described, we use the following formula. It provides the cumulative probability of obtaining a value for the exponential random variable of less than or equal to some specific value denoted by x_0.

> **EXPONENTIAL DISTRIBUTION: CUMULATIVE PROBABILITIES**
>
> $$P(x \leq x_0) = 1 - e^{-x_0/\mu} \tag{6.5}$$

For the Schips loading dock example, x = loading time in minutes and μ = 15 minutes. Using equation (6.5),

$$P(x \leq x_0) = 1 - e^{-x_0/15}$$

Hence, the probability that loading a truck will take 6 minutes or less is

$$P(x \leq 6) = 1 - e^{-6/15} = .3297$$

Using equation (6.5), we calculate the probability of loading a truck in 18 minutes or less.

$$P(x \leq 18) = 1 - e^{-18/15} = .6988$$

Thus, the probability that loading a truck will take between 6 minutes and 18 minutes is equal to $.6988 - .3297 = .3691$. Probabilities for any other interval can be computed similarly.

A property of the exponential distribution is that the mean and standard deviation are equal.

In the preceding example, the mean time it takes to load a truck is μ = 15 minutes. A property of the exponential distribution is that the mean of the distribution and the standard deviation of the distribution are *equal*. Thus, the standard deviation for the time it takes to load a truck is σ = 15 minutes. The variance is $\sigma^2 = (15)^2 = 225$.

Relationship Between the Poisson and Exponential Distributions

In Section 5.6 we introduced the Poisson distribution as a discrete probability distribution that is often useful in examining the number of occurrences of an event over a specified interval of time or space. Recall that the Poisson probability function is

$$f(x) = \frac{\mu^x e^{-\mu}}{x!}$$

where

$$\mu = \text{expected value or mean number of}$$
$$\text{occurrences over a specified interval}$$

If arrivals follow a Poisson distribution, the time between arrivals must follow an exponential distribution.

The continuous exponential probability distribution is related to the discrete Poisson distribution. If the Poisson distribution provides an appropriate description of the number of occurrences per interval, the exponential distribution provides a description of the length of the interval between occurrences.

To illustrate this relationship, suppose the number of cars that arrive at a car wash during one hour is described by a Poisson probability distribution with a mean of 10 cars per hour. The Poisson probability function that gives the probability of x arrivals per hour is

$$f(x) = \frac{10^x e^{-10}}{x!}$$

Because the average number of arrivals is 10 cars per hour, the average time between cars arriving is

$$\frac{1 \text{ hour}}{10 \text{ cars}} = .1 \text{ hour/car}$$

Thus, the corresponding exponential distribution that describes the time between the arrivals has a mean of $\mu = .1$ hour per car; as a result, the appropriate exponential probability density function is

$$f(x) = \frac{1}{.1} e^{-x/.1} = 10 e^{-10x}$$

NOTES AND COMMENTS

As we can see in Figure 6.10, the exponential distribution is skewed to the right. Indeed, the skewness measure for exponential distributions is 2. The exponential distribution gives us a good idea what a skewed distribution looks like.

Exercises

Methods

32. Consider the following exponential probability density function.

$$f(x) = \frac{1}{8} e^{-x/8} \qquad \text{for } x \geq 0$$

    a.   Find $P(x \leq 6)$.
    b.   Find $P(x \leq 4)$.
    c.   Find $P(x \geq 6)$.
    d.   Find $P(4 \leq x \leq 6)$.

33. Consider the following exponential probability density function.

$$f(x) = \frac{1}{3} e^{-x/3} \qquad \text{for } x \geq 0$$

    a.   Write the formula for $P(x \leq x_0)$.
    b.   Find $P(x \leq 2)$.
    c.   Find $P(x \geq 3)$.
    d.   Find $P(x \leq 5)$.
    e.   Find $P(2 \leq x \leq 5)$.

Applications

34. Battery life between charges for the Motorola Droid Razr Maxx is 20 hours when the primary use is talk time (*The Wall Street Journal,* March 7, 2012). The battery life drops to 7 hours when the phone is primarily used for Internet applications over cellular. Assume that the battery life in both cases follows an exponential distribution.
    a.   Show the probability density function for battery life for the Droid Razr Maxx phone when its primary use is talk time.
    b.   What is the probability that the battery charge for a randomly selected Droid Razr Maxx phone will last no more than 15 hours when its primary use is talk time?
    c.   What is the probability that the battery charge for a randomly selected Droid Razr Maxx phone will last more than 20 hours when its primary use is talk time?

d. What is the probability that the battery charge for a randomly selected Droid Razr Maxx phone will last no more than 5 hours when its primary use is Internet applications?

35. The time between arrivals of vehicles at a particular intersection follows an exponential probability distribution with a mean of 12 seconds.
    a. Sketch this exponential probability distribution.
    b. What is the probability that the arrival time between vehicles is 12 seconds or less?
    c. What is the probability that the arrival time between vehicles is 6 seconds or less?
    d. What is the probability of 30 or more seconds between vehicle arrivals?

36. Comcast Corporation is the largest cable television company, the second largest Internet service provider, and the fourth largest telephone service provider in the United States. Generally known for quality and reliable service, the company periodically experiences unexpected service interruptions. On January 14, 2014, such an interruption occurred for the Comcast customers living in southwest Florida. When customers called the Comcast office, a recorded message told them that the company was aware of the service outage and that it was anticipated that service would be restored in two hours. Assume that two hours is the mean time to do the repair and that the repair time has an exponential probability distribution.
    a. What is the probability that the cable service will be repaired in one hour or less?
    b. What is the probability that the repair will take between one hour and two hours?
    c. For a customer who calls the Comcast office at 1:00 P.M., what is the probability that the cable service will not be repaired by 5:00 P.M.?

37. Wendy's restaurant has been recognized for having the fastest average service time among fast food restaurants. In a benchmark study, Wendy's average service time of 2.2 minutes was less than those of Burger King, Chick-fil-A, Krystal, McDonald's, Taco Bell, and Taco John's (*QSR Magazine* website, December 2014). Assume that the service time for Wendy's has an exponential distribution.
    a. What is the probability that a service time is less than or equal to one minute?
    b. What is the probability that a service time is between 30 seconds and one minute?
    c. Suppose a manager of a Wendy's is considering instituting a policy such that if the time it takes to serve you exceeds five minutes, your food is free. What is the probability that you will get your food for free? Comment.

38. The Boston Fire Department receives 911 calls at a mean rate of 1.6 calls per hour (Mass.gov website, November 2012). Suppose the number of calls per hour follows a Poisson probability distribution.
    a. What is the mean time between 911 calls to the Boston Fire Department in minutes?
    b. Using the mean in part (a), show the probability density function for the time between 911 calls in minutes.
    c. What is the probability that there will be less than one hour between 911 calls?
    d. What is the probability that there will be 30 minutes or more between 911 calls?
    e. What is the probability that there will be more than 5 minutes, but less than 20 minutes between 911 calls?

Summary

This chapter extended the discussion of probability distributions to the case of continuous random variables. The major conceptual difference between discrete and continuous probability distributions involves the method of computing probabilities. With discrete distributions, the probability function $f(x)$ provides the probability that the random variable x assumes various values. With continuous distributions, the probability density function $f(x)$ does not provide probability values directly. Instead, probabilities are given by areas under the curve or graph of the probability density function $f(x)$. Because the area under the curve above a single point is zero, we observe that the probability of any particular value is zero for a continuous random variable.

Three continuous probability distributions—the uniform, normal, and exponential distributions—were treated in detail. The normal distribution is used widely in statistical inference and will be used extensively throughout the remainder of the text.

Glossary

Continuity correction factor A value of .5 that is added to or subtracted from a value of x when the continuous normal distribution is used to approximate the discrete binomial distribution.

Exponential probability distribution A continuous probability distribution that is useful in computing probabilities for the time it takes to complete a task.

Normal probability distribution A continuous probability distribution. Its probability density function is bell-shaped and determined by its mean μ and standard deviation σ.

Probability density function A function used to compute probabilities for a continuous random variable. The area under the graph of a probability density function over an interval represents probability.

Standard normal probability distribution A normal distribution with a mean of zero and a standard deviation of one.

Uniform probability distribution A continuous probability distribution for which the probability that the random variable will assume a value in any interval is the same for each interval of equal length.

Key Formulas

Uniform Probability Density Function

$$f(x) = \begin{cases} \dfrac{1}{b-a} & \text{for } a \le x \le b \\ 0 & \text{elsewhere} \end{cases} \tag{6.1}$$

Normal Probability Density Function

$$f(x) = \frac{1}{\sigma\sqrt{2\pi}}\, e^{-\frac{1}{2}\left(\frac{x-\mu}{\sigma}\right)^2} \tag{6.2}$$

Converting to the Standard Normal Random Variable

$$z = \frac{x - \mu}{\sigma} \tag{6.3}$$

Exponential Probability Density Function

$$f(x) = \frac{1}{\mu}\, e^{-x/\mu} \qquad \text{for } x \ge 0 \tag{6.4}$$

Exponential Distribution: Cumulative Probabilities

$$P(x \le x_0) = 1 - e^{-x_0/\mu} \tag{6.5}$$

Supplementary Exercises

39. A business executive, transferred from Chicago to Atlanta, needs to sell her house in Chicago quickly. The executive's employer has offered to buy the house for $210,000, but the offer expires at the end of the week. The executive does not currently have a better offer but can afford to leave the house on the market for another month. From conversations with her realtor, the executive believes the price she will get by leaving the house on the market for another month is uniformly distributed between $200,000 and $225,000.
    a. If she leaves the house on the market for another month, what is the mathematical expression for the probability density function of the sales price?
    b. If she leaves it on the market for another month, what is the probability she will get at least $215,000 for the house?
    c. If she leaves it on the market for another month, what is the probability she will get less than $210,000?
    d. Should the executive leave the house on the market for another month? Why or why not?

40. The NCAA estimates that the yearly value of a full athletic scholarship at in-state public universities is $19,000 (*The Wall Street Journal,* March 12, 2012). Assume the scholarship value is normally distributed with a standard deviation of $2100.
    a. For the 10% of athletic scholarships of least value, how much are they worth?
    b. What percentage of athletic scholarships are valued at $22,000 or more?
    c. For the 3% of athletic scholarships that are most valuable, how much are they worth?

41. Motorola used the normal distribution to determine the probability of defects and the number of defects expected in a production process. Assume a production process produces items with a mean weight of 10 ounces. Calculate the probability of a defect and the expected number of defects for a 1000-unit production run in the following situations.
    a. The process standard deviation is .15, and the process control is set at plus or minus one standard deviation. Units with weights less than 9.85 or greater than 10.15 ounces will be classified as defects.
    b. Through process design improvements, the process standard deviation can be reduced to .05. Assume the process control remains the same, with weights less than 9.85 or greater than 10.15 ounces being classified as defects.
    c. What is the advantage of reducing process variation, thereby causing process control limits to be at a greater number of standard deviations from the mean?

42. During early 2012, economic hardship was stretching the limits of France's welfare system. One indicator of the level of hardship was the increase in the number of people bringing items to a Paris pawnbroker; the number of people bringing items to the pawnbroker had increased to 658 per day (*Bloomberg Businessweek*, March 5–March 11, 2012). Assume the number of people bringing items to the pawnshop per day in 2012 is normally distributed with a mean of 658.
    a. Suppose you learn that on 3% of the days, 610 or fewer people brought items to the pawnshop. What is the standard deviation of the number of people bringing items to the pawnshop per day?
    b. On any given day, what is the probability that between 600 and 700 people bring items to the pawnshop?
    c. How many people bring items to the pawnshop on the busiest 3% of days?

43. The port of South Louisiana, located along 54 miles of the Mississippi River between New Orleans and Baton Rouge, is the largest bulk cargo port in the world. The U.S. Army Corps of Engineers reports that the port handles a mean of 4.5 million tons of cargo per week (*USA Today*, September 25, 2012). Assume that the number of tons of cargo handled per week is normally distributed with a standard deviation of .82 million tons.
    a. What is the probability that the port handles less than 5 million tons of cargo per week?
    b. What is the probability that the port handles 3 or more million tons of cargo per week?

c. What is the probability that the port handles between 3 million and 4 million tons of cargo per week?

d. Assume that 85% of the time the port can handle the weekly cargo volume without extending operating hours. What is the number of tons of cargo per week that will require the port to extend its operating hours?

44. Ward Doering Auto Sales is considering offering a special service contract that will cover the total cost of any service work required on leased vehicles. From experience, the company manager estimates that yearly service costs are approximately normally distributed, with a mean of $150 and a standard deviation of $25.

a. If the company offers the service contract to customers for a yearly charge of $200, what is the probability that any one customer's service costs will exceed the contract price of $200?

b. What is Ward's expected profit per service contract?

45. The XO Group Inc. conducted a survey of 13,000 brides and grooms married in the United States and found that the average cost of a wedding is $29,858 (XO Group website, January 5, 2015). Assume that the cost of a wedding is normally distributed with a mean of $29,858 and a standard deviation of $5600.

a. What is the probability that a wedding costs less than $20,000?

b. What is the probability that a wedding costs between $20,000 and $30,000?

c. For a wedding to be among the 5% most expensive, how much would it have to cost?

46. Assume that the test scores from a college admissions test are normally distributed, with a mean of 450 and a standard deviation of 100.

a. What percentage of the people taking the test score between 400 and 500?

b. Suppose someone receives a score of 630. What percentage of the people taking the test score better? What percentage score worse?

c. If a particular university will not admit anyone scoring below 480, what percentage of the persons taking the test would be acceptable to the university?

47. According to the National Association of Colleges and Employers, the average starting salary for new college graduates in health sciences is $51,541. The average starting salary for new college graduates in business is $53,901 (National Association of Colleges and Employers website, January 5, 2015). Assume that starting salaries are normally distributed and that the standard deviation for starting salaries for new college graduates in health sciences is $11,000. Assume that the standard deviation for starting salaries for new college graduates in business is $15,000.

a. What is the probability that a new college graduate in business will earn a starting salary of at least $65,000?

b. What is the probability that a new college graduate in health sciences will earn a starting salary of at least $65,000?

c. What is the probability that a new college graduate in health sciences will earn a starting salary less than $40,000?

d. How much would a new college graduate in business have to earn in order to have a starting salary higher than 99% of all starting salaries of new college graduates in the health sciences?

48. A machine fills containers with a particular product. The standard deviation of filling weights is known from past data to be .6 ounce. If only 2% of the containers hold less than 18 ounces, what is the mean filling weight for the machine? That is, what must μ equal? Assume the filling weights have a normal distribution.

49. Consider a multiple-choice examination with 50 questions. Each question has four possible answers. Assume that a student who has done the homework and attended lectures has a 75% probability of answering any question correctly.

a. A student must answer 43 or more questions correctly to obtain a grade of A. What percentage of the students who have done their homework and attended lectures will obtain a grade of A on this multiple-choice examination?

    b.   A student who answers 35 to 39 questions correctly will receive a grade of C. What percentage of students who have done their homework and attended lectures will obtain a grade of C on this multiple-choice examination?

    c.   A student must answer 30 or more questions correctly to pass the examination. What percentage of the students who have done their homework and attended lectures will pass the examination?

    d.   Assume that a student has not attended class and has not done the homework for the course. Furthermore, assume that the student will simply guess at the answer to each question. What is the probability that this student will answer 30 or more questions correctly and pass the examination?

50.   A blackjack player at a Las Vegas casino learned that the house will provide a free room if play is for four hours at an average bet of $50. The player's strategy provides a probability of .49 of winning on any one hand, and the player knows that there are 60 hands per hour. Suppose the player plays for four hours at a bet of $50 per hand.

    a.   What is the player's expected payoff?

    b.   What is the probability the player loses $1000 or more?

    c.   What is the probability the player wins?

    d.   Suppose the player starts with $1500. What is the probability of going broke?

51.   The Information Systems Audit and Control Association surveyed office workers to learn about the anticipated usage of office computers for personal holiday shopping (*USA Today*, November 11, 2009). Assume that the number of hours a worker spends doing holiday shopping on an office computer follows an exponential distribution.

    a.   The study reported that there is a .53 probability that a worker uses an office computer for holiday shopping 5 hours or less. Is the mean time spent using an office computer for holiday shopping closest to 5.8, 6.2, 6.6, or 7 hours?

    b.   Using the mean time from part (a), what is the probability that a worker uses an office computer for holiday shopping more than 10 hours?

    c.   What is the probability that a worker uses an office computer for holiday shopping between 4 and 8 hours?

52.   The website for the Bed and Breakfast Inns of North America gets approximately seven visitors per minute (*Time*, September 2001). Suppose the number of website visitors per minute follows a Poisson probability distribution.

    a.   What is the mean time between visits to the website?

    b.   Show the exponential probability density function for the time between website visits.

    c.   What is the probability no one will access the website in a 1-minute period?

    d.   What is the probability no one will access the website in a 12-second period?

53.   Do you dislike waiting in line? Supermarket chain Kroger has used computer simulation and information technology to reduce the average waiting time for customers at 2300 stores. Using a new system called *QueVision*, which allows Kroger to better predict when shoppers will be checking out, the company was able to decrease average customer waiting time to just 26 seconds (*InformationWeek* website and *The Wall Street Journal* website, January 5, 2015).

    a.   Assume that Kroger waiting times are exponentially distributed. Show the probability density function of waiting time at Kroger.

    b.   What is the probability that a customer will have to wait between 15 and 30 seconds?

    c.   What is the probability that a customer will have to wait more than 2 minutes?

54.   The time (in minutes) between telephone calls at an insurance claims office has the following exponential probability distribution.

$$f(x) = .50e^{-.50x} \qquad \text{for } x \geq 0$$

    a.   What is the mean time between telephone calls?

    b.   What is the probability of having 30 seconds or less between telephone calls?

c.   What is the probability of having 1 minute or less between telephone calls?

d.   What is the probability of having 5 or more minutes without a telephone call?

Case Problem   # Specialty Toys

Specialty Toys, Inc., sells a variety of new and innovative children's toys. Management learned that the preholiday season is the best time to introduce a new toy, because many families use this time to look for new ideas for December holiday gifts. When Specialty discovers a new toy with good market potential, it chooses an October market entry date.

In order to get toys in its stores by October, Specialty places one-time orders with its manufacturers in June or July of each year. Demand for children's toys can be highly volatile. If a new toy catches on, a sense of shortage in the marketplace often increases the demand to high levels and large profits can be realized. However, new toys can also flop, leaving Specialty stuck with high levels of inventory that must be sold at reduced prices. The most important question the company faces is deciding how many units of a new toy should be purchased to meet anticipated sales demand. If too few are purchased, sales will be lost; if too many are purchased, profits will be reduced because of low prices realized in clearance sales.

For the coming season, Specialty plans to introduce a new product called Weather Teddy. This variation of a talking teddy bear is made by a company in Taiwan. When a child presses Teddy's hand, the bear begins to talk. A built-in barometer selects one of five responses that predict the weather conditions. The responses range from "It looks to be a very nice day! Have fun" to "I think it may rain today. Don't forget your umbrella." Tests with the product show that, even though it is not a perfect weather predictor, its predictions are surprisingly good. Several of Specialty's managers claimed Teddy gave predictions of the weather that were as good as many local television weather forecasters.

As with other products, Specialty faces the decision of how many Weather Teddy units to order for the coming holiday season. Members of the management team suggested order quantities of 15,000, 18,000, 24,000, or 28,000 units. The wide range of order quantities suggested indicates considerable disagreement concerning the market potential. The product management team asks you for an analysis of the stock-out probabilities for various order quantities, an estimate of the profit potential, and to help make an order quantity recommendation. Specialty expects to sell Weather Teddy for $24 based on a cost of $16 per unit. If inventory remains after the holiday season, Specialty will sell all surplus inventory for $5 per unit. After reviewing the sales history of similar products, Specialty's senior sales forecaster predicted an expected demand of 20,000 units with a .95 probability that demand would be between 10,000 units and 30,000 units.

Managerial Report

Prepare a managerial report that addresses the following issues and recommends an order quantity for the Weather Teddy product.

1.   Use the sales forecaster's prediction to describe a normal probability distribution that can be used to approximate the demand distribution. Sketch the distribution and show its mean and standard deviation.

2.   Compute the probability of a stock-out for the order quantities suggested by members of the management team.

3.   Compute the projected profit for the order quantities suggested by the management team under three scenarios: worst case in which sales = 10,000 units, most likely case in which sales = 20,000 units, and best case in which sales = 30,000 units.

4.   One of Specialty's managers felt that the profit potential was so great that the order quantity should have a 70% chance of meeting demand and only a 30% chance of

any stock-outs. What quantity would be ordered under this policy, and what is the projected profit under the three sales scenarios?

5. Provide your own recommendation for an order quantity and note the associated profit projections. Provide a rationale for your recommendation.

Appendix 6.1   Continuous Probability Distributions with Minitab

Let us demonstrate the Minitab procedure for computing continuous probabilities by referring to the Grear Tire Company problem where tire mileage was described by a normal distribution with $\mu = 36{,}500$ and $\sigma = 5000$. One question asked was: What is the probability that the tire mileage will exceed 40,000 miles?

For continuous probability distributions, Minitab provides the cumulative probability that the random variable takes on a value less than or equal to a specified constant. For the Grear tire mileage question, Minitab can be used to determine the cumulative probability that the tire mileage will be less than or equal to 40,000 miles. After obtaining the cumulative probability, we must subtract it from 1 to determine the probability that the tire mileage will exceed 40,000 miles.

Prior to using Minitab to compute a probability, we must enter the specified constant into a column of the worksheet. For the Grear tire mileage question we enter 40,000 into column C1 of the Minitab worksheet. The steps in using Minitab to compute the cumulative probability follow.

Step 1. Select the **Calc** menu
Step 2. Choose **Probability Distributions**
Step 3. Choose **Normal**
Step 4. When the Normal Distribution dialog box appears:
Select **Cumulative probability**
Enter 36500 in the **Mean** box
Enter 5000 in the **Standard deviation** box
Enter C1 in the **Input column** box (the column containing 40,000)
Click **OK**

Minitab shows that this probability is .7580. Because we are interested in the probability that the tire mileage will be greater than 40,000, the desired probability is $1 - .7580 = .2420$.

A second question in the Grear Tire Company problem was: What mileage guarantee should Grear set to ensure that no more than 10% of the tires qualify for the guarantee? Here we are given a probability and want to find the corresponding value for the random variable. Minitab uses an inverse calculation routine to find the value of the random variable associated with a given cumulative probability. First, we must enter the cumulative probability into a column of the Minitab worksheet. In this case, the desired cumulative probability of .10 is entered into column C1. Then, the first three steps of the Minitab procedure are as already listed. In step 4, we select **Inverse cumulative probability** instead of **Cumulative probability** and complete the remaining parts of the step. Minitab then displays the mileage guarantee of 30,092 miles.

Minitab is capable of computing probabilities for other continuous probability distributions, including the exponential probability distribution. To compute exponential probabilities, follow the procedure shown previously for the normal probability distribution and choose the **Exponential** option in step 3. Step 4 is as shown, with the exception that entering the standard deviation is not required. Output for cumulative probabilities and inverse cumulative probabilities is identical to that described for the normal probability distribution.

Appendix 6.2 # Continuous Probability Distributions with Excel

Excel provides the capability for computing probabilities for several continuous probability distributions, including the normal and exponential probability distributions. In this appendix, we describe how Excel can be used to compute probabilities for any normal distribution. The procedures for the exponential and other continuous distributions are similar to the one we describe for the normal distribution.

Let us return to the Grear Tire Company problem where the tire mileage was described by a normal distribution with $\mu = 36{,}500$ and $\sigma = 5000$. Assume we are interested in the probability that tire mileage will exceed 40,000 miles.

Excel's NORM.DIST function can be used to compute cumulative probabilities for a normal distribution. The general form of the function is NORM.DIST(x,μ,σ,cumulative). For the fourth argument, TRUE is specified if a cumulative probability is desired. Thus, to compute the cumulative probability that the tire mileage will be less than or equal to 40,000 miles we would enter the following formula into any cell of an Excel worksheet:

$$=\text{NORM.DIST}(40000,36500,5000,\text{TRUE})$$

At this point, .7580 will appear in the cell where the formula was entered, indicating that the probability of tire mileage being less than or equal to 40,000 miles is .7580. Therefore, the probability that tire mileage will exceed 40,000 miles is $1 - .7580 = .2420$.

Excel's NORM.INV function uses an inverse computation to find the x value corresponding to a given cumulative probability. For instance, suppose we want to find the guaranteed mileage Grear should offer so that no more than 10% of the tires will be eligible for the guarantee. We would enter the following formula into any cell of an Excel worksheet:

$$=\text{NORM.INV}(.1,36500,5000)$$

At this point, 30092 will appear in the cell where the formula was entered, indicating that the probability of a tire lasting 30,092 miles or less is .10.

The Excel function for computing exponential probabilities is EXPON.DIST. This function requires three inputs: x, the value of the variable; lambda, which is $1/\mu$, and TRUE if you would like the cumulative probability. For example, consider an exponential probability distribution with mean $\mu = 15$. The probability that the exponential variable is less than or equal to 6 can be computed by the Excel formula

$$=\text{EXPON.DIST}(6,1/15,\text{TRUE})$$

If you need help inserting functions in a worksheet, Excel's Insert Function dialog box may be used (see Appendix E).

CHAPTER 7

Sampling and Sampling Distributions

CONTENTS

STATISTICS IN PRACTICE:
MEADWESTVACO CORPORATION

STATISTICS *in* PRACTICE

MEADWESTVACO CORPORATION*
STAMFORD, CONNECTICUT

MeadWestvaco Corporation, a leading producer of packaging, coated and specialty papers, and specialty chemicals, employs more than 17,000 people. It operates worldwide in 30 countries and serves customers located in approximately 100 countries. MeadWestvaco's internal consulting group uses sampling to provide a variety of information that enables the company to obtain significant productivity benefits and remain competitive.

For example, MeadWestvaco maintains large woodland holdings, which supply the trees, or raw material, for many of the company's products. Managers need reliable and accurate information about the timberlands and forests to evaluate the company's ability to meet its future raw material needs. What is the present volume in the forests? What is the past growth of the forests? What is the projected future growth of the forests? With answers to these important questions MeadWestvaco's managers can develop plans for the future, including long-term planting and harvesting schedules for the trees.

How does MeadWestvaco obtain the information it needs about its vast forest holdings? Data collected from sample plots throughout the forests are the basis for learning about the population of trees owned by the company. To identify the sample plots, the timberland holdings are first divided into three sections based on location and types of trees. Using maps and random numbers, MeadWestvaco analysts identify random samples of 1/5- to 1/7-acre plots in each section of the forest. MeadWestvaco foresters collect data from these sample plots to learn about the forest population.

Random sampling of its forest holdings enables MeadWestvaco Corporation to meet future raw material needs.

Foresters throughout the organization participate in the field data collection process. Periodically, two-person teams gather information on each tree in every sample plot. The sample data are entered into the company's continuous forest inventory (CFI) computer system. Reports from the CFI system include a number of frequency distribution summaries containing statistics on types of trees, present forest volume, past forest growth rates, and projected future forest growth and volume. Sampling and the associated statistical summaries of the sample data provide the reports essential for the effective management of MeadWestvaco's forests and timberlands.

In this chapter you will learn about simple random sampling and the sample selection process. In addition, you will learn how statistics such as the sample mean and sample proportion are used to estimate the population mean and population proportion. The important concept of a sampling distribution is also introduced.

*The authors are indebted to Dr. Edward P. Winkofsky for providing this Statistics in Practice.

In Chapter 1 we presented the following definitions of an element, a population, and a sample.

- An *element* is the entity on which data are collected.
- A *population* is the collection of all the elements of interest.
- A *sample* is a subset of the population.

The reason we select a sample is to collect data to make an inference and answer research questions about a population.

Let us begin by citing two examples in which sampling was used to answer a research question about a population.

1. Members of a political party in Texas were considering supporting a particular candidate for election to the U.S. Senate, and party leaders wanted to estimate the proportion of registered voters in the state favoring the candidate. A sample of 400 registered voters in Texas was selected and 160 of the 400 voters indicated a preference for the candidate. Thus, an estimate of the proportion of the population of registered voters favoring the candidate is 160/400 = .40.

2. A tire manufacturer is considering producing a new tire designed to provide an increase in mileage over the firm's current line of tires. To estimate the mean useful life of the new tires, the manufacturer produced a sample of 120 tires for testing. The test results provided a sample mean of 36,500 miles. Hence, an estimate of the mean useful life for the population of new tires was 36,500 miles.

A sample mean provides an estimate of a population mean, and a sample proportion provides an estimate of a population proportion. With estimates such as these, some estimation error can be expected. This chapter provides the basis for determining how large that error might be.

It is important to realize that sample results provide only *estimates* of the values of the corresponding population characteristics. We do not expect exactly .40, or 40%, of the population of registered voters to favor the candidate, nor do we expect the sample mean of 36,500 miles to exactly equal the mean mileage for the population of all new tires produced. The reason is simply that the sample contains only a portion of the population. Some sampling error is to be expected. With proper sampling methods, the sample results will provide "good" estimates of the population parameters. But how good can we expect the sample results to be? Fortunately, statistical procedures are available for answering this question.

Let us define some of the terms used in sampling. The **sampled population** is the population from which the sample is drawn, and a **frame** is a list of the elements that the sample will be selected from. In the first example, the sampled population is all registered voters in Texas, and the frame is a list of all the registered voters. Because the number of registered voters in Texas is a finite number, the first example is an illustration of sampling from a finite population. In Section 7.2, we discuss how a simple random sample can be selected when sampling from a finite population.

The sampled population for the tire mileage example is more difficult to define because the sample of 120 tires was obtained from a production process at a particular point in time. We can think of the sampled population as the conceptual population of all the tires that could have been made by the production process at that particular point in time. In this sense the sampled population is considered infinite, making it impossible to construct a frame to draw the sample from. In Section 7.2, we discuss how to select a random sample in such a situation.

In this chapter, we show how simple random sampling can be used to select a sample from a finite population and describe how a random sample can be taken from an infinite population that is generated by an ongoing process. We then show how data obtained from a sample can be used to compute estimates of a population mean, a population standard deviation, and a population proportion. In addition, we introduce the important concept of a sampling distribution. As we will show, knowledge of the appropriate sampling distribution enables us to make statements about how close the sample estimates are to the corresponding population parameters. The last section discusses some alternatives to simple random sampling that are often employed in practice.

7.1 The Electronics Associates Sampling Problem

The director of personnel for Electronics Associates, Inc. (EAI), has been assigned the task of developing a profile of the company's 2500 managers. The characteristics to be identified include the mean annual salary for the managers and the proportion of managers having completed the company's management training program.

Using the 2500 managers as the population for this study, we can find the annual salary and the training program status for each individual by referring to the firm's personnel records. The data set containing this information for all 2500 managers in the population is in the file named EAI.

Using the EAI data and the formulas presented in Chapter 3, we computed the population mean and the population standard deviation for the annual salary data.

$$\text{Population mean:} \quad \mu = \$51,800$$
$$\text{Population standard deviation:} \quad \sigma = \$4000$$

The data for the training program status show that 1500 of the 2500 managers completed the training program.

Numerical characteristics of a population are called **parameters**. Letting p denote the proportion of the population that completed the training program, we see that $p = 1500/2500 = .60$. The population mean annual salary ($\mu = \$51,800$), the population standard deviation of annual salary ($\sigma = \$4000$), and the population proportion that completed the training program ($p = .60$) are parameters of the population of EAI managers.

Often the cost of collecting information from a sample is substantially less than from a population, especially when personal interviews must be conducted to collect the information.

Now, suppose that the necessary information on all the EAI managers was not readily available in the company's database. The question we now consider is how the firm's director of personnel can obtain estimates of the population parameters by using a sample of managers rather than all 2500 managers in the population. Suppose that a sample of 30 managers will be used. Clearly, the time and the cost of developing a profile would be substantially less for 30 managers than for the entire population. If the personnel director could be assured that a sample of 30 managers would provide adequate information about the population of 2500 managers, working with a sample would be preferable to working with the entire population. Let us explore the possibility of using a sample for the EAI study by first considering how we can identify a sample of 30 managers.

(7.2) Selecting a Sample

In this section we describe how to select a sample. We first describe how to sample from a finite population and then describe how to select a sample from an infinite population.

Sampling from a Finite Population

Other methods of probability sampling are described in Section 7.8

Statisticians recommend selecting a probability sample when sampling from a finite population because a probability sample allows them to make valid statistical inferences about the population. The simplest type of probability sample is one in which each sample of size n has the same probability of being selected. It is called a simple random sample. A simple random sample of size n from a finite population of size N is defined as follows.

> **SIMPLE RANDOM SAMPLE (FINITE POPULATION)**
>
> A **simple random sample** of size n from a finite population of size N is a sample selected such that each possible sample of size n has the same probability of being selected.

We describe how Excel and Minitab can be used to generate a simple random sample in the chapter appendices.

One procedure for selecting a simple random sample from a finite population is to use a table of random numbers to choose the elements for the sample one at a time in such a way that, at each step, each of the elements remaining in the population has the same probability of being selected. Sampling n elements in this way will satisfy the definition of a simple random sample from a finite population.

TABLE 7.1   RANDOM NUMBERS

63271	59986	71744	51102	15141	80714	58683	93108	13554	79945
88547	09896	95436	79115	08303	01041	20030	63754	08459	28364
55957	57243	83865	09911	19761	66535	40102	26646	60147	15702
46276	87453	44790	67122	45573	84358	21625	16999	13385	22782
55363	07449	34835	15290	76616	67191	12777	21861	68689	03263
69393	92785	49902	58447	42048	30378	87618	26933	40640	16281
13186	29431	88190	04588	38733	81290	89541	70290	40113	08243
17726	28652	56836	78351	47327	18518	92222	55201	27340	10493
36520	64465	05550	30157	82242	29520	69753	72602	23756	54935
81628	36100	39254	56835	37636	02421	98063	89641	64953	99337
84649	48968	75215	75498	49539	74240	03466	49292	36401	45525
63291	11618	12613	75055	43915	26488	41116	64531	56827	30825
70502	53225	03655	05915	37140	57051	48393	91322	25653	06543
06426	24771	59935	49801	11082	66762	94477	02494	88215	27191
20711	55609	29430	70165	45406	78484	31639	52009	18873	96927
41990	70538	77191	25860	55204	73417	83920	69468	74972	38712
72452	36618	76298	26678	89334	33938	95567	29380	75906	91807
37042	40318	57099	10528	09925	89773	41335	96244	29002	46453
53766	52875	15987	46962	67342	77592	57651	95508	80033	69828
90585	58955	53122	16025	84299	53310	67380	84249	25348	04332
32001	96293	37203	64516	51530	37069	40261	61374	05815	06714
62606	64324	46354	72157	67248	20135	49804	09226	64419	29457
10078	28073	85389	50324	14500	15562	64165	06125	71353	77669
91561	46145	24177	15294	10061	98124	75732	00815	83452	97355
13091	98112	53959	79607	52244	63303	10413	63839	74762	50289

The random numbers in the table are shown in groups of five for readability.

To select a simple random sample from the finite population of EAI managers, we first construct a frame by assigning each manager a number. For example, we can assign the managers the numbers 1 to 2500 in the order that their names appear in the EAI personnel file. Next, we refer to the table of random numbers shown in Table 7.1. Using the first row of the table, each digit, 6, 3, 2, . . . , is a random digit having an equal chance of occurring. Because the largest number in the population list of EAI managers, 2500, has four digits, we will select random numbers from the table in sets or groups of four digits. Even though we may start the selection of random numbers anywhere in the table and move systematically in a direction of our choice, we will use the first row of Table 7.1 and move from left to right. The first 7 four-digit random numbers are

6327   1599   8671   7445   1102   1514   1807

Because the numbers in the table are random, these four-digit numbers are equally likely.

We can now use these four-digit random numbers to give each manager in the population an equal chance of being included in the random sample. The first number, 6327, is greater than 2500. It does not correspond to one of the numbered managers in the population, and hence is discarded. The second number, 1599, is between 1 and 2500. Thus the first manager selected for the random sample is number 1599 on the list of EAI managers. Continuing this process, we ignore the numbers 8671 and 7445 before identifying managers number 1102, 1514, and 1807 to be included in the random sample. This process continues until the simple random sample of 30 EAI managers has been obtained.

In implementing this simple random sample selection process, it is possible that a random number used previously may appear again in the table before the complete sample of

30 EAI managers has been selected. Because we do not want to select a manager more than one time, any previously used random numbers are ignored because the corresponding manager is already included in the sample. Selecting a sample in this manner is referred to as **sampling without replacement**. If we selected a sample such that previously used random numbers are acceptable and specific managers could be included in the sample two or more times, we would be **sampling with replacement**. Sampling with replacement is a valid way of identifying a simple random sample. However, sampling without replacement is the sampling procedure used most often in practice. When we refer to simple random sampling, we will assume the sampling is without replacement.

Sampling from an Infinite Population

Sometimes we want to select a sample from a population, but the population is infinitely large or the elements of the population are being generated by an ongoing process for which there is no limit on the number of elements that can be generated. Thus, it is not possible to develop a list of all the elements in the population. This is considered the infinite population case. With an infinite population, we cannot select a simple random sample because we cannot construct a frame consisting of all the elements. In the infinite population case, statisticians recommend selecting what is called a random sample.

RANDOM SAMPLE (INFINITE POPULATION)

A **random sample** of size n from an infinite population is a sample selected such that the following conditions are satisfied.

1. Each element selected comes from the same population.
2. Each element is selected independently.

Care and judgment must be exercised in implementing the selection process for obtaining a random sample from an infinite population. Each case may require a different selection procedure. Let us consider two examples to see what we mean by the conditions (1) each element selected comes from the same population and (2) each element is selected independently.

A common quality control application involves a production process where there is no limit on the number of elements that can be produced. The conceptual population we are sampling from is all the elements that could be produced (not just the ones that are produced) by the ongoing production process. Because we cannot develop a list of all the elements that could be produced, the population is considered infinite. To be more specific, let us consider a production line designed to fill boxes of a breakfast cereal with a mean weight of 24 ounces of breakfast cereal per box. Samples of 12 boxes filled by this process are periodically selected by a quality control inspector to determine if the process is operating properly or if, perhaps, a machine malfunction has caused the process to begin underfilling or overfilling the boxes.

With a production operation such as this, the biggest concern in selecting a random sample is to make sure that condition 1, the sampled elements are selected from the same population, is satisfied. To ensure that this condition is satisfied, the boxes must be selected at approximately the same point in time. This way the inspector avoids the possibility of selecting some boxes when the process is operating properly and other boxes when the process is not operating properly and is underfilling or overfilling the boxes. With a production process such as this, the second condition, each element is selected independently, is satisfied by designing the production process so that each box of cereal is filled independently. With this assumption, the quality control inspector only needs to worry about satisfying the same population condition.

As another example of selecting a random sample from an infinite population, consider the population of customers arriving at a fast-food restaurant. Suppose an employee is asked to select and interview a sample of customers in order to develop a profile of customers who visit the restaurant. The customer arrival process is ongoing and there is no way to obtain a list of all customers in the population. So, for practical purposes, the population for this ongoing process is considered infinite. As long as a sampling procedure is designed so that all the elements in the sample are customers of the restaurant and they are selected independently, a random sample will be obtained. In this case, the employee collecting the sample needs to select the sample from people who come into the restaurant and make a purchase to ensure that the same population condition is satisfied. If, for instance, the employee selected someone for the sample who came into the restaurant just to use the restroom, that person would not be a customer and the same population condition would be violated. So, as long as the interviewer selects the sample from people making a purchase at the restaurant, condition 1 is satisfied. Ensuring that the customers are selected independently can be more difficult.

The purpose of the second condition of the random sample selection procedure (each element is selected independently) is to prevent selection bias. In this case, selection bias would occur if the interviewer were free to select customers for the sample arbitrarily. The interviewer might feel more comfortable selecting customers in a particular age group and might avoid customers in other age groups. Selection bias would also occur if the interviewer selected a group of five customers who entered the restaurant together and asked all of them to participate in the sample. Such a group of customers would be likely to exhibit similar characteristics, which might provide misleading information about the population of customers. Selection bias such as this can be avoided by ensuring that the selection of a particular customer does not influence the selection of any other customer. In other words, the elements (customers) are selected independently.

McDonald's, the fast-food restaurant leader, implemented a random sampling procedure for this situation. The sampling procedure was based on the fact that some customers presented discount coupons. Whenever a customer presented a discount coupon, the next customer served was asked to complete a customer profile questionnaire. Because arriving customers presented discount coupons randomly and independently of other customers, this sampling procedure ensured that customers were selected independently. As a result, the sample satisfied the requirements of a random sample from an infinite population.

Situations involving sampling from an infinite population are usually associated with a process that operates over time. Examples include parts being manufactured on a production line, repeated experimental trials in a laboratory, transactions occurring at a bank, telephone calls arriving at a technical support center, and customers entering a retail store. In each case, the situation may be viewed as a process that generates elements from an infinite population. As long as the sampled elements are selected from the same population and are selected independently, the sample is considered a random sample from an infinite population.

NOTES AND COMMENTS

1. In this section we have been careful to define two types of samples: a simple random sample from a finite population and a random sample from an infinite population. In the remainder of the text, we will generally refer to both of these as either a *random sample* or simply a *sample*. We will not make a distinction of the sample being a "simple" random sample unless it is necessary for the exercise or discussion.

2. Statisticians who specialize in sample surveys from finite populations use sampling methods that provide probability samples. With a probability sample, each possible sample has a known probability of selection and a random process is used to select the elements for the sample. Simple random sampling is one of these methods. In Section 7.8, we describe some other probability sampling methods: stratified random sampling, cluster sampling, and systematic sampling. We use the term "simple" in simple random sampling to clarify that this is the probability sampling method that assures each sample of size n has the same probability of being selected.

3. The number of different simple random samples of size n that can be selected from a finite population of size N is

$$\frac{N!}{n!(N-n)!}$$

In this formula, $N!$ and $n!$ are the factorial formulas discussed in Chapter 4. For the EAI problem with $N = 2500$ and $n = 30$, this expression can be used to show that approximately 2.75×10^{69} different simple random samples of 30 EAI managers can be obtained.

Exercises

Methods

1. Consider a finite population with five elements labeled A, B, C, D, and E. Ten possible simple random samples of size 2 can be selected.
a.   List the 10 samples beginning with AB, AC, and so on.
b.   Using simple random sampling, what is the probability that each sample of size 2 is selected?
c.   Assume random number 1 corresponds to A, random number 2 corresponds to B, and so on. List the simple random sample of size 2 that will be selected by using the random digits 8 0 5 7 5 3 2.

2. Assume a finite population has 350 elements. Using the last three digits of each of the following five-digit random numbers (e.g., 601, 022, 448, . . .), determine the first four elements that will be selected for the simple random sample.

98601   73022   83448   02147   34229   27553   84147   93289   14209

Applications

3. *Fortune* publishes data on sales, profits, assets, stockholders' equity, market value, and earnings per share for the 500 largest U.S. industrial corporations (*Fortune* 500, 2012). Assume that you want to select a simple random sample of 10 corporations from the *Fortune* 500 list. Use the last three digits in column 9 of Table 7.1, beginning with 554. Read down the column and identify the numbers of the 10 corporations that would be selected.

4. The 10 most active stocks on the New York Stock Exchange for a given week, are shown here.

AT&T	Alcatel Lucent	Exxon Mobile	Petrobras	Vale SA
Pfizer	Verizon	Gen. Elect.	Citigroup	Ford

Exchange authorities decided to investigate trading practices using a sample of three of these stocks.
a.   Beginning with the first random digit in column 6 of Table 7.1, read down the column to select a simple random sample of three stocks for the exchange authorities.
b.   Using the information in the third Note and Comment, determine how many different simple random samples of size 3 can be selected from the list of 10 stocks.

5. A student government organization is interested in estimating the proportion of students who favor a mandatory "pass-fail" grading policy for elective courses. A list of names and addresses of the 645 students enrolled during the current quarter is available from the registrar's office. Using three-digit random numbers in row 10 of Table 7.1 and moving across the row from left to right, identify the first 10 students who would be selected using simple random sampling. The three-digit random numbers begin with 816, 283, and 610.

6. The *County and City Data Book,* published by the Census Bureau, lists information on 3139 counties throughout the United States. Assume that a national study will collect data from 30 randomly selected counties. Use four-digit random numbers from the last column of Table 7.1 to identify the numbers corresponding to the first five counties selected for the sample. Ignore the first digits and begin with the four-digit random numbers 9945, 8364, 5702, and so on.

7. Assume that we want to identify a simple random sample of 12 of the 372 doctors practicing in a particular city. The doctors' names are available from a local medical organization. Use the eighth column of five-digit random numbers in Table 7.1 to identify the 12 doctors for the sample. Ignore the first two random digits in each five-digit grouping of the random numbers. This process begins with random number 108 and proceeds down the column of random numbers.

8. The following stocks make up the Dow Jones Industrial Average (*Barron's*, July 30, 2012).

1. 3M	11. Disney	21. McDonald's
2. AT&T	12. DuPont	22. Merck
3. Alcoa	13. ExxonMobil	23. Microsoft
4. American Express	14. General Electric	24. J.P. Morgan
5. Bank of America	15. Hewlett-Packard	25. Pfizer
6. Boeing	16. Home Depot	26. Procter & Gamble
7. Caterpillar	17. IBM	27. Travelers
8. Chevron	18. Intel	28. United Technologies
9. Cisco Systems	19. Johnson & Johnson	29. Verizon
10. Coca-Cola	20. Kraft Foods	30. Wal-Mart

Suppose you would like to select a sample of six of these companies to conduct an in-depth study of management practices. Use the first two digits in each row of the ninth column of Table 7.1 to select a simple random sample of six companies.

9. *The Wall Street Journal* provides the net asset value, the year-to-date percent return, and the three-year percent return for 748 mutual funds (*The Wall Street Journal,* December 15, 2014). Assume that a simple random sample of 12 of the 748 mutual funds will be selected for a follow-up study on the size and performance of mutual funds. Use the fourth column of the random numbers in Table 7.1, beginning with 51102, to select the simple random sample of 12 mutual funds. Begin with mutual fund 102 and use the *last* three digits in each row of the fourth column for your selection process. What are the numbers of the 12 mutual funds in the simple random sample?

10. Indicate which of the following situations involve sampling from a finite population and which involve sampling from an infinite population. In cases where the sampled population is finite, describe how you would construct a frame.
   a. Obtain a sample of licensed drivers in the state of New York.
   b. Obtain a sample of boxes of cereal produced by the Breakfast Choice company.
   c. Obtain a sample of cars crossing the Golden Gate Bridge on a typical weekday.
   d. Obtain a sample of students in a statistics course at Indiana University.
   e. Obtain a sample of the orders that are processed by a mail-order firm.

7.3 Point Estimation

Now that we have described how to select a simple random sample, let us return to the EAI problem. A simple random sample of 30 managers and the corresponding data on annual salary and management training program participation are as shown in Table 7.2. The notation x_1, x_2, and so on is used to denote the annual salary of the first manager in the sample, the annual salary of the second manager in the sample, and so on. Participation in the management training program is indicated by Yes in the management training program column.

To estimate the value of a population parameter, we compute a corresponding characteristic of the sample, referred to as a **sample statistic**. For example, to estimate the population

TABLE 7.2 ANNUAL SALARY AND TRAINING PROGRAM STATUS FOR A SIMPLE RANDOM SAMPLE OF 30 EAI MANAGERS

Annual Salary ($)	Management Training Program	Annual Salary ($)	Management Training Program
$x_1 = 49{,}094.30$	Yes	$x_{16} = 51{,}766.00$	Yes
$x_2 = 53{,}263.90$	Yes	$x_{17} = 52{,}541.30$	No
$x_3 = 49{,}643.50$	Yes	$x_{18} = 44{,}980.00$	Yes
$x_4 = 49{,}894.90$	Yes	$x_{19} = 51{,}932.60$	Yes
$x_5 = 47{,}621.60$	No	$x_{20} = 52{,}973.00$	Yes
$x_6 = 55{,}924.00$	Yes	$x_{21} = 45{,}120.90$	Yes
$x_7 = 49{,}092.30$	Yes	$x_{22} = 51{,}753.00$	Yes
$x_8 = 51{,}404.40$	Yes	$x_{23} = 54{,}391.80$	No
$x_9 = 50{,}957.70$	Yes	$x_{24} = 50{,}164.20$	No
$x_{10} = 55{,}109.70$	Yes	$x_{25} = 52{,}973.60$	No
$x_{11} = 45{,}922.60$	Yes	$x_{26} = 50{,}241.30$	No
$x_{12} = 57{,}268.40$	No	$x_{27} = 52{,}793.90$	No
$x_{13} = 55{,}688.80$	Yes	$x_{28} = 50{,}979.40$	Yes
$x_{14} = 51{,}564.70$	No	$x_{29} = 55{,}860.90$	Yes
$x_{15} = 56{,}188.20$	No	$x_{30} = 57{,}309.10$	No

mean μ and the population standard deviation σ for the annual salary of EAI managers, we use the data in Table 7.2 to calculate the corresponding sample statistics: the sample mean and the sample standard deviation s. Using the formulas for a sample mean and a sample standard deviation presented in Chapter 3, the sample mean is

$$\bar{x} = \frac{\Sigma x_i}{n} = \frac{1{,}554{,}420}{30} = \$51{,}814$$

and the sample standard deviation is

$$s = \sqrt{\frac{\Sigma(x_i - \bar{x})^2}{n - 1}} = \sqrt{\frac{325{,}009{,}260}{29}} = \$3348$$

To estimate p, the proportion of managers in the population who completed the management training program, we use the corresponding sample proportion $\bar{p}$. Let x denote the number of managers in the sample who completed the management training program. The data in Table 7.2 show that $x = 19$. Thus, with a sample size of $n = 30$, the sample proportion is

$$\bar{p} = \frac{x}{n} = \frac{19}{30} = .63$$

By making the preceding computations, we perform the statistical procedure called *point estimation*. We refer to the sample mean $\bar{x}$ as the **point estimator** of the population mean μ, the sample standard deviation s as the point estimator of the population standard deviation σ, and the sample proportion $\bar{p}$ as the point estimator of the population proportion p. The numerical value obtained for $\bar{x}$, s, or $\bar{p}$ is called the **point estimate**. Thus, for the simple random sample of 30 EAI managers shown in Table 7.2, $\$51{,}814$ is the point estimate of μ, $\$3348$ is the point estimate of σ, and .63 is the point estimate of p. Table 7.3 summarizes the sample results and compares the point estimates to the actual values of the population parameters.

As is evident from Table 7.3, the point estimates differ somewhat from the corresponding population parameters. This difference is to be expected because a sample, and not a census of the entire population, is being used to develop the point estimates. In the next

TABLE 7.3   SUMMARY OF POINT ESTIMATES OBTAINED FROM A SIMPLE RANDOM SAMPLE OF 30 EAI MANAGERS

Population Parameter	Parameter Value	Point Estimator	Point Estimate
μ = Population mean annual salary	$51,800	$\bar{x}$ = Sample mean annual salary	$51,814
σ = Population standard deviation for annual salary	$4000	s = Sample standard deviation for annual salary	$3348
p = Population proportion having completed the management training program	.60	$\bar{p}$ = Sample proportion having completed the management training program	.63

chapter, we will show how to construct an interval estimate in order to provide information about how close the point estimate is to the population parameter.

Practical Advice

The subject matter of most of the rest of the book is concerned with statistical inference. Point estimation is a form of statistical inference. We use a sample statistic to make an inference about a population parameter. When making inferences about a population based on a sample, it is important to have a close correspondence between the sampled population and the target population. The **target population** is the population we want to make inferences about, while the sampled population is the population from which the sample is actually taken. In this section, we have described the process of drawing a simple random sample from the population of EAI managers and making point estimates of characteristics of that same population. So the sampled population and the target population are identical, which is the desired situation. But in other cases, it is not as easy to obtain a close correspondence between the sampled and target populations.

Consider the case of an amusement park selecting a sample of its customers to learn about characteristics such as age and time spent at the park. Suppose all the sample elements were selected on a day when park attendance was restricted to employees of a single company. Then the sampled population would be composed of employees of that company and members of their families. If the target population we wanted to make inferences about were typical park customers over a typical summer, then we might encounter a significant difference between the sampled population and the target population. In such a case, we would question the validity of the point estimates being made. Park management would be in the best position to know whether a sample taken on a particular day was likely to be representative of the target population.

In summary, whenever a sample is used to make inferences about a population, we should make sure that the study is designed so that the sampled population and the target population are in close agreement. Good judgment is a necessary ingredient of sound statistical practice.

Exercises

Methods

SELF*test*

11. The following data are from a simple random sample.

    5   8   10   7   10   14

a. What is the point estimate of the population mean?

b. What is the point estimate of the population standard deviation?

12. A survey question for a sample of 150 individuals yielded 75 Yes responses, 55 No responses, and 20 No Opinions.

a. What is the point estimate of the proportion in the population who respond Yes?

b. What is the point estimate of the proportion in the population who respond No?

Applications

SELF*test*

13. A sample of 5 months of sales data provided the following information:

Month:	1	2	3	4	5
Units Sold:	94	100	85	94	92

a. Develop a point estimate of the population mean number of units sold per month.

b. Develop a point estimate of the population standard deviation.

DATA *file*

Morningstar

14. Morningstar publishes ratings data on 1208 company stocks (Morningstar website, October 24, 2012). A sample of 40 of these stocks is contained in the DATAfile named Morningstar. Use the Morningstar data set to answer the following questions.

a. Develop a point estimate of the proportion of the stocks that receive Morningstar's highest rating of 5 Stars.

b. Develop a point estimate of the proportion of the Morningstar stocks that are rated Above Average with respect to business risk.

c. Develop a point estimate of the proportion of the Morningstar stocks that are rated 2 Stars or less.

15. The National Football League (NFL) polls fans to develop a rating for each football game (NFL website, October 24, 2012). Each game is rated on a scale from 0 (forgettable) to 100 (memorable). The fan ratings for a random sample of 12 games follow.

57	61	86	74	72	73
20	57	80	79	83	74

a. Develop a point estimate of mean fan rating for the population of NFL games.

b. Develop a point estimate of the standard deviation for the population of NFL games.

16. A sample of 426 U.S. adults age 50 and older were asked how important a variety of issues were in choosing whom to vote for in the 2012 presidential election (*AARP Bulletin*, March 2012).

a. What is the sampled population for this study?

b. Social Security and Medicare was cited as "very important" by 350 respondents. Estimate the proportion of the population of U.S. adults age 50 and over who believe this issue is very important.

c. Education was cited as "very important" by 74% of the respondents. Estimate the number of respondents who believe this issue is very important.

d. Job Growth was cited as "very important" by 354 respondents. Estimate the proportion of U.S. adults age 50 and over who believe job growth is very important.

e. What is the target population for the inferences being made in parts (b) and (d)? Is it the same as the sampled population you identified in part (a)? Suppose you later learn that the sample was restricted to members of the American Association of Retired People (AARP). Would you still feel the inferences being made in parts (b) and (d) are valid? Why or why not?

17. One of the questions in the Pew Internet & American Life Project asked adults if they used the Internet at least occasionally (Pew website, October 23, 2012). The results showed that 454 out of 478 adults aged 18–29 answered Yes; 741 out of 833 adults aged 30–49 answered Yes; 1058 out of 1644 adults aged 50 and over answered Yes.

a. Develop a point estimate of the proportion of adults aged 18–29 who use the Internet.
b. Develop a point estimate of the proportion of adults aged 30–49 who use the Internet.
c. Develop a point estimate of the proportion of adults aged 50 and over who use the Internet.
d. Comment on any relationship between age and Internet use that seems apparent.
e. Suppose your target population of interest is that of all adults (18 years of age and over). Develop an estimate of the proportion of that population who use the Internet.

7.4 Introduction to Sampling Distributions

In the preceding section we said that the sample mean $\bar{x}$ is the point estimator of the population mean μ, and the sample proportion $\bar{p}$ is the point estimator of the population proportion p. For the simple random sample of 30 EAI managers shown in Table 7.2, the point estimate of μ is $\bar{x} = \$51,814$ and the point estimate of p is $\bar{p} = .63$. Suppose we select another simple random sample of 30 EAI managers and obtain the following point estimates:

$$\text{Sample mean: } \bar{x} = \$52,670$$
$$\text{Sample proportion: } \bar{p} = .70$$

Note that different values of $\bar{x}$ and $\bar{p}$ were obtained. Indeed, a second simple random sample of 30 EAI managers cannot be expected to provide the same point estimates as the first sample.

The ability to understand the material in subsequent chapters depends heavily on the ability to understand and use the sampling distributions presented in this chapter.

Now, suppose we repeat the process of selecting a simple random sample of 30 EAI managers over and over again, each time computing the values of $\bar{x}$ and $\bar{p}$. Table 7.4 contains a portion of the results obtained for 500 simple random samples, and Table 7.5 shows the frequency and relative frequency distributions for the 500 $\bar{x}$ values. Figure 7.1 shows the relative frequency histogram for the $\bar{x}$ values.

In Chapter 5 we defined a random variable as a numerical description of the outcome of an experiment. If we consider the process of selecting a simple random sample as an experiment, the sample mean $\bar{x}$ is the numerical description of the outcome of the experiment. Thus, the sample mean $\bar{x}$ is a random variable. As a result, just like other random variables, $\bar{x}$ has a mean or expected value, a standard deviation, and a probability distribution. Because the various possible values of $\bar{x}$ are the result of different simple random samples, the probability distribution of $\bar{x}$ is called the **sampling distribution** of $\bar{x}$. Knowledge of this sampling distribution and its properties will enable us to make probability statements about how close the sample mean $\bar{x}$ is to the population mean μ.

TABLE 7.4 VALUES OF $\bar{x}$ AND $\bar{p}$ FROM 500 SIMPLE RANDOM SAMPLES
OF 30 EAI MANAGERS

Sample Number	Sample Mean ($\bar{x}$)	Sample Proportion ($\bar{p}$)
1	51,814	.63
2	52,670	.70
3	51,780	.67
4	51,588	.53
.	.	.
.	.	.
.	.	.
500	51,752	.50

TABLE 7.5 FREQUENCY AND RELATIVE FREQUENCY DISTRIBUTIONS OF $\bar{x}$ FROM 500 SIMPLE RANDOM SAMPLES OF 30 EAI MANAGERS

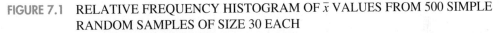

Mean Annual Salary ($)	Frequency	Relative Frequency
49,500.00–49,999.99	2	.004
50,000.00–50,499.99	16	.032
50,500.00–50,999.99	52	.104
51,000.00–51,499.99	101	.202
51,500.00–51,999.99	133	.266
52,000.00–52,499.99	110	.220
52,500.00–52,999.99	54	.108
53,000.00–53,499.99	26	.052
53,500.00–53,999.99	6	.012
Totals 500		1.000

FIGURE 7.1 RELATIVE FREQUENCY HISTOGRAM OF $\bar{x}$ VALUES FROM 500 SIMPLE RANDOM SAMPLES OF SIZE 30 EACH

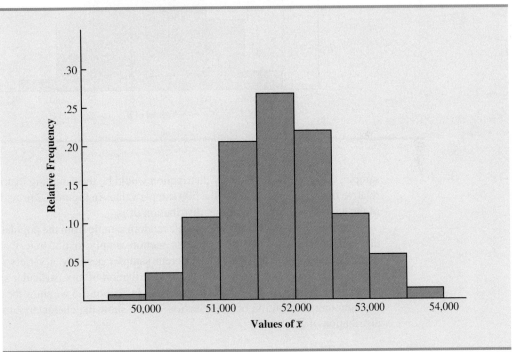

Let us return to Figure 7.1. We would need to enumerate every possible sample of 30 managers and compute each sample mean to completely determine the sampling distribution of $\bar{x}$. However, the histogram of 500 $\bar{x}$ values gives an approximation of this sampling distribution. From the approximation we observe the bell-shaped appearance of the distribution. We note that the largest concentration of the $\bar{x}$ values and the mean of the 500 $\bar{x}$ values is near the population mean $\mu = \$51,800$. We will describe the properties of the sampling distribution of $\bar{x}$ more fully in the next section.

The 500 values of the sample proportion $\bar{p}$ are summarized by the relative frequency histogram in Figure 7.2. As in the case of $\bar{x}$, $\bar{p}$ is a random variable. If every possible sample of size 30 were selected from the population and if a value of $\bar{p}$ were computed for each

FIGURE 7.2   RELATIVE FREQUENCY HISTOGRAM OF $\bar{p}$ VALUES FROM 500 SIMPLE
RANDOM SAMPLES OF SIZE 30 EACH

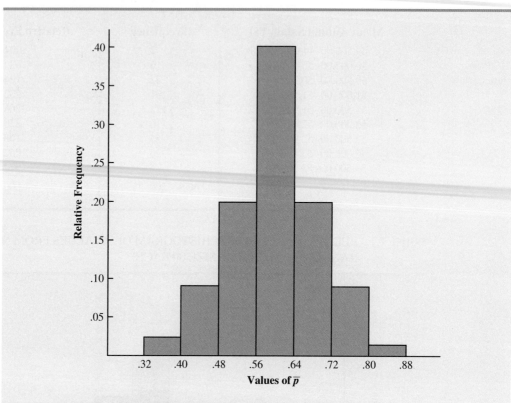

sample, the resulting probability distribution would be the sampling distribution of $\bar{p}$. The
relative frequency histogram of the 500 sample values in Figure 7.2 provides a general idea
of the appearance of the sampling distribution of $\bar{p}$.

In practice, we select only one simple random sample from the population. We repeated
the sampling process 500 times in this section simply to illustrate that many different
samples are possible and that the different samples generate a variety of values for the
sample statistics $\bar{x}$ and $\bar{p}$. The probability distribution of any particular sample statistic is
called the sampling distribution of the statistic. In Section 7.5 we show the characteristics of
the sampling distribution of $\bar{x}$. In Section 7.6 we show the characteristics of the sampling
distribution of $\bar{p}$.

7.5   Sampling Distribution of $\bar{x}$

In the previous section we said that the sample mean $\bar{x}$ is a random variable and its
probability distribution is called the sampling distribution of $\bar{x}$.

SAMPLING DISTRIBUTION OF $\bar{x}$

The sampling distribution of $\bar{x}$ is the probability distribution of all possible values
of the sample mean $\bar{x}$.

This section describes the properties of the sampling distribution of $\bar{x}$. Just as with other probability distributions we studied, the sampling distribution of $\bar{x}$ has an expected value or mean, a standard deviation, and a characteristic shape or form. Let us begin by considering the mean of all possible $\bar{x}$ values, which is referred to as the expected value of $\bar{x}$.

Expected Value of $\bar{x}$

In the EAI sampling problem we saw that different simple random samples result in a variety of values for the sample mean $\bar{x}$. Because many different values of the random variable $\bar{x}$ are possible, we are often interested in the mean of all possible values of $\bar{x}$ that can be generated by the various simple random samples. The mean of the $\bar{x}$ random variable is the expected value of $\bar{x}$. Let $E(\bar{x})$ represent the expected value of $\bar{x}$ and μ represent the mean of the population from which we are selecting a simple random sample. It can be shown that with simple random sampling, $E(\bar{x})$ and μ are equal.

The expected value of $\bar{x}$ equals the mean of the population from which the sample is selected.

EXPECTED VALUE OF $\bar{x}$

$$E(\bar{x}) = \mu \qquad (7.1)$$

where

$$E(\bar{x}) = \text{the expected value of } \bar{x}$$
$$\mu = \text{the population mean}$$

This result shows that with simple random sampling, the expected value or mean of the sampling distribution of $\bar{x}$ is equal to the mean of the population. In Section 7.1 we saw that the mean annual salary for the population of EAI managers is $\mu = \$51,800$. Thus, according to equation (7.1), the mean of all possible sample means for the EAI study is also $\$51,800$.

When the expected value of a point estimator equals the population parameter, we say the point estimator is **unbiased**. Thus, equation (7.1) shows that $\bar{x}$ is an unbiased estimator of the population mean μ.

Standard Deviation of $\bar{x}$

Let us define the standard deviation of the sampling distribution of $\bar{x}$. We will use the following notation.

$$\sigma_{\bar{x}} = \text{the standard deviation of } \bar{x}$$
$$\sigma = \text{the standard deviation of the population}$$
$$n = \text{the sample size}$$
$$N = \text{the population size}$$

It can be shown that the formula for the standard deviation of $\bar{x}$ depends on whether the population is finite or infinite. The two formulas for the standard deviation of $\bar{x}$ follow.

STANDARD DEVIATION OF $\bar{x}$

Finite Population	*Infinite Population*	
$\sigma_{\bar{x}} = \sqrt{\dfrac{N-n}{N-1}}\left(\dfrac{\sigma}{\sqrt{n}}\right)$	$\sigma_{\bar{x}} = \dfrac{\sigma}{\sqrt{n}}$	(7.2)

In comparing the two formulas in (7.2), we see that the factor $\sqrt{(N-n)/(N-1)}$ is required for the finite population case but not for the infinite population case. This factor is commonly referred to as the **finite population correction factor**. In many practical sampling situations, we find that the population involved, although finite, is "large," whereas the sample size is relatively "small." In such cases the finite population correction factor $\sqrt{(N-n)/(N-1)}$ is close to 1. As a result, the difference between the values of the standard deviation of $\bar{x}$ for the finite and infinite population cases becomes negligible. Then, $\sigma_{\bar{x}} = \sigma/\sqrt{n}$ becomes a good approximation to the standard deviation of $\bar{x}$ even though the population is finite. This observation leads to the following general guideline, or rule of thumb, for computing the standard deviation of $\bar{x}$.

USE THE FOLLOWING EXPRESSION TO COMPUTE THE STANDARD DEVIATION OF $\bar{x}$

$$\sigma_{\bar{x}} = \frac{\sigma}{\sqrt{n}} \tag{7.3}$$

whenever

1. The population is infinite; or
2. The population is finite *and* the sample size is less than or equal to 5% of the population size; that is, $n/N \leq .05$.

Problem 21 shows that when $n/N \leq .05$, the finite population correction factor has little effect on the value of $\sigma_{\bar{x}}$.

In cases where $n/N > .05$, the finite population version of formula (7.2) should be used in the computation of $\sigma_{\bar{x}}$. Unless otherwise noted, throughout the text we will assume that the population size is "large," $n/N \leq .05$, and expression (7.3) can be used to compute $\sigma_{\bar{x}}$.

To compute $\sigma_{\bar{x}}$, we need to know σ, the standard deviation of the population. To further emphasize the difference between $\sigma_{\bar{x}}$ and σ, we refer to the standard deviation of $\bar{x}$, $\sigma_{\bar{x}}$, as the **standard error** of the mean. In general, the term *standard error* refers to the standard deviation of a point estimator. Later we will see that the value of the standard error of the mean is helpful in determining how far the sample mean may be from the population mean. Let us now return to the EAI example and compute the standard error of the mean associated with simple random samples of 30 EAI managers.

The term standard error *is used throughout statistical inference to refer to the standard deviation of a point estimator.*

In Section 7.1 we saw that the standard deviation of annual salary for the population of 2500 EAI managers is $\sigma = 4000$. In this case, the population is finite, with $N = 2500$. However, with a sample size of 30, we have $n/N = 30/2500 = .012$. Because the sample size is less than 5% of the population size, we can ignore the finite population correction factor and use equation (7.3) to compute the standard error.

$$\sigma_{\bar{x}} = \frac{\sigma}{\sqrt{n}} = \frac{4000}{\sqrt{30}} = 730.3$$

Form of the Sampling Distribution of $\bar{x}$

The preceding results concerning the expected value and standard deviation for the sampling distribution of $\bar{x}$ are applicable for any population. The final step in identifying the characteristics of the sampling distribution of $\bar{x}$ is to determine the form or shape of the sampling distribution. We will consider two cases: (1) The population has a normal distribution; and (2) the population does not have a normal distribution.

Population has a normal distribution In many situations it is reasonable to assume that the population from which we are selecting a random sample has a normal, or nearly normal, distribution. When the population has a normal distribution, the sampling distribution of $\bar{x}$ is normally distributed for any sample size.

Population does not have a normal distribution When the population from which we are selecting a random sample does not have a normal distribution, the **central limit theorem** is helpful in identifying the shape of the sampling distribution of $\bar{x}$. A statement of the central limit theorem as it applies to the sampling distribution of $\bar{x}$ follows.

CENTRAL LIMIT THEOREM

In selecting random samples of size n from a population, the sampling distribution of the sample mean $\bar{x}$ can be approximated by a *normal distribution* as the sample size becomes large.

Figure 7.3 shows how the central limit theorem works for three different populations; each column refers to one of the populations. The top panel of the figure shows that none of the populations are normally distributed. Population I follows a uniform distribution. Population II is often called the rabbit-eared distribution. It is symmetric, but the more likely values fall in the tails of the distribution. Population III is shaped like the exponential distribution; it is skewed to the right.

The bottom three panels of Figure 7.3 show the shape of the sampling distribution for samples of size $n = 2$, $n = 5$, and $n = 30$. When the sample size is 2, we see that the shape of each sampling distribution is different from the shape of the corresponding population distribution. For samples of size 5, we see that the shapes of the sampling distributions for populations I and II begin to look similar to the shape of a normal distribution. Even though the shape of the sampling distribution for population III begins to look similar to the shape of a normal distribution, some skewness to the right is still present. Finally, for samples of size 30, the shapes of each of the three sampling distributions are approximately normal.

From a practitioner standpoint, we often want to know how large the sample size needs to be before the central limit theorem applies and we can assume that the shape of the sampling distribution is approximately normal. Statistical researchers have investigated this question by studying the sampling distribution of $\bar{x}$ for a variety of populations and a variety of sample sizes. General statistical practice is to assume that, for most applications, the sampling distribution of $\bar{x}$ can be approximated by a normal distribution whenever the sample is size 30 or more. In cases where the population is highly skewed or outliers are present, samples of size 50 may be needed. Finally, if the population is discrete, the sample size needed for a normal approximation often depends on the population proportion. We say more about this issue when we discuss the sampling distribution of $\bar{p}$ in Section 7.6.

Sampling Distribution of $\bar{x}$ for the EAI Problem

Let us return to the EAI problem where we previously showed that $E(\bar{x}) = \$51,800$ and $\sigma_{\bar{x}} = 730.3$. At this point, we do not have any information about the population distribution; it may or may not be normally distributed. If the population has a normal distribution, the sampling distribution of $\bar{x}$ is normally distributed. If the population does not have a normal distribution, the simple random sample of 30 managers and the central limit theorem enable us to conclude that the sampling distribution of $\bar{x}$ can be approximated by a normal distribution. In either case, we are comfortable proceeding with the conclusion that the sampling distribution of $\bar{x}$ can be described by the normal distribution shown in Figure 7.4.

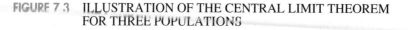

FIGURE 7.3   ILLUSTRATION OF THE CENTRAL LIMIT THEOREM
FOR THREE POPULATIONS

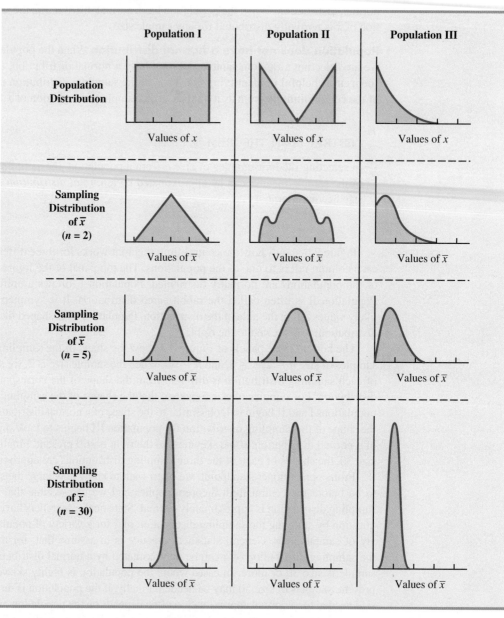

Practical Value of the Sampling Distribution of $\bar{x}$

Whenever a simple random sample is selected and the value of the sample mean is used to estimate the value of the population mean μ, we cannot expect the sample mean to exactly equal the population mean. The practical reason we are interested in the sampling distribution of $\bar{x}$ is that it can be used to provide probability information about the difference between the sample mean and the population mean. To demonstrate this use, let us return to the EAI problem.

Suppose the personnel director believes the sample mean will be an acceptable estimate of the population mean if the sample mean is within \$500 of the population mean. However, it is not possible to guarantee that the sample mean will be within \$500 of the population

FIGURE 7.4   SAMPLING DISTRIBUTION OF $\bar{x}$ FOR THE MEAN ANNUAL SALARY
OF A SIMPLE RANDOM SAMPLE OF 30 EAI MANAGERS

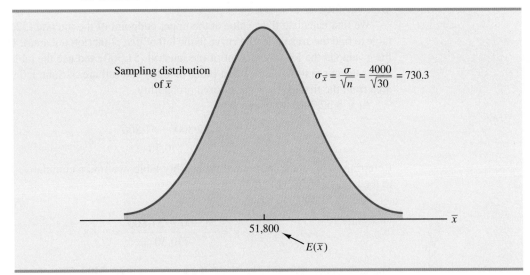

mean. Indeed, Table 7.5 and Figure 7.1 show that some of the 500 sample means differed
by more than $2000 from the population mean. So we must think of the personnel director's
request in probability terms. That is, the personnel director is concerned with the following
question: What is the probability that the sample mean computed using a simple random
sample of 30 EAI managers will be within $500 of the population mean?

Because we have identified the properties of the sampling distribution of $\bar{x}$ (see Figure 7.4),
we will use this distribution to answer the probability question. Refer to the sampling distribution of $\bar{x}$ shown again in Figure 7.5. With a population mean of $51,800, the personnel
director wants to know the probability that $\bar{x}$ is between $51,300 and $52,300. This probability is given by the darkly shaded area of the sampling distribution shown in Figure 7.5.

FIGURE 7.5   PROBABILITY OF A SAMPLE MEAN BEING WITHIN $500
OF THE POPULATION MEAN FOR A SIMPLE RANDOM
SAMPLE OF 30 EAI MANAGERS

Because the sampling distribution is normally distributed, with mean 51,800 and standard error of the mean 730.3, we can use the standard normal probability table to find the area or probability.

We first calculate the z value at the upper endpoint of the interval (52,300) and use the table to find the area under the curve to the left of that point (left tail area). Then we compute the z value at the lower endpoint of the interval (51,300) and use the table to find the area under the curve to the left of that point (another left tail area). Subtracting the second tail area from the first gives us the desired probability.

At $\bar{x} = 52,300$, we have

$$z = \frac{52,300 - 51,800}{730.30} = .68$$

Referring to the standard normal probability table, we find a cumulative probability (area to the left of $z = .68$) of .7517.

At $\bar{x} = 51,300$, we have

$$z = \frac{51,300 - 51,800}{730.30} = -.68$$

The area under the curve to the left of $z = -.68$ is .2483. Therefore, $P(51,300 \le \bar{x} \le 52,300) = P(z \le .68) - P(z < -.68) = .7517 - .2483 = .5034$.

The sampling distribution of $\bar{x}$ can be used to provide probability information about how close the sample mean $\bar{x}$ is to the population mean μ.

The preceding computations show that a simple random sample of 30 EAI managers has a .5034 probability of providing a sample mean $\bar{x}$ that is within $500 of the population mean. Thus, there is a $1 - .5034 = .4966$ probability that the difference between $\bar{x}$ and $\mu = \$51,800$ will be more than $500. In other words, a simple random sample of 30 EAI managers has roughly a 50–50 chance of providing a sample mean within the allowable $500. Perhaps a larger sample size should be considered. Let us explore this possibility by considering the relationship between the sample size and the sampling distribution of $\bar{x}$.

Relationship Between the Sample Size and the Sampling Distribution of $\bar{x}$

Suppose that in the EAI sampling problem we select a simple random sample of 100 EAI managers instead of the 30 originally considered. Intuitively, it would seem that with more data provided by the larger sample size, the sample mean based on $n = 100$ should provide a better estimate of the population mean than the sample mean based on $n = 30$. To see how much better, let us consider the relationship between the sample size and the sampling distribution of $\bar{x}$.

First note that $E(\bar{x}) = \mu$ regardless of the sample size. Thus, the mean of all possible values of $\bar{x}$ is equal to the population mean μ regardless of the sample size n. However, note that the standard error of the mean, $\sigma_{\bar{x}} = \sigma/\sqrt{n}$, is related to the square root of the sample size. Whenever the sample size is increased, the standard error of the mean $\sigma_{\bar{x}}$ decreases. With $n = 30$, the standard error of the mean for the EAI problem is 730.3. However, with the increase in the sample size to $n = 100$, the standard error of the mean is decreased to

$$\sigma_{\bar{x}} = \frac{\sigma}{\sqrt{n}} = \frac{4000}{\sqrt{100}} = 400$$

The sampling distributions of $\bar{x}$ with $n = 30$ and $n = 100$ are shown in Figure 7.6. Because the sampling distribution with $n = 100$ has a smaller standard error, the values of $\bar{x}$ have less variation and tend to be closer to the population mean than the values of $\bar{x}$ with $n = 30$.

FIGURE 7.6 A COMPARISON OF THE SAMPLING DISTRIBUTIONS OF $\bar{x}$ FOR SIMPLE RANDOM SAMPLES OF $n = 30$ AND $n = 100$ EAI MANAGERS

We can use the sampling distribution of $\bar{x}$ for the case with $n = 100$ to compute the probability that a simple random sample of 100 EAI managers will provide a sample mean that is within \$500 of the population mean. Because the sampling distribution is normal, with mean 51,800 and standard error of the mean 400, we can use the standard normal probability table to find the area or probability.

At $\bar{x} = 52,300$ (see Figure 7.7), we have

$$z = \frac{52{,}300 - 51{,}800}{400} = 1.25$$

FIGURE 7.7 PROBABILITY OF A SAMPLE MEAN BEING WITHIN \$500 OF THE POPULATION MEAN FOR A SIMPLE RANDOM SAMPLE OF 100 EAI MANAGERS

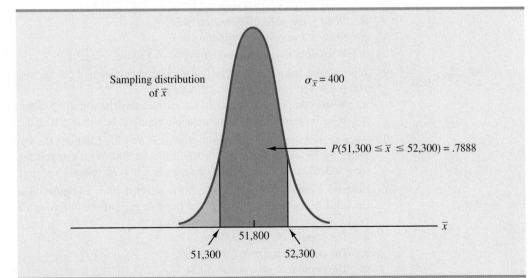

Referring to the standard normal probability table, we find a cumulative probability corresponding to $z = 1.25$ of .8944.

At $\bar{x} = 51,300$, we have

$$z = \frac{51,300 - 51,800}{400} = -1.25$$

The cumulative probability corresponding to $z = -1.25$ is .1056. Therefore, $P(51,300 \leq \bar{x} \leq 52,300) = P(z \leq 1.25) - P(z \leq -1.25) = .8944 - .1056 = .7888$. Thus, by increasing the sample size from 30 to 100 EAI managers, we increase the probability of obtaining a sample mean within $500 of the population mean from .5034 to .7888.

The important point in this discussion is that as the sample size is increased, the standard error of the mean decreases. As a result, the larger sample size provides a higher probability that the sample mean is within a specified distance of the population mean.

NOTES AND COMMENTS

1. In presenting the sampling distribution of $\bar{x}$ for the EAI problem, we took advantage of the fact that the population mean $\mu = 51,800$ and the population standard deviation $\sigma = 4000$ were known. However, usually the values of the population mean μ and the population standard deviation σ that are needed to determine the sampling distribution of $\bar{x}$ will be unknown. In Chapter 8 we will show how the sample mean $\bar{x}$ and the sample standard deviation s are used when μ and σ are unknown.

2. The theoretical proof of the central limit theorem requires independent observations in the sample. This condition is met for infinite populations and for finite populations where sampling is done with replacement. Although the central limit theorem does not directly address sampling without replacement from finite populations, general statistical practice applies the findings of the central limit theorem when the population size is large.

Exercises

Methods

18. A population has a mean of 200 and a standard deviation of 50. A sample of size 100 will be taken and the sample mean $\bar{x}$ will be used to estimate the population mean.
    a. What is the expected value of $\bar{x}$?
    b. What is the standard deviation of $\bar{x}$?
    c. Show the sampling distribution of $\bar{x}$.
    d. What does the sampling distribution of $\bar{x}$ show?

19. A population has a mean of 200 and a standard deviation of 50. Suppose a sample of size 100 is selected and $\bar{x}$ is used to estimate μ.
    a. What is the probability that the sample mean will be within ± 5 of the population mean?
    b. What is the probability that the sample mean will be within ± 10 of the population mean?

20. Assume the population standard deviation is $\sigma = 25$. Compute the standard error of the mean, $\sigma_{\bar{x}}$, for sample sizes of 50, 100, 150, and 200. What can you say about the size of the standard error of the mean as the sample size is increased?

21. Suppose a random sample of size 50 is selected from a population with $\sigma = 10$. Find the value of the standard error of the mean in each of the following cases (use the finite population correction factor if appropriate).
    a. The population size is infinite.
    b. The population size is $N = 50,000$.
    c. The population size is $N = 5000$.
    d. The population size is $N = 500$.

Applications

22. Refer to the EAI sampling problem. Suppose a simple random sample of 60 managers is used.
    a. Sketch the sampling distribution of $\bar{x}$ when simple random samples of size 60 are used.
    b. What happens to the sampling distribution of $\bar{x}$ if simple random samples of size 120 are used?
    c. What general statement can you make about what happens to the sampling distribution of $\bar{x}$ as the sample size is increased? Does this generalization seem logical? Explain.

23. In the EAI sampling problem (see Figure 7.5), we showed that for $n = 30$, there was .5034 probability of obtaining a sample mean within $\pm\$500$ of the population mean.
    a. What is the probability that $\bar{x}$ is within $500 of the population mean if a sample of size 60 is used?
    b. Answer part (a) for a sample of size 120.

24. *Barron's* reported that the average number of weeks an individual is unemployed is 17.5 weeks. Assume that for the population of all unemployed individuals the population mean length of unemployment is 17.5 weeks and that the population standard deviation is 4 weeks. Suppose you would like to select a sample of 50 unemployed individuals for a follow-up study.
    a. Show the sampling distribution of $\bar{x}$, the sample mean average for a sample of 50 unemployed individuals.
    b. What is the probability that a simple random sample of 50 unemployed individuals will provide a sample mean within 1 week of the population mean?
    c. What is the probability that a simple random sample of 50 unemployed individuals will provide a sample mean within 1/2 week of the population mean?

25. The College Board reported the following mean scores for the three parts of the Scholastic Aptitude Test (SAT) (*The World Almanac*, 2009):

Critical Reading	502
Mathematics	515
Writing	494

    Assume that the population standard deviation on each part of the test is $\sigma = 100$.
    a. What is the probability a sample of 90 test takers will provide a sample mean test score within 10 points of the population mean of 502 on the Critical Reading part of the test?
    b. What is the probability a sample of 90 test takers will provide a sample mean test score within 10 points of the population mean of 515 on the Mathematics part of the test? Compare this probability to the value computed in part (a).
    c. What is the probability a sample of 100 test takers will provide a sample mean test score within 10 of the population mean of 494 on the writing part of the test? Comment on the differences between this probability and the values computed in parts (a) and (b).

26. For the year 2010, 33% of taxpayers with adjusted gross incomes between $30,000 and $60,000 itemized deductions on their federal income tax return (*The Wall Street Journal*, October 25, 2012). The mean amount of deductions for this population of taxpayers was $16,642. Assume the standard deviation is $\sigma = \$2400$.
    a. What is the probability that a sample of taxpayers from this income group who have itemized deductions will show a sample mean within $200 of the population mean for each of the following sample sizes: 30, 50, 100, and 400?
    b. What is the advantage of a larger sample size when attempting to estimate the population mean?

27. The Economic Policy Institute periodically issues reports on wages of entry level workers. The institute reported that entry level wages for male college graduates were $21.68 per hour and for female college graduates were $18.80 per hour in 2011 (Economic Policy

Institute website, March 30, 2012). Assume the standard deviation for male graduates is $2.30, and for female graduates it is $2.05.

   a. What is the probability that a sample of 50 male graduates will provide a sample mean within $.50 of the population mean, $21.68?

   b. What is the probability that a sample of 50 female graduates will provide a sample mean within $.50 of the population mean, $18.80?

   c. In which of the preceding two cases, part (a) or part (b), do we have a higher probability of obtaining a sample estimate within $.50 of the population mean? Why?

   d. What is the probability that a sample of 120 female graduates will provide a sample mean more than $.30 below the population mean?

28. The state of California has a mean annual rainfall of 22 inches, whereas the state of New York has a mean annual rainfall of 42 inches (Current Results website, October 27, 2012). Assume that the standard deviation for both states is 4 inches. A sample of 30 years of rainfall for California and a sample of 45 years of rainfall for New York has been taken.

   a. Show the probability distribution of the sample mean annual rainfall for California.

   b. What is the probability that the sample mean is within 1 inch of the population mean for California?

   c. What is the probability that the sample mean is within 1 inch of the population mean for New York?

   d. In which case, part (b) or part (c), is the probability of obtaining a sample mean within 1 inch of the population mean greater? Why?

29. The mean preparation fee H&R Block charged retail customers last year was $183 (*The Wall Street Journal,* March 7, 2012). Use this price as the population mean and assume the population standard deviation of preparation fees is $50.

   a. What is the probability that the mean price for a sample of 30 H&R Block retail customers is within $8 of the population mean?

   b. What is the probability that the mean price for a sample of 50 H&R Block retail customers is within $8 of the population mean?

   c. What is the probability that the mean price for a sample of 100 H&R Block retail customers is within $8 of the population mean?

   d. Which, if any, of the sample sizes in parts (a), (b), and (c) would you recommend to have at least a .95 probability that the sample mean is within $8 of the population mean?

30. To estimate the mean age for a population of 4000 employees, a simple random sample of 40 employees is selected.

   a. Would you use the finite population correction factor in calculating the standard error of the mean? Explain.

   b. If the population standard deviation is $\sigma = 8.2$ years, compute the standard error both with and without the finite population correction factor. What is the rationale for ignoring the finite population correction factor whenever $n/N \leq .05$?

   c. What is the probability that the sample mean age of the employees will be within ± 2 years of the population mean age?

(7.6) Sampling Distribution of $\bar{p}$

The sample proportion $\bar{p}$ is the point estimator of the population proportion p. The formula for computing the sample proportion is

$$\bar{p} = \frac{x}{n}$$

where

   x = the number of elements in the sample that possess the characteristic of interest

   n = sample size

As noted in Section 7.4, the sample proportion $\bar{p}$ is a random variable and its probability distribution is called the sampling distribution of $\bar{p}$.

SAMPLING DISTRIBUTION OF $\bar{p}$

The sampling distribution of $\bar{p}$ is the probability distribution of all possible values of the sample proportion $\bar{p}$.

To determine how close the sample proportion $\bar{p}$ is to the population proportion p, we need to understand the properties of the sampling distribution of $\bar{p}$: the expected value of $\bar{p}$, the standard deviation of $\bar{p}$, and the shape or form of the sampling distribution of $\bar{p}$.

Expected Value of $\bar{p}$

The expected value of $\bar{p}$, the mean of all possible values of $\bar{p}$, is equal to the population proportion p.

EXPECTED VALUE OF $\bar{p}$

$$E(\bar{p}) = p \qquad (7.4)$$

where

$$E(\bar{p}) = \text{the expected value of } \bar{p}$$
$$p = \text{the population proportion}$$

Because $E(\bar{p}) = p$, $\bar{p}$ is an unbiased estimator of p. Recall from Section 7.1 we noted that $p = .60$ for the EAI population, where p is the proportion of the population of managers who participated in the company's management training program. Thus, the expected value of $\bar{p}$ for the EAI sampling problem is .60.

Standard Deviation of $\bar{p}$

Just as we found for the standard deviation of $\bar{x}$, the standard deviation of $\bar{p}$ depends on whether the population is finite or infinite. The two formulas for computing the standard deviation of $\bar{p}$ follow.

STANDARD DEVIATION OF $\bar{p}$

| *Finite Population* | *Infinite Population* |
| $\sigma_{\bar{p}} = \sqrt{\dfrac{N-n}{N-1}} \sqrt{\dfrac{p(1-p)}{n}}$ | $\sigma_{\bar{p}} = \sqrt{\dfrac{p(1-p)}{n}}$ |

(7.5)

Comparing the two formulas in (7.5), we see that the only difference is the use of the finite population correction factor $\sqrt{(N-n)/(N-1)}$.

As was the case with the sample mean $\bar{x}$, the difference between the expressions for the finite population and the infinite population becomes negligible if the size of the finite population is large in comparison to the sample size. We follow the same rule of thumb that we recommended for the sample mean. That is, if the population is finite with $n/N \leq .05$, we will use $\sigma_{\bar{p}} = \sqrt{p(1 - p)/n}$. However, if the population is finite with $n/N > .05$, the finite population correction factor should be used. Again, unless specifically noted, throughout the text we will assume that the population size is large in relation to the sample size and thus the finite population correction factor is unnecessary.

In Section 7.5 we used the term standard error of the mean to refer to the standard deviation of $\bar{x}$. We stated that in general the term standard error refers to the standard deviation of a point estimator. Thus, for proportions we use *standard error of the proportion* to refer to the standard deviation of $\bar{p}$. Let us now return to the EAI example and compute the standard error of the proportion associated with simple random samples of 30 EAI managers.

For the EAI study we know that the population proportion of managers who participated in the management training program is $p = .60$. With $n/N = 30/2500 = .012$, we can ignore the finite population correction factor when we compute the standard error of the proportion. For the simple random sample of 30 managers, $\sigma_{\bar{p}}$ is

$$\sigma_{\bar{p}} = \sqrt{\frac{p(1 - p)}{n}} = \sqrt{\frac{.60(1 - .60)}{30}} = .0894$$

Form of the Sampling Distribution of $\bar{p}$

Now that we know the mean and standard deviation of the sampling distribution of $\bar{p}$, the final step is to determine the form or shape of the sampling distribution. The sample proportion is $\bar{p} = x/n$. For a simple random sample from a large population, the value of x is a binomial random variable indicating the number of elements in the sample with the characteristic of interest. Because n is a constant, the probability of x/n is the same as the binomial probability of x, which means that the sampling distribution of $\bar{p}$ is also a discrete probability distribution and that the probability for each value of x/n is the same as the probability of x.

In Chapter 6 we also showed that a binomial distribution can be approximated by a normal distribution whenever the sample size is large enough to satisfy the following two conditions:

$$np \geq 5 \quad \text{and} \quad n(1 - p) \geq 5$$

Assuming these two conditions are satisfied, the probability distribution of x in the sample proportion, $\bar{p} = x/n$, can be approximated by a normal distribution. And because n is a constant, the sampling distribution of $\bar{p}$ can also be approximated by a normal distribution. This approximation is stated as follows:

> The sampling distribution of $\bar{p}$ can be approximated by a normal distribution whenever $np \geq 5$ and $n(1 - p) \geq 5$.

In practical applications, when an estimate of a population proportion is desired, we find that sample sizes are almost always large enough to permit the use of a normal approximation for the sampling distribution of $\bar{p}$.

Recall that for the EAI sampling problem we know that the population proportion of managers who participated in the training program is $p = .60$. With a simple random sample of size 30, we have $np = 30(.60) = 18$ and $n(1 - p) = 30(.40) = 12$. Thus, the sampling distribution of $\bar{p}$ can be approximated by a normal distribution shown in Figure 7.8.

FIGURE 7.8   SAMPLING DISTRIBUTION OF $\bar{p}$ FOR THE PROPORTION OF EAI MANAGERS WHO PARTICIPATED IN THE MANAGEMENT TRAINING PROGRAM

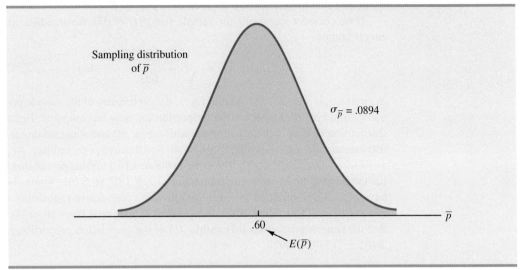

Practical Value of the Sampling Distribution of $\bar{p}$

The practical value of the sampling distribution of $\bar{p}$ is that it can be used to provide probability information about the difference between the sample proportion and the population proportion. For instance, suppose that in the EAI problem the personnel director wants to know the probability of obtaining a value of $\bar{p}$ that is within .05 of the population proportion of EAI managers who participated in the training program. That is, what is the probability of obtaining a sample with a sample proportion $\bar{p}$ between .55 and .65? The darkly shaded area in Figure 7.9 shows this probability. Using the fact that the sampling distribution of $\bar{p}$ can be approximated by a normal distribution with a mean of .60 and a standard error of the proportion of $\sigma_{\bar{p}} = .0894$, we find that the standard normal random variable corresponding to $\bar{p} = .65$ has a value of $z = (.65 - .60)/.0894 = .56$. Referring to the standard normal probability table, we see that the cumulative probability corresponding to $z = .56$ is .7123. Similarly, at $\bar{p} = .55$, we find $z = (.55 - .60)/.0894 = -.56$. From the standard normal

FIGURE 7.9   PROBABILITY OF OBTAINING $\bar{p}$ BETWEEN .55 AND .65

probability table, we find the cumulative probability corresponding to $z = -.56$ is .2877. Thus, the probability of selecting a sample that provides a sample proportion $\bar{p}$ within .05 of the population proportion p is given by $.7123 - .2877 = .4246$.

If we consider increasing the sample size to $n = 100$, the standard error of the proportion becomes

$$\sigma_{\bar{p}} = \sqrt{\frac{.60(1 - .60)}{100}} = .049$$

With a sample size of 100 EAI managers, the probability of the sample proportion having a value within .05 of the population proportion can now be computed. Because the sampling distribution is approximately normal, with mean .60 and standard deviation .049, we can use the standard normal probability table to find the area or probability. At $\bar{p} = .65$, we have $z = (.65 - .60)/.049 = 1.02$. Referring to the standard normal probability table, we see that the cumulative probability corresponding to $z = 1.02$ is .8461. Similarly, at $\bar{p} = .55$, we have $z = (.55 - .60)/.049 = -1.02$. We find the cumulative probability corresponding to $z = -1.02$ is .1539. Thus, if the sample size is increased from 30 to 100, the probability that the sample proportion $\bar{p}$ is within .05 of the population proportion p will increase to $.8461 - .1539 = .6922$.

Exercises

Methods

31. A sample of size 100 is selected from a population with $p = .40$.
    a. What is the expected value of $\bar{p}$?
    b. What is the standard error of $\bar{p}$?
    c. Show the sampling distribution of $\bar{p}$.
    d. What does the sampling distribution of $\bar{p}$ show?

 32. A population proportion is .40. A sample of size 200 will be taken and the sample proportion $\bar{p}$ will be used to estimate the population proportion.
    a. What is the probability that the sample proportion will be within $\pm.03$ of the population proportion?
    b. What is the probability that the sample proportion will be within $\pm.05$ of the population proportion?

33. Assume that the population proportion is .55. Compute the standard error of the proportion, $\sigma_{\bar{p}}$, for sample sizes of 100, 200, 500, and 1000. What can you say about the size of the standard error of the proportion as the sample size is increased?

34. The population proportion is .30. What is the probability that a sample proportion will be within $\pm.04$ of the population proportion for each of the following sample sizes?
    a. $n = 100$
    b. $n = 200$
    c. $n = 500$
    d. $n = 1000$
    e. What is the advantage of a larger sample size?

Applications

 35. The president of Doerman Distributors, Inc., believes that 30% of the firm's orders come from first-time customers. A random sample of 100 orders will be used to estimate the proportion of first-time customers.
    a. Assume that the president is correct and $p = .30$. What is the sampling distribution of $\bar{p}$ for this study?

b.   What is the probability that the sample proportion $\bar{p}$ will be between .20 and .40?

c.   What is the probability that the sample proportion will be between .25 and .35?

36.   *The Wall Street Journal* reported that the age at first startup for 55% of entrepreneurs was 29 years of age or less and the age at first startup for 45% of entrepreneurs was 30 years of age or more (*The Wall Street Journal*, March 19, 2012).

a.   Suppose a sample of 200 entrepreneurs will be taken to learn about the most important qualities of entrepreneurs. Show the sampling distribution of $\bar{p}$ where $\bar{p}$ is the sample proportion of entrepreneurs whose first startup was at 29 years of age or less.

b.   What is the probability that the sample proportion in part (a) will be within ±.05 of its population proportion?

c.   Suppose a sample of 200 entrepreneurs will be taken to learn about the most important qualities of entrepreneurs. Show the sampling distribution of $\bar{p}$ where $\bar{p}$ is now the sample proportion of entrepreneurs whose first startup was at 30 years of age or more.

d.   What is the probability that the sample proportion in part (c) will be within ±.05 of its population proportion?

e.   Is the probability different in parts (b) and (d)? Why?

f.   Answer part (b) for a sample of size 400. Is the probability smaller? Why?

37.   People end up tossing 12% of what they buy at the grocery store (*Reader's Digest*, March 2009). Assume this is the true population proportion and that you plan to take a sample survey of 540 grocery shoppers to further investigate their behavior.

a.   Show the sampling distribution of $\bar{p}$, the proportion of groceries thrown out by your sample respondents.

b.   What is the probability that your survey will provide a sample proportion within ±.03 of the population proportion?

c.   What is the probability that your survey will provide a sample proportion within ±.015 of the population proportion?

38.   Forty-two percent of primary care doctors think their patients receive unnecessary medical care (*Reader's Digest*, December 2011/January 2012).

a.   Suppose a sample of 300 primary care doctors were taken. Show the sampling distribution of the proportion of the doctors who think their patients receive unnecessary medical care.

b.   What is the probability that the sample proportion will be within ±.03 of the population proportion?

c.   What is the probability that the sample proportion will be within ±.05 of the population proportion?

d.   What would be the effect of taking a larger sample on the probabilities in parts (b) and (c)? Why?

39.   In 2008 the Better Business Bureau settled 75% of complaints they received (*USA Today*, March 2, 2009). Suppose you have been hired by the Better Business Bureau to investigate the complaints they received this year involving new car dealers. You plan to select a sample of new car dealer complaints to estimate the proportion of complaints the Better Business Bureau is able to settle. Assume the population proportion of complaints settled for new car dealers is .75, the same as the overall proportion of complaints settled in 2008.

a.   Suppose you select a sample of 450 complaints involving new car dealers. Show the sampling distribution of $\bar{p}$.

b.   Based upon a sample of 450 complaints, what is the probability that the sample proportion will be within .04 of the population proportion?

c.   Suppose you select a sample of 200 complaints involving new car dealers. Show the sampling distribution of $\bar{p}$.

d.   Based upon the smaller sample of only 200 complaints, what is the probability that the sample proportion will be within .04 of the population proportion?

e.   As measured by the increase in probability, how much do you gain in precision by taking the larger sample in part (b)?

40. The Grocery Manufacturers of America reported that 76% of consumers read the ingredients listed on a product's label. Assume the population proportion is $p = .76$ and a sample of 400 consumers is selected from the population.

a. Show the sampling distribution of the sample proportion $\bar{p}$ where $\bar{p}$ is the proportion of the sampled consumers who read the ingredients listed on a product's label.

b. What is the probability that the sample proportion will be within $\pm.03$ of the population proportion?

c. Answer part (b) for a sample of 750 consumers.

41. The Food Marketing Institute shows that 17% of households spend more than $100 per week on groceries. Assume the population proportion is $p = .17$ and a sample of 800 households will be selected from the population.

a. Show the sampling distribution of $\bar{p}$, the sample proportion of households spending more than $100 per week on groceries.

b. What is the probability that the sample proportion will be within $\pm.02$ of the population proportion?

c. Answer part (b) for a sample of 1600 households.

7.7 Properties of Point Estimators

In this chapter we showed how sample statistics such as a sample mean $\bar{x}$, a sample standard deviation s, and a sample proportion $\bar{p}$ can be used as point estimators of their corresponding population parameters μ, σ, and p. It is intuitively appealing that each of these sample statistics is the point estimator of its corresponding population parameter. However, before using a sample statistic as a point estimator, statisticians check to see whether the sample statistic demonstrates certain properties associated with good point estimators. In this section we discuss three properties of good point estimators: unbiased, efficiency, and consistency.

Because several different sample statistics can be used as point estimators of different population parameters, we use the following general notation in this section.

$$\theta = \text{the population parameter of interest}$$
$$\hat{\theta} = \text{the sample statistic or point estimator of } \theta$$

The notation θ is the Greek letter theta, and the notation $\hat{\theta}$ is pronounced "theta-hat." In general, θ represents any population parameter such as a population mean, population standard deviation, population proportion, and so on; $\hat{\theta}$ represents the corresponding sample statistic such as the sample mean, sample standard deviation, and sample proportion.

Unbiased

If the expected value of the sample statistic is equal to the population parameter being estimated, the sample statistic is said to be an *unbiased estimator* of the population parameter.

UNBIASED

The sample statistic $\hat{\theta}$ is an unbiased estimator of the population parameter θ if

$$E(\hat{\theta}) = \theta$$

where

$$E(\hat{\theta}) = \text{the expected value of the sample statistic } \hat{\theta}$$

FIGURE 7.10 **EXAMPLES OF UNBIASED AND BIASED POINT ESTIMATORS**

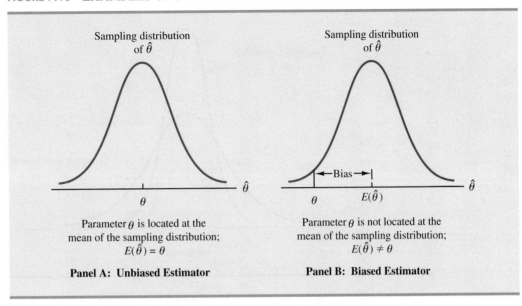

Hence, the expected value, or mean, of all possible values of an unbiased sample statistic is equal to the population parameter being estimated.

Figure 7.10 shows the cases of unbiased and biased point estimators. In the illustration showing the unbiased estimator, the mean of the sampling distribution is equal to the value of the population parameter. The estimation errors balance out in this case, because sometimes the value of the point estimator $\hat{\theta}$ may be less than θ and other times it may be greater than θ. In the case of a biased estimator, the mean of the sampling distribution is less than or greater than the value of the population parameter. In the illustration in Panel B of Figure 7.10, $E(\hat{\theta})$ is greater than θ; thus, the sample statistic has a high probability of overestimating the value of the population parameter. The amount of the bias is shown in the figure.

In discussing the sampling distributions of the sample mean and the sample proportion, we stated that $E(\bar{x}) = \mu$ and $E(\bar{p}) = p$. Thus, both $\bar{x}$ and $\bar{p}$ are unbiased estimators of their corresponding population parameters μ and p.

In the case of the sample standard deviation s and the sample variance s^2, it can be shown that $E(s^2) = \sigma^2$. Thus, we conclude that the sample variance s^2 is an unbiased estimator of the population variance σ^2. In fact, when we first presented the formulas for the sample variance and the sample standard deviation in Chapter 3, $n - 1$ rather than n was used in the denominator. The reason for using $n - 1$ rather than n is to make the sample variance an unbiased estimator of the population variance.

Efficiency

When sampling from a normal population, the standard error of the sample mean is less than the standard error of the sample median. Thus, the sample mean is more efficient than the sample median.

Assume that a simple random sample of n elements can be used to provide two unbiased point estimators of the same population parameter. In this situation, we would prefer to use the point estimator with the smaller standard error, because it tends to provide estimates closer to the population parameter. The point estimator with the smaller standard error is said to have greater **relative efficiency** than the other.

Figure 7.11 shows the sampling distributions of two unbiased point estimators, $\hat{\theta}_1$ and $\hat{\theta}_2$. Note that the standard error of $\hat{\theta}_1$ is less than the standard error of $\hat{\theta}_2$; thus,

FIGURE 7.11   SAMPLING DISTRIBUTIONS OF TWO UNBIASED POINT ESTIMATORS

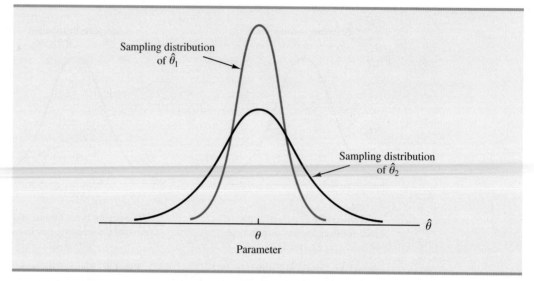

values of $\hat{\theta}_1$ have a greater chance of being close to the parameter θ than do values of $\hat{\theta}_2$. Because the standard error of point estimator $\hat{\theta}_1$ is less than the standard error of point estimator $\hat{\theta}_2$, $\hat{\theta}_1$ is relatively more efficient than $\hat{\theta}_2$ and is the preferred point estimator.

Consistency

A third property associated with good point estimators is **consistency.** Loosely speaking, a point estimator is consistent if the values of the point estimator tend to become closer to the population parameter as the sample size becomes larger. In other words, a large sample size tends to provide a better point estimate than a small sample size. Note that for the sample mean $\bar{x}$, we showed that the standard error of $\bar{x}$ is given by $\sigma_{\bar{x}} = \sigma/\sqrt{n}$. Because $\sigma_{\bar{x}}$ is related to the sample size such that larger sample sizes provide smaller values for $\sigma_{\bar{x}}$, we conclude that a larger sample size tends to provide point estimates closer to the population mean μ. In this sense, we can say that the sample mean $\bar{x}$ is a consistent estimator of the population mean μ. Using a similar rationale, we can also conclude that the sample proportion $\bar{p}$ is a consistent estimator of the population proportion p.

NOTES AND COMMENTS

In Chapter 3 we stated that the mean and the median are two measures of central location. In this chapter we discussed only the mean. The reason is that in sampling from a normal population, where the population mean and population median are identical, the standard error of the median is approximately 25% larger than the standard error of the mean. Recall that in the EAI problem where $n = 30$, the standard error of the mean is $\sigma_{\bar{x}} = 730.3$. The standard error of the median for this problem would be $1.25 \times (730.3) = 913$. As a result, the sample mean is more efficient and will have a higher probability of being within a specified distance of the population mean.

Other Sampling Methods

We described simple random sampling as a procedure for sampling from a finite population and discussed the properties of the sampling distributions of $\bar{x}$ and $\bar{p}$ when simple random sampling is used. Other methods such as stratified random sampling, cluster sampling, and systematic sampling provide advantages over simple random sampling in some of these situations. In this section we briefly introduce these alternative sampling methods. A more in-depth treatment is provided in Chapter 22, which is located on the website that accompanies the text.

This section provides a brief introduction to survey sampling methods other than simple random sampling.

Stratified Random Sampling

Stratified random sampling works best when the variance among elements in each stratum is relatively small.

In **stratified random sampling**, the elements in the population are first divided into groups called *strata,* such that each element in the population belongs to one and only one stratum. The basis for forming the strata, such as department, location, age, industry type, and so on, is at the discretion of the designer of the sample. However, the best results are obtained when the elements within each stratum are as much alike as possible. Figure 7.12 is a diagram of a population divided into *H* strata.

After the strata are formed, a simple random sample is taken from each stratum. Formulas are available for combining the results for the individual stratum samples into one estimate of the population parameter of interest. The value of stratified random sampling depends on how homogeneous the elements are within the strata. If elements within strata are alike, the strata will have low variances. Thus relatively small sample sizes can be used to obtain good estimates of the strata characteristics. If strata are homogeneous, the stratified random sampling procedure provides results just as precise as those of simple random sampling by using a smaller total sample size.

Cluster Sampling

Cluster sampling works best when each cluster provides a small-scale representation of the population.

In **cluster sampling**, the elements in the population are first divided into separate groups called *clusters.* Each element of the population belongs to one and only one cluster (see Figure 7.13). A simple random sample of the clusters is then taken. All elements within each sampled cluster form the sample. Cluster sampling tends to provide the best results when the elements within the clusters are not alike. In the ideal case, each cluster is a representative small-scale version of the entire population. The value of cluster sampling depends on how representative each cluster is of the entire population. If all clusters are alike in this regard, sampling a small number of clusters will provide good estimates of the population parameters.

FIGURE 7.12   DIAGRAM FOR STRATIFIED RANDOM SAMPLING

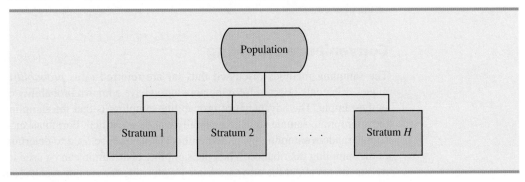

FIGURE 7.13   DIAGRAM FOR CLUSTER SAMPLING

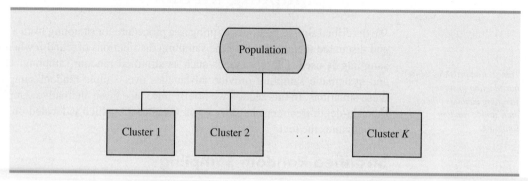

One of the primary applications of cluster sampling is area sampling, where clusters are city blocks or other well-defined areas. Cluster sampling generally requires a larger total sample size than either simple random sampling or stratified random sampling. However, it can result in cost savings because of the fact that when an interviewer is sent to a sampled cluster (e.g., a city-block location), many sample observations can be obtained in a relatively short time. Hence, a larger sample size may be obtainable with a significantly lower total cost.

Systematic Sampling

In some sampling situations, especially those with large populations, it is time-consuming to select a simple random sample by first finding a random number and then counting or searching through the list of the population until the corresponding element is found. An alternative to simple random sampling is **systematic sampling**. For example, if a sample size of 50 is desired from a population containing 5000 elements, we will sample one element for every 5000/50 = 100 elements in the population. A systematic sample for this case involves selecting randomly one of the first 100 elements from the population list. Other sample elements are identified by starting with the first sampled element and then selecting every 100th element that follows in the population list. In effect, the sample of 50 is identified by moving systematically through the population and identifying every 100th element after the first randomly selected element. The sample of 50 usually will be easier to identify in this way than it would be if simple random sampling were used. Because the first element selected is a random choice, a systematic sample is usually assumed to have the properties of a simple random sample. This assumption is especially applicable when the list of elements in the population is a random ordering of the elements.

Convenience Sampling

The sampling methods discussed thus far are referred to as *probability sampling* techniques. Elements selected from the population have a known probability of being included in the sample. The advantage of probability sampling is that the sampling distribution of the appropriate sample statistic generally can be identified. Formulas such as the ones for simple random sampling presented in this chapter can be used to determine the properties of the sampling distribution. Then the sampling distribution can be used to make probability statements about the error associated with using the sample results to make inferences about the population.

Convenience sampling is a *nonprobability sampling* technique. As the name implies, the sample is identified primarily by convenience. Elements are included in the sample without prespecified or known probabilities of being selected. For example, a professor conducting research at a university may use student volunteers to constitute a sample simply because they are readily available and will participate as subjects for little or no cost. Similarly, an inspector may sample a shipment of oranges by selecting oranges haphazardly from among several crates. Labeling each orange and using a probability method of sampling would be impractical. Samples such as wildlife captures and volunteer panels for consumer research are also convenience samples.

Convenience samples have the advantage of relatively easy sample selection and data collection; however, it is impossible to evaluate the "goodness" of the sample in terms of its representativeness of the population. A convenience sample may provide good results or it may not; no statistically justified procedure allows a probability analysis and inference about the quality of the sample results. Sometimes researchers apply statistical methods designed for probability samples to a convenience sample, arguing that the convenience sample can be treated as though it were a probability sample. However, this argument cannot be supported, and we should be cautious in interpreting the results of convenience samples that are used to make inferences about populations.

Judgment Sampling

One additional nonprobability sampling technique is **judgment sampling**. In this approach, the person most knowledgeable on the subject of the study selects elements of the population that he or she feels are most representative of the population. Often this method is a relatively easy way of selecting a sample. For example, a reporter may sample two or three senators, judging that those senators reflect the general opinion of all senators. However, the quality of the sample results depends on the judgment of the person selecting the sample. Again, great caution is warranted in drawing conclusions based on judgment samples used to make inferences about populations.

NOTES AND COMMENTS

We recommend using probability sampling methods when sampling from finite populations: simple random sampling, stratified random sampling, cluster sampling, or systematic sampling. For these methods, formulas are available for evaluating the "goodness" of the sample results in terms of the closeness of the results to the population parameters being estimated. An evaluation of the goodness cannot be made with convenience or judgment sampling. Thus, great care should be used in interpreting the results based on nonprobability sampling methods.

Summary

In this chapter we presented the concepts of sampling and sampling distributions. We demonstrated how a simple random sample can be selected from a finite population and how a random sample can be collected from an infinite population. The data collected from such samples can be used to develop point estimates of population parameters. Because different samples provide different values for the point estimators, point estimators such as $\bar{x}$ and $\bar{p}$ are random variables. The probability distribution of such a random variable is called a sampling distribution. In particular, we described the sampling distributions of the sample mean $\bar{x}$ and the sample proportion $\bar{p}$.

In considering the characteristics of the sampling distributions of $\bar{x}$ and $\bar{p}$, we stated that $E(\bar{x}) = \mu$ and $E(\bar{p}) = p$. Thus $\bar{x}$ and $\bar{p}$ are unbiased estimators. After developing the standard deviation or standard error formulas for these estimators, we described the conditions necessary for the sampling distributions of $\bar{x}$ and $\bar{p}$ to follow a normal distribution. Other sampling methods including stratified random sampling, cluster sampling, systematic sampling, convenience sampling, and judgment sampling were discussed.

Glossary

Central limit theorem A theorem that enables one to use the normal probability distribution to approximate the sampling distribution of $\bar{x}$ whenever the sample size is large.

Cluster sampling A probability sampling method in which the population is first divided into clusters and then a simple random sample of the clusters is taken.

Consistency A property of a point estimator that is present whenever larger sample sizes tend to provide point estimates closer to the population parameter.

Convenience sampling A nonprobability method of sampling whereby elements are selected for the sample on the basis of convenience.

Finite population correction factor The term $\sqrt{(N - n)/(N - 1)}$ that is used in the formulas for $\sigma_{\bar{x}}$ and $\sigma_{\bar{p}}$ whenever a finite population, rather than an infinite population, is being sampled. The generally accepted rule of thumb is to ignore the finite population correction factor whenever $n/N \leq .05$.

Frame A listing of the elements the sample will be selected from.

Judgment sampling A nonprobability method of sampling whereby elements are selected for the sample based on the judgment of the person doing the study.

Parameter A numerical characteristic of a population, such as a population mean μ, a population standard deviation σ, a population proportion p, and so on.

Point estimate The value of a point estimator used in a particular instance as an estimate of a population parameter.

Point estimator The sample statistic, such as $\bar{x}$, s, or $\bar{p}$, that provides the point estimate of the population parameter.

Random sample A random sample from an infinite population is a sample selected such that the following conditions are satisfied: (1) Each element selected comes from the same population; (2) each element is selected independently.

Relative efficiency Given two unbiased point estimators of the same population parameter, the point estimator with the smaller standard error is more efficient.

Sampling distribution A probability distribution consisting of all possible values of a sample statistic.

Sampled population The population from which the sample is taken.

Sample statistic A sample characteristic, such as a sample mean $\bar{x}$, a sample standard deviation s, a sample proportion $\bar{p}$, and so on. The value of the sample statistic is used to estimate the value of the corresponding population parameter.

Sampling without replacement Once an element has been included in the sample, it is removed from the population and cannot be selected a second time.

Sampling with replacement Once an element has been included in the sample, it is returned to the population. A previously selected element can be selected again and therefore may appear in the sample more than once.

Simple random sample A simple random sample of size n from a finite population of size N is a sample selected such that each possible sample of size n has the same probability of being selected.

Standard error The standard deviation of a point estimator.

Stratified random sampling A probability sampling method in which the population is first divided into strata and a simple random sample is then taken from each stratum.

Systematic sampling A probability sampling method in which we randomly select one of the first k elements and then select every kth element thereafter.

Target population The population for which statistical inferences such as point estimates are made. It is important for the target population to correspond as closely as possible to the sampled population.

Unbiased A property of a point estimator that is present when the expected value of the point estimator is equal to the population parameter it estimates.

Key Formulas

Expected Value of $\bar{x}$

$$E(\bar{x}) = \mu \qquad (7.1)$$

Standard Deviation of $\bar{x}$ (Standard Error)

Finite Population   *Infinite Population*

$$\sigma_{\bar{x}} = \sqrt{\frac{N-n}{N-1}}\left(\frac{\sigma}{\sqrt{n}}\right) \qquad \sigma_{\bar{x}} = \frac{\sigma}{\sqrt{n}} \qquad (7.2)$$

Expected Value of $\bar{p}$

$$E(\bar{p}) = p \qquad (7.4)$$

Standard Deviation of $\bar{p}$ (Standard Error)

Finite Population   *Infinite Population*

$$\sigma_{\bar{p}} = \sqrt{\frac{N-n}{N-1}}\sqrt{\frac{p(1-p)}{n}} \qquad \sigma_{\bar{p}} = \sqrt{\frac{p(1-p)}{n}} \qquad (7.5)$$

Supplementary Exercises

DATA *file*

ShadowStocks

42. Jack Lawler, a financial analyst, wants to prepare an article on the Shadow Stock portfolio developed by the American Association of Individual Investors (AAII). A list of the 30 companies in the Shadow Stock portfolio as of March 2014 is contained in the DATAfile named ShadowStocks (AAII website March 27, 2014). Jack would like to select a simple random sample of 5 of these companies for an interview concerning management practices.
    a. In the DATAfile the Shadow Stock companies are listed in column A of an Excel worksheet. In column B we have generated a random number for each of the companies. Use these random numbers to select a simple random sample of 5 of these companies for Jack.
    b. Generate a new set of random numbers and use them to select a new simple random sample. Did you select the same companies?

43. The latest available data showed health expenditures were $8086 per person in the United States or 17.6% of gross domestic product (Centers for Medicare & Medicaid Services website, April 1, 2012). Use $8086 as the population mean and suppose a survey research firm will take a sample of 100 people to investigate the nature of their health expenditures. Assume the population standard deviation is $2500.
    a. Show the sampling distribution of the mean amount of health care expenditures for a sample of 100 people.

b. What is the probability the sample mean will be within ±$200 of the population mean?

c. What is the probability the sample mean will be greater than $9000? If the survey research firm reports a sample mean greater than $9000, would you question whether the firm followed correct sampling procedures? Why or why not?

44. Foot Locker uses sales per square foot as a measure of store productivity. Sales are currently running at an annual rate of $406 per square foot (*The Wall Street Journal*, March 7, 2012). You have been asked by management to conduct a study of a sample of 64 Foot Locker stores. Assume the standard deviation in annual sales per square foot for the population of all 3400 Foot Locker stores is $80.

a. Show the sampling distribution of $\bar{x}$, the sample mean annual sales per square foot for a sample of 64 Foot Locker stores.

b. What is the probability that the sample mean will be within $15 of the population mean?

c. Suppose you find a sample mean of $380. What is the probability of finding a sample mean of $380 or less? Would you consider such a sample to be an unusually low-performing group of stores?

45. Allegiant Airlines charges a mean base fare of $89. In addition, the airline charges for making a reservation on its website, checking bags, and inflight beverages. These additional charges average $39 per passenger (*Bloomberg Businessweek*, October 8–14, 2012). Suppose a random sample of 60 passengers is taken to determine the total cost of their flight on Allegiant Airlines. The population standard deviation of total flight cost is known to be $40.

a. What is the population mean cost per flight?

b. What is the probability the sample mean will be within $10 of the population mean cost per flight?

c. What is the probability the sample mean will be within $5 of the population mean cost per flight?

46. After deducting grants based on need, the average cost to attend the University of Southern California (USC) is $27,175 (*U.S. News & World Report, America's Best Colleges*, 2009 ed.). Assume the population standard deviation is $7400. Suppose that a random sample of 60 USC students will be taken from this population.

a. What is the value of the standard error of the mean?

b. What is the probability that the sample mean will be more than $27,175?

c. What is the probability that the sample mean will be within $1000 of the population mean?

d. How would the probability in part (c) change if the sample size were increased to 100?

47. Three firms carry inventories that differ in size. Firm A's inventory contains 2000 items, firm B's inventory contains 5000 items, and firm C's inventory contains 10,000 items. The population standard deviation for the cost of the items in each firm's inventory is $\sigma = 144$. A statistical consultant recommends that each firm take a sample of 50 items from its inventory to provide statistically valid estimates of the average cost per item. Managers of the small firm state that because it has the smallest population, it should be able to make the estimate from a much smaller sample than that required by the larger firms. However, the consultant states that to obtain the same standard error and thus the same precision in the sample results, all firms should use the same sample size regardless of population size.

a. Using the finite population correction factor, compute the standard error for each of the three firms given a sample of size 50.

b. What is the probability that for each firm the sample mean $\bar{x}$ will be within ±25 of the population mean μ?

48. A researcher reports survey results by stating that the standard error of the mean is 20. The population standard deviation is 500.
    a. How large was the sample used in this survey?
    b. What is the probability that the point estimate was within ± 25 of the population mean?

49. A production process is checked periodically by a quality control inspector. The inspector selects simple random samples of 30 finished products and computes the sample mean product weights $\bar{x}$. If test results over a long period of time show that 5% of the $\bar{x}$ values are over 2.1 pounds and 5% are under 1.9 pounds, what are the mean and the standard deviation for the population of products produced with this process?

50. Fifteen percent of Australians smoke. By introducing tough laws banning brand labels on cigarette packages, Australia hopes to reduce the percentage of people smoking to 10% by 2018 (Reuters website, October 23, 2012). Answer the following questions based on a sample of 240 Australians.
    a. Show the sampling distribution of $\bar{p}$, the proportion of Australians who are smokers.
    b. What is the probability the sample proportion will be within $\pm .04$ of the population proportion?
    c. What is the probability the sample proportion will be within $\pm .02$ of the population proportion?

51. A market research firm conducts telephone surveys with a 40% historical response rate. What is the probability that in a new sample of 400 telephone numbers, at least 150 individuals will cooperate and respond to the questions? In other words, what is the probability that the sample proportion will be at least $150/400 = .375$?

52. Advertisers contract with Internet service providers and search engines to place ads on websites. They pay a fee based on the number of potential customers who click on their ad. Unfortunately, click fraud—the practice of someone clicking on an ad solely for the purpose of driving up advertising revenue—has become a problem. Forty percent of advertisers claim they have been a victim of click fraud (*Businessweek,* March 13, 2006). Suppose a simple random sample of 380 advertisers will be taken to learn more about how they are affected by this practice.
    a. What is the probability that the sample proportion will be within $\pm .04$ of the population proportion experiencing click fraud?
    b. What is the probability that the sample proportion will be greater than .45?

53. The proportion of individuals insured by the All-Driver Automobile Insurance Company who received at least one traffic ticket during a five-year period is .15.
    a. Show the sampling distribution of $\bar{p}$ if a random sample of 150 insured individuals is used to estimate the proportion having received at least one ticket.
    b. What is the probability that the sample proportion will be within $\pm .03$ of the population proportion?

54. Lori Jeffrey is a successful sales representative for a major publisher of college textbooks. Historically, Lori obtains a book adoption on 25% of her sales calls. Viewing her sales calls for one month as a sample of all possible sales calls, assume that a statistical analysis of the data yields a standard error of the proportion of .0625.
    a. How large was the sample used in this analysis? That is, how many sales calls did Lori make during the month?
    b. Let $\bar{p}$ indicate the sample proportion of book adoptions obtained during the month. Show the sampling distribution of $\bar{p}$.
    c. Using the sampling distribution of $\bar{p}$, compute the probability that Lori will obtain book adoptions on 30% or more of her sales calls during a one-month period.

Case Problem   Marion Dairies

Last year Marion Dairies decided to enter the yogurt market, and it began cautiously by producing, distributing, and marketing a single flavor—a blueberry-flavored yogurt that it calls Blugurt. The company's initial venture into the yogurt market has been very successful; sales of Blugurt are higher than expected, and consumers' ratings of the product have a mean of 80 and a standard deviation of 25 on a 100-point scale for which 100 is the most favorable score and zero is the least favorable score. Past experience has also shown Marion Dairies that a consumer who rates one of its products with a score greater than 75 on this scale will consider purchasing the product, and a score of 75 or less indicates that the consumer will not consider purchasing the product.

Emboldened by the success and popularity of its blueberry-flavored yogurt, Marion Dairies management is now considering the introduction of a second flavor. Marion's marketing department is pressing to extend the product line through the introduction of a strawberry-flavored yogurt that would be called Strawgurt, but senior managers are concerned about whether or not Strawgurt will increase Marion's market share by appealing to potential customers who do not like Blugurt. That is, the goal in offering the new product is to increase the market share rather than cannibalize existing sales of Blugurt. The marketing department has proposed giving tastes of both Blugurt and Strawgurt to a simple random sample of 50 customers and asking each of them to rate the two yogurts on the 100-point scale. If the mean score given to Blugurt by this sample of consumers is 75 or less, Marion's senior management believes the sample can be used to assess whether Strawgurt will appeal to potential customers who do not like Blugurt.

Managerial Report

Prepare a managerial report that addresses the following issues.

1. Calculate the probability that the mean score of Blugert given by the simple random sample of Marion Dairies customers will be 75 or less.

2. If the Marketing Department increases the sample size to 150, what is the probability that the mean score of Blugert given by the simple random sample of Marion Dairies customers will be 75 or less?

3. Explain to Marion Dairies senior management why the probability that the mean score of Blugert given by the simple random sample of Marion Dairies customers will be 75 or less differs for these two sample sizes.

Appendix 7.1   The Expected Value and Standard Deviation of $\bar{x}$

In this appendix we present the mathematical basis for the expressions for $E(\bar{x})$, the expected value of $\bar{x}$ as given by equation (7.1), and $\sigma_{\bar{x}}$, the standard deviation of $\bar{x}$ as given by equation (7.2).

Expected Value of $\bar{x}$

Assume a population with mean μ and variance σ^2. A simple random sample of size n is selected with individual observations denoted $x_1, x_2, \ldots, x_n$. A sample mean $\bar{x}$ is computed as follows.

$$\bar{x} = \frac{\Sigma x_i}{n}$$

With repeated simple random samples of size n, $\bar{x}$ is a random variable that assumes different numerical values depending on the specific n items selected. The expected value of the random variable $\bar{x}$ is the mean of all possible $\bar{x}$ values.

$$\text{Mean of } \bar{x} = E(\bar{x}) = E\left(\frac{\Sigma x_i}{n}\right)$$

$$= \frac{1}{n}[E(x_1 + x_2 + \cdots + x_n)]$$

$$= \frac{1}{n}[E(x_1) + E(x_2) + \cdots + E(x_n)]$$

For any x_i we have $E(x_i) = \mu$; therefore we can write

$$E(\bar{x}) = \frac{1}{n}(\mu + \mu + \cdots + \mu)$$

$$= \frac{1}{n}(n\mu) = \mu$$

This result shows that the mean of all possible $\bar{x}$ values is the same as the population mean μ. That is, $E(\bar{x}) = \mu$.

Standard Deviation of $\bar{x}$

Again assume a population with mean μ, variance σ^2, and a sample mean given by

$$\bar{x} = \frac{\Sigma x_i}{n}$$

With repeated simple random samples of size n, we know that $\bar{x}$ is a random variable that takes different numerical values depending on the specific n items selected. What follows is the derivation of the expression for the standard deviation of the $\bar{x}$ values, $\sigma_{\bar{x}}$, for the case of an infinite population. The derivation of the expression for $\sigma_{\bar{x}}$ for a finite population when sampling is done without replacement is more difficult and is beyond the scope of this text.

Returning to the infinite population case, recall that a simple random sample from an infinite population consists of observations $x_1, x_2, \ldots, x_n$ that are independent. The following two expressions are general formulas for the variance of random variables.

$$Var(ax) = a^2\, Var(x)$$

where a is a constant and x is a random variable, and

$$Var(x + y) = Var(x) + Var(y)$$

where x and y are *independent* random variables. Using the two preceding equations, we can develop the expression for the variance of the random variable $\bar{x}$ as follows.

$$Var(\bar{x}) = Var\left(\frac{\Sigma x_i}{n}\right) = Var\left(\frac{1}{n}\Sigma x_i\right)$$

Then, with $1/n$ a constant, we have

$$Var(\bar{x}) = \left(\frac{1}{n}\right)^2 Var(\Sigma x_i)$$

$$= \left(\frac{1}{n}\right)^2 Var(x_1 + x_2 + \cdots + x_n)$$

In the infinite population case, the random variables $x_1, x_2, \ldots, x_n$ are independent, which enables us to write

$$Var(\bar{x}) = \left(\frac{1}{n}\right)^2 [Var(x_1) + Var(x_2) + \cdots + Var(x_n)]$$

For any x_i, we have $Var(x_i) = \sigma^2$; therefore we have

$$Var(\bar{x}) = \left(\frac{1}{n}\right)^2 (\sigma^2 + \sigma^2 + \cdots + \sigma^2)$$

With n values of σ^2 in this expression, we have

$$Var(\bar{x}) = \left(\frac{1}{n}\right)^2 (n\sigma^2) = \frac{\sigma^2}{n}$$

Taking the square root provides the formula for the standard deviation of $\bar{x}$.

$$\sigma_{\bar{x}} = \sqrt{Var(\bar{x})} = \frac{\sigma}{\sqrt{n}}$$

Appendix 7.2   Random Sampling with Minitab

If a list of the elements in a population is available in a Minitab file, Minitab can be used to select a simple random sample. For example, a list of the top 100 metropolitan areas in the United States and Canada is provided in column 1 of the data set MetAreas (*Places Rated Almanac—The Millennium Edition 2000*). Column 2 contains the overall rating of each metropolitan area. The first 10 metropolitan areas in the data set and their corresponding ratings are shown in Table 7.6.

Suppose that you would like to select a simple random sample of 30 metropolitan areas in order to do an in-depth study of the cost of living in the United States and Canada. The following steps can be used to select the sample.

Step 1. Select the **Calc** pull-down menu
Step 2. Choose **Random Data**
Step 3. Choose **Sample From Columns**

TABLE 7.6   OVERALL RATING FOR THE FIRST 10 METROPOLITAN AREAS
IN THE DATA SET METAREAS

DATA *file*

MetAreas

Metropolitan Area	Rating
Albany, NY	64.18
Albuquerque, NM	66.16
Appleton, WI	60.56
Atlanta, GA	69.97
Austin, TX	71.48
Baltimore, MD	69.75
Birmingham, AL	69.59
Boise City, ID	68.36
Boston, MA	68.99
Buffalo, NY	66.10

Step 4. When the Sample From Columns dialog box appears:

Enter 30 in the **Number of rows to sample** box

Enter C1 C2 in the **From columns** box below

Enter C3 C4 in the **Store samples in** box

Step 5. Click **OK**

The random sample of 30 metropolitan areas appears in columns C3 and C4.

Appendix 7.3   Random Sampling with Excel

If a list of the elements in a population is available in an Excel file, Excel can be used to select a simple random sample. For example, a list of the top 100 metropolitan areas in the United States and Canada is provided in column A of the data set MetAreas (*Places Rated Almanac—The Millennium Edition 2000*). Column B contains the overall rating of each metropolitan area. The first 10 metropolitan areas in the data set and their corresponding ratings are shown in Table 7.6. Assume that you would like to select a simple random sample of 30 metropolitan areas in order to do an in-depth study of the cost of living in the United States and Canada.

The rows of any Excel data set can be placed in a random order by adding an extra column to the data set and filling the column with random numbers using the =RAND() function. Then, using Excel's sort ascending capability on the random number column, the rows of the data set will be reordered randomly. The random sample of size *n* appears in the first *n* rows of the reordered data set.

In the MetAreas data set, labels are in row 1 and the 100 metropolitan areas are in rows 2 to 101. The following steps can be used to select a simple random sample of 30 metropolitan areas.

Step 1. Enter =RAND() in cell C2

Step 2. Copy cell C2 to cells C3:C101

Step 3. Select any cell in Column C

Step 4. Click the **Home** tab on the Ribbon

Step 5. In the **Editing** group, click **Sort & Filter**

Step 6. Click **Sort Smallest to Largest**

The random sample of 30 metropolitan areas appears in rows 2 to 31 of the reordered data set. The random numbers in column C are no longer necessary and can be deleted if desired.

CHAPTER 8

Interval Estimation

CONTENTS

STATISTICS *in* PRACTICE

FOOD LION*
SALISBURY, NORTH CAROLINA

Founded in 1957 as Food Town, Food Lion is one of the largest supermarket chains in the United States, with 1300 stores in 11 Southeastern and Mid-Atlantic states. The company sells more than 24,000 different products and offers nationally and regionally advertised brand-name merchandise, as well as a growing number of high-quality private label products manufactured especially for Food Lion. The company maintains its low price leadership and quality assurance through operating efficiencies such as standard store formats, innovative warehouse design, energy-efficient facilities, and data synchronization with suppliers. Food Lion looks to a future of continued innovation, growth, price leadership, and service to its customers.

Being in an inventory-intense business, Food Lion made the decision to adopt the LIFO (last-in, first-out) method of inventory valuation. This method matches current costs against current revenues, which minimizes the effect of radical price changes on profit and loss results. In addition, the LIFO method reduces net income thereby reducing income taxes during periods of inflation.

Food Lion establishes a LIFO index for each of seven inventory pools: Grocery, Paper/Household, Pet Supplies, Health & Beauty Aids, Dairy, Cigarette/Tobacco, and Beer/Wine. For example, a LIFO index of 1.008 for the Grocery pool would indicate that the company's grocery inventory value at current costs reflects a .8% increase due to inflation over the most recent one-year period.

A LIFO index for each inventory pool requires that the year-end inventory count for each product be valued

Davis Turner/Bloomberg/Getty Images

As an inventory-intense business, Food Lion adopted the LIFO method of inventory valuation.

at the current year-end cost and at the preceding year-end cost. To avoid excessive time and expense associated with counting the inventory in all 1200 store locations, Food Lion selects a random sample of 50 stores. Year-end physical inventories are taken in each of the sample stores. The current-year and preceding-year costs for each item are then used to construct the required LIFO indexes for each inventory pool.

For a recent year, the sample estimate of the LIFO index for the Health & Beauty Aids inventory pool was 1.015. Using a 95% confidence level, Food Lion computed a margin of error of .006 for the sample estimate. Thus, the interval from 1.009 to 1.021 provided a 95% confidence interval estimate of the population LIFO index. This level of precision was judged to be very good.

In this chapter you will learn how to compute the margin of error associated with sample estimates. You will also learn how to use this information to construct and interpret interval estimates of a population mean and a population proportion.

*The authors are indebted to Keith Cunningham, Tax Director, and Bobby Harkey, Staff Tax Accountant, at Food Lion for providing this Statistics in Practice.

In Chapter 7, we stated that a point estimator is a sample statistic used to estimate a population parameter. For instance, the sample mean $\bar{x}$ is a point estimator of the population mean μ and the sample proportion $\bar{p}$ is a point estimator of the population proportion p. Because a point estimator cannot be expected to provide the exact value of the population parameter, an **interval estimate** is often computed by adding and subtracting a value, called the **margin of error**, to the point estimate. The general form of an interval estimate is as follows:

$$\text{Point estimate} \pm \text{Margin of error}$$

The purpose of an interval estimate is to provide information about how close the point estimate, provided by the sample, is to the value of the population parameter.

In this chapter we show how to compute interval estimates of a population mean μ and a population proportion p. The general form of an interval estimate of a population mean is

$$\bar{x} \pm \text{Margin of error}$$

Similarly, the general form of an interval estimate of a population proportion is

$$\bar{p} \pm \text{Margin of error}$$

The sampling distributions of $\bar{x}$ and $\bar{p}$ play key roles in computing these interval estimates.

8.1 Population Mean: σ Known

In order to develop an interval estimate of a population mean, either the population standard deviation σ or the sample standard deviation s must be used to compute the margin of error. In most applications σ is not known, and s is used to compute the margin of error. In some applications, large amounts of relevant historical data are available and can be used to estimate the population standard deviation prior to sampling. Also, in quality control applications where a process is assumed to be operating correctly, or "in control," it is appropriate to treat the population standard deviation as known. We refer to such cases as the **σ known** case. In this section we introduce an example in which it is reasonable to treat σ as known and show how to construct an interval estimate for this case.

Each week Lloyd's Department Store selects a simple random sample of 100 customers in order to learn about the amount spent per shopping trip. With x representing the amount spent per shopping trip, the sample mean $\bar{x}$ provides a point estimate of μ, the mean amount spent per shopping trip for the population of all Lloyd's customers. Lloyd's has been using the weekly survey for several years. Based on the historical data, Lloyd's now assumes a known value of $\sigma = \$20$ for the population standard deviation. The historical data also indicate that the population follows a normal distribution.

DATA *file*
Lloyd's

During the most recent week, Lloyd's surveyed 100 customers ($n = 100$) and obtained a sample mean of $\bar{x} = \$82$. The sample mean amount spent provides a point estimate of the population mean amount spent per shopping trip, μ. In the discussion that follows, we show how to compute the margin of error for this estimate and develop an interval estimate of the population mean.

Margin of Error and the Interval Estimate

In Chapter 7 we showed that the sampling distribution of $\bar{x}$ can be used to compute the probability that $\bar{x}$ will be within a given distance of μ. In the Lloyd's example, the his-torical data show that the population of amounts spent is normally distributed with a standard deviation of $\sigma = 20$. So, using what we learned in Chapter 7, we can conclude that the sampling distribution of $\bar{x}$ follows a normal distribution with a standard error of $\sigma_{\bar{x}} = \sigma/\sqrt{n} = 20/\sqrt{100} = 2$. This sampling distribution is shown in Figure 8.1.[1] Because the sampling distribution shows how values of $\bar{x}$ are distributed around the population mean μ, the sampling distribution of $\bar{x}$ provides information about the possible differences between $\bar{x}$ and μ.

---

[1] We use the fact that the population of amounts spent has a normal distribution to conclude that the sampling distribution of $\bar{x}$ has a normal distribution. If the population did not have a normal distribution, we could rely on the central limit theorem and the sample size of $n = 100$ to conclude that the sampling distribution of $\bar{x}$ is approximately normal. In either case, the sampling distribution of $\bar{x}$ would appear as shown in Figure 8.1.

FIGURE 8.1   SAMPLING DISTRIBUTION OF THE SAMPLE MEAN AMOUNT SPENT
FROM SIMPLE RANDOM SAMPLES OF 100 CUSTOMERS

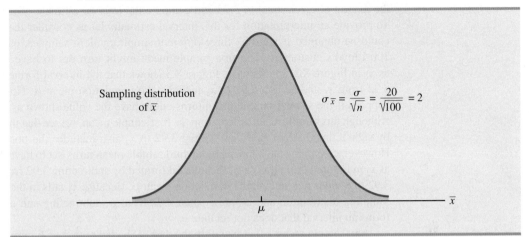

Using the standard normal probability table, we find that 95% of the values of any normally distributed random variable are within ± 1.96 standard deviations of the mean. Thus, when the sampling distribution of $\bar{x}$ is normally distributed, 95% of the $\bar{x}$ values must be within $\pm 1.96\sigma_{\bar{x}}$ of the mean μ. In the Lloyd's example we know that the sampling distribution of $\bar{x}$ is normally distributed with a standard error of $\sigma_{\bar{x}} = 2$. Because $\pm 1.96\sigma_{\bar{x}} = 1.96(2) = 3.92$, we can conclude that 95% of all $\bar{x}$ values obtained using a sample size of $n = 100$ will be within ± 3.92 of the population mean μ. See Figure 8.2.

FIGURE 8.2   SAMPLING DISTRIBUTION OF $\bar{x}$ SHOWING THE LOCATION OF SAMPLE
MEANS THAT ARE WITHIN 3.92 OF μ

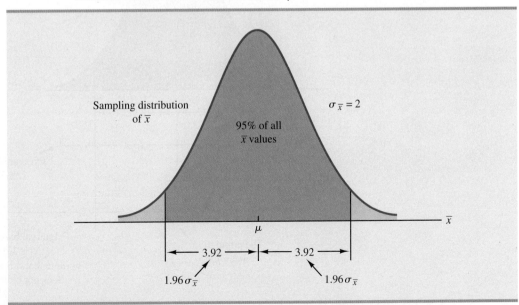

In the introduction to this chapter we said that the general form of an interval estimate of the population mean μ is $\bar{x} \pm$ margin of error. For the Lloyd's example, suppose we set the margin of error equal to 3.92 and compute the interval estimate of μ using $\bar{x} \pm 3.92$. To provide an interpretation for this interval estimate, let us consider the values of $\bar{x}$ that could be obtained if we took three *different* simple random samples, each consisting of 100 Lloyd's customers. The first sample mean might turn out to have the value shown as $\bar{x}_1$ in Figure 8.3. In this case, Figure 8.3 shows that the interval formed by subtracting 3.92 from $\bar{x}_1$ and adding 3.92 to $\bar{x}_1$ includes the population mean μ. Now consider what happens if the second sample mean turns out to have the value shown as $\bar{x}_2$ in Figure 8.3. Although this sample mean differs from the first sample mean, we see that the interval formed by subtracting 3.92 from $\bar{x}_2$ and adding 3.92 to $\bar{x}_2$ also includes the population mean μ. However, consider what happens if the third sample mean turns out to have the value shown as $\bar{x}_3$ in Figure 8.3. In this case, the interval formed by subtracting 3.92 from $\bar{x}_3$ and adding 3.92 to $\bar{x}_3$ does not include the population mean μ. Because $\bar{x}_3$ falls in the upper tail of the sampling distribution and is farther than 3.92 from μ, subtracting and adding 3.92 to $\bar{x}_3$ forms an interval that does not include μ.

Any sample mean $\bar{x}$ that is within the darkly shaded region of Figure 8.3 will provide an interval that contains the population mean μ. Because 95% of all possible sample means are in the darkly shaded region, 95% of all intervals formed by subtracting 3.92 from $\bar{x}$ and adding 3.92 to $\bar{x}$ will include the population mean μ.

FIGURE 8.3   INTERVALS FORMED FROM SELECTED SAMPLE MEANS AT LOCATIONS $\bar{x}_1$, $\bar{x}_2$, AND $\bar{x}_3$

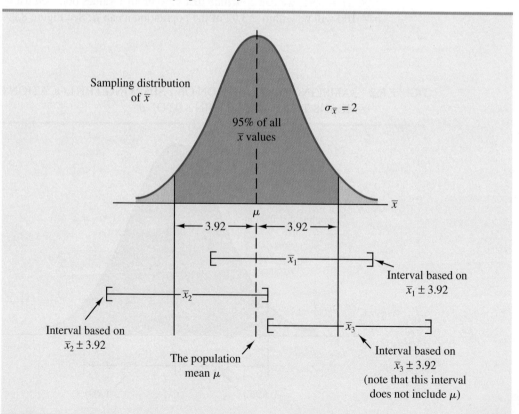

Recall that during the most recent week, the quality assurance team at Lloyd's surveyed 100 customers and obtained a sample mean amount spent of $\bar{x} = 82$. Using $\bar{x} \pm 3.92$ to construct the interval estimate, we obtain 82 ± 3.92. Thus, the specific interval estimate of μ based on the data from the most recent week is $82 - 3.92 = 78.08$ to $82 + 3.92 = 85.92$. Because 95% of all the intervals constructed using $\bar{x} \pm 3.92$ will contain the population mean, we say that we are 95% confident that the interval 78.08 to 85.92 includes the population mean μ. We say that this interval has been established at the 95% **confidence level**. The value .95 is referred to as the **confidence coefficient**, and the interval 78.08 to 85.92 is called the 95% **confidence interval**.

This discussion provides insight as to why the interval is called a 95% confidence interval.

With the margin of error given by $z_{\alpha/2}(\sigma/\sqrt{n})$, the general form of an interval estimate of a population mean for the σ known case follows.

INTERVAL ESTIMATE OF A POPULATION MEAN: σ KNOWN

$$\bar{x} \pm z_{\alpha/2}\frac{\sigma}{\sqrt{n}} \qquad (8.1)$$

where $(1 - \alpha)$ is the confidence coefficient and $z_{\alpha/2}$ is the z value providing an area of $\alpha/2$ in the upper tail of the standard normal probability distribution.

Let us use expression (8.1) to construct a 95% confidence interval for the Lloyd's example. For a 95% confidence interval, the confidence coefficient is $(1 - \alpha) = .95$ and thus, $\alpha = .05$. Using the standard normal probability table, an area of $\alpha/2 = .05/2 = .025$ in the upper tail provides $z_{.025} = 1.96$. With the Lloyd's sample mean $\bar{x} = 82$, $\sigma = 20$, and a sample size $n = 100$, we obtain

$$82 \pm 1.96\frac{20}{\sqrt{100}}$$

$$82 \pm 3.92$$

Thus, using expression (8.1), the margin of error is 3.92 and the 95% confidence interval is $82 - 3.92 = 78.08$ to $82 + 3.92 = 85.92$.

Although a 95% confidence level is frequently used, other confidence levels such as 90% and 99% may be considered. Values of $z_{\alpha/2}$ for the most commonly used confidence levels are shown in Table 8.1. Using these values and expression (8.1), the 90% confidence interval for the Lloyd's example is

$$82 \pm 1.645\frac{20}{\sqrt{100}}$$

$$82 \pm 3.29$$

TABLE 8.1   VALUES OF $Z_{\alpha/2}$ FOR THE MOST COMMONLY USED CONFIDENCE LEVELS

Confidence Level	α	$\alpha/2$	$z_{\alpha/2}$
90%	.10	.05	1.645
95%	.05	.025	1.960
99%	.01	.005	2.576

Thus, at 90% confidence, the margin of error is 3.29 and the confidence interval is $82 - 3.29 = 78.71$ to $82 + 3.29 = 85.29$. Similarly, the 99% confidence interval is

$$82 \pm 2.576 \frac{20}{\sqrt{100}}$$

$$82 \pm 5.15$$

Thus, at 99% confidence, the margin of error is 5.15 and the confidence interval is $82 - 5.15 = 76.85$ to $82 + 5.15 = 87.15$.

Comparing the results for the 90%, 95%, and 99% confidence levels, we see that in order to have a higher degree of confidence, the margin of error and thus the width of the confidence interval must be larger.

Practical Advice

If the population follows a normal distribution, the confidence interval provided by expression (8.1) is exact. In other words, if expression (8.1) were used repeatedly to generate 95% confidence intervals, exactly 95% of the intervals generated would contain the population mean. If the population does not follow a normal distribution, the confidence interval provided by expression (8.1) will be approximate. In this case, the quality of the approximation depends on both the distribution of the population and the sample size.

In most applications, a sample size of $n \geq 30$ is adequate when using expression (8.1) to develop an interval estimate of a population mean. If the population is not normally distributed but is roughly symmetric, sample sizes as small as 15 can be expected to provide good approximate confidence intervals. With smaller sample sizes, expression (8.1) should only be used if the analyst believes, or is willing to assume, that the population distribution is at least approximately normal.

NOTES AND COMMENTS

1. The interval estimation procedure discussed in this section is based on the assumption that the population standard deviation σ is known. By σ known we mean that historical data or other information are available that permit us to obtain a good estimate of the population standard deviation prior to taking the sample that will be used to develop an estimate of the population mean. So technically we don't mean that σ is actually known with certainty. We just mean that we obtained a good estimate of the standard deviation prior to sampling and thus we won't be using the same sample to estimate both the population mean and the population standard deviation.

2. The sample size n appears in the denominator of the interval estimation expression (8.1). Thus, if a particular sample size provides too wide an interval to be of any practical use, we may want to consider increasing the sample size. With n in the denominator, a larger sample size will provide a smaller margin of error, a narrower interval, and greater precision. The procedure for determining the size of a simple random sample necessary to obtain a desired precision is discussed in Section 8.3.

Exercises

Methods

1. A simple random sample of 40 items resulted in a sample mean of 25. The population standard deviation is $\sigma = 5$.
   a. What is the standard error of the mean, $\sigma_{\bar{x}}$?
   b. At 95% confidence, what is the margin of error?

SELF*test*

2. A simple random sample of 50 items from a population with $\sigma = 6$ resulted in a sample mean of 32.
   a. Provide a 90% confidence interval for the population mean.
   b. Provide a 95% confidence interval for the population mean.
   c. Provide a 99% confidence interval for the population mean.

3. A simple random sample of 60 items resulted in a sample mean of 80. The population standard deviation is $\sigma = 15$.
   a. Compute the 95% confidence interval for the population mean.
   b. Assume that the same sample mean was obtained from a sample of 120 items. Provide a 95% confidence interval for the population mean.
   c. What is the effect of a larger sample size on the interval estimate?

4. A 95% confidence interval for a population mean was reported to be 152 to 160. If $\sigma = 15$, what sample size was used in this study?

SELF*test*

Applications

DATA *file*

Houston

5. Data were collected on the amount spent by 64 customers for lunch at a major Houston restaurant. These data are contained in the file named Houston. Based upon past studies the population standard deviation is known with $\sigma = \$6$.
   a. At 99% confidence, what is the margin of error?
   b. Develop a 99% confidence interval estimate of the mean amount spent for lunch.

DATA *file*

TravelTax

6. In an attempt to assess total daily travel taxes in various cities, the Global Business Travel Association conducted a study of daily travel taxes on lodging, rental car, and meals (GBTA Foundation website, October 30, 2012). The data contained in the DATAfile named TravelTax are consistent with the findings of that study for business travel to Chicago. Assume the population standard deviation is known to be $8.50 and develop a 95% confidence interval of the population mean total daily travel taxes for Chicago.

DATA *file*

Setters

7. The average annual cost of the first year of owning and caring for a large dog is $1843 (*US News and World Report*, September 9, 2013). The Irish Red and White Setter Association of America has requested a study to estimate the annual first-year cost for owners of this breed. A sample of 50 will be used. Based on past studies, the population standard deviation is assumed known with $\sigma = \$255$.
   a. What is the margin of error for a 95% confidence interval of the mean cost of the first year of owning and caring for this breed?
   b. The DATAfile Setters contains data collected from fifty owners of Irish Setters on the cost of the first year of owning and caring for their dogs. Use these data data set to compute the sample mean. Using this sample, what is the 95% confidence interval for the mean cost of the first year of owning and caring for an Irish Red and White Setter?

8. Studies show that massage therapy has a variety of health benefits and it is not too expensive (*The Wall Street Journal*, March 13, 2012). A sample of 10 typical one-hour massage therapy sessions showed an average charge of $59. The population standard deviation for a one-hour session is $\sigma = \$5.50$.
   a. What assumptions about the population should we be willing to make if a margin of error is desired?
   b. Using 95% confidence, what is the margin of error?
   c. Using 99% confidence, what is the margin of error?

DATA *file*

TobaccoFires

9. The mean cost to repair the smoke and fire damage that results from home fires of all causes is $11,389 (HomeAdvisor website, December 2014). How does the damage that results from home fires caused by careless use of tobacco compare? The DATAfile named TobaccoFires provides the cost to repair smoke and fire damage associated with a sample of 55 fires caused by careless use of tobacco products. Using past years' data, the population standard deviation can be assumed known with $\sigma = \$3027$. What is the 95% confidence interval estimate of the mean cost to repair smoke and fire damage that results from

home fires caused by careless use of tobacco? How does this compare with the mean cost to repair the smoke and fire damage that results from home fires of all causes?

10. Costs are rising for all kinds of medical care. The mean monthly rent at assisted-living facilities was reported to have increased 17% over the last five years to $3486 (*The Wall Street Journal*, October 27, 2012). Assume this cost estimate is based on a sample of 120 facilities and, from past studies, it can be assumed that the population standard deviation is $\sigma = \$650$.

    a. Develop a 90% confidence interval estimate of the population mean monthly rent.

    b. Develop a 95% confidence interval estimate of the population mean monthly rent.

    c. Develop a 99% confidence interval estimate of the population mean monthly rent.

    d. What happens to the width of the confidence interval as the confidence level is increased? Does this seem reasonable? Explain.

(8.2) Population Mean: σ Unknown

When developing an interval estimate of a population mean we usually do not have a good estimate of the population standard deviation either. In these cases, we must use the same sample to estimate both μ and σ. This situation represents the σ **unknown** case. When s is used to estimate σ, the margin of error and the interval estimate for the population mean are based on a probability distribution known as the *t* **distribution**. Although the mathematical development of the *t* distribution is based on the assumption of a normal distribution for the population we are sampling from, research shows that the *t* distribution can be successfully applied in many situations where the population deviates significantly from normal. Later in this section we provide guidelines for using the *t* distribution if the population is not normally distributed.

William Sealy Gosset, writing under the name "Student," is the founder of the t distribution. Gosset, an Oxford graduate in mathematics, worked for the Guinness Brewery in Dublin, Ireland. He developed the t distribution while working on small-scale materials and temperature experiments.

The *t* distribution is a family of similar probability distributions, with a specific *t* distribution depending on a parameter known as the **degrees of freedom**. The *t* distribution with one degree of freedom is unique, as is the *t* distribution with two degrees of freedom, with three degrees of freedom, and so on. As the number of degrees of freedom increases, the difference between the *t* distribution and the standard normal distribution becomes smaller and smaller. Figure 8.4 shows *t* distributions with 10 and 20 degrees of freedom and their

FIGURE 8.4   COMPARISON OF THE STANDARD NORMAL DISTRIBUTION WITH *t* DISTRIBUTIONS HAVING 10 AND 20 DEGREES OF FREEDOM

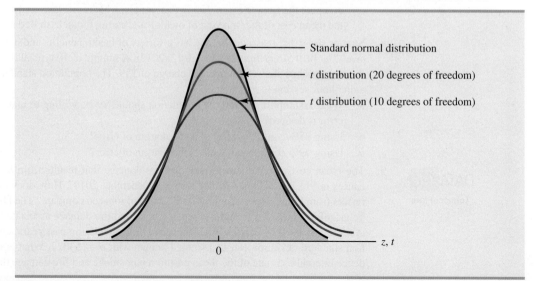

relationship to the standard normal probability distribution. Note that a t distribution with more degrees of freedom exhibits less variability and more closely resembles the standard normal distribution. Note also that the mean of the t distribution is zero.

We place a subscript on t to indicate the area in the upper tail of the t distribution. For example, just as we used $z_{.025}$ to indicate the z value providing a .025 area in the upper tail of a standard normal distribution, we will use $t_{.025}$ to indicate a .025 area in the upper tail of a t distribution. In general, we will use the notation $t_{\alpha/2}$ to represent a t value with an area of $\alpha/2$ in the upper tail of the t distribution. See Figure 8.5.

As the degrees of freedom increase, the t distribution approaches the standard normal distribution.

Table 2 in Appendix B contains a table for the t distribution. A portion of this table is shown in Table 8.2. Each row in the table corresponds to a separate t distribution with the degrees of freedom shown. For example, for a t distribution with 9 degrees of freedom, $t_{.025} = 2.262$. Similarly, for a t distribution with 60 degrees of freedom, $t_{.025} = 2.000$. As the degrees of freedom continue to increase, $t_{.025}$ approaches $z_{.025} = 1.96$. In fact, the standard normal distribution z values can be found in the infinite degrees of freedom row (labeled ∞) of the t distribution table. If the degrees of freedom exceed 100, the infinite degrees of freedom row can be used to approximate the actual t value; in other words, for more than 100 degrees of freedom, the standard normal z value provides a good approximation to the t value.

Margin of Error and the Interval Estimate

In Section 8.1 we showed that an interval estimate of a population mean for the σ known case is

$$\bar{x} \pm z_{\alpha/2} \frac{\sigma}{\sqrt{n}}$$

To compute an interval estimate of μ for the σ unknown case, the sample standard deviation s is used to estimate σ, and $z_{\alpha/2}$ is replaced by the t distribution value $t_{\alpha/2}$. The margin

FIGURE 8.5　t DISTRIBUTION WITH $\alpha/2$ AREA OR PROBABILITY IN THE UPPER TAIL

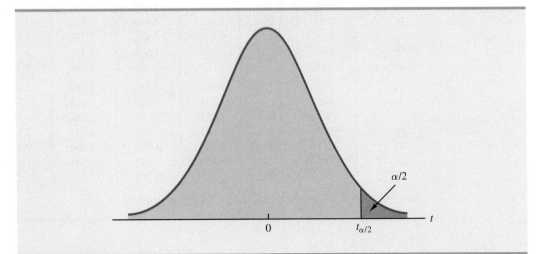

TABLE 8.2 SELECTED VALUES FROM THE T DISTRIBUTION TABLE*

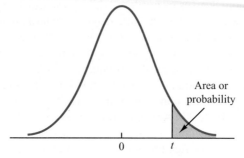

Degrees of Freedom	Area in Upper Tail						
	.20	.10	.05	.025	.01	.05	.005
1	1.376	3.078	6.314	12.706	31.821	31.821	63.656
2	1.061	1.886	2.920	4.303	6.965	6.965	9.925
3	.978	1.638	2.353	3.182	4.541	4.541	5.841
4	.941	1.533	2.132	2.776	3.747	3.747	4.604
5	.920	1.476	2.015	2.571	3.365	3.365	4.032
6	.906	1.440	1.943	2.447	3.143	3.143	3.707
7	.896	1.415	1.895	2.365	2.998	2.998	3.499
8	.889	1.397	1.860	2.306	2.896	2.896	3.355
9	.883	1.383	1.833	2.262	2.821	2.821	3.250
⋮	⋮	⋮	⋮	⋮	⋮	⋮	⋮
60	.848	1.296	1.671	2.000	2.390	2.390	2.660
61	.848	1.296	1.670	2.000	2.389	2.389	2.659
62	.847	1.295	1.670	1.999	2.388	2.388	2.657
63	.847	1.295	1.669	1.998	2.387	2.387	2.656
64	.847	1.295	1.669	1.998	2.386	2.386	2.655
65	.847	1.295	1.669	1.997	2.385	2.385	2.654
66	.847	1.295	1.668	1.997	2.384	2.384	2.652
67	.847	1.294	1.668	1.996	2.383	2.383	2.651
68	.847	1.294	1.668	1.995	2.382	2.382	2.650
69	.847	1.294	1.667	1.995	2.382	2.382	2.649
⋮	⋮	⋮	⋮	⋮	⋮	⋮	⋮
90	.846	1.291	1.662	1.987	2.368	2.368	2.632
91	.846	1.291	1.662	1.986	2.368	2.368	2.631
92	.846	1.291	1.662	1.986	2.368	2.368	2.630
93	.846	1.291	1.661	1.986	2.367	2.367	2.630
94	.845	1.291	1.661	1.986	2.367	2.367	2.629
95	.845	1.291	1.661	1.985	2.366	2.366	2.629
96	.845	1.290	1.661	1.985	2.366	2.366	2.628
97	.845	1.290	1.661	1.985	2.365	2.365	2.627
98	.845	1.290	1.661	1.984	2.365	2.365	2.627
99	.845	1.290	1.660	1.984	2.364	2.364	2.626
100	.845	1.290	1.660	1.984	2.364	2.364	2.626
∞	.842	1.282	1.645	1.960	2.326	2.326	2.576

*Note: A more extensive table is provided as Table 2 of Appendix B.

of error is then given by $t_{\alpha/2}s/\sqrt{n}$. With this margin of error, the general expression for an interval estimate of a population mean when σ is unknown follows.

INTERVAL ESTIMATE OF A POPULATION MEAN: σ UNKNOWN

$$\bar{x} \pm t_{\alpha/2}\frac{s}{\sqrt{n}} \tag{8.2}$$

where s is the sample standard deviation, $(1 - \alpha)$ is the confidence coefficient, and $t_{\alpha/2}$ is the t value providing an area of $\alpha/2$ in the upper tail of the t distribution with $n - 1$ degrees of freedom.

The reason the number of degrees of freedom associated with the t value in expression (8.2) is $n - 1$ concerns the use of s as an estimate of the population standard deviation σ. The expression for the sample standard deviation is

$$s = \sqrt{\frac{\Sigma(x_i - \bar{x})^2}{n - 1}}$$

Degrees of freedom refer to the number of independent pieces of information that go into the computation of $\Sigma(x_i - \bar{x})^2$. The n pieces of information involved in computing $\Sigma(x_i - \bar{x})^2$ are as follows: $x_1 - \bar{x}, x_2 - \bar{x}, \ldots, x_n - \bar{x}$. In Section 3.2 we indicated that $\Sigma(x_i - \bar{x}) = 0$ for any data set. Thus, only $n - 1$ of the $x_i - \bar{x}$ values are independent; that is, if we know $n - 1$ of the values, the remaining value can be determined exactly by using the condition that the sum of the $x_i - \bar{x}$ values must be 0. Thus, $n - 1$ is the number of degrees of freedom associated with $\Sigma(x_i - \bar{x})^2$ and hence the number of degrees of freedom for the t distribution in expression (8.2).

To illustrate the interval estimation procedure for the σ unknown case, we will consider a study designed to estimate the mean credit card debt for the population of U.S. households. A sample of $n = 70$ households provided the credit card balances shown in Table 8.3. For this situation, no previous estimate of the population standard deviation σ is available. Thus, the sample data must be used to estimate both the population mean and the population standard deviation. Using the data in Table 8.3, we compute the sample

TABLE 8.3 CREDIT CARD BALANCES FOR A SAMPLE OF 70 HOUSEHOLDS

DATA *file*

NewBalance

9430	14661	7159	9071	9691	11032
7535	12195	8137	3603	11448	6525
4078	10544	9467	16804	8279	5239
5604	13659	12595	13479	5649	6195
5179	7061	7917	14044	11298	12584
4416	6245	11346	6817	4353	15415
10676	13021	12806	6845	3467	15917
1627	9719	4972	10493	6191	12591
10112	2200	11356	615	12851	9743
6567	10746	7117	13627	5337	10324
13627	12744	9465	12557	8372	
18719	5742	19263	6232	7445	

mean $\bar{x} = \$9312$ and the sample standard deviation $s = \$4007$. With 95% confidence and $n - 1 = 69$ degrees of freedom, Table 8.2 can be used to obtain the appropriate value for $t_{.025}$. We want the t value in the row with 69 degrees of freedom, and the column corresponding to .025 in the upper tail. The value shown is $t_{.025} = 1.995$.

We use expression (8.2) to compute an interval estimate of the population mean credit card balance.

$$9312 \pm 1.995 \, \frac{4007}{\sqrt{70}}$$

$$9312 \pm 955$$

The point estimate of the population mean is $9312, the margin of error is $955, and the 95% confidence interval is $9312 - 955 = \$8357$ to $9312 + 955 = \$10{,}267$. Thus, we are 95% confident that the mean credit card balance for the population of all households is between $8357 and $10,267.

The procedures used by Minitab and Excel to develop confidence intervals for a population mean are described in Appendixes 8.1 and 8.2. For the household credit card balances study, the results of the Minitab interval estimation procedure are shown in Figure 8.6. The sample of 70 households provides a sample mean credit card balance of $9312, a sample standard deviation of $4007, a standard error of the mean of $479, and a 95% confidence interval of $8357 to $10,267.

Practical Advice

If the population follows a normal distribution, the confidence interval provided by expression (8.2) is exact and can be used for any sample size. If the population does not follow a normal distribution, the confidence interval provided by expression (8.2) will be approximate. In this case, the quality of the approximation depends on both the distribution of the population and the sample size.

Larger sample sizes are needed if the distribution of the population is highly skewed or includes outliers.

In most applications, a sample size of $n \geq 30$ is adequate when using expression (8.2) to develop an interval estimate of a population mean. However, if the population distribution is highly skewed or contains outliers, most statisticians would recommend increasing the sample size to 50 or more. If the population is not normally distributed but is roughly symmetric, sample sizes as small as 15 can be expected to provide good approximate confidence intervals. With smaller sample sizes, expression (8.2) should only be used if the analyst believes, or is willing to assume, that the population distribution is at least approximately normal.

Using a Small Sample

In the following example we develop an interval estimate for a population mean when the sample size is small. As we already noted, an understanding of the distribution of the population becomes a factor in deciding whether the interval estimation procedure provides acceptable results.

Scheer Industries is considering a new computer-assisted program to train maintenance employees to do machine repairs. In order to fully evaluate the program, the director of

FIGURE 8.6   MINITAB CONFIDENCE INTERVAL FOR THE CREDIT CARD BALANCE SURVEY

Variable	N	Mean	StDev	SE Mean	95% CI
NewBalance	70	9312	4007	479	(8357, 10267)

TABLE 8.4 TRAINING TIME IN DAYS FOR A SAMPLE OF 20 SCHEER
INDUSTRIES EMPLOYEES

DATA *file*

Scheer

52	59	54	42
44	50	42	48
55	54	60	55
44	62	62	57
45	46	43	56

manufacturing requested an estimate of the population mean time required for maintenance employees to complete the computer-assisted training.

A sample of 20 employees is selected, with each employee in the sample completing the training program. Data on the training time in days for the 20 employees are shown in Table 8.4. A histogram of the sample data appears in Figure 8.7. What can we say about the distribution of the population based on this histogram? First, the sample data do not support the conclusion that the distribution of the population is normal, yet we do not see any evidence of skewness or outliers. Therefore, using the guidelines in the previous subsection, we conclude that an interval estimate based on the t distribution appears acceptable for the sample of 20 employees.

We continue by computing the sample mean and sample standard deviation as follows.

$$\bar{x} = \frac{\Sigma x_i}{n} = \frac{1030}{20} = 51.5 \text{ days}$$

$$s = \sqrt{\frac{\Sigma(x_i - \bar{x})^2}{n-1}} = \sqrt{\frac{889}{20-1}} = 6.84 \text{ days}$$

FIGURE 8.7 HISTOGRAM OF TRAINING TIMES FOR THE SCHEER INDUSTRIES SAMPLE

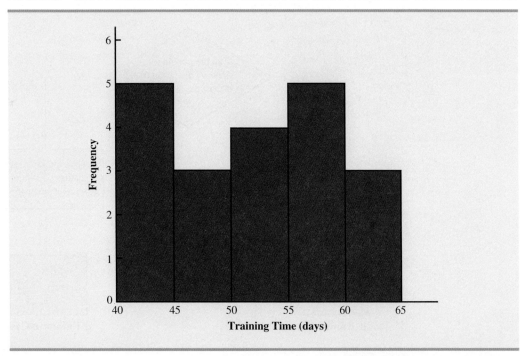

For a 95% confidence interval, we use Table 2 of Appendix B and $n - 1 = 19$ degrees of freedom to obtain $t_{.025} = 2.093$. Expression (8.2) provides the interval estimate of the population mean.

$$51.5 \pm 2.093 \left(\frac{6.84}{\sqrt{20}} \right)$$

$$51.5 \pm 3.2$$

The point estimate of the population mean is 51.5 days. The margin of error is 3.2 days and the 95% confidence interval is $51.5 - 3.2 = 48.3$ days to $51.5 + 3.2 = 54.7$ days.

Using a histogram of the sample data to learn about the distribution of a population is not always conclusive, but in many cases it provides the only information available. The histogram, along with judgment on the part of the analyst, can often be used to decide whether expression (8.2) can be used to develop the interval estimate.

Summary of Interval Estimation Procedures

We provided two approaches to developing an interval estimate of a population mean. For the σ known case, σ and the standard normal distribution are used in expression (8.1) to compute the margin of error and to develop the interval estimate. For the σ unknown case, the sample standard deviation s and the t distribution are used in expression (8.2) to compute the margin of error and to develop the interval estimate.

A summary of the interval estimation procedures for the two cases is shown in Figure 8.8. In most applications, a sample size of $n \geq 30$ is adequate. If the population has a normal or approximately normal distribution, however, smaller sample sizes may be used. For the σ unknown case a sample size of $n \geq 50$ is recommended if the population distribution is believed to be highly skewed or has outliers.

FIGURE 8.8   SUMMARY OF INTERVAL ESTIMATION PROCEDURES
FOR A POPULATION MEAN

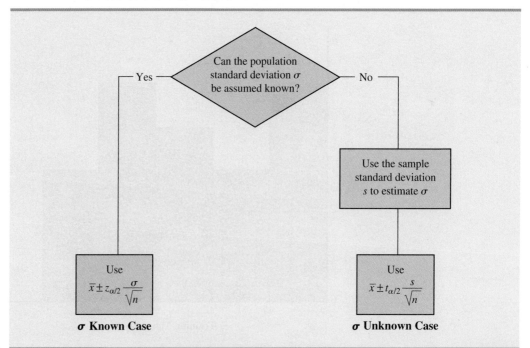

NOTES AND COMMENTS

1. When σ is known, the margin of error, $z_{\alpha/2}(\sigma/\sqrt{n})$, is fixed and is the same for all samples of size n. When σ is unknown, the margin of error, $t_{\alpha/2}(s/\sqrt{n})$, varies from sample to sample. This variation occurs because the sample standard deviation s varies depending upon the sample selected. A large value for s provides a larger margin of error, while a small value for s provides a smaller margin of error.

2. What happens to confidence interval estimates when the population is skewed? Consider a population that is skewed to the right with large data values stretching the distribution to the right. When such skewness exists, the sample mean $\bar{x}$ and the sample standard deviation s are positively correlated. Larger values of s tend to be associated with larger values of $\bar{x}$. Thus, when $\bar{x}$ is larger than the population mean, s tends to be larger than σ. This skewness causes the margin of error, $t_{\alpha/2}(s/\sqrt{n})$, to be larger than it would be with σ known. The confidence interval with the larger margin of error tends to include the population mean μ more often than it would if the true value of σ were used. But when $\bar{x}$ is smaller than the population mean, the correlation between $\bar{x}$ and s causes the margin of error to be small. In this case, the confidence interval with the smaller margin of error tends to miss the population mean more than it would if we knew σ and used it. For this reason, we recommend using larger sample sizes with highly skewed population distributions.

Exercises

Methods

11. For a t distribution with 16 degrees of freedom, find the area, or probability, in each region.
    a. To the right of 2.120
    b. To the left of 1.337
    c. To the left of -1.746
    d. To the right of 2.583
    e. Between -2.120 and 2.120
    f. Between -1.746 and 1.746

12. Find the t value(s) for each of the following cases.
    a. Upper tail area of .025 with 12 degrees of freedom
    b. Lower tail area of .05 with 50 degrees of freedom
    c. Upper tail area of .01 with 30 degrees of freedom
    d. Where 90% of the area falls between these two t values with 25 degrees of freedom
    e. Where 95% of the area falls between these two t values with 45 degrees of freedom

SELF*test*

13. The following sample data are from a normal population: 10, 8, 12, 15, 13, 11, 6, 5.
    a. What is the point estimate of the population mean?
    b. What is the point estimate of the population standard deviation?
    c. With 95% confidence, what is the margin of error for the estimation of the population mean?
    d. What is the 95% confidence interval for the population mean?

14. A simple random sample with $n = 54$ provided a sample mean of 22.5 and a sample standard deviation of 4.4.
    a. Develop a 90% confidence interval for the population mean.
    b. Develop a 95% confidence interval for the population mean.
    c. Develop a 99% confidence interval for the population mean.
    d. What happens to the margin of error and the confidence interval as the confidence level is increased?

Applications

15. Sales personnel for Skillings Distributors submit weekly reports listing the customer contacts made during the week. A sample of 65 weekly reports showed a sample mean of 19.5 customer contacts per week. The sample standard deviation was 5.2. Provide 90% and 95% confidence intervals for the population mean number of weekly customer contacts for the sales personnel.

CorporateBonds

16. A sample containing years to maturity and yield for 40 corporate bonds are contained in the data file named CorporateBonds (*Barron's*, April 2, 2012).
    a. What is the sample mean years to maturity for corporate bonds and what is the sample standard deviation?
    b. Develop a 95% confidence interval for the population mean years to maturity.
    c. What is the sample mean yield on corporate bonds and what is the sample standard deviation?
    d. Develop a 95% confidence interval for the population mean yield on corporate bonds.

17. The International Air Transport Association surveys business travelers to develop quality ratings for transatlantic gateway airports. The maximum possible rating is 10. Suppose a simple random sample of 50 business travelers is selected and each traveler is asked to provide a rating for the Miami International Airport. The ratings obtained from the sample of 50 business travelers follow.

Miami

6	4	6	8	7	7	6	3	3	8	10	4	8
7	8	7	5	9	5	8	4	3	8	5	5	4
4	4	8	4	5	6	2	5	9	9	8	4	8
9	9	5	9	7	8	3	10	8	9	6		

Develop a 95% confidence interval estimate of the population mean rating for Miami.

JobSearch

18. Older people often have a hard time finding work. AARP reported on the number of weeks it takes a worker aged 55 plus to find a job. The data on number of weeks spent searching for a job contained in the file JobSearch are consistent with the AARP findings.
    a. Provide a point estimate of the population mean number of weeks it takes a worker aged 55 plus to find a job.
    b. At 95% confidence, what is the margin of error?
    c. What is the 95% confidence interval estimate of the mean?
    d. Discuss the degree of skewness found in the sample data. What suggestion would you make for a repeat of this study?

HongKongMeals

19. The mean cost of a meal for two in a mid-range restaurant in Tokyo is $40 (Numbeo.com website, December 14, 2014). How do prices for comparable meals in Hong Kong compare? The DATAfile HongKongMeals contains the costs for a sample of 42 recent meals for two in Hong Kong mid-range restaurants.
    a. With 95% confidence, what is the margin of error?
    b. What is the 95% confidence interval estimate of the population mean?
    c. How do prices for meals for two in mid-range restaurants in Hong Kong compare to prices for comparable meals in Tokyo restaurants?

AutoInsurance

20. The average annual premium for automobile insurance in the United States is $1503 (Insure.com website, March 6, 2014). The following annual premiums ($) are representative of the website's findings for the state of Michigan.

1905	3112	2312
2725	2545	2981
2677	2525	2627
2600	2370	2857
2962	2545	2675
2184	2529	2115
2332	2442	

Assume the population is approximately normal.

a. Provide a point estimate of the mean annual automobile insurance premium in Michigan.

b. Develop a 95% confidence interval for the mean annual automobile insurance premium in Michigan.

c. Does the 95% confidence interval for the annual automobile insurance premium in Michigan include the national average for the United States? What is your interpretation of the relationship between auto insurance premiums in Michigan and the national average?

TeleHealth

21. Health insurers are beginning to offer telemedicine services online that replace the common office visit. Wellpoint provides a video service that allows subscribers to connect with a physician online and receive prescribed treatments (*Bloomberg Businessweek,* March 4–9, 2014). Wellpoint claims that users of its LiveHealth Online service saved a significant amount of money on a typical visit. The data shown below ($), for a sample of 20 online doctor visits, are consistent with the savings per visit reported by Wellpoint.

92	34	40
105	83	55
56	49	40
76	48	96
93	74	73
78	93	100
53	82	

Assuming the population is roughly symmetric, construct a 95% confidence interval for the mean savings for a televisit to the doctor as opposed to an office visit.

Guardians

22. Marvel Studio's motion picture *Guardians of the Galaxy* opened over the first two days of the 2014 Labor Day weekend to a record-breaking $94.3 million in ticket sales revenue in North America (*The Hollywood Reporter*, August 3, 2014). The ticket sales revenue in dollars for a sample of 30 theaters is as follows.

a. What is the 95% confidence interval estimate for the mean ticket sales revenue per theater? Interpret this result.

b. Using the movie ticket price of $8.11 per ticket, what is the estimate of the mean number of customers per theater?

c. The movie was shown in 4080 theaters. Estimate the total number of customers who saw *Guardians of the Galaxy* and the total box office ticket sales for the weekend.

(8.3) Determining the Sample Size

If a desired margin of error is selected prior to sampling, the procedures in this section can be used to determine the sample size necessary to satisfy the margin of error requirement.

In providing practical advice in the two preceding sections, we commented on the role of the sample size in providing good approximate confidence intervals when the population is not normally distributed. In this section, we focus on another aspect of the sample size issue. We describe how to choose a sample size large enough to provide a desired margin of error. To understand how this process works, we return to the σ known case presented in Section 8.1. Using expression (8.1), the interval estimate is

$$\bar{x} \pm z_{\alpha/2} \frac{\sigma}{\sqrt{n}}$$

The quantity $z_{\alpha/2}(\sigma/\sqrt{n})$ is the margin of error. Thus, we see that $z_{\alpha/2}$, the population standard deviation σ, and the sample size n combine to determine the margin of error. Once we select a confidence coefficient $1 - \alpha$, $z_{\alpha/2}$ can be determined. Then, if we have a value for σ, we can determine the sample size n needed to provide any desired margin of error. Development of the formula used to compute the required sample size n follows.

Let E = the desired margin of error:

$$E = z_{\alpha/2} \frac{\sigma}{\sqrt{n}}$$

Solving for $\sqrt{n}$, we have

$$\sqrt{n} = \frac{z_{\alpha/2}\sigma}{E}$$

Squaring both sides of this equation, we obtain the following expression for the sample size.

Equation (8.3) can be used to provide a good sample size recommendation. However, judgment on the part of the analyst should be used to determine whether the final sample size should be adjusted upward.

SAMPLE SIZE FOR AN INTERVAL ESTIMATE OF A POPULATION MEAN

$$n = \frac{(z_{\alpha/2})^2\sigma^2}{E^2} \tag{8.3}$$

This sample size provides the desired margin of error at the chosen confidence level.

In equation (8.3), E is the margin of error that the user is willing to accept, and the value of $z_{\alpha/2}$ follows directly from the confidence level to be used in developing the interval estimate. Although user preference must be considered, 95% confidence is the most frequently chosen value ($z_{.025} = 1.96$).

Finally, use of equation (8.3) requires a value for the population standard deviation σ. However, even if σ is unknown, we can use equation (8.3) provided we have a preliminary or *planning value* for σ. In practice, one of the following procedures can be chosen.

A planning value for the population standard deviation σ must be specified before the sample size can be determined. Three methods of obtaining a planning value for σ are discussed here.

1. Use the estimate of the population standard deviation computed from data of previous studies as the planning value for σ.
2. Use a pilot study to select a preliminary sample. The sample standard deviation from the preliminary sample can be used as the planning value for σ.
3. Use judgment or a "best guess" for the value of σ. For example, we might begin by estimating the largest and smallest data values in the population. The difference between the largest and smallest values provides an estimate of the range for the data. Finally, the range divided by 4 is often suggested as a rough approximation of the standard deviation and thus an acceptable planning value for σ.

Let us demonstrate the use of equation (8.3) to determine the sample size by considering the following example. A previous study that investigated the cost of renting automobiles in the United States found a mean cost of approximately $55 per day for renting a midsize automobile. Suppose that the organization that conducted this study would like to conduct a new study in order to estimate the population mean daily rental cost for a midsize automobile in the United States. In designing the new study, the project director specifies that the population mean daily rental cost be estimated with a margin of error of $2 and a 95% level of confidence.

The project director specified a desired margin of error of $E = 2$, and the 95% level of confidence indicates $z_{.025} = 1.96$. Thus, we only need a planning value for the population standard deviation σ in order to compute the required sample size. At this point, an analyst reviewed the sample data from the previous study and found that the sample standard

Equation (8.3) provides the minimum sample size needed to satisfy the desired margin of error requirement. If the computed sample size is not an integer, rounding up to the next integer value will provide a margin of error slightly smaller than required.

deviation for the daily rental cost was $9.65. Using 9.65 as the planning value for σ, we obtain

$$n = \frac{(z_{\alpha/2})^2 \sigma^2}{E^2} = \frac{(1.96)^2 (9.65)^2}{2^2} = 89.43$$

Thus, the sample size for the new study needs to be at least 89.43 midsize automobile rentals in order to satisfy the project director's $2 margin-of-error requirement. In cases where the computed n is not an integer, we round up to the next integer value; hence, the recommended sample size is 90 midsize automobile rentals.

Exercises

Methods

23. How large a sample should be selected to provide a 95% confidence interval with a margin of error of 10? Assume that the population standard deviation is 40.

SELF*test*

24. The range for a set of data is estimated to be 36.
    a. What is the planning value for the population standard deviation?
    b. At 95% confidence, how large a sample would provide a margin of error of 3?
    c. At 95% confidence, how large a sample would provide a margin of error of 2?

Applications

SELF*test*

25. Refer to the Scheer Industries example in Section 8.2. Use 6.84 days as a planning value for the population standard deviation.
    a. Assuming 95% confidence, what sample size would be required to obtain a margin of error of 1.5 days?
    b. If the precision statement was made with 90% confidence, what sample size would be required to obtain a margin of error of 2 days?

26. The U.S. Energy Information Administration (US EIA) reported that the average price for a gallon of regular gasoline is $3.94 (US EIA website, April 6, 2012). The US EIA updates its estimates of average gas prices on a weekly basis. Assume the standard deviation is $.25 for the price of a gallon of regular gasoline and recommend the appropriate sample size for the US EIA to use if they wish to report each of the following margins of error at 95% confidence.
    a. The desired margin of error is $.10.
    b. The desired margin of error is $.07.
    c. The desired margin of error is $.05.

27. Annual starting salaries for college graduates with degrees in business administration are generally expected to be between $30,000 and $45,000. Assume that a 95% confidence interval estimate of the population mean annual starting salary is desired. What is the planning value for the population standard deviation? How large a sample should be taken if the desired margin of error is
    a. $500?
    b. $200?
    c. $100?
    d. Would you recommend trying to obtain the $100 margin of error? Explain.

28. Many medical professionals believe that eating too much red meat increases the risk of heart disease and cancer (WebMD website, March 12, 2014). Suppose you would like to conduct a survey to determine the yearly consumption of beef by a typical American and want to use 3 pounds as the desired margin of error for a confidence interval estimate of

the population mean amount of beef consumed annually. Use 25 pounds as a planning value for the population standard deviation and recommend a sample size for each of the following situations.

a. A 90% confidence interval is desired for the mean amount of beef consumed.
b. A 95% confidence interval is desired for the mean amount of beef consumed.
c. A 99% confidence interval is desired for the mean amount of beef consumed.
d. When the desired margin of error is set, what happens to the sample size as the confidence level is increased? Would you recommend using a 99% confidence interval in this case? Discuss.

29. Customers arrive at a movie theater at the advertised movie time only to find that they have to sit through several previews and prepreview ads before the movie starts. Many complain that the time devoted to previews is too long (*The Wall Street Journal*, October 12, 2012). A preliminary sample conducted by *The Wall Street Journal* showed that the standard deviation of the amount of time devoted to previews was 4 minutes. Use that as a planning value for the standard deviation in answering the following questions.

a. If we want to estimate the population mean time for previews at movie theaters with a margin of error of 75 seconds, what sample size should be used? Assume 95% confidence.
b. If we want to estimate the population mean time for previews at movie theaters with a margin of error of 1 minute, what sample size should be used? Assume 95% confidence.

30. There has been a trend toward less driving in the last few years, especially by young people. From 2001 to 2009 the annual vehicle miles traveled by people from 16 to 34 years of age decreased from 10,300 to 7900 miles per person (U.S. PIRG and Education Fund website, April 6, 2012). Assume the standard deviation was 2000 miles in 2009. Suppose you would like to conduct a survey to develop a 95% confidence interval estimate of the annual vehicle-miles per person for people 16 to 34 years of age at the current time. A margin of error of 100 miles is desired. How large a sample should be used for the current survey?

8.4 Population Proportion

In the introduction to this chapter we said that the general form of an interval estimate of a population proportion p is

$$\bar{p} \pm \text{Margin of error}$$

The sampling distribution of $\bar{p}$ plays a key role in computing the margin of error for this interval estimate.

In Chapter 7 we said that the sampling distribution of $\bar{p}$ can be approximated by a normal distribution whenever $np \geq 5$ and $n(1 - p) \geq 5$. Figure 8.9 shows the normal approximation of the sampling distribution of $\bar{p}$. The mean of the sampling distribution of $\bar{p}$ is the population proportion p, and the standard error of $\bar{p}$ is

$$\sigma_{\bar{p}} = \sqrt{\frac{p(1 - p)}{n}} \tag{8.4}$$

Because the sampling distribution of $\bar{p}$ is normally distributed, if we choose $z_{\alpha/2}\sigma_{\bar{p}}$ as the margin of error in an interval estimate of a population proportion, we know that $100(1 - \alpha)\%$ of the intervals generated will contain the true population proportion. But $\sigma_{\bar{p}}$ cannot be used directly in the computation of the margin of error because p will not be known; p is what we are trying to estimate. So $\bar{p}$ is substituted for p and the margin of error for an interval estimate of a population proportion is given by

$$\text{Margin of error} = z_{\alpha/2} \sqrt{\frac{\bar{p}(1 - \bar{p})}{n}} \tag{8.5}$$

FIGURE 8.9   NORMAL APPROXIMATION OF THE SAMPLING DISTRIBUTION OF $\bar{p}$

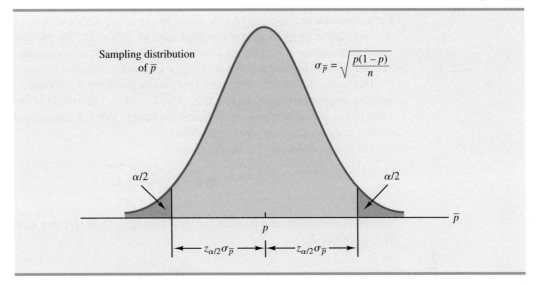

With this margin of error, the general expression for an interval estimate of a population proportion is as follows.

When developing confidence intervals for proportions, the quantity $z_{\alpha/2}\sqrt{\bar{p}(1-\bar{p})/n}$ provides the margin of error.

INTERVAL ESTIMATE OF A POPULATION PROPORTION

$$\bar{p} \pm z_{\alpha/2}\sqrt{\frac{\bar{p}(1-\bar{p})}{n}} \qquad (8.6)$$

where $1 - \alpha$ is the confidence coefficient and $z_{\alpha/2}$ is the z value providing an area of $\alpha/2$ in the upper tail of the standard normal distribution.

TeeTimes

The following example illustrates the computation of the margin of error and interval estimate for a population proportion. A national survey of 900 women golfers was conducted to learn how women golfers view their treatment at golf courses in the United States. The survey found that 396 of the women golfers were satisfied with the availability of tee times. Thus, the point estimate of the proportion of the population of women golfers who are satisfied with the availability of tee times is 396/900 = .44. Using expression (8.6) and a 95% confidence level,

$$\bar{p} \pm z_{\alpha/2}\sqrt{\frac{\bar{p}(1-\bar{p})}{n}}$$

$$.44 \pm 1.96\sqrt{\frac{.44(1 - .44)}{900}}$$

$$.44 \pm .0324$$

Thus, the margin of error is .0324 and the 95% confidence interval estimate of the population proportion is .4076 to .4724. Using percentages, the survey results enable us to state with 95% confidence that between 40.76% and 47.24% of all women golfers are satisfied with the availability of tee times.

Determining the Sample Size

Let us consider the question of how large the sample size should be to obtain an estimate of a population proportion at a specified level of precision. The rationale for the sample size determination in developing interval estimates of p is similar to the rationale used in Section 8.3 to determine the sample size for estimating a population mean.

Previously in this section we said that the margin of error associated with an interval estimate of a population proportion is $z_{\alpha/2}\sqrt{\bar{p}(1-\bar{p})/n}$. The margin of error is based on the value of $z_{\alpha/2}$, the sample proportion $\bar{p}$, and the sample size n. Larger sample sizes provide a smaller margin of error and better precision.

Let E denote the desired margin of error.

$$E = z_{\alpha/2}\sqrt{\frac{\bar{p}(1-\bar{p})}{n}}$$

Solving this equation for n provides a formula for the sample size that will provide a margin of error of size E.

$$n = \frac{(z_{\alpha/2})^2\bar{p}(1-\bar{p})}{E^2}$$

Note, however, that we cannot use this formula to compute the sample size that will provide the desired margin of error because $\bar{p}$ will not be known until after we select the sample. What we need, then, is a planning value for $\bar{p}$ that can be used to make the computation. Using p^* to denote the planning value for $\bar{p}$, the following formula can be used to compute the sample size that will provide a margin of error of size E.

SAMPLE SIZE FOR AN INTERVAL ESTIMATE OF A POPULATION PROPORTION

$$n = \frac{(z_{\alpha/2})^2 p^*(1-p^*)}{E^2} \tag{8.7}$$

In practice, the planning value p^* can be chosen by one of the following procedures.

1. Use the sample proportion from a previous sample of the same or similar units.
2. Use a pilot study to select a preliminary sample. The sample proportion from this sample can be used as the planning value, p^*.
3. Use judgment or a "best guess" for the value of p^*.
4. If none of the preceding alternatives apply, use a planning value of $p^* = .50$.

Let us return to the survey of women golfers and assume that the company is interested in conducting a new survey to estimate the current proportion of the population of women golfers who are satisfied with the availability of tee times. How large should the sample be if the survey director wants to estimate the population proportion with a margin of error of .025 at 95% confidence? With $E = .025$ and $z_{\alpha/2} = 1.96$, we need a planning value p^* to answer the sample size question. Using the previous survey result of $\bar{p} = .44$ as the planning value p^*, equation (8.7) shows that

$$n = \frac{(z_{\alpha/2})^2 p^*(1-p^*)}{E^2} = \frac{(1.96)^2(.44)(1-.44)}{(.025)^2} = 1514.5$$

TABLE 8.5 SOME POSSIBLE VALUES FOR $p^*(1 - p^*)$

p^*	$p^*(1 - p^*)$	
.10	$(.10)(.90) = .09$	
.30	$(.30)(.70) = .21$	
.40	$(.40)(.60) = .24$	
.50	$(.50)(.50) = .25$	← Largest value for $p^*(1 - p^*)$
.60	$(.60)(.40) = .24$	
.70	$(.70)(.30) = .21$	
.90	$(.90)(.10) = .09$	

Thus, the sample size must be at least 1514.5 women golfers to satisfy the margin of error requirement. Rounding up to the next integer value indicates that a sample of 1515 women golfers is recommended to satisfy the margin of error requirement.

The fourth alternative suggested for selecting a planning value p^* is to use $p^* = .50$. This value of p^* is frequently used when no other information is available. To understand why, note that the numerator of equation (8.7) shows that the sample size is proportional to the quantity $p^*(1 - p^*)$. A larger value for the quantity $p^*(1 - p^*)$ will result in a larger sample size. Table 8.5 gives some possible values of $p^*(1 - p^*)$. Note that the largest value of $p^*(1 - p^*)$ occurs when $p^* = .50$. Thus, in case of any uncertainty about an appropriate planning value, we know that $p^* = .50$ will provide the largest sample size recommendation. In effect, we play it safe by recommending the largest necessary sample size. If the sample proportion turns out to be different from the .50 planning value, the margin of error will be smaller than anticipated. Thus, in using $p^* = .50$, we guarantee that the sample size will be sufficient to obtain the desired margin of error.

In the survey of women golfers example, a planning value of $p^* = .50$ would have provided the sample size

$$n = \frac{(z_{\alpha/2})^2 p^*(1 - p^*)}{E^2} = \frac{(1.96)^2(.50)(1 - .50)}{(.025)^2} = 1536.6$$

Thus, a slightly larger sample size of 1537 women golfers would be recommended.

NOTES AND COMMENTS

1. The desired margin of error for estimating a population proportion is almost always .10 or less. In national public opinion polls conducted by organizations such as Gallup and Harris, a .03 or .04 margin of error is common. With such margins of error, equation (8.7) will almost always provide a sample size that is large enough to satisfy the requirements of $np \geq 5$ and $n(1 - p) \geq 5$ for using a normal distribution as an approximation for the sampling distribution of $\bar{x}$.

2. The binomial distribution can also be used to calculate an exact confidence interval for one proportion. This method is more accurate and more powerful than the normal approximation method. However, the calculations for the normal approximation method are simpler, and the accuracy and power of confidence intervals calculated using the normal approximation method improve as the sample size increases.

Exercises

Methods

☑SELF*test*

31. A simple random sample of 400 individuals provides 100 Yes responses.
    a. What is the point estimate of the proportion of the population that would provide Yes responses?
    b. What is your estimate of the standard error of the proportion, $\sigma_{\bar{p}}$?
    c. Compute the 95% confidence interval for the population proportion.

32. A simple random sample of 800 elements generates a sample proportion $\bar{p} = .70$.
    a. Provide a 90% confidence interval for the population proportion.
    b. Provide a 95% confidence interval for the population proportion.

33. In a survey, the planning value for the population proportion is $p^* = .35$. How large a sample should be taken to provide a 95% confidence interval with a margin of error of .05?

34. At 95% confidence, how large a sample should be taken to obtain a margin of error of .03 for the estimation of a population proportion? Assume that past data are not available for developing a planning value for p^*.

Applications

☑SELF*test*

35. The Consumer Reports National Research Center conducted a telephone survey of 2000 adults to learn about the major economic concerns for the future (*Consumer Reports,* January 2009). The survey results showed that 1760 of the respondents think the future health of Social Security is a major economic concern.
    a. What is the point estimate of the population proportion of adults who think the future health of Social Security is a major economic concern.
    b. At 90% confidence, what is the margin of error?
    c. Develop a 90% confidence interval for the population proportion of adults who think the future health of Social Security is a major economic concern.
    d. Develop a 95% confidence interval for this population proportion.

36. According to statistics reported on CNBC, a surprising number of motor vehicles are not covered by insurance. Sample results, consistent with the CNBC report, showed 46 of 200 vehicles were not covered by insurance.
    a. What is the point estimate of the proportion of vehicles not covered by insurance?
    b. Develop a 95% confidence interval for the population proportion.

DATA *file*
ChildOutlook

37. One of the questions on a survey of 1000 adults asked if today's children will be better off than their parents (Rasmussen Reports website, October 26, 2012). Representative data are shown in the DATAfile named ChildOutlook. A response of Yes indicates that the adult surveyed did think today's children will be better off than their parents. A response of No indicates that the adult surveyed did not think today's children will be better off than their parents. A response of Not Sure was given by 23% of the adults surveyed.
    a. What is the point estimate of the proportion of the population of adults who do think that today's children will be better off than their parents?
    b. At 95% confidence, what is the margin of error?
    c. What is the 95% confidence interval for the proportion of adults who do think that today's children will be better off than their parents?
    d. What is the 95% confidence interval for the proportion of adults who do not think that today's children will be better off than their parents?
    e. Which of the confidence intervals in parts (c) and (d) has the smaller margin of error? Why?

CasualDining

38. According to *Franchise Business Review*, over 50% of all food franchises earn a profit of less than $50,000 a year. In a sample of 142 casual dining restaurants, 81 earned a profit of less than $50,000 last year.
    a. What is the point estimate of the proportion of casual dining restaurants that earned a profit of less than $50,000 last year?
    b. Determine the margin of error and provide a 95% confidence interval for the proportion of casual dining restaurants that earned a profit of less than $50,000 last year.
    c. How large a sample is needed if the desired margin of error is .03?

SELFtest

39. In 16% of all homes with a stay-at-home parent, the father is the stay-at-home parent (*Pew Research*, June 5, 2014). An independent research firm has been charged with conducting a sample survey to obtain more current information.
    a. What sample size is needed if the research firm's goal is to estimate the current proportion of homes with a stay-at-home parent in which the father is the stay-at-home parent with a margin of error of .03? Use a 95% confidence level.
    b. Repeat part (a) using a 99% confidence level.

40. For many years businesses have struggled with the rising cost of health care. But recently, the increases have slowed due to less inflation in health care prices and employees paying for a larger portion of health care benefits. A recent Mercer survey showed that 52% of U.S. employers were likely to require higher employee contributions for health care coverage in 2009. Suppose the survey was based on a sample of 800 companies. Compute the margin of error and a 95% confidence interval for the proportion of companies likely to require higher employee contributions for health care coverage in 2009.

41. Fewer young people are driving. In 1983, 87% of 19-year-olds had a driver's license. Twenty-five years later that percentage had dropped to 75% (University of Michigan Transportation Research Institute website, April 7, 2012). Suppose these results are based on a random sample of 1200 19-year-olds in 1983 and again in 2008.
    a. At 95% confidence, what is the margin of error and the interval estimate of the number of 19-year-old drivers in 1983?
    b. At 95% confidence, what is the margin of error and the interval estimate of the number of 19-year-old drivers in 2008?
    c. Is the margin of error the same in parts (a) and (b)? Why or why not?

42. A poll for the presidential campaign sampled 491 potential voters in June. A primary purpose of the poll was to obtain an estimate of the proportion of potential voters who favored each candidate. Assume a planning value of $p^* = .50$ and a 95% confidence level.
    a. For $p^* = .50$, what was the planned margin of error for the June poll?
    b. Closer to the November election, better precision and smaller margins of error are desired. Assume the following margins of error are requested for surveys to be conducted during the presidential campaign. Compute the recommended sample size for each survey.

Survey	Margin of Error
September	.04
October	.03
Early November	.02
Pre-Election Day	.01

43. The Pew Research Center Internet Project, conducted on the 25th anniversary of the Internet, involved a survey of 857 Internet users (Pew Research Center website, April 1, 2014). It provided a variety of statistics on Internet users. For instance, in 2014, 87% of American adults were Internet users. In 1995 only 14% of American adults used the Internet.

   a. The sample survey showed that 90% of respondents said the Internet has been a good thing for them personally. Develop a 95% confidence interval for the proportion of respondents who say the Internet has been a good thing for them personally.

   b. The sample survey showed that 67% of Internet users said the Internet has generally strengthened their relationship with family and friends. Develop a 95% confidence interval for the proportion of respondents who say the Internet has strengthened their relationship with family and friends.

   c. Fifty-six percent of Internet users have seen an online group come together to help a person or community solve a problem, whereas only 25% have left an online group because of unpleasant interaction. Develop a 95% confidence interval for the proportion of Internet users who say online groups have helped solve a problem.

   d. Compare the margin of error for the interval estimates in parts (a), (b), and (c). How is the margin of error related to the sample proportion?

Summary

In this chapter we presented methods for developing interval estimates of a population mean and a population proportion. A point estimator may or may not provide a good estimate of a population parameter. The use of an interval estimate provides a measure of the precision of an estimate. Both the interval estimate of the population mean and the population proportion are of the form: point estimate $\pm$ margin of error.

We presented interval estimates for a population mean for two cases. In the σ known case, historical data or other information is used to develop an estimate of σ prior to taking a sample. Analysis of new sample data then proceeds based on the assumption that σ is known. In the σ unknown case, the sample data are used to estimate both the population mean and the population standard deviation. The final choice of which interval estimation procedure to use depends upon the analyst's understanding of which method provides the best estimate of σ.

In the σ known case, the interval estimation procedure is based on the assumed value of σ and the use of the standard normal distribution. In the σ unknown case, the interval estimation procedure uses the sample standard deviation s and the t distribution. In both cases the quality of the interval estimates obtained depends on the distribution of the population and the sample size. If the population is normally distributed the interval estimates will be exact in both cases, even for small sample sizes. If the population is not normally distributed, the interval estimates obtained will be approximate. Larger sample sizes will provide better approximations, but the more highly skewed the population is, the larger the sample size needs to be to obtain a good approximation. Practical advice about the sample size necessary to obtain good approximations was included in Sections 8.1 and 8.2. In most cases a sample of size 30 or more will provide good approximate confidence intervals.

The general form of the interval estimate for a population proportion is $\bar{p} \pm$ margin of error. In practice the sample sizes used for interval estimates of a population proportion are generally large. Thus, the interval estimation procedure is based on the standard normal distribution.

Often a desired margin of error is specified prior to developing a sampling plan. We showed how to choose a sample size large enough to provide the desired precision.

Glossary

Confidence coefficient The confidence level expressed as a decimal value. For example, .95 is the confidence coefficient for a 95% confidence level.

Confidence interval Another name for an interval estimate.

Confidence level The confidence associated with an interval estimate. For example, if an interval estimation procedure provides intervals such that 95% of the intervals formed using the procedure will include the population parameter, the interval estimate is said to be constructed at the 95% confidence level.

Degrees of freedom A parameter of the t distribution. When the t distribution is used in the computation of an interval estimate of a population mean, the appropriate t distribution has $n - 1$ degrees of freedom, where n is the size of the sample.

Interval estimate An estimate of a population parameter that provides an interval believed to contain the value of the parameter. For the interval estimates in this chapter, it has the form: point estimate ± margin of error.

Margin of error The ± value added to and subtracted from a point estimate in order to develop an interval estimate of a population parameter.

t distribution A family of probability distributions that can be used to develop an interval estimate of a population mean whenever the population standard deviation σ is unknown and is estimated by the sample standard deviation s.

σ known The case when historical data or other information provides a good value for the population standard deviation prior to taking a sample. The interval estimation procedure uses this known value of σ in computing the margin of error.

σ unknown The more common case when no good basis exists for estimating the population standard deviation prior to taking the sample. The interval estimation procedure uses the sample standard deviation s in computing the margin of error.

Key Formulas

Interval Estimate of a Population Mean: σ Known

$$\bar{x} \pm z_{\alpha/2}\frac{\sigma}{\sqrt{n}} \tag{8.1}$$

Interval Estimate of a Population Mean: σ Unknown

$$\bar{x} \pm t_{\alpha/2}\frac{s}{\sqrt{n}} \tag{8.2}$$

Sample Size for an Interval Estimate of a Population Mean

$$n = \frac{(z_{\alpha/2})^2\sigma^2}{E^2} \tag{8.3}$$

Interval Estimate of a Population Proportion

$$\bar{p} \pm z_{\alpha/2}\sqrt{\frac{\bar{p}(1-\bar{p})}{n}} \tag{8.6}$$

Sample Size for an Interval Estimate of a Population Proportion

$$n = \frac{(z_{\alpha/2})^2 p^*(1-p^*)}{E^2} \tag{8.7}$$

Supplementary Exercises

44. A sample survey of 54 discount brokers showed that the mean price charged for a trade of 100 shares at $50 per share was $33.77. The survey is conducted annually. With the historical data available, assume a known population standard deviation of $15.
    a. Using the sample data, what is the margin of error associated with a 95% confidence interval?
    b. Develop a 95% confidence interval for the mean price charged by discount brokers for a trade of 100 shares at $50 per share.

45. A survey conducted by the American Automobile Association showed that a family of four spends an average of $215.60 per day while on vacation. Suppose a sample of 64 families of four vacationing at Niagara Falls resulted in a sample mean of $252.45 per day and a sample standard deviation of $74.50.
    a. Develop a 95% confidence interval estimate of the mean amount spent per day by a family of four visiting Niagara Falls.
    b. Based on the confidence interval from part (a), does it appear that the population mean amount spent per day by families visiting Niagara Falls differs from the mean reported by the American Automobile Association? Explain.

46. The 92 million Americans of age 50 and over control 50 percent of all discretionary income. AARP estimates that the average annual expenditure on restaurants and carryout food was $1873 for individuals in this age group. Suppose this estimate is based on a sample of 80 persons and that the sample standard deviation is $550.
    a. At 95% confidence, what is the margin of error?
    b. What is the 95% confidence interval for the population mean amount spent on restaurants and carryout food?
    c. What is your estimate of the total amount spent by Americans of age 50 and over on restaurants and carryout food?
    d. If the amount spent on restaurants and carryout food is skewed to the right, would you expect the median amount spent to be greater or less than $1873?

Russia

47. Russia has recently started a push for stronger smoking regulations much like those in Western countries concerning cigarette advertising, smoking in public places, and so on. The DATAfile named Russia contains sample data on smoking habits of Russians that are consistent with those reported by *The Wall Street Journal* (*The Wall Street Journal*, October 16, 2012). Analyze the data using Excel and answer the following questions.
    a. Develop a point estimate and a 95% confidence interval for the proportion of Russians who smoke.
    b. Develop a point estimate and a 95% confidence interval for the mean annual per capita consumption (number of cigarettes) of a Russian.
    c. For those Russians who do smoke, estimate the number of cigarettes smoked per day.

DrugCost

48. The Health Care Cost Institute tracks health care expenditures for beneficiaries under the age of 65 who are covered by employer-sponsored private health insurance (Health Care Cost Institute website, November 4, 2012). The data contained in the DATAfile named DrugCost are consistent with the institute's findings concerning annual prescription costs per employee. Analyze the data using Excel and answer the following questions.
    a. Develop a 90% confidence interval for the annual cost of prescription drugs.
    b. Develop a 90% confidence interval for the amount of out-of-pocket expense per employee.
    c. What is your point estimate of the proportion of employees who incurred no prescription drug costs?
    d. Which, if either, of the confidence intervals in parts (a) and (b) has a larger margin of error. Why?

Standing

49. A recent article reported that there are approximately 11 minutes of actual playing time in a typical National Football League (NFL) game (*The Wall Street Journal,* January 15, 2010). The article included information about the amount of time devoted to replays, the amount of time devoted to commercials, and the amount of time the players spend standing around between plays. Data consistent with the findings published in *The Wall Street Journal* are in the DATAfile named Standing. These data provide the amount of time players spend standing around between plays for a sample of 60 NFL games.
    a. Use the Standing data set to develop a point estimate of the number of minutes during an NFL game that players are standing around between plays. Compare this to the actual playing time reported in the article. Are you surprised?
    b. What is the sample standard deviation?
    c. Develop a 95% confidence interval for the number of minutes players spend standing around between plays.

50. Mileage tests are conducted for a particular model of automobile. If a 98% confidence interval with a margin of error of 1 mile per gallon is desired, how many automobiles should be used in the test? Assume that preliminary mileage tests indicate the standard deviation is 2.6 miles per gallon.

51. In developing patient appointment schedules, a medical center wants to estimate the mean time that a staff member spends with each patient. How large a sample should be taken if the desired margin of error is two minutes at a 95% level of confidence? How large a sample should be taken for a 99% level of confidence? Use a planning value for the population standard deviation of eight minutes.

52. Annual salary plus bonus data for chief executive officers are presented in the *Business-Week* Annual Pay Survey. A preliminary sample showed that the standard deviation is $675 with data provided in thousands of dollars. How many chief executive officers should be in a sample if we want to estimate the population mean annual salary plus bonus with a margin of error of $100,000? (*Note:* The desired margin of error would be $E = 100$ if the data are in thousands of dollars.) Use 95% confidence.

53. The National Center for Education Statistics reported that 47% of college students work to pay for tuition and living expenses. Assume that a sample of 450 college students was used in the study.
    a. Provide a 95% confidence interval for the population proportion of college students who work to pay for tuition and living expenses.
    b. Provide a 99% confidence interval for the population proportion of college students who work to pay for tuition and living expenses.
    c. What happens to the margin of error as the confidence is increased from 95% to 99%?

54. A *USA Today*/CNN/Gallup survey of 369 working parents found 200 who said they spend too little time with their children because of work commitments.
    a. What is the point estimate of the proportion of the population of working parents who feel they spend too little time with their children because of work commitments?
    b. At 95% confidence, what is the margin of error?
    c. What is the 95% confidence interval estimate of the population proportion of working parents who feel they spend too little time with their children because of work commitments?

55. The Pew Research Center has conducted extensive research on the young adult population (Pew Research website, November 6, 2012). One finding was that 93% of adults aged 18 to 29 use the Internet. Another finding was that 21% of those aged 18 to 28 are married. Assume the sample size associated with both findings is 500.
    a. Develop a 95% confidence interval for the proportion of adults aged 18 to 29 who use the Internet.
    b. Develop a 99% confidence interval for the proportion of adults aged 18 to 28 who are married.
    c. In which case, part (a) or part (b), is the margin of error larger? Explain why.

56. A survey of 750 likely voters in Ohio was conducted by the Rasmussen Poll just prior to the general election (Rasmussen Reports website, November 4, 2012). The state of the economy was thought to be an important determinant of how people would vote. Among other things, the survey found that 165 of the respondents rated the economy as good or excellent and 315 rated the economy as poor.
    a. Develop a point estimate of the proportion of likely voters in Ohio who rated the economy as good or excellent.
    b. Construct a 95% confidence interval for the proportion of likely voters in Ohio who rated the economy as good or excellent.
    c. Construct a 95% confidence interval for the proportion of likely voters in Ohio who rated the economy as poor.
    d. Which of the confidence intervals in parts (b) and (c) is wider? Why?

57. The *Centers for Disease Control* reported the percentage of people 18 years of age and older who smoke (CDC website, December 14, 2014). Suppose that a study designed to collect new data on smokers and nonsmokers uses a preliminary estimate of the proportion who smoke of .30.
    a. How large a sample should be taken to estimate the proportion of smokers in the population with a margin of error of .02? Use 95% confidence.
    b. Assume that the study uses your sample size recommendation in part (a) and finds 520 smokers. What is the point estimate of the proportion of smokers in the population?
    c. What is the 95% confidence interval for the proportion of smokers in the population?

58. A well-known bank credit card firm wishes to estimate the proportion of credit card holders who carry a nonzero balance at the end of the month and incur an interest charge. Assume that the desired margin of error is .03 at 98% confidence.
    a. How large a sample should be selected if it is anticipated that roughly 70% of the firm's card holders carry a nonzero balance at the end of the month?
    b. How large a sample should be selected if no planning value for the proportion could be specified?

59. Workers in several industries were surveyed to determine the proportion of workers who feel their industry is understaffed. In the government sector, 37% of the respondents said they were understaffed, in the health care sector 33% said they were understaffed, and in the education sector 28% said they were understaffed (*USA Today,* January 11, 2010). Suppose that 200 workers were surveyed in each industry.
    a. Construct a 95% confidence interval for the proportion of workers in each of these industries who feel their industry is understaffed.
    b. Assuming the same sample size will be used in each industry, how large would the sample need to be to ensure that the margin of error is .05 or less for each of the three confidence intervals?

60. Although airline schedules and cost are important factors for business travelers when choosing an airline carrier, a *USA Today* survey found that business travelers list an airline's frequent flyer program as the most important factor. From a sample of $n = 1993$ business travelers who responded to the survey, 618 listed a frequent flyer program as the most important factor.
    a. What is the point estimate of the proportion of the population of business travelers who believe a frequent flyer program is the most important factor when choosing an airline carrier?
    b. Develop a 95% confidence interval estimate of the population proportion.
    c. How large a sample would be required to report the margin of error of .01 at 95% confidence? Would you recommend that *USA Today* attempt to provide this degree of precision? Why or why not?

Case Problem 1 *Young Professional* Magazine

Young Professional magazine was developed for a target audience of recent college graduates who are in their first 10 years in a business/professional career. In its two years of publication, the magazine has been fairly successful. Now the publisher is interested in expanding the magazine's advertising base. Potential advertisers continually ask about the demographics and interests of subscribers to *Young Professional*. To collect this information, the magazine commissioned a survey to develop a profile of its subscribers. The survey results will be used to help the magazine choose articles of interest and provide advertisers with a profile of subscribers. As a new employee of the magazine, you have been asked to help analyze the survey results.

DATA *file*

Professional

Some of the survey questions follow:

1. What is your age?
2. Are you: Male_____   Female_____
3. Do you plan to make any real estate purchases in the next two years? Yes_____   No_____
4. What is the approximate total value of financial investments, exclusive of your home, owned by you or members of your household?
5. How many stock/bond/mutual fund transactions have you made in the past year?
6. Do you have broadband access to the Internet at home? Yes_____   No_____
7. Please indicate your total household income last year. _____
8. Do you have children? Yes_____   No_____

The file entitled Professional contains the responses to these questions. Table 8.6 shows the portion of the file pertaining to the first five survey respondents.

Managerial Report

Prepare a managerial report summarizing the results of the survey. In addition to statistical summaries, discuss how the magazine might use these results to attract advertisers. You might also comment on how the survey results could be used by the magazine's editors to identify topics that would be of interest to readers. Your report should address the following issues, but do not limit your analysis to just these areas.

1. Develop appropriate descriptive statistics to summarize the data.
2. Develop 95% confidence intervals for the mean age and household income of subscribers.

TABLE 8.6 PARTIAL SURVEY RESULTS FOR *YOUNG PROFESSIONAL* MAGAZINE

Age	Gender	Real Estate Purchases	Value of Investments($)	Number of Transactions	Broadband Access	Household Income($)	Children
38	Female	No	12200	4	Yes	75200	Yes
30	Male	No	12400	4	Yes	70300	Yes
41	Female	No	26800	5	Yes	48200	No
28	Female	Yes	19600	6	No	95300	No
31	Female	Yes	15100	5	No	73300	Yes
⋮	⋮	⋮	⋮	⋮	⋮	⋮	⋮

3. Develop 95% confidence intervals for the proportion of subscribers who have broadband access at home and the proportion of subscribers who have children.
4. Would *Young Professional* be a good advertising outlet for online brokers? Justify your conclusion with statistical data.
5. Would this magazine be a good place to advertise for companies selling educational software and computer games for young children?
6. Comment on the types of articles you believe would be of interest to readers of *Young Professional*.

Case Problem 2   Gulf Real Estate Properties

Gulf Real Estate Properties, Inc., is a real estate firm located in southwest Florida. The company, which advertises itself as "expert in the real estate market," monitors condominium sales by collecting data on location, list price, sale price, and number of days it takes to sell each unit. Each condominium is classified as *Gulf View* if it is located directly on the Gulf of Mexico or *No Gulf View* if it is located on the bay or a golf course, near but not on the Gulf. Sample data from the Multiple Listing Service in Naples, Florida, provided recent sales data for 40 Gulf View condominiums and 18 No Gulf View condominiums. Prices are in thousands of dollars. The data are shown in Table 8.7.

Managerial Report

1. Use appropriate descriptive statistics to summarize each of the three variables for the 40 Gulf View condominiums.
2. Use appropriate descriptive statistics to summarize each of the three variables for the 18 No Gulf View condominiums.
3. Compare your summary results. Discuss any specific statistical results that would help a real estate agent understand the condominium market.
4. Develop a 95% confidence interval estimate of the population mean sales price and population mean number of days to sell for Gulf View condominiums. Interpret your results.
5. Develop a 95% confidence interval estimate of the population mean sales price and population mean number of days to sell for No Gulf View condominiums. Interpret your results.
6. Assume the branch manager requested estimates of the mean selling price of Gulf View condominiums with a margin of error of $40,000 and the mean selling price of No Gulf View condominiums with a margin of error of $15,000. Using 95% confidence, how large should the sample sizes be?
7. Gulf Real Estate Properties just signed contracts for two new listings: a Gulf View condominium with a list price of $589,000 and a No Gulf View condominium with a list price of $285,000. What is your estimate of the final selling price and number of days required to sell each of these units?

Case Problem 3   Metropolitan Research, Inc.

Metropolitan Research, Inc., a consumer research organization, conducts surveys designed to evaluate a wide variety of products and services available to consumers. In one particular study, Metropolitan looked at consumer satisfaction with the performance

TABLE 8.7   SALES DATA FOR GULF REAL ESTATE PROPERTIES

Gulf View Condominiums			No Gulf View Condominiums		
List Price	**Sale Price**	**Days to Sell**	**List Price**	**Sale Price**	**Days to Sell**
495.0	475.0	130	217.0	217.0	182
379.0	350.0	71	148.0	135.5	338
529.0	519.0	85	186.5	179.0	122
552.5	534.5	95	239.0	230.0	150
334.9	334.9	119	279.0	267.5	169
550.0	505.0	92	215.0	214.0	58
169.9	165.0	197	279.0	259.0	110
210.0	210.0	56	179.9	176.5	130
975.0	945.0	73	149.9	144.9	149
314.0	314.0	126	235.0	230.0	114
315.0	305.0	88	199.8	192.0	120
885.0	800.0	282	210.0	195.0	61
975.0	975.0	100	226.0	212.0	146
469.0	445.0	56	149.9	146.5	137
329.0	305.0	49	160.0	160.0	281
365.0	330.0	48	322.0	292.5	63
332.0	312.0	88	187.5	179.0	48
520.0	495.0	161	247.0	227.0	52
425.0	405.0	149			
675.0	669.0	142			
409.0	400.0	28			
649.0	649.0	29			
319.0	305.0	140			
425.0	410.0	85			
359.0	340.0	107			
469.0	449.0	72			
895.0	875.0	129			
439.0	430.0	160			
435.0	400.0	206			
235.0	227.0	91			
638.0	618.0	100			
629.0	600.0	97			
329.0	309.0	114			
595.0	555.0	45			
339.0	315.0	150			
215.0	200.0	48			
395.0	375.0	135			
449.0	425.0	53			
499.0	465.0	86			
439.0	428.5	158			

DATA *file*

GulfProp

of automobiles produced by a major Detroit manufacturer. A questionnaire sent to owners of one of the manufacturer's full-sized cars revealed several complaints about early transmission problems. To learn more about the transmission failures, Metropolitan used a sample of actual transmission repairs provided by a transmission repair firm in the Detroit area. The following data show the actual number of miles driven for 50 vehicles at the time of transmission failure.

DATA *file*

Auto

85,092	32,609	59,465	77,437	32,534	64,090	32,464	59,902
39,323	89,641	94,219	116,803	92,857	63,436	65,605	85,861
64,342	61,978	67,998	59,817	101,769	95,774	121,352	69,568
74,276	66,998	40,001	72,069	25,066	77,098	69,922	35,662
74,425	67,202	118,444	53,500	79,294	64,544	86,813	116,269
37,831	89,341	73,341	85,288	138,114	53,402	85,586	82,256
77,539	88,798						

Managerial Report

1. Use appropriate descriptive statistics to summarize the transmission failure data.
2. Develop a 95% confidence interval for the mean number of miles driven until transmission failure for the population of automobiles with transmission failure. Provide a managerial interpretation of the interval estimate.
3. Discuss the implication of your statistical findings in terms of the belief that some owners of the automobiles experienced early transmission failures.
4. How many repair records should be sampled if the research firm wants the population mean number of miles driven until transmission failure to be estimated with a margin of error of 5000 miles? Use 95% confidence.
5. What other information would you like to gather to evaluate the transmission failure problem more fully?

Appendix 8.1   Interval Estimation with Minitab

We describe the use of Minitab in constructing confidence intervals for a population mean and a population proportion.

Population Mean: σ Known

DATA *file*

Lloyd's

We illustrate interval estimation using the Lloyd's example in Section 8.1. The amounts spent per shopping trip for the sample of 100 customers are in column C1 of a Minitab worksheet. The population standard deviation $\sigma = 20$ is assumed known. The following steps can be used to compute a 95% confidence interval estimate of the population mean.

Step 1. Select the **Stat** menu
Step 2. Choose **Basic Statistics**
Step 3. Choose **1-Sample Z**
Step 4. When the One-Sample Z dialog box appears:
Select **One or more samples, each in a column** from the pull-down menu
Enter C1 in the box immediately below the pull-down menu
Enter 20 in the **Known Standard deviation** box
Step 5. Click **OK**

The Minitab default is a 95% confidence level. In order to specify a different confidence level such as 90%, add the following to step 4.

Select **Options**
When the One-Sample Z-Options dialog box appears:
Enter 90 in the **Confidence level** box
Click **OK**

Population Mean: σ Unknown

NewBalance

We illustrate interval estimation using the data in Table 8.3 showing the credit card balances for a sample of 70 households. The data are in column C1 of a Minitab worksheet. In this case the population standard deviation σ will be estimated by the sample standard deviation s. The following steps can be used to compute a 95% confidence interval estimate of the population mean.

Step 1. Select the **Stat** menu
Step 2. Choose **Basic Statistics**
Step 3. Choose **1-Sample t**
Step 4. When the One-Sample t dialog box appears:
        Select **One or more samples, each in a column** from the pull-down menu
        Enter C1 in the box immediately below the pull-down menu
Step 5. Click **OK**

The Minitab default is a 95% confidence level. In order to specify a different confidence level such as 90%, add the following to step 4.

        Select **Options**
        When the One-Sample t-Options dialog box appears:
            Enter 90 in the **Confidence level** box
        Click **OK**

Population Proportion

TeeTimes

We illustrate interval estimation using the survey data for women golfers presented in Section 8.4. The data are in column C1 of a Minitab worksheet. Individual responses are recorded as Yes if the golfer is satisfied with the availability of tee times and No otherwise. The following steps can be used to compute a 95% confidence interval estimate of the proportion of women golfers who are satisfied with the availability of tee times.

Step 1. Select the **Stat** menu
Step 2. Choose **Basic Statistics**
Step 3. Choose **1 Proportion**
Step 4. When the One-Sample Proportion dialog box appears:
        Select **One or more samples, each in a column** from the pull-down menu
        Enter C1 in the box immediately below the pull-down menu
Step 5. Select **Options**
Step 6. When the One-Sample Proportion-Options dialog box appears:
        Select **Normal approximation** from the Method pull down menu
        Click **OK**
Step 7. Click **OK**

The Minitab default is a 95% confidence level. In order to specify a different confidence level such as 90%, enter 90 in the **Confidence Level** box when the 1 Proportion-Options dialog box appears in step 6.

Note: Minitab's 1 Proportion routine uses an alphabetical ordering of the responses and selects the *second response* for the population proportion of interest. In the women golfers example, Minitab used the alphabetical ordering No-Yes and then provided the confidence interval for the proportion of Yes responses. Because Yes was the response of interest, the Minitab output was fine. However, if Minitab's alphabetical ordering does not provide the response of interest, select any cell in the column and use the sequence: Editor > Column > Value Order. It will provide you with the option of entering a user-specified order, but you must list the response of interest second in the define-an-order box.

*You can also select the **Exact** from the Method pull-down menu when calculating a confidence interval for one proportion. This method uses the binomial distribution for calculating a confidence interval for one population proportion.*

Appendix 8.2   Interval Estimation Using Excel

We describe the use of Excel in constructing confidence intervals for a population mean and a population proportion.

Population Mean: σ Known

Lloyd's

We illustrate interval estimation using the Lloyd's example in Section 8.1. The population standard deviation $\sigma = 20$ is assumed known. The amounts spent for the sample of 100 customers are in column A of an Excel worksheet. Excel's AVERAGE and CONFIDENCE.NORM functions can be used to compute the point estimate and the margin of error for an estimate of the population mean.

> **Step 1.** Select cell C1 and enter the Excel formula =AVERAGE(A2:A101)
> **Step 2.** Select cell C2 and enter the Excel formula =CONFIDENCE.NORM(.05,20,100)

The three inputs of the CONFIDENCE.NORM function are

$$\text{Alpha} = 1 - \text{confidence coefficient} = 1 - .95 = .05$$
$$\text{The population standard deviation} = 20$$
$$\text{The sample size} = 100$$

The point estimate of the population mean (82) in cell C1 and the margin of error (3.92) in cell C2 allow the confidence interval for the population mean to be easily computed.

Population Mean: σ Unknown

NewBalance

We illustrate interval estimation using the data in Table 8.3, which show the credit card balances for a sample of 70 households. The data are in column A of an Excel worksheet. The following steps can be used to compute the point estimate and the margin of error for an interval estimate of a population mean. We will use Excel's Descriptive Statistics Tool described in Chapter 3.

> **Step 1.** Click the **Data** tab on the Ribbon
> **Step 2.** In the **Analysis** group, click **Data Analysis**
> **Step 3.** Choose **Descriptive Statistics** from the list of Analysis Tools
> **Step 4.** When the Descriptive Statistics dialog box appears:
> > Enter A1:A71 in the **Input Range** box
> > Select **Grouped by Columns**
> > Select **Labels in First Row**
> > Select **Output Range**
> > Enter C1 in the Output Range box
> > Select **Summary Statistics**
> > Select **Confidence Level for Mean**
> > > Enter 95 in the Confidence Level for Mean box
> > Click **OK**

The summary statistics will appear in columns C and D. The point estimate of the population mean appears in cell D3. The margin of error, labeled "Confidence Level(95.0%)," appears in cell D16. The point estimate ($9312) and the margin of error ($955) allow the confidence interval for the population mean to be easily computed. The output from this Excel procedure is shown in Figure 8.10.

FIGURE 8.10   INTERVAL ESTIMATION OF THE POPULATION MEAN CREDIT CARD
BALANCE USING EXCEL

	A	B	C	D	E	F
1	NewBalance		*NewBalance*			
2	9430				Point Estimate	
3	7535		Mean	9312		
4	4078		Standard Error	478.9281		
5	5604		Median	9466		
6	5179		Mode	13627		
7	4416		Standard Deviation	4007		
8	10676		Sample Variance	16056048		
9	1627		Kurtosis	-0.2960		
10	10112		Skewness	0.1879		
11	6567		Range	18648		
12	13627		Minimum	615		
13	18719		Maximum	19263		
14	14661		Sum	651840		
15	12195		Count	70	Margin of Error	
16	10544		Confidence Level(95.0%)	955		
17	13659					
70	9743					
71	10324					
72						

Note: Rows 18 to 69 are hidden.

Population Proportion

We illustrate interval estimation using the survey data for women golfers presented in
Section 8.4. The data are in column A of an Excel worksheet. Individual responses are
recorded as Yes if the golfer is satisfied with the availability of tee times and No otherwise.
Excel does not offer a built-in routine to handle the estimation of a population proportion;
however, it is relatively easy to develop an Excel template that can be used for this purpose.
The template shown in Figure 8.11 provides the 95% confidence interval estimate of the
proportion of women golfers who are satisfied with the availability of tee times. Note that
the background worksheet in Figure 8.11 shows the cell formulas that provide the interval
estimation results shown in the foreground worksheet. The following steps are necessary to
use the template for this data set.

DATA *file*

Interval p

> **Step 1.** Enter the data range A2:A901 into the =COUNTA cell formula in cell D3
> **Step 2.** Enter Yes as the response of interest in cell D4
> **Step 3.** Enter the data range A2:A901 into the =COUNTIF cell formula in cell D5
> **Step 4.** Enter .95 as the confidence coefficient in cell D8

The template automatically provides the confidence interval in cells D15 and D16.

This template can be used to compute the confidence interval for a population proportion for other applications. For instance, to compute the interval estimate for a new data set,
enter the new sample data into column A of the worksheet and then make the changes to

FIGURE 8.11 EXCEL TEMPLATE FOR INTERVAL ESTIMATION OF A POPULATION PROPORTION

	A	B	C	D	E
1	**Response**		**Interval Estimate of a Population Proportion**		
2	Yes				
3	No		Sample Size	=COUNTA(A2:A901)	
4	Yes		Response of Interest	Yes	
5	Yes		Count for Response	=COUNTIF(A2:A901,D4)	
6	No		Sample Proportion	=D5/D3	
7	No				
8	No		Confidence Coefficient	0.95	
9	Yes		z Value	=NORM.S.INV(0.5+D8/2)	
10	Yes				
11	Yes		Standard Error	=SQRT(D6*(1-D6)/D3)	
12	No		Margin of Error	=D9*D11	
13	No				
14	Yes		Point Estimate	=D6	
15	No		Lower Limit	=D14-D12	
16	No		Upper Limit	=D14+D12	
17	Yes				
18	No				
901	Yes				
902					

	A	B	C	D	E	F	G
1	Response		**Interval Estimate of a Population Proportion**				
2	Yes						
3	No		Sample Size	900	Enter the response of interest		
4	Yes		Response of Interest	Yes			
5	Yes		Count for Response	396			
6	No		Sample Proportion	0.4400			
7	No						
8	No		Confidence Coefficient	0.95	Enter the confidence coefficient		
9	Yes		z Value	1.960			
10	Yes						
11	Yes		Standard Error	0.0165			
12	No		Margin of Error	0.0324			
13	No						
14	Yes		Point Estimate	0.4400			
15	No		Lower Limit	0.4076			
16	No		Upper Limit	0.4724			
17	Yes						
18	No						
901	Yes						
902							

DATA *file*

TeeTimes

Note: Rows 19 to 900 are hidden.

the four cells as shown. If the new sample data have already been summarized, the sample data do not have to be entered into the worksheet. In this case, enter the sample size into cell D3 and the sample proportion into cell D6; the worksheet template will then provide the confidence interval for the population proportion. The worksheet in Figure 8.11 is available in the file Interval p on the website that accompanies this book.

CHAPTER 9

Hypothesis Tests

CONTENTS

STATISTICS *in* PRACTICE

JOHN MORRELL & COMPANY*
CINCINNATI, OHIO

John Morrell & Company, which began in England in 1827, is considered the oldest continuously operating meat manufacturer in the United States. It is a wholly owned and independently managed subsidiary of Smithfield Foods, Smithfield, Virginia. John Morrell & Company offers an extensive product line of processed meats and fresh pork to consumers under 13 regional brands including John Morrell, E-Z-Cut, Tobin's First Prize, Dinner Bell, Hunter, Kretschmar, Rath, Rodeo, Shenson, Farmers Hickory Brand, Iowa Quality, and Peyton's. Each regional brand enjoys high brand recognition and loyalty among consumers.

Market research at Morrell provides management with up-to-date information on the company's various products and how the products compare with competing brands of similar products. A recent study compared a Beef Pot Roast made by Morrell to similar beef products from two major competitors. In the three-product comparison test, a sample of consumers was used to indicate how the products rated in terms of taste, appearance, aroma, and overall preference.

One research question concerned whether the Beef Pot Roast made by Morrell was the preferred choice of more than 50% of the consumer population. Letting p indicate the population proportion preferring Morrell's product, the hypothesis test for the research question is as follows:

$$H_0: p \leq .50$$
$$H_a: p > .50$$

The null hypothesis H_0 indicates the preference for Morrell's product is less than or equal to 50%. If the sample data support rejecting H_0 in favor of the

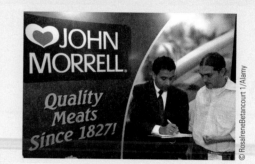

Market research at Morrell provides up-to-date information on their various products and how they compare with competing brands.

alternative hypothesis H_a, Morrell will draw the research conclusion that in a three-product comparison, their Beef Pot Roast is preferred by more than 50% of the consumer population.

In an independent taste test study using a sample of 224 consumers in Cincinnati, Milwaukee, and Los Angeles, 150 consumers selected the Beef Pot Roast made by Morrell as the preferred product. Using statistical hypothesis testing procedures, the null hypothesis H_0 was rejected. The study provided statistical evidence supporting H_a and the conclusion that the Morrell product is preferred by more than 50% of the consumer population.

The point estimate of the population proportion was $\bar{p} = 150/224 = .67$. Thus, the sample data provided support for a food magazine advertisement showing that in a three-product taste comparison, Beef Pot Roast made by Morrell was "preferred 2 to 1 over the competition."

In this chapter we will discuss how to formulate hypotheses and how to conduct tests like the one used by Morrell. Through the analysis of sample data, we will be able to determine whether a hypothesis should or should not be rejected.

---

*The authors are indebted to Marty Butler, Vice President of Marketing, John Morrell, for providing this Statistics in Practice.

In Chapters 7 and 8 we showed how a sample could be used to develop point and interval estimates of population parameters. In this chapter we continue the discussion of statistical inference by showing how hypothesis testing can be used to determine whether a statement about the value of a population parameter should or should not be rejected.

In hypothesis testing we begin by making a tentative assumption about a population parameter. This tentative assumption is called the **null hypothesis** and is denoted by H_0. We then define another hypothesis, called the **alternative hypothesis**, which is the opposite of what is stated in the null hypothesis. The alternative hypothesis is denoted by H_a.

The hypothesis testing procedure uses data from a sample to test the two competing statements indicated by H_0 and H_a.

This chapter shows how hypothesis tests can be conducted about a population mean and a population proportion. We begin by providing examples that illustrate approaches to developing null and alternative hypotheses.

9.1 Developing Null and Alternative Hypotheses

It is not always obvious how the null and alternative hypotheses should be formulated. Care must be taken to structure the hypotheses appropriately so that the hypothesis testing conclusion provides the information the researcher or decision maker wants. The context of the situation is very important in determining how the hypotheses should be stated. All hypothesis testing applications involve collecting a sample and using the sample results to provide evidence for drawing a conclusion. Good questions to consider when formulating the null and alternative hypotheses are, What is the purpose of collecting the sample? What conclusions are we hoping to make?

Learning to correctly formulate hypotheses will take some practice. Expect some initial confusion over the proper choice of the null and alternative hypotheses. The examples in this section are intended to provide guidelines.

In the chapter introduction, we stated that the null hypothesis H_0 is a tentative assumption about a population parameter such as a population mean or a population proportion. The alternative hypothesis H_a is a statement that is the opposite of what is stated in the null hypothesis. In some situations it is easier to identify the alternative hypothesis first and then develop the null hypothesis. In other situations it is easier to identify the null hypothesis first and then develop the alternative hypothesis. We will illustrate these situations in the following examples.

The Alternative Hypothesis as a Research Hypothesis

Many applications of hypothesis testing involve an attempt to gather evidence in support of a research hypothesis. In these situations, it is often best to begin with the alternative hypothesis and make it the conclusion that the researcher hopes to support. Consider a particular automobile that currently attains a fuel efficiency of 24 miles per gallon in city driving. A product research group has developed a new fuel injection system designed to increase the miles-per-gallon rating. The group will run controlled tests with the new fuel injection system looking for statistical support for the conclusion that the new fuel injection system provides more miles per gallon than the current system.

Several new fuel injection units will be manufactured, installed in test automobiles, and subjected to research-controlled driving conditions. The sample mean miles per gallon for these automobiles will be computed and used in a hypothesis test to determine if it can be concluded that the new system provides more than 24 miles per gallon. In terms of the population mean miles per gallon μ, the research hypothesis $\mu > 24$ becomes the alternative hypothesis. Since the current system provides an average or mean of 24 miles per gallon, we will make the tentative assumption that the new system is not any better than the current system and choose $\mu \leq 24$ as the null hypothesis. The null and alternative hypotheses are:

$$H_0: \mu \leq 24$$
$$H_a: \mu > 24$$

If the sample results lead to the conclusion to reject H_0, the inference can be made that $H_a: \mu > 24$ is true. The researchers have the statistical support to state that the new fuel injection system increases the mean number of miles per gallon. The production of automobiles with the new fuel injection system should be considered. However, if the sample results lead to the conclusion that H_0 cannot be rejected, the researchers cannot conclude

The conclusion that the research hypothesis is true is made if the sample data provide sufficient evidence to show that the null hypothesis can be rejected.

that the new fuel injection system is better than the current system. Production of automobiles with the new fuel injection system on the basis of better gas mileage cannot be justified. Perhaps more research and further testing can be conducted.

Successful companies stay competitive by developing new products, new methods, new systems, and the like, that are better than what is currently available. Before adopting something new, it is desirable to conduct research to determine if there is statistical support for the conclusion that the new approach is indeed better. In such cases, the research hypothesis is stated as the alternative hypothesis. For example, a new teaching method is developed that is believed to be better than the current method. The alternative hypothesis is that the new method is better. The null hypothesis is that the new method is no better than the old method. A new sales force bonus plan is developed in an attempt to increase sales. The alternative hypothesis is that the new bonus plan increases sales. The null hypothesis is that the new bonus plan does not increase sales. A new drug is developed with the goal of lowering blood pressure more than an existing drug. The alternative hypothesis is that the new drug lowers blood pressure more than the existing drug. The null hypothesis is that the new drug does not provide lower blood pressure than the existing drug. In each case, rejection of the null hypothesis H_0 provides statistical support for the research hypothesis. We will see many examples of hypothesis tests in research situations such as these throughout this chapter and in the remainder of the text.

The Null Hypothesis as an Assumption to Be Challenged

Of course, not all hypothesis tests involve research hypotheses. In the following discussion we consider applications of hypothesis testing where we begin with a belief or an assumption that a statement about the value of a population parameter is true. We will then use a hypothesis test to challenge the assumption and determine if there is statistical evidence to conclude that the assumption is incorrect. In these situations, it is helpful to develop the null hypothesis first. The null hypothesis H_0 expresses the belief or assumption about the value of the population parameter. The alternative hypothesis H_a is that the belief or assumption is incorrect.

As an example, consider the situation of a manufacturer of soft drink products. The label on a soft drink bottle states that it contains 67.6 fluid ounces. We consider the label correct provided the population mean filling weight for the bottles is *at least* 67.6 fluid ounces. Without any reason to believe otherwise, we would give the manufacturer the benefit of the doubt and assume that the statement provided on the label is correct. Thus, in a hypothesis test about the population mean fluid weight per bottle, we would begin with the assumption that the label is correct and state the null hypothesis as $\mu \geq 67.6$. The challenge to this assumption would imply that the label is incorrect and the bottles are being underfilled. This challenge would be stated as the alternative hypothesis $\mu < 67.6$. Thus, the null and alternative hypotheses are:

$$H_0: \mu \geq 67.6$$
$$H_a: \mu < 67.6$$

A manufacturer's product information is usually assumed to be true and stated as the null hypothesis. The conclusion that the information is incorrect can be made if the null hypothesis is rejected.

A government agency with the responsibility for validating manufacturing labels could select a sample of soft drinks bottles, compute the sample mean filling weight, and use the sample results to test the preceding hypotheses. If the sample results lead to the conclusion to reject H_0, the inference that $H_a: \mu < 67.6$ is true can be made. With this statistical support, the agency is justified in concluding that the label is incorrect and underfilling of the bottles is occurring. Appropriate action to force the manufacturer to comply with labeling standards would be considered. However, if the sample results indicate H_0 cannot be rejected, the assumption that the manufacturer's labeling is correct cannot be rejected. With this conclusion, no action would be taken.

Let us now consider a variation of the soft drink bottle filling example by viewing the same situation from the manufacturer's point of view. The bottle-filling operation has been designed to fill soft drink bottles with 67.6 fluid ounces as stated on the label. The company does not want to underfill the containers because that could result in an underfilling complaint from customers or, perhaps, a government agency. However, the company does not want to overfill containers either because putting more soft drink than necessary into the containers would be an unnecessary cost. The company's goal would be to adjust the bottle-filling operation so that the population mean filling weight per bottle is 67.6 fluid ounces as specified on the label.

Although this is the company's goal, from time to time any production process can get out of adjustment. If this occurs in our example, underfilling or overfilling of the soft drink bottles will occur. In either case, the company would like to know about it in order to correct the situation by readjusting the bottle-filling operation to the designed 67.6 fluid ounces. In a hypothesis testing application, we would again begin with the assumption that the production process is operating correctly and state the null hypothesis as $\mu = 67.6$ fluid ounces. The alternative hypothesis that challenges this assumption is that $\mu \neq 67.6$, which indicates either overfilling or underfilling is occurring. The null and alternative hypotheses for the manufacturer's hypothesis test are:

$$H_0: \mu = 67.6$$
$$H_a: \mu \neq 67.6$$

Suppose that the soft drink manufacturer uses a quality control procedure to periodically select a sample of bottles from the filling operation and computes the sample mean filling weight per bottle. If the sample results lead to the conclusion to reject H_0, the inference is made that $H_a: \mu \neq 67.6$ is true. We conclude that the bottles are not being filled properly and the production process should be adjusted to restore the population mean to 67.6 fluid ounces per bottle. However, if the sample results indicate H_0 cannot be rejected, the assumption that the manufacturer's bottle filling operation is functioning properly cannot be rejected. In this case, no further action would be taken and the production operation would continue to run.

The two preceding forms of the soft drink manufacturing hypothesis test show that the null and alternative hypotheses may vary depending upon the point of view of the researcher or decision maker. To correctly formulate hypotheses it is important to understand the context of the situation and structure the hypotheses to provide the information the researcher or decision maker wants.

Summary of Forms for Null and Alternative Hypotheses

The hypothesis tests in this chapter involve two population parameters: the population mean and the population proportion. Depending on the situation, hypothesis tests about a population parameter may take one of three forms: two use inequalities in the null hypothesis; the third uses an equality in the null hypothesis. For hypothesis tests involving a population mean, we let μ_0 denote the hypothesized value and we must choose one of the following three forms for the hypothesis test.

The three possible forms of hypotheses H_0 and H_a are shown here. Note that the equality always appears in the null hypothesis H_0.

$$H_0: \mu \geq \mu_0 \qquad H_0: \mu \leq \mu_0 \qquad H_0: \mu = \mu_0$$
$$H_a: \mu < \mu_0 \qquad H_a: \mu > \mu_0 \qquad H_a: \mu \neq \mu_0$$

For reasons that will be clear later, the first two forms are called one-tailed tests. The third form is called a two-tailed test.

In many situations, the choice of H_0 and H_a is not obvious and judgment is necessary to select the proper form. However, as the preceding forms show, the equality part of the expression (either $\geq$, $\leq$, or $=$) *always* appears in the null hypothesis. In selecting the proper form of H_0 and H_a, keep in mind that the alternative hypothesis is often what the test is attempting to establish. Hence, asking whether the user is looking for evidence to support $\mu < \mu_0$, $\mu > \mu_0$, or $\mu \neq \mu_0$ will help determine H_a. The following exercises are designed to provide practice in choosing the proper form for a hypothesis test involving a population mean.

Exercises

1. The manager of the Danvers-Hilton Resort Hotel stated that the mean guest bill for a weekend is $600 or less. A member of the hotel's accounting staff noticed that the total charges for guest bills have been increasing in recent months. The accountant will use a sample of future weekend guest bills to test the manager's claim.
   a. Which form of the hypotheses should be used to test the manager's claim? Explain.

   $$H_0: \mu \geq 600 \qquad H_0: \mu \leq 600 \qquad H_0: \mu = 600$$
   $$H_a: \mu < 600 \qquad H_a: \mu > 600 \qquad H_a: \mu \neq 600$$

   b. What conclusion is appropriate when H_0 cannot be rejected?
   c. What conclusion is appropriate when H_0 can be rejected?

✔SELF*test*

2. The manager of an automobile dealership is considering a new bonus plan designed to increase sales volume. Currently, the mean sales volume is 14 automobiles per month. The manager wants to conduct a research study to see whether the new bonus plan increases sales volume. To collect data on the plan, a sample of sales personnel will be allowed to sell under the new bonus plan for a one-month period.
   a. Develop the null and alternative hypotheses most appropriate for this situation.
   b. Comment on the conclusion when H_0 cannot be rejected.
   c. Comment on the conclusion when H_0 can be rejected.

3. A production line operation is designed to fill cartons with laundry detergent to a mean weight of 32 ounces. A sample of cartons is periodically selected and weighed to determine whether underfilling or overfilling is occurring. If the sample data lead to a conclusion of underfilling or overfilling, the production line will be shut down and adjusted to obtain proper filling.
   a. Formulate the null and alternative hypotheses that will help in deciding whether to shut down and adjust the production line.
   b. Comment on the conclusion and the decision when H_0 cannot be rejected.
   c. Comment on the conclusion and the decision when H_0 can be rejected.

4. Because of high production-changeover time and costs, a director of manufacturing must convince management that a proposed manufacturing method reduces costs before the new method can be implemented. The current production method operates with a mean cost of $220 per hour. A research study will measure the cost of the new method over a sample production period.
   a. Develop the null and alternative hypotheses most appropriate for this study.
   b. Comment on the conclusion when H_0 cannot be rejected.
   c. Comment on the conclusion when H_0 can be rejected.

(9.2) Type I and Type II Errors

The null and alternative hypotheses are competing statements about the population. Either the null hypothesis H_0 is true or the alternative hypothesis H_a is true, but not both. Ideally the hypothesis testing procedure should lead to the acceptance of H_0 when H_0 is true and

TABLE 9.1   ERRORS AND CORRECT CONCLUSIONS IN HYPOTHESIS TESTING

		Population Condition	
		H_0 **True**	H_a **True**
Conclusion	**Accept H_0**	Correct Conclusion	Type II Error
	Reject H_0	Type I Error	Correct Conclusion

the rejection of H_0 when H_a is true. Unfortunately, the correct conclusions are not always possible. Because hypothesis tests are based on sample information, we must allow for the possibility of errors. Table 9.1 illustrates the two kinds of errors that can be made in hypothesis testing.

The first row of Table 9.1 shows what can happen if the conclusion is to accept H_0. If H_0 is true, this conclusion is correct. However, if H_a is true, we make a **Type II error**; that is, we accept H_0 when it is false. The second row of Table 9.1 shows what can happen if the conclusion is to reject H_0. If H_0 is true, we make a **Type I error**; that is, we reject H_0 when it is true. However, if H_a is true, rejecting H_0 is correct.

Recall the hypothesis testing illustration discussed in Section 9.1 in which an automobile product research group developed a new fuel injection system designed to increase the miles-per-gallon rating of a particular automobile. With the current model obtaining an average of 24 miles per gallon, the hypothesis test was formulated as follows.

$$H_0: \mu \leq 24$$
$$H_a: \mu > 24$$

The alternative hypothesis, $H_a: \mu > 24$, indicates that the researchers are looking for sample evidence to support the conclusion that the population mean miles per gallon with the new fuel injection system is greater than 24.

In this application, the Type I error of rejecting H_0 when it is true corresponds to the researchers claiming that the new system improves the miles-per-gallon rating ($\mu > 24$) when in fact the new system is not any better than the current system. In contrast, the Type II error of accepting H_0 when it is false corresponds to the researchers concluding that the new system is not any better than the current system ($\mu \leq 24$) when in fact the new system improves miles-per-gallon performance.

For the miles-per-gallon rating hypothesis test, the null hypothesis is $H_0: \mu \leq 24$. Suppose the null hypothesis is true as an equality; that is, $\mu = 24$. The probability of making a Type I error when the null hypothesis is true as an equality is called the **level of significance**. Thus, for the miles-per-gallon rating hypothesis test, the level of significance is the probability of rejecting $H_0: \mu \leq 24$ when $\mu = 24$. Because of the importance of this concept, we now restate the definition of level of significance.

LEVEL OF SIGNIFICANCE

The level of significance is the probability of making a Type I error when the null hypothesis is true as an equality.

The Greek symbol α (alpha) is used to denote the level of significance, and common choices for α are .05 and .01.

In practice, the person responsible for the hypothesis test specifies the level of significance. By selecting α, that person is controlling the probability of making a Type I error. If the cost of making a Type I error is high, small values of α are preferred. If the cost of making a Type I error is not too high, larger values of α are typically used. Applications of hypothesis testing that only control for the Type I error are called *significance tests*. Many applications of hypothesis testing are of this type.

If the sample data are consistent with the null hypothesis H_0, we will follow the practice of concluding "do not reject H_0." This conclusion is preferred over "accept H_0," because the conclusion to accept H_0 puts us at risk of making a Type II error.

Although most applications of hypothesis testing control for the probability of making a Type I error, they do not always control for the probability of making a Type II error. Hence, if we decide to accept H_0, we cannot determine how confident we can be with that decision. Because of the uncertainty associated with making a Type II error when conducting significance tests, statisticians usually recommend that we use the statement "do not reject H_0" instead of "accept H_0." Using the statement "do not reject H_0" carries the recommendation to withhold both judgment and action. In effect, by not directly accepting H_0, the statistician avoids the risk of making a Type II error. Whenever the probability of making a Type II error has not been determined and controlled, we will not make the statement "accept H_0." In such cases, only two conclusions are possible: *do not reject H_0 or reject H_0*.

Although controlling for a Type II error in hypothesis testing is not common, it can be done. In Sections 9.7 and 9.8 we will illustrate procedures for determining and controlling the probability of making a Type II error. If proper controls have been established for this error, action based on the "accept H_0" conclusion can be appropriate.

NOTES AND COMMENTS

Walter Williams, syndicated columnist and professor of economics at George Mason University, points out that the possibility of making a Type I or a Type II error is always present in decision making (*The Cincinnati Enquirer,* August 14, 2005). He notes that the Food and Drug Administration (FDA) runs the risk of making these errors in its drug approval process. The FDA must either approve a new drug or not approve it. Thus the FDA runs the risk of making a Type I error by approving a new drug that is not safe and effective, or making a Type II error by failing to approve a new drug that is safe and effective. Regardless of the decision made, the possibility of making a costly error cannot be eliminated.

Exercises

✓SELF*test*

5. Duke Energy reported that the cost of electricity for an efficient home in a particular neighborhood of Cincinnati, Ohio, was $104 per month (*Home Energy Report,* Duke Energy, March 2012). A researcher believes that the cost of electricity for a comparable neighborhood in Chicago, Illinois, is higher. A sample of homes in this Chicago neighborhood will be taken and the sample mean monthly cost of electricity will be used to test the following null and alternative hypotheses.

$$H_0: \mu \leq 104$$
$$H_a: \mu > 104$$

   a. Assume the sample data led to rejection of the null hypothesis. What would be your conclusion about the cost of electricity in the Chicago neighborhood?
   b. What is the Type I error in this situation? What are the consequences of making this error?
   c. What is the Type II error in this situation? What are the consequences of making this error?

6. The label on a 3-quart container of orange juice states that the orange juice contains an average of 1 gram of fat or less. Answer the following questions for a hypothesis test that could be used to test the claim on the label.
    a. Develop the appropriate null and alternative hypotheses.
    b. What is the Type I error in this situation? What are the consequences of making this error?
    c. What is the Type II error in this situation? What are the consequences of making this error?

7. Carpetland salespersons average $8000 per week in sales. Steve Contois, the firm's vice president, proposes a compensation plan with new selling incentives. Steve hopes that the results of a trial selling period will enable him to conclude that the compensation plan increases the average sales per salesperson.
    a. Develop the appropriate null and alternative hypotheses.
    b. What is the Type I error in this situation? What are the consequences of making this error?
    c. What is the Type II error in this situation? What are the consequences of making this error?

8. Suppose a new production method will be implemented if a hypothesis test supports the conclusion that the new method reduces the mean operating cost per hour.
    a. State the appropriate null and alternative hypotheses if the mean cost for the current production method is $220 per hour.
    b. What is the Type I error in this situation? What are the consequences of making this error?
    c. What is the Type II error in this situation? What are the consequences of making this error?

9.3 Population Mean: σ Known

In Chapter 8 we said that the σ known case corresponds to applications in which historical data and/or other information are available that enable us to obtain a good estimate of the population standard deviation prior to sampling. In such cases the population standard deviation can, for all practical purposes, be considered known. In this section we show how to conduct a hypothesis test about a population mean for the σ known case.

The methods presented in this section are exact if the sample is selected from a population that is normally distributed. In cases where it is not reasonable to assume the population is normally distributed, these methods are still applicable if the sample size is large enough. We provide some practical advice concerning the population distribution and the sample size at the end of this section.

One-Tailed Test

One-tailed tests about a population mean take one of the following two forms.

Lower Tail Test	Upper Tail Test
$H_0: \mu \geq \mu_0$	$H_0: \mu \leq \mu_0$
$H_a: \mu < \mu_0$	$H_a: \mu > \mu_0$

Let us consider an example involving a lower tail test.

The Federal Trade Commission (FTC) periodically conducts statistical studies designed to test the claims that manufacturers make about their products. For example, the label on a large can of Hilltop Coffee states that the can contains 3 pounds of coffee. The FTC knows that Hilltop's production process cannot place exactly 3 pounds of coffee in each can, even if the mean filling weight for the population of all cans filled is 3 pounds per can. However, as long as the population mean filling weight is at least 3 pounds per can, the rights of consumers will be protected. Thus, the FTC interprets the label information on a large can of coffee as a claim by Hilltop that the population mean filling weight is at least 3 pounds per can. We will show how the FTC can check Hilltop's claim by conducting a lower tail hypothesis test.

The first step is to develop the null and alternative hypotheses for the test. If the population mean filling weight is at least 3 pounds per can, Hilltop's claim is correct. This establishes the null hypothesis for the test. However, if the population mean weight is less than 3 pounds per can, Hilltop's claim is incorrect. This establishes the alternative hypothesis. With μ denoting the population mean filling weight, the null and alternative hypotheses are as follows:

$$H_0: \mu \geq 3$$
$$H_a: \mu < 3$$

Note that the hypothesized value of the population mean is $\mu_0 = 3$.

If the sample data indicate that H_0 cannot be rejected, the statistical evidence does not support the conclusion that a label violation has occurred. Hence, no action should be taken against Hilltop. However, if the sample data indicate H_0 can be rejected, we will conclude that the alternative hypothesis, $H_a: \mu < 3$, is true. In this case a conclusion of underfilling and a charge of a label violation against Hilltop would be justified.

Suppose a sample of 36 cans of coffee is selected and the sample mean $\bar{x}$ is computed as an estimate of the population mean μ. If the value of the sample mean $\bar{x}$ is less than 3 pounds, the sample results will cast doubt on the null hypothesis. What we want to know is how much less than 3 pounds must $\bar{x}$ be before we would be willing to declare the difference significant and risk making a Type I error by falsely accusing Hilltop of a label violation. A key factor in addressing this issue is the value the decision maker selects for the level of significance.

As noted in the preceding section, the level of significance, denoted by α, is the probability of making a Type I error by rejecting H_0 when the null hypothesis is true as an equality. The decision maker must specify the level of significance. If the cost of making a Type I error is high, a small value should be chosen for the level of significance. If the cost is not high, a larger value is more appropriate. In the Hilltop Coffee study, the director of the FTC's testing program made the following statement: "If the company is meeting its weight specifications at $\mu = 3$, I do not want to take action against them. But, I am willing to risk a 1% chance of making such an error." From the director's statement, we set the level of significance for the hypothesis test at $\alpha = .01$. Thus, we must design the hypothesis test so that the probability of making a Type I error when $\mu = 3$ is .01.

For the Hilltop Coffee study, by developing the null and alternative hypotheses and specifying the level of significance for the test, we carry out the first two steps required in conducting every hypothesis test. We are now ready to perform the third step of hypothesis testing: collect the sample data and compute the value of what is called a test statistic.

Test statistic For the Hilltop Coffee study, previous FTC tests show that the population standard deviation can be assumed known with a value of $\sigma = .18$. In addition, these tests also show that the population of filling weights can be assumed to have a normal distribution. From the study of sampling distributions in Chapter 7 we know that if the population from which we are sampling is normally distributed, the sampling distribution of $\bar{x}$ will also be normally distributed. Thus, for the Hilltop Coffee study, the sampling distribution of $\bar{x}$ is normally distributed. With a known value of $\sigma = .18$ and a sample size of $n = 36$, Figure 9.1 shows the sampling distribution of $\bar{x}$ when the null hypothesis is true as an equality; that is, when $\mu = \mu_0 = 3$.[1] Note that the standard error of $\bar{x}$ is given by $\sigma_{\bar{x}} = \sigma / \sqrt{n} = .18 / \sqrt{36} = .03$.

Because the sampling distribution of $\bar{x}$ is normally distributed, the sampling distribution of

The standard error of $\bar{x}$ is the standard deviation of the sampling distribution of $\bar{x}$.

$$z = \frac{\bar{x} - \mu_0}{\sigma_{\bar{x}}} = \frac{\bar{x} - 3}{.03}$$

---

[1]In constructing sampling distributions for hypothesis tests, it is assumed that H_0 is satisfied as an equality.

FIGURE 9.1   SAMPLING DISTRIBUTION OF $\bar{x}$ FOR THE HILLTOP COFFEE STUDY WHEN
THE NULL HYPOTHESIS IS TRUE AS AN EQUALITY ($\mu = 3$)

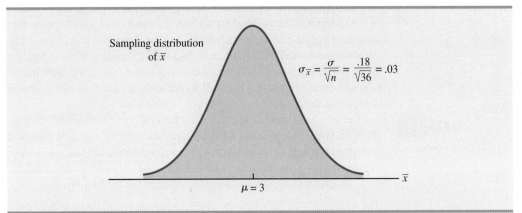

is a standard normal distribution. A value of $z = -1$ means that the value of $\bar{x}$ is one standard error below the hypothesized value of the mean, a value of $z = -2$ means that the value of $\bar{x}$ is two standard errors below the hypothesized value of the mean, and so on. We can use the standard normal probability table to find the lower tail probability corresponding to any z value. For instance, the lower tail area at $z = -3.00$ is .0013. Hence, the probability of obtaining a value of z that is three or more standard errors below the mean is .0013. As a result, the probability of obtaining a value of $\bar{x}$ that is 3 or more standard errors below the hypothesized population mean $\mu_0 = 3$ is also .0013. Such a result is unlikely if the null hypothesis is true.

For hypothesis tests about a population mean in the σ known case, we use the standard normal random variable z as a **test statistic** to determine whether $\bar{x}$ deviates from the hypothesized value of μ enough to justify rejecting the null hypothesis. With $\sigma_{\bar{x}} = \sigma/\sqrt{n}$, the test statistic is as follows.

TEST STATISTIC FOR HYPOTHESIS TESTS ABOUT A POPULATION MEAN:
σ KNOWN

$$z = \frac{\bar{x} - \mu_0}{\sigma/\sqrt{n}} \tag{9.1}$$

The key question for a lower tail test is, How small must the test statistic z be before we choose to reject the null hypothesis? Two approaches can be used to answer this question: the p-value approach and the critical value approach.

p-value approach   The p-value approach uses the value of the test statistic z to compute a probability called a **p-value**.

A small p-value indicates the value of the test statistic is unusual given the assumption that H_0 is true.

---

p-VALUE

A **p-value** is a probability that provides a measure of the evidence against the null hypothesis provided by the sample. Smaller p-values indicate more evidence against H_0.

The p-value is used to determine whether the null hypothesis should be rejected.

Let us see how the *p*-value is computed and used. The value of the test statistic is used to compute the *p*-value. The method used depends on whether the test is a lower tail, an upper tail, or a two-tailed test. For a lower tail test, the *p*-value is the probability of obtaining a value for the test statistic as small as or smaller than that provided by the sample. Thus, to compute the *p*-value for the lower tail test in the σ known case, we use the standard normal distribution to find the probability that *z* is less than or equal to the value of the test statistic. After computing the *p*-value, we must then decide whether it is small enough to reject the null hypothesis; as we will show, this decision involves comparing the *p*-value to the level of significance.

Coffee

Let us now compute the *p*-value for the Hilltop Coffee lower tail test. Suppose the sample of 36 Hilltop coffee cans provides a sample mean of $\bar{x} = 2.92$ pounds. Is $\bar{x} = 2.92$ small enough to cause us to reject H_0? Because this is a lower tail test, the *p*-value is the area under the standard normal curve for values of $z \leq$ the value of the test statistic. Using $\bar{x} = 2.92$, $\sigma = .18$, and $n = 36$, we compute the value of the test statistic *z*.

$$z = \frac{\bar{x} - \mu_0}{\sigma/\sqrt{n}} = \frac{2.92 - 3}{.18/\sqrt{36}} = -2.67$$

Thus, the *p*-value is the probability that *z* is less than or equal to -2.67 (the lower tail area corresponding to the value of the test statistic).

Using the standard normal probability table, we find that the lower tail area at $z = -2.67$ is .0038. Figure 9.2 shows that $\bar{x} = 2.92$ corresponds to $z = -2.67$ and a *p*-value = .0038. This *p*-value indicates a small probability of obtaining a sample mean of $\bar{x} = 2.92$ (and a test statistic of -2.67) or smaller when sampling from a population with $\mu = 3$. This *p*-value

FIGURE 9.2   *p*-VALUE FOR THE HILLTOP COFFEE STUDY WHEN $\bar{x} = 2.92$ AND $z = -2.67$

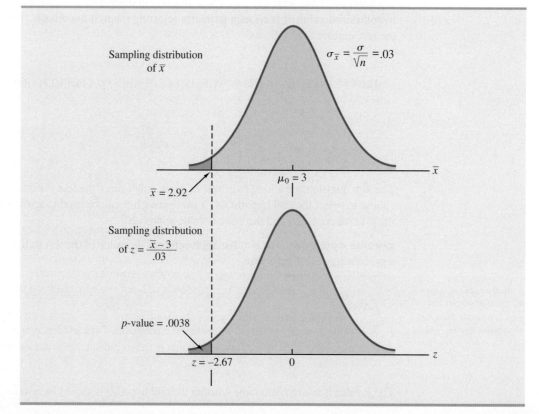

does not provide much support for the null hypothesis, but is it small enough to cause us to reject H_0? The answer depends upon the level of significance for the test.

As noted previously, the director of the FTC's testing program selected a value of .01 for the level of significance. The selection of $\alpha = .01$ means that the director is willing to tolerate a probability of .01 of rejecting the null hypothesis when it is true as an equality ($\mu_0 = 3$). The sample of 36 coffee cans in the Hilltop Coffee study resulted in a p-value = .0038, which means that the probability of obtaining a value of $\bar{x} = 2.92$ or less when the null hypothesis is true as an equality is .0038. Because .0038 is less than or equal to $\alpha = .01$, we reject H_0. Therefore, we find sufficient statistical evidence to reject the null hypothesis at the .01 level of significance.

We can now state the general rule for determining whether the null hypothesis can be rejected when using the p-value approach. For a level of significance α, the rejection rule using the p-value approach is as follows:

> **REJECTION RULE USING p-VALUE**
>
> Reject H_0 if p-value $\leq \alpha$

In the Hilltop Coffee test, the p-value of .0038 resulted in the rejection of the null hypothesis. Although the basis for making the rejection decision involves a comparison of the p-value to the level of significance specified by the FTC director, the observed p-value of .0038 means that we would reject H_0 for any value of $\alpha \geq .0038$. For this reason, the p-value is also called the *observed level of significance*.

Different decision makers may express different opinions concerning the cost of making a Type I error and may choose a different level of significance. By providing the p-value as part of the hypothesis testing results, another decision maker can compare the reported p-value to his or her own level of significance and possibly make a different decision with respect to rejecting H_0.

Critical value approach The critical value approach requires that we first determine a value for the test statistic called the **critical value**. For a lower tail test, the critical value serves as a benchmark for determining whether the value of the test statistic is small enough to reject the null hypothesis. It is the value of the test statistic that corresponds to an area of α (the level of significance) in the lower tail of the sampling distribution of the test statistic. In other words, the critical value is the largest value of the test statistic that will result in the rejection of the null hypothesis. Let us return to the Hilltop Coffee example and see how this approach works.

In the σ known case, the sampling distribution for the test statistic z is a standard normal distribution. Therefore, the critical value is the value of the test statistic that corresponds to an area of $\alpha = .01$ in the lower tail of a standard normal distribution. Using the standard normal probability table, we find that $z = -2.33$ provides an area of .01 in the lower tail (see Figure 9.3). Thus, if the sample results in a value of the test statistic that is less than or equal to -2.33, the corresponding p-value will be less than or equal to .01; in this case, we should reject the null hypothesis. Hence, for the Hilltop Coffee study the critical value rejection rule for a level of significance of .01 is

$$\text{Reject } H_0 \text{ if } z \leq -2.33$$

In the Hilltop Coffee example, $\bar{x} = 2.92$ and the test statistic is $z = -2.67$. Because $z = -2.67 < -2.33$, we can reject H_0 and conclude that Hilltop Coffee is underfilling cans.

FIGURE 9.3   CRITICAL VALUE $= -2.33$ FOR THE HILLTOP COFFEE HYPOTHESIS TEST

We can generalize the rejection rule for the critical value approach to handle any level of significance. The rejection rule for a lower tail test follows.

REJECTION RULE FOR A LOWER TAIL TEST: CRITICAL VALUE APPROACH

$$\text{Reject } H_0 \text{ if } z \leq -z_\alpha$$

where $-z_\alpha$ is the critical value; that is, the z value that provides an area of α in the lower tail of the standard normal distribution.

Summary The p-value approach to hypothesis testing and the critical value approach will always lead to the same rejection decision; that is, whenever the p-value is less than or equal to α, the value of the test statistic will be less than or equal to the critical value. The advantage of the p-value approach is that the p-value tells us *how* significant the results are (the observed level of significance). If we use the critical value approach, we only know that the results are significant at the stated level of significance.

At the beginning of this section, we said that one-tailed tests about a population mean take one of the following two forms:

Lower Tail Test	Upper Tail Test
$H_0: \mu \geq \mu_0$	$H_0: \mu \leq \mu_0$
$H_a: \mu < \mu_0$	$H_a: \mu > \mu_0$

We used the Hilltop Coffee study to illustrate how to conduct a lower tail test. We can use the same general approach to conduct an upper tail test. The test statistic z is still computed using equation (9.1). But, for an upper tail test, the p-value is the probability of obtaining a value for the test statistic as large as or larger than that provided by the sample. Thus, to compute the p-value for the upper tail test in the σ known case, we must use the standard normal distribution to find the probability that z is greater than or equal to the value of the test statistic. Using the critical value approach causes us to reject the null hypothesis if the value of the test statistic is greater than or equal to the critical value z_α; in other words, we reject H_0 if $z \geq z_\alpha$.

Let us summarize the steps involved in computing p-values for one-tailed hypothesis tests.

COMPUTATION OF p-VALUES FOR ONE-TAILED TESTS

1. Compute the value of the test statistic using equation (9.1).
2. **Lower tail test:** Using the standard normal distribution, compute the probability that z is less than or equal to the value of the test statistic (area in the lower tail).
3. **Upper tail test:** Using the standard normal distribution, compute the probability that z is greater than or equal to the value of the test statistic (area in the upper tail).

Two-Tailed Test

In hypothesis testing, the general form for a **two-tailed test** about a population mean is as follows:

$$H_0: \mu = \mu_0$$
$$H_a: \mu \neq \mu_0$$

In this subsection we show how to conduct a two-tailed test about a population mean for the σ known case. As an illustration, we consider the hypothesis testing situation facing MaxFlight, Inc.

The U.S. Golf Association (USGA) establishes rules that manufacturers of golf equipment must meet if their products are to be acceptable for use in USGA events. MaxFlight uses a high-technology manufacturing process to produce golf balls with a mean driving distance of 295 yards. Sometimes, however, the process gets out of adjustment and produces golf balls with a mean driving distance different from 295 yards. When the mean distance falls below 295 yards, the company worries about losing sales because the golf balls do not provide as much distance as advertised. When the mean distance passes 295 yards, MaxFlight's golf balls may be rejected by the USGA for exceeding the overall distance standard concerning carry and roll.

MaxFlight's quality control program involves taking periodic samples of 50 golf balls to monitor the manufacturing process. For each sample, a hypothesis test is conducted to determine whether the process has fallen out of adjustment. Let us develop the null and alternative hypotheses. We begin by assuming that the process is functioning correctly; that is, the golf balls being produced have a mean distance of 295 yards. This assumption establishes the null hypothesis. The alternative hypothesis is that the mean distance is not equal to 295 yards. With a hypothesized value of $\mu_0 = 295$, the null and alternative hypotheses for the MaxFlight hypothesis test are as follows:

$$H_0: \mu = 295$$
$$H_a: \mu \neq 295$$

If the sample mean $\bar{x}$ is significantly less than 295 yards or significantly greater than 295 yards, we will reject H_0. In this case, corrective action will be taken to adjust the manufacturing process. On the other hand, if $\bar{x}$ does not deviate from the hypothesized mean $\mu_0 = 295$ by a significant amount, H_0 will not be rejected and no action will be taken to adjust the manufacturing process.

The quality control team selected $\alpha = .05$ as the level of significance for the test. Data from previous tests conducted when the process was known to be in adjustment show that

FIGURE 9.4   SAMPLING DISTRIBUTION OF $\bar{x}$ FOR THE MAXFLIGHT HYPOTHESIS TEST

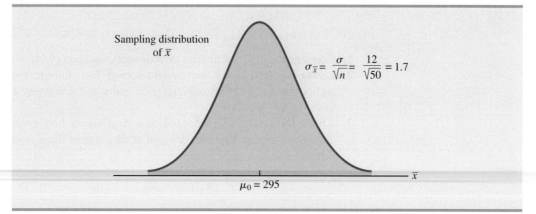

the population standard deviation can be assumed known with a value of $\sigma = 12$. Thus, with a sample size of $n = 50$, the standard error of $\bar{x}$ is

$$\sigma_{\bar{x}} = \frac{\sigma}{\sqrt{n}} = \frac{12}{\sqrt{50}} = 1.7$$

Because the sample size is large, the central limit theorem (see Chapter 7) allows us to conclude that the sampling distribution of $\bar{x}$ can be approximated by a normal distribution. Figure 9.4 shows the sampling distribution of $\bar{x}$ for the MaxFlight hypothesis test with a hypothesized population mean of $\mu_0 = 295$.

GolfTest

Suppose that a sample of 50 golf balls is selected and that the sample mean is $\bar{x} = 297.6$ yards. This sample mean provides support for the conclusion that the population mean is larger than 295 yards. Is this value of $\bar{x}$ enough larger than 295 to cause us to reject H_0 at the .05 level of significance? In the previous section we described two approaches that can be used to answer this question: the p-value approach and the critical value approach.

p-value approach   Recall that the p-value is a probability used to determine whether the null hypothesis should be rejected. For a two-tailed test, values of the test statistic in *either* tail provide evidence against the null hypothesis. For a two-tailed test, the p-value is the probability of obtaining a value for the test statistic *as unlikely as or more unlikely than* that provided by the sample. Let us see how the p-value is computed for the MaxFlight hypothesis test.

First we compute the value of the test statistic. For the σ known case, the test statistic z is a standard normal random variable. Using equation (9.1) with $\bar{x} = 297.6$, the value of the test statistic is

$$z = \frac{\bar{x} - \mu_0}{\sigma/\sqrt{n}} = \frac{297.6 - 295}{12/\sqrt{50}} = 1.53$$

Now to compute the p-value we must find the probability of obtaining a value for the test statistic *at least as unlikely as* $z = 1.53$. Clearly values of $z \geq 1.53$ are *at least as unlikely*. But, because this is a two-tailed test, values of $z \leq -1.53$ are also *at least as unlikely as* the value of the test statistic provided by the sample. In Figure 9.5, we see that the two-tailed p-value in this case is given by $P(z \leq -1.53) + P(z \geq 1.53)$. Because the normal curve is symmetric, we can compute this probability by finding the upper tail area at $z = 1.53$ and doubling it. The table for the standard normal distribution shows that $P(z < 1.53) = .9370$. Thus, the upper tail area is $P(z \geq 1.53) = 1.0000 - .9370 = .0630$. Doubling this, we find the p-value for the MaxFlight two-tailed hypothesis test is p-value $= 2(.0630) = .1260$.

FIGURE 9.5   *p*-VALUE FOR THE MAXFLIGHT HYPOTHESIS TEST

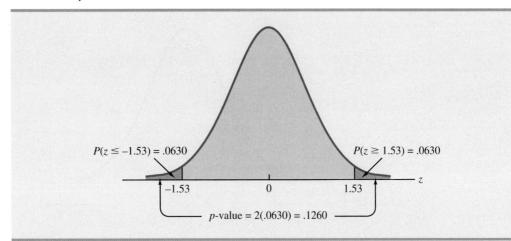

Next we compare the *p*-value to the level of significance to see whether the null hypothesis should be rejected. With a level of significance of $\alpha = .05$, we do not reject H_0 because the *p*-value $= .1260 > .05$. Because the null hypothesis is not rejected, no action will be taken to adjust the MaxFlight manufacturing process.

The computation of the *p*-value for a two-tailed test may seem a bit confusing as compared to the computation of the *p*-value for a one-tailed test. But it can be simplified by following three steps.

COMPUTATION OF *p*-VALUES FOR TWO-TAILED TESTS

1. Compute the value of the test statistic using equation (9.1).
2. If the value of the test statistic is in the upper tail, compute the probability that z is greater than or equal to the value of the test statistic (the upper tail area). If the value of the test statistic is in the lower tail, compute the probability that z is less than or equal to the value of the test statistic (the lower tail area).
3. Double the probability (or tail area) from step 2 to obtain the *p*-value.

Critical value approach   Before leaving this section, let us see how the test statistic z can be compared to a critical value to make the hypothesis testing decision for a two-tailed test. Figure 9.6 shows that the critical values for the test will occur in both the lower and upper tails of the standard normal distribution. With a level of significance of $\alpha = .05$, the area in each tail corresponding to the critical values is $\alpha/2 = .05/2 = .025$. Using the standard normal probability table, we find the critical values for the test statistic are $-z_{.025} = -1.96$ and $z_{.025} = 1.96$. Thus, using the critical value approach, the two-tailed rejection rule is

$$\text{Reject } H_0 \text{ if } z \leq -1.96 \text{ or if } z \geq 1.96$$

Because the value of the test statistic for the MaxFlight study is $z = 1.53$, the statistical evidence will not permit us to reject the null hypothesis at the .05 level of significance.

Summary and Practical Advice

We presented examples of a lower tail test and a two-tailed test about a population mean. Based upon these examples, we can now summarize the hypothesis testing procedures about a population mean for the σ known case as shown in Table 9.2. Note that μ_0 is the hypothesized value of the population mean.

FIGURE 9.6 CRITICAL VALUES FOR THE MAXFLIGHT HYPOTHESIS TEST

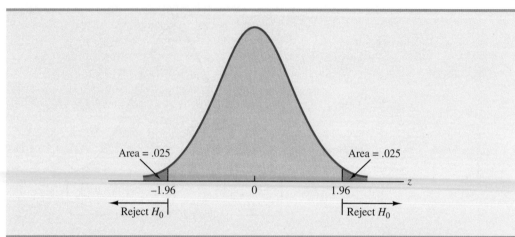

TABLE 9.2 SUMMARY OF HYPOTHESIS TESTS ABOUT A POPULATION MEAN: σ KNOWN CASE

	Lower Tail Test	**Upper Tail Test**	**Two-Tailed Test**
Hypotheses	$H_0: \mu \geq \mu_0$ $H_a: \mu < \mu_0$	$H_0: \mu \leq \mu_0$ $H_a: \mu > \mu_0$	$H_0: \mu = \mu_0$ $H_a: \mu \neq \mu_0$
Test Statistic	$z = \dfrac{\bar{x} - \mu_0}{\sigma/\sqrt{n}}$	$z = \dfrac{\bar{x} - \mu_0}{\sigma/\sqrt{n}}$	$z = \dfrac{\bar{x} - \mu_0}{\sigma/\sqrt{n}}$
Rejection Rule: **p-Value Approach**	Reject H_0 if p-value $\leq \alpha$	Reject H_0 if p-value $\leq \alpha$	Reject H_0 if p-value $\leq \alpha$
Rejection Rule: **Critical Value** **Approach**	Reject H_0 if $z \leq -z_\alpha$	Reject H_0 if $z \geq z_\alpha$	Reject H_0 if $z \leq -z_{\alpha/2}$ or if $z \geq z_{\alpha/2}$

The hypothesis testing steps followed in the two examples presented in this section are common to every hypothesis test.

STEPS OF HYPOTHESIS TESTING

Step 1. Develop the null and alternative hypotheses.
Step 2. Specify the level of significance.
Step 3. Collect the sample data and compute the value of the test statistic.

p-Value Approach

Step 4. Use the value of the test statistic to compute the p-value.
Step 5. Reject H_0 if the p-value $\leq \alpha$.
Step 6. Interpret the statistical conclusion in the context of the application.

Critical Value Approach

Step 4. Use the level of significance to determine the critical value and the rejection rule.
Step 5. Use the value of the test statistic and the rejection rule to determine whether to reject H_0.
Step 6. Interpret the statistical conclusion in the context of the application.

Practical advice about the sample size for hypothesis tests is similar to the advice we provided about the sample size for interval estimation in Chapter 8. In most applications, a sample size of $n \geq 30$ is adequate when using the hypothesis testing procedure described in this section. In cases where the sample size is less than 30, the distribution of the population from which we are sampling becomes an important consideration. If the population is normally distributed, the hypothesis testing procedure that we described is exact and can be used for any sample size. If the population is not normally distributed but is at least roughly symmetric, sample sizes as small as 15 can be expected to provide acceptable results.

Relationship Between Interval Estimation and Hypothesis Testing

In Chapter 8 we showed how to develop a confidence interval estimate of a population mean. For the σ known case, the $(1 - \alpha)\%$ confidence interval estimate of a population mean is given by

$$\bar{x} \pm z_{\alpha/2} \frac{\sigma}{\sqrt{n}}$$

In this chapter, we showed that a two-tailed hypothesis test about a population mean takes the following form:

$$H_0: \mu = \mu_0$$
$$H_a: \mu \neq \mu_0$$

where μ_0 is the hypothesized value for the population mean.

Suppose that we follow the procedure described in Chapter 8 for constructing a $100(1 - \alpha)\%$ confidence interval for the population mean. We know that $100(1 - \alpha)\%$ of the confidence intervals generated will contain the population mean and $100\alpha\%$ of the confidence intervals generated will not contain the population mean. Thus, if we reject H_0 whenever the confidence interval does not contain μ_0, we will be rejecting the null hypothesis when it is true ($\mu = \mu_0$) with probability α. Recall that the level of significance is the probability of rejecting the null hypothesis when it is true. So constructing a $100(1 - \alpha)\%$ confidence interval and rejecting H_0 whenever the interval does not contain μ_0 is equivalent to conducting a two-tailed hypothesis test with α as the level of significance. The procedure for using a confidence interval to conduct a two-tailed hypothesis test can now be summarized.

A CONFIDENCE INTERVAL APPROACH TO TESTING A HYPOTHESIS OF THE FORM

$$H_0: \mu = \mu_0$$
$$H_a: \mu \neq \mu_0$$

1. Select a simple random sample from the population and use the value of the sample mean $\bar{x}$ to develop the confidence interval for the population mean μ.

$$\bar{x} \pm z_{\alpha/2} \frac{\sigma}{\sqrt{n}}$$

For a two-tailed hypothesis test, the null hypothesis can be rejected if the confidence interval does not include μ_0.

2. If the confidence interval contains the hypothesized value μ_0, do not reject H_0. Otherwise, reject[2] H_0.

---

[2]To be consistent with the rule for rejecting H_0 when the p-value $\leq \alpha$, we would also reject H_0 using the confidence interval approach if μ_0 happens to be equal to one of the end points of the $100(1 - \alpha)\%$ confidence interval.

Let us illustrate by conducting the MaxFlight hypothesis test using the confidence interval approach. The MaxFlight hypothesis test takes the following form:

$$H_0: \mu = 295$$
$$H_a: \mu \neq 295$$

To test these hypotheses with a level of significance of $\alpha = .05$, we sampled 50 golf balls and found a sample mean distance of $\bar{x} = 297.6$ yards. Recall that the population standard deviation is $\sigma = 12$. Using these results with $z_{.025} = 1.96$, we find that the 95% confidence interval estimate of the population mean is

$$\bar{x} \pm z_{.025}\frac{\sigma}{\sqrt{n}}$$
$$297.6 \pm 1.96\frac{12}{\sqrt{50}}$$
$$297.6 \pm 3.3$$

or

$$294.3 \text{ to } 300.9$$

This finding enables the quality control manager to conclude with 95% confidence that the mean distance for the population of golf balls is between 294.3 and 300.9 yards. Because the hypothesized value for the population mean, $\mu_0 = 295$, is in this interval, the hypothesis testing conclusion is that the null hypothesis, $H_0: \mu = 295$, cannot be rejected.

Note that this discussion and example pertain to two-tailed hypothesis tests about a population mean. However, the same confidence interval and two-tailed hypothesis testing relationship exists for other population parameters. The relationship can also be extended to one-tailed tests about population parameters. Doing so, however, requires the development of one-sided confidence intervals, which are rarely used in practice.

NOTES AND COMMENTS

We have shown how to use *p*-values. The smaller the *p*-value the greater the evidence against H_0 and the more the evidence in favor of H_a. Here are some guidelines statisticians suggest for interpreting small *p*-values.

- Less than .01—Overwhelming evidence to conclude H_a is true.

- Between .01 and .05—Strong evidence to conclude H_a is true.
- Between .05 and .10—Weak evidence to conclude H_a is true.
- Greater than .10—Insufficient evidence to conclude H_a is true.

Exercises

Note to Student: Some of the exercises that follow ask you to use the *p*-value approach and others ask you to use the critical value approach. Both methods will provide the same hypothesis testing conclusion. We provide exercises with both methods to give you practice using both. In later sections and in following chapters, we will generally emphasize the *p*-value approach as the preferred method, but you may select either based on personal preference.

Methods

9. Consider the following hypothesis test:

$$H_0: \mu \geq 20$$
$$H_a: \mu < 20$$

A sample of 50 provided a sample mean of 19.4. The population standard deviation is 2.
a. Compute the value of the test statistic.
b. What is the p-value?
c. Using $\alpha = .05$, what is your conclusion?
d. What is the rejection rule using the critical value? What is your conclusion?

 10. Consider the following hypothesis test:

$$H_0: \mu \leq 25$$
$$H_a: \mu > 25$$

A sample of 40 provided a sample mean of 26.4. The population standard deviation is 6.
a. Compute the value of the test statistic.
b. What is the p-value?
c. At $\alpha = .01$, what is your conclusion?
d. What is the rejection rule using the critical value? What is your conclusion?

 11. Consider the following hypothesis test:

$$H_0: \mu = 15$$
$$H_a: \mu \neq 15$$

A sample of 50 provided a sample mean of 14.15. The population standard deviation is 3.
a. Compute the value of the test statistic.
b. What is the p-value?
c. At $\alpha = .05$, what is your conclusion?
d. What is the rejection rule using the critical value? What is your conclusion?

12. Consider the following hypothesis test:

$$H_0: \mu \geq 80$$
$$H_a: \mu < 80$$

A sample of 100 is used and the population standard deviation is 12. Compute the p-value and state your conclusion for each of the following sample results. Use $\alpha = .01$.
a. $\bar{x} = 78.5$
b. $\bar{x} = 77$
c. $\bar{x} = 75.5$
d. $\bar{x} = 81$

13. Consider the following hypothesis test:

$$H_0: \mu \leq 50$$
$$H_a: \mu > 50$$

A sample of 60 is used and the population standard deviation is 8. Use the critical value approach to state your conclusion for each of the following sample results. Use $\alpha = .05$.
a. $\bar{x} = 52.5$
b. $\bar{x} = 51$
c. $\bar{x} = 51.8$

14. Consider the following hypothesis test:

$$H_0: \mu = 22$$
$$H_a: \mu \neq 22$$

A sample of 75 is used and the population standard deviation is 10. Compute the p-value and state your conclusion for each of the following sample results. Use $\alpha = .01$.
   a. $\bar{x} = 23$
   b. $\bar{x} = 25.1$
   c. $\bar{x} = 20$

Applications

SELF*test*

15. Individuals filing federal income tax returns prior to March 31 received an average refund of $1056. Consider the population of "last-minute" filers who mail their tax return during the last five days of the income tax period (typically April 10 to April 15).
   a. A researcher suggests that a reason individuals wait until the last five days is that on average these individuals receive lower refunds than do early filers. Develop appropriate hypotheses such that rejection of H_0 will support the researcher's contention.
   b. For a sample of 400 individuals who filed a tax return between April 10 and 15, the sample mean refund was $910. Based on prior experience a population standard deviation of $\sigma = \$1600$ may be assumed. What is the p-value?
   c. At $\alpha = .05$, what is your conclusion?
   d. Repeat the preceding hypothesis test using the critical value approach.

16. In a study entitled How Undergraduate Students Use Credit Cards, it was reported that undergraduate students have a mean credit card balance of $3173. This figure was an all-time high and had increased 44% over the previous five years. Assume that a current study is being conducted to determine if it can be concluded that the mean credit card balance for undergraduate students has continued to increase compared to the original report. Based on previous studies, use a population standard deviation $\sigma = \$1000$.
   a. State the null and alternative hypotheses.
   b. What is the p-value for a sample of 180 undergraduate students with a sample mean credit card balance of $3325?
   c. Using a .05 level of significance, what is your conclusion?

17. The mean hourly wage for employees in goods-producing industries is currently $24.57 (Bureau of Labor Statistics website, April, 12, 2012). Suppose we take a sample of employees from the manufacturing industry to see if the mean hourly wage differs from the reported mean of $24.57 for the goods-producing industries.
   a. State the null and alternative hypotheses we should use to test whether the population mean hourly wage in the manufacturing industry differs from the population mean hourly wage in the goods-producing industries.
   b. Suppose a sample of 30 employees from the manufacturing industry showed a sample mean of $23.89 per hour. Assume a population standard deviation of $2.40 per hour and compute the p-value.
   c. With $\alpha = .05$ as the level of significance, what is your conclusion?
   d. Repeat the preceding hypothesis test using the critical value approach.

18. Young millennials, adults aged 18 to 34, are viewed as the future of the restaurant industry. During 2011, this group consumed a mean of 192 restaurant meals per person (NPD Group website, November 7, 2012). Conduct a hypothesis test to determine if the poor economy caused a change in the frequency of consuming restaurant meals by young millennials in 2012.

a. Formulate hypotheses that can be used to determine whether the annual mean number of restaurant meals per person has changed for young millennials in 2012.

b. Based on a sample, the NPD Group stated that the mean number of restaurant meals consumed by young millennials in 2012 was 182. Assume the sample size was 150 and that, based on past studies, the population standard deviation can be assumed to be $\sigma = 55$. Use the sample results to compute the test statistic and p-value for your hypothesis test.

c. At $\alpha = .05$, what is your conclusion?

19. The Internal Revenue Service (IRS) provides a toll-free help line for taxpayers to call in and get answers to questions as they prepare their tax returns. In recent years, the IRS has been inundated with taxpayer calls and has redesigned its phone service as well as posted answers to frequently asked questions on its website (*The Cincinnati Enquirer*, January 7, 2010). According to a report by a taxpayer advocate, callers using the new system can expect to wait on hold for an unreasonably long time of 12 minutes before being able to talk to an IRS employee. Suppose you select a sample of 50 callers after the new phone service has been implemented; the sample results show a mean waiting time of 10 minutes before an IRS employee comes on the line. Based upon data from past years, you decide it is reasonable to assume that the standard deviation of waiting time is 8 minutes. Using your sample results, can you conclude that the actual mean waiting time turned out to be significantly less than the 12-minute claim made by the taxpayer advocate? Use $\alpha = .05$.

20. Annual expenditure for prescription drugs was $838 per person in the Northeast of the country (Hospital Care Cost Institute website, November 7, 2012). A sample of 60 individuals in the Midwest showed a per person annual expenditure for prescription drugs of $745. Use a population standard deviation of $300 to answer the following questions.

a. Formulate hypotheses for a test to determine whether the sample data support the conclusion that the population annual expenditure for prescription drugs per person is lower in the Midwest than in the Northeast.

b. What is the value of the test statistic?

c. What is the p-value?

d. At $\alpha = .01$, what is your conclusion?

Fowle

21. Fowle Marketing Research, Inc., bases charges to a client on the assumption that telephone surveys can be completed in a mean time of 15 minutes or less. If a longer mean survey time is necessary, a premium rate is charged. A sample of 35 surveys provided the survey times shown in the file named Fowle. Based upon past studies, the population standard deviation is assumed known with $\sigma = 4$ minutes. Is the premium rate justified?

a. Formulate the null and alternative hypotheses for this application.

b. Compute the value of the test statistic.

c. What is the p-value?

d. At $\alpha = .01$, what is your conclusion?

22. CCN and ActMedia provided a television channel targeted to individuals waiting in supermarket checkout lines. The channel showed news, short features, and advertisements. The length of the program was based on the assumption that the population mean time a shopper stands in a supermarket checkout line is 8 minutes. A sample of actual waiting times will be used to test this assumption and determine whether actual mean waiting time differs from this standard.

a. Formulate the hypotheses for this application.

b. A sample of 120 shoppers showed a sample mean waiting time of 8.4 minutes. Assume a population standard deviation of $\sigma = 3.2$ minutes. What is the p-value?

c. At $\alpha = .05$, what is your conclusion?

d. Compute a 95% confidence interval for the population mean. Does it support your conclusion?

9.4 Population Mean: σ Unknown

In this section we describe how to conduct hypothesis tests about a population mean for the σ unknown case. Because the σ unknown case corresponds to situations in which an estimate of the population standard deviation cannot be developed prior to sampling, the sample must be used to develop an estimate of both μ and σ. Thus, to conduct a hypothesis test about a population mean for the σ unknown case, the sample mean $\bar{x}$ is used as an estimate of μ and the sample standard deviation s is used as an estimate of σ.

The steps of the hypothesis testing procedure for the σ unknown case are the same as those for the σ known case described in Section 9.3. But, with σ unknown, the computation of the test statistic and p-value is a bit different. Recall that for the σ known case, the sampling distribution of the test statistic has a standard normal distribution. For the σ unknown case, however, the sampling distribution of the test statistic follows the t distribution; it has slightly more variability because the sample is used to develop estimates of both μ and σ.

In Section 8.2 we showed that an interval estimate of a population mean for the σ unknown case is based on a probability distribution known as the t distribution. Hypothesis tests about a population mean for the σ unknown case are also based on the t distribution. For the σ unknown case, the test statistic has a t distribution with $n - 1$ degrees of freedom.

TEST STATISTIC FOR HYPOTHESIS TESTS ABOUT A POPULATION MEAN: σ UNKNOWN

$$t = \frac{\bar{x} - \mu_0}{s/\sqrt{n}} \tag{9.2}$$

In Chapter 8 we said that the t distribution is based on an assumption that the population from which we are sampling has a normal distribution. However, research shows that this assumption can be relaxed considerably when the sample size is large enough. We provide some practical advice concerning the population distribution and sample size at the end of the section.

One-Tailed Test

DATA *file*

AirRating

Let us consider an example of a one-tailed test about a population mean for the σ unknown case. A business travel magazine wants to classify transatlantic gateway airports according to the mean rating for the population of business travelers. A rating scale with a low score of 0 and a high score of 10 will be used, and airports with a population mean rating greater than 7 will be designated as superior service airports. The magazine staff surveyed a sample of 60 business travelers at each airport to obtain the ratings data. The sample for London's Heathrow Airport provided a sample mean rating of $\bar{x} = 7.25$ and a sample standard deviation of $s = 1.052$. Do the data indicate that Heathrow should be designated as a superior service airport?

We want to develop a hypothesis test for which the decision to reject H_0 will lead to the conclusion that the population mean rating for the Heathrow Airport is *greater* than 7. Thus, an upper tail test with $H_a: \mu > 7$ is required. The null and alternative hypotheses for this upper tail test are as follows:

$$H_0: \mu \leq 7$$
$$H_a: \mu > 7$$

We will use $\alpha = .05$ as the level of significance for the test.

Using equation (9.2) with $\bar{x} = 7.25$, $\mu_0 = 7$, $s = 1.052$, and $n = 60$, the value of the test statistic is

$$t = \frac{\bar{x} - \mu_0}{s/\sqrt{n}} = \frac{7.25 - 7}{1.052/\sqrt{60}} = 1.84$$

The sampling distribution of t has $n - 1 = 60 - 1 = 59$ degrees of freedom. Because the test is an upper tail test, the p-value is $P(t \geq 1.84)$, that is, the upper tail area corresponding to the value of the test statistic.

The t distribution table provided in most textbooks will not contain sufficient detail to determine the exact p-value, such as the p-value corresponding to $t = 1.84$. For instance, using Table 2 in Appendix B, the t distribution with 59 degrees of freedom provides the following information.

Area in Upper Tail	.20	.10	.05	.025	.01	.005
t Value (59 df)	.848	1.296	1.671	2.001	2.391	2.662

$t = 1.84$

We see that $t = 1.84$ is between 1.671 and 2.001. Although the table does not provide the exact p-value, the values in the "Area in Upper Tail" row show that the p-value must be less than .05 and greater than .025. With a level of significance of $\alpha = .05$, this placement is all we need to know to make the decision to reject the null hypothesis and conclude that Heathrow should be classified as a superior service airport.

Appendix F shows how to compute p-values using Excel or Minitab.

Because it is cumbersome to use a t table to compute p-values, and only approximate values are obtained, we show how to compute the exact p-value using Excel or Minitab. The directions can be found in Appendix F at the end of this text. Using Excel or Minitab with $t = 1.84$ provides the upper tail p-value of .0354 for the Heathrow Airport hypothesis test. With $.0354 < .05$, we reject the null hypothesis and conclude that Heathrow should be classified as a superior service airport.

The decision whether to reject the null hypothesis in the σ unknown case can also be made using the critical value approach. The critical value corresponding to an area of $\alpha = .05$ in the upper tail of a t distribution with 59 degrees of freedom is $t_{.05} = 1.671$. Thus the rejection rule using the critical value approach is to reject H_0 if $t \geq 1.671$. Because $t = 1.84 > 1.671$, H_0 is rejected. Heathrow should be classified as a superior service airport.

Two-Tailed Test

To illustrate how to conduct a two-tailed test about a population mean for the σ unknown case, let us consider the hypothesis testing situation facing Holiday Toys. The company manufactures and distributes its products through more than 1000 retail outlets. In planning production levels for the coming winter season, Holiday must decide how many units of each product to produce prior to knowing the actual demand at the retail level. For this year's most important new toy, Holiday's marketing director is expecting demand to average 40 units per retail outlet. Prior to making the final production decision based upon this estimate, Holiday decided to survey a sample of 25 retailers in order to develop more information about the demand for the new product. Each retailer was provided with information about the features of the new toy along with the cost and the suggested selling price. Then each retailer was asked to specify an anticipated order quantity.

With μ denoting the population mean order quantity per retail outlet, the sample data will be used to conduct the following two-tailed hypothesis test:

$$H_0: \mu = 40$$
$$H_a: \mu \neq 40$$

If H_0 cannot be rejected, Holiday will continue its production planning based on the marketing director's estimate that the population mean order quantity per retail outlet will be $\mu = 40$ units. However, if H_0 is rejected, Holiday will immediately reevaluate its production plan for the product. A two-tailed hypothesis test is used because Holiday wants to reevaluate the production plan if the population mean quantity per retail outlet is less than anticipated or greater than anticipated. Because no historical data are available (it's a new product), the population mean μ and the population standard deviation must both be estimated using $\bar{x}$ and s from the sample data.

DATA *file*

Orders

The sample of 25 retailers provided a mean of $\bar{x} = 37.4$ and a standard deviation of $s = 11.79$ units. Before going ahead with the use of the t distribution, the analyst constructed a histogram of the sample data in order to check on the form of the population distribution. The histogram of the sample data showed no evidence of skewness or any extreme outliers, so the analyst concluded that the use of the t distribution with $n - 1 = 24$ degrees of freedom was appropriate. Using equation (9.2) with $\bar{x} = 37.4$, $\mu_0 = 40$, $s = 11.79$, and $n = 25$, the value of the test statistic is

$$t = \frac{\bar{x} - \mu_0}{s/\sqrt{n}} = \frac{37.4 - 40}{11.79/\sqrt{25}} = -1.10$$

Because we have a two-tailed test, the p-value is two times the area under the curve of the t distribution for $t \leq -1.10$. Using Table 2 in Appendix B, the t distribution table for 24 degrees of freedom provides the following information.

Area in Upper Tail	.20	.10	.05	.025	.01	.005
t-Value (24 *df*)	.857	1.318	1.711	2.064	2.492	2.797

$$t = 1.10$$

The t distribution table only contains positive t values. Because the t distribution is symmetric, however, the upper tail area at $t = 1.10$ is the same as the lower tail area at $t = -1.10$. We see that $t = 1.10$ is between 0.857 and 1.318. From the "Area in Upper Tail" row, we see that the area in the upper tail at $t = 1.10$ is between .20 and .10. When we double these amounts, we see that the p-value must be between .40 and .20. With a level of significance of $\alpha = .05$, we now know that the p-value is greater than α. Therefore, H_0 cannot be rejected. Sufficient evidence is not available to conclude that Holiday should change its production plan for the coming season.

Appendix F shows how the p-value for this test can be computed using Excel or Minitab. The p-value obtained is .2822. With a level of significance of $\alpha = .05$, we cannot reject H_0 because .2822 > .05.

The test statistic can also be compared to the critical value to make the two-tailed hypothesis testing decision. With $\alpha = .05$ and the t distribution with 24 degrees of freedom, $-t_{.025} = -2.064$ and $t_{.025} = 2.064$ are the critical values for the two-tailed test. The rejection rule using the test statistic is

$$\text{Reject } H_0 \text{ if } t \leq -2.064 \text{ or if } t \geq 2.064$$

TABLE 9.3   SUMMARY OF HYPOTHESIS TESTS ABOUT A POPULATION MEAN:
             σ UNKNOWN CASE

	Lower Tail Test	**Upper Tail Test**	**Two-Tailed Test**
Hypotheses	$H_0: \mu \geq \mu_0$ $H_a: \mu < \mu_0$	$H_0: \mu \leq \mu_0$ $H_a: \mu > \mu_0$	$H_0: \mu = \mu_0$ $H_a: \mu \neq \mu_0$
Test Statistic	$t = \dfrac{\bar{x} - \mu_0}{s/\sqrt{n}}$	$t = \dfrac{\bar{x} - \mu_0}{s/\sqrt{n}}$	$t = \dfrac{\bar{x} - \mu_0}{s/\sqrt{n}}$
Rejection Rule: **p-Value Approach**	Reject H_0 if p-value $\leq \alpha$	Reject H_0 if p-value $\leq \alpha$	Reject H_0 if p-value $\leq \alpha$
Rejection Rule: **Critical Value** **Approach**	Reject H_0 if $t \leq -t_\alpha$	Reject H_0 if $t \geq t_\alpha$	Reject H_0 if $t \leq -t_{\alpha/2}$ or if $t \geq t_{\alpha/2}$

Based on the test statistic $t = -1.10$, H_0 cannot be rejected. This result indicates that Holiday should continue its production planning for the coming season based on the expectation that $\mu = 40$.

Summary and Practical Advice

Table 9.3 provides a summary of the hypothesis testing procedures about a population mean for the σ unknown case. The key difference between these procedures and the ones for the σ known case is that s is used, instead of σ, in the computation of the test statistic. For this reason, the test statistic follows the t distribution.

The applicability of the hypothesis testing procedures of this section is dependent on the distribution of the population being sampled from and the sample size. When the population is normally distributed, the hypothesis tests described in this section provide exact results for any sample size. When the population is not normally distributed, the procedures are approximations. Nonetheless, we find that sample sizes of 30 or greater will provide good results in most cases. If the population is approximately normal, small sample sizes (e.g., $n < 15$) can provide acceptable results. If the population is highly skewed or contains outliers, sample sizes approaching 50 are recommended.

Exercises

Methods

23. Consider the following hypothesis test:

$$H_0: \mu \leq 12$$
$$H_a: \mu > 12$$

A sample of 25 provided a sample mean $\bar{x} = 14$ and a sample standard deviation $s = 4.32$.
   a.   Compute the value of the test statistic.
   b.   Use the t distribution table (Table 2 in Appendix B) to compute a range for the p-value.
   c.   At $\alpha = .05$, what is your conclusion?
   d.   What is the rejection rule using the critical value? What is your conclusion?

✓SELF*test* 24. Consider the following hypothesis test:

$$H_0: \mu = 18$$
$$H_a: \mu \neq 18$$

A sample of 48 provided a sample mean $\bar{x} = 17$ and a sample standard deviation $s = 4.5$.

a. Compute the value of the test statistic.
b. Use the t distribution table (Table 2 in Appendix B) to compute a range for the p-value.
c. At $\alpha = .05$, what is your conclusion?
d. What is the rejection rule using the critical value? What is your conclusion?

25. Consider the following hypothesis test:

$$H_0: \mu \geq 45$$
$$H_a: \mu < 45$$

A sample of 36 is used. Identify the p-value and state your conclusion for each of the following sample results. Use $\alpha = .01$.

a. $\bar{x} = 44$ and $s = 5.2$
b. $\bar{x} = 43$ and $s = 4.6$
c. $\bar{x} = 46$ and $s = 5.0$

26. Consider the following hypothesis test:

$$H_0: \mu = 100$$
$$H_a: \mu \neq 100$$

A sample of 65 is used. Identify the p-value and state your conclusion for each of the following sample results. Use $\alpha = .05$.

a. $\bar{x} = 103$ and $s = 11.5$
b. $\bar{x} = 96.5$ and $s = 11.0$
c. $\bar{x} = 102$ and $s = 10.5$

Applications

✓SELF*test* 27. Which is cheaper: eating out or dining in? The mean cost of a flank steak, broccoli, and rice bought at the grocery store is $13.04 (Money.msn website, November 7, 2012). A sample of 100 neighborhood restaurants showed a mean price of $12.75 and a standard deviation of $2 for a comparable restaurant meal.

a. Develop appropriate hypotheses for a test to determine whether the sample data support the conclusion that the mean cost of a restaurant meal is less than fixing a comparable meal at home.
b. Using the sample from the 100 restaurants, what is the p-value?
c. At $\alpha = .05$, what is your conclusion?
d. Repeat the preceding hypothesis test using the critical value approach.

28. A shareholders' group, in lodging a protest, claimed that the mean tenure for a chief executive office (CEO) was at least nine years. A survey of companies reported in *The Wall Street Journal* found a sample mean tenure of $\bar{x} = 7.27$ years for CEOs with a standard deviation of $s = 6.38$ years.

a. Formulate hypotheses that can be used to challenge the validity of the claim made by the shareholders' group.
b. Assume 85 companies were included in the sample. What is the p-value for your hypothesis test?
c. At $\alpha = .01$, what is your conclusion?

Administrator

29. The national mean annual salary for a school administrator is $90,000 a year (*The Cincinnati Enquirer*, April 7, 2012). A school official took a sample of 25 school administrators in the state of Ohio to learn about salaries in that state to see if they differed from the national average.
    a. Formulate hypotheses that can be used to determine whether the population mean annual administrator salary in Ohio differs from the national mean of $90,000.
    b. The sample data for 25 Ohio administrators is contained in the file named Administrator. What is the *p*-value for your hypothesis test in part (a)?
    c. At $\alpha = .05$, can your null hypothesis be rejected? What is your conclusion?
    d. Repeat the preceding hypothesis test using the critical value approach.

ChildCare

30. The time married men with children spend on child care averages 6.4 hours per week (*Time*, March 12, 2012). You belong to a professional group on family practices that would like to do its own study to determine if the time married men in your area spend on child care per week differs from the reported mean of 6.4 hours per week. A sample of 40 married couples will be used with the data collected showing the hours per week the husband spends on child care. The sample data are contained in the file ChildCare.
    a. What are the hypotheses if your group would like to determine if the population mean number of hours married men are spending in child care differs from the mean reported by *Time* in your area?
    b. What is the sample mean and the *p*-value?
    c. Select your own level of significance. What is your conclusion?

31. The Coca-Cola Company reported that the mean per capita annual sales of its beverages in the United States was 423 eight-ounce servings (Coca-Cola Company website, February 3, 2009). Suppose you are curious whether the consumption of Coca-Cola beverages is higher in Atlanta, Georgia, the location of Coca-Cola's corporate headquarters. A sample of 36 individuals from the Atlanta area showed a sample mean annual consumption of 460.4 eight-ounce servings with a standard deviation of $s = 101.9$ ounces. Using $\alpha = .05$, do the sample results support the conclusion that mean annual consumption of Coca-Cola beverage products is higher in Atlanta?

UsedCars

32. According to the National Automobile Dealers Association, the mean price for used cars is $10,192. A manager of a Kansas City used car dealership reviewed a sample of 50 recent used car sales at the dealership in an attempt to determine whether the population mean price for used cars at this particular dealership differed from the national mean. The prices for the sample of 50 cars are shown in the file named UsedCars.
    a. Formulate the hypotheses that can be used to determine whether a difference exists in the mean price for used cars at the dealership.
    b. What is the *p*-value?
    c. At $\alpha = .05$, what is your conclusion?

33. The mean annual premium for automobile insurance in the United States is $1503 (Insure.com website, March 6, 2014). Being from Pennsylvania, you believe automobile insurance is cheaper there and wish to develop statistical support for your opinion. A sample of 25 automobile insurance policies from the state of Pennsylvania showed a mean annual premium of $1440 with a standard deviation of $s = \$165$.
    a. Develop a hypothesis test that can be used to determine whether the mean annual premium in Pennsylvania is lower than the national mean annual premium.
    b. What is a point estimate of the difference between the mean annual premium in Pennsylvania and the national mean?
    c. At $\alpha = .05$, test for a significant difference. What is your conclusion?

34. Joan's Nursery specializes in custom-designed landscaping for residential areas. The estimated labor cost associated with a particular landscaping proposal is based on the number of plantings of trees, shrubs, and so on to be used for the project. For cost-estimating purposes, managers use two hours of labor time for the planting of a

medium-sized tree. Actual times from a sample of 10 plantings during the past month follow (times in hours).

| 1.7 | 1.5 | 2.6 | 2.2 | 2.4 | 2.3 | 2.6 | 3.0 | 1.4 | 2.3 |

With a .05 level of significance, test to see whether the mean tree-planting time differs from two hours.

a. State the null and alternative hypotheses.
b. Compute the sample mean.
c. Compute the sample standard deviation.
d. What is the p-value?
e. What is your conclusion?

9.5 Population Proportion

In this section we show how to conduct a hypothesis test about a population proportion p. Using p_0 to denote the hypothesized value for the population proportion, the three forms for a hypothesis test about a population proportion are as follows.

$$
\begin{array}{ccc}
H_0: p \geq p_0 & H_0: p \leq p_0 & H_0: p = p_0 \\
H_a: p < p_0 & H_a: p > p_0 & H_a: p \neq p_0
\end{array}
$$

The first form is called a lower tail test, the second form is called an upper tail test, and the third form is called a two-tailed test.

Hypothesis tests about a population proportion are based on the difference between the sample proportion $\bar{p}$ and the hypothesized population proportion p_0. The methods used to conduct the hypothesis test are similar to those used for hypothesis tests about a population mean. The only difference is that we use the sample proportion and its standard error to compute the test statistic. The p-value approach or the critical value approach is then used to determine whether the null hypothesis should be rejected.

Let us consider an example involving a situation faced by Pine Creek golf course. Over the past year, 20% of the players at Pine Creek were women. In an effort to increase the proportion of women players, Pine Creek implemented a special promotion designed to attract women golfers. One month after the promotion was implemented, the course manager requested a statistical study to determine whether the proportion of women players at Pine Creek had increased. Because the objective of the study is to determine whether the proportion of women golfers increased, an upper tail test with $H_a: p > .20$ is appropriate. The null and alternative hypotheses for the Pine Creek hypothesis test are as follows:

$$
\begin{array}{c}
H_0: p \leq .20 \\
H_a: p > .20
\end{array}
$$

If H_0 can be rejected, the test results will give statistical support for the conclusion that the proportion of women golfers increased and the promotion was beneficial. The course manager specified that a level of significance of $\alpha = .05$ be used in carrying out this hypothesis test.

The next step of the hypothesis testing procedure is to select a sample and compute the value of an appropriate test statistic. To show how this step is done for the Pine Creek upper tail test, we begin with a general discussion of how to compute the value of the test statistic for any form of a hypothesis test about a population proportion. The sampling distribution of $\bar{p}$, the point estimator of the population parameter p, is the basis for developing the test statistic.

When the null hypothesis is true as an equality, the expected value of $\bar{p}$ equals the hypothesized value p_0; that is, $E(\bar{p}) = p_0$. The standard error of $\bar{p}$ is given by

$$
\sigma_{\bar{p}} = \sqrt{\frac{p_0(1 - p_0)}{n}}
$$

In Chapter 7 we said that if $np \geq 5$ and $n(1 - p) \geq 5$, the sampling distribution of $\bar{p}$ can be approximated by a normal distribution.[3] Under these conditions, which usually apply in practice, the quantity

$$z = \frac{\bar{p} - p_0}{\sigma_{\bar{p}}}$$ (9.3)

has a standard normal probability distribution. With $\sigma_{\bar{p}} = \sqrt{p_0(1 - p_0)/n}$, the standard normal random variable z is the test statistic used to conduct hypothesis tests about a population proportion.

> **TEST STATISTIC FOR HYPOTHESIS TESTS ABOUT A POPULATION PROPORTION**
>
> $$z = \frac{\bar{p} - p_0}{\sqrt{\dfrac{p_0(1 - p_0)}{n}}}$$ (9.4)

DATA *file*

WomenGolf

We can now compute the test statistic for the Pine Creek hypothesis test. Suppose a random sample of 400 players was selected, and that 100 of the players were women. The proportion of women golfers in the sample is

$$\bar{p} = \frac{100}{400} = .25$$

Using equation (9.4), the value of the test statistic is

$$z = \frac{\bar{p} - p_0}{\sqrt{\dfrac{p_0(1 - p_0)}{n}}} = \frac{.25 - .20}{\sqrt{\dfrac{.20(1 - .20)}{400}}} = \frac{.05}{.02} = 2.50$$

Because the Pine Creek hypothesis test is an upper tail test, the p-value is the probability that z is greater than or equal to $z = 2.50$; that is, it is the upper tail area corresponding to $z \geq 2.50$. Using the standard normal probability table, we find that the area to the left of $z = 2.50$ is .9938. Thus, the p-value for the Pine Creek test is $1.0000 - .9938 = .0062$. Figure 9.7 shows this p-value calculation.

Recall that the course manager specified a level of significance of $\alpha = .05$. A p-value $= .0062 < .05$ gives sufficient statistical evidence to reject H_0 at the .05 level of significance. Thus, the test provides statistical support for the conclusion that the special promotion increased the proportion of women players at the Pine Creek golf course.

The decision whether to reject the null hypothesis can also be made using the critical value approach. The critical value corresponding to an area of .05 in the upper tail of a normal probability distribution is $z_{.05} = 1.645$. Thus, the rejection rule using the critical value approach is to reject H_0 if $z \geq 1.645$. Because $z = 2.50 > 1.645$, H_0 is rejected.

Again, we see that the p-value approach and the critical value approach lead to the same hypothesis testing conclusion, but the p-value approach provides more information. With a p-value $= .0062$, the null hypothesis would be rejected for any level of significance greater than or equal to .0062.

---

[3]In most applications involving hypothesis tests of a population proportion, sample sizes are large enough to use the normal approximation. The exact sampling distribution of $\bar{p}$ is discrete with the probability for each value of $\bar{p}$ given by the binomial distribution. So hypothesis testing is a bit more complicated for small samples when the normal approximation cannot be used.

FIGURE 9.7   CALCULATION OF THE p-VALUE FOR THE PINE CREEK HYPOTHESIS TEST

Area = .9938

p-value = $P(z \geq 2.50)$ = .0062

2.5

z

Summary

The procedure used to conduct a hypothesis test about a population proportion is similar to the procedure used to conduct a hypothesis test about a population mean. Although we only illustrated how to conduct a hypothesis test about a population proportion for an upper tail test, similar procedures can be used for lower tail and two-tailed tests. Table 9.4 provides a summary of the hypothesis tests about a population proportion. We assume that $np \geq 5$ and $n(1 - p) \geq 5$; thus the normal probability distribution can be used to approximate the sampling distribution of $\bar{p}$.

TABLE 9.4   SUMMARY OF HYPOTHESIS TESTS ABOUT A POPULATION PROPORTION

	Lower Tail Test	Upper Tail Test	Two-Tailed Test
Hypotheses	$H_0: p \geq p_0$ $H_a: p < p_0$	$H_0: p \leq p_0$ $H_a: p > p_0$	$H_0: p = p_0$ $H_a: p \neq p_0$
Test Statistic	$z = \dfrac{\bar{p} - p_0}{\sqrt{\dfrac{p_0(1 - p_0)}{n}}}$	$z = \dfrac{\bar{p} - p_0}{\sqrt{\dfrac{p_0(1 - p_0)}{n}}}$	$z = \dfrac{\bar{p} - p_0}{\sqrt{\dfrac{p_0(1 - p_0)}{n}}}$
Rejection Rule: p-**Value Approach**	Reject H_0 if p-value $\leq \alpha$	Reject H_0 if p-value $\leq \alpha$	Reject H_0 if p-value $\leq \alpha$
Rejection Rule: **Critical Value** **Approach**	Reject H_0 if $z \leq -z_\alpha$	Reject H_0 if $z \geq z_\alpha$	Reject H_0 if $z \leq -z_{\alpha/2}$ or if $z \geq z_{\alpha/2}$

NOTES AND COMMENTS

The binomial distribution can also be used to perform an exact hypothesis test for one proportion. This method is more accurate and more powerful than the normal approximation method. However, the calculations for the normal approximation method are simpler, and the accuracy and power of hypothesis tests performed using the normal approximation method improves as the sample size increases.

Exercises

Methods

35. Consider the following hypothesis test:

$$H_0: p = .20$$
$$H_a: p \neq .20$$

A sample of 400 provided a sample proportion $\bar{p} = .175$.
    a. Compute the value of the test statistic.
    b. What is the p-value?
    c. At $\alpha = .05$, what is your conclusion?
    d. What is the rejection rule using the critical value? What is your conclusion?

36. Consider the following hypothesis test:

$$H_0: p \geq .75$$
$$H_a: p < .75$$

A sample of 300 items was selected. Compute the p-value and state your conclusion for each of the following sample results. Use $\alpha = .05$.
    a. $\bar{p} = .68$ c. $\bar{p} = .70$
    b. $\bar{p} = .72$ d. $\bar{p} = .77$

Applications

37. The U.S. Bureau of Labor Statistics reports that 11.3% of U.S. workers belong to unions (BLS website, January 2014). Suppose a sample of 400 U.S. workers is collected in 2014 to determine whether union efforts to organize have increased union membership.
    a. Formulate the hypotheses that can be used to determine whether union membership increased in 2014.
    b. If the sample results show that 52 of the workers belonged to unions, what is the p-value for your hypothesis test?
    c. At $\alpha = .05$, what is your conclusion?

38. A study by *Consumer Reports* showed that 64% of supermarket shoppers believe super-market brands to be as good as national name brands. To investigate whether this result applies to its own product, the manufacturer of a national name-brand ketchup asked a sample of shoppers whether they believed that supermarket ketchup was as good as the national brand ketchup.
    a. Formulate the hypotheses that could be used to determine whether the percentage of supermarket shoppers who believe that the supermarket ketchup was as good as the national brand ketchup differed from 64%.
    b. If a sample of 100 shoppers showed 52 stating that the supermarket brand was as good as the national brand, what is the p-value?
    c. At $\alpha = .05$, what is your conclusion?
    d. Should the national brand ketchup manufacturer be pleased with this conclusion? Explain.

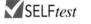

HomeState

39. What percentage of the population live in their state of birth? According to the U.S. Census Bureau's American Community Survey, the figure ranges from 25% in Nevada to 78.7% in Louisiana (*AARP Bulletin*, March 2014). The average percentage across all states and the District of Columbia is 57.7%. The data in the DATAfile Homestate are consistent with the findings in the American Community Survey. The data are for a random sample of 120 Arkansas residents and for a random sample of 180 Virginia residents.

a. Formulate hypotheses that can be used to determine whether the percentage of stay-at-home residents in the two states differs from the overall average of 57.7%.
b. Estimate the proportion of stay-at-home residents in Arkansas. Does this proportion differ significantly from the mean proportion for all states? Use $\alpha = .05$.
c. Estimate the proportion of stay-at-home residents in Virginia. Does this proportion differ significantly from the mean proportion for all states? Use $\alpha = .05$.
d. Would you expect the proportion of stay-at-home residents to be higher in Virginia than in Arkansas? Support your conclusion with the results obtained in parts (b) and (c).

40. Last year, 46% of business owners gave a holiday gift to their employees. A survey of business owners conducted this year indicates that 35% plan to provide a holiday gift to their employees. Suppose the survey results are based on a sample of 60 business owners.
a. How many business owners in the survey plan to provide a holiday gift to their employees this year?
b. Suppose the business owners in the sample did as they plan. Compute the p-value for a hypothesis test that can be used to determine if the proportion of business owners providing holiday gifts had decreased from last year.
c. Using a .05 level of significance, would you conclude that the proportion of business owners providing gifts decreased? What is the smallest level of significance for which you could draw such a conclusion?

41. Ten years ago 53% of American families owned stocks or stock funds. Sample data collected by the Investment Company Institute indicate that the percentage is now 46% (*The Wall Street Journal*, October 5, 2012).
a. Develop appropriate hypotheses such that rejection of H_0 will support the conclusion that a smaller proportion of American families own stocks or stock funds in 2012 than 10 years ago.
b. Assume the Investment Company Institute sampled 300 American families to estimate that the percent owning stocks or stock funds was 46% in 2012. What is the p-value for your hypothesis test?
c. At $\alpha = .01$, what is your conclusion?

42. According to the University of Nevada Center for Logistics Management, 6% of all merchandise sold in the United States gets returned. A Houston department store sampled 80 items sold in January and found that 12 of the items were returned.
a. Construct a point estimate of the proportion of items returned for the population of sales transactions at the Houston store.
b. Construct a 95% confidence interval for the proportion of returns at the Houston store.
c. Is the proportion of returns at the Houston store significantly different from the returns for the nation as a whole? Provide statistical support for your answer.

DATA *file*

Eagle

43. Eagle Outfitters is a chain of stores specializing in outdoor apparel and camping gear. They are considering a promotion that involves mailing discount coupons to all their credit card customers. This promotion will be considered a success if more than 10% of those receiving the coupons use them. Before going national with the promotion, coupons were sent to a sample of 100 credit card customers.
a. Develop hypotheses that can be used to test whether the population proportion of those who will use the coupons is sufficient to go national.
b. The file Eagle contains the sample data. Develop a point estimate of the population proportion.
c. Use $\alpha = .05$ to conduct your hypothesis test. Should Eagle go national with the promotion?

DATA *file*

LawSuit

44. One of the reasons health care costs have been rising rapidly in recent years is the increasing cost of malpractice insurance for physicians. Also, fear of being sued causes doctors to run more precautionary tests (possibly unnecessary) just to make sure they are not guilty

of missing something (*Reader's Digest*, October 2012). These precautionary tests also add to health care costs. Data in the DATAfile named LawSuit are consistent with findings in the *Reader's Digest* article and can be used to estimate the proportion of physicians over the age of 55 who have been sued at least once.

a. Formulate hypotheses that can be used to see if these data can support a finding that more than half of physicians over the age of 55 have been sued at least once.

b. Use Excel and the DATAfile named LawSuit to compute the sample proportion of physicians over the age of 55 who have been sued at least once. What is the *p*-value for your hypothesis test?

c. At $\alpha = .01$, what is your conclusion?

45. The American Association of Individual Investors conducts a weekly survey of its members to measure the percent who are bullish, bearish, and neutral on the stock market for the next six months. For the week ending November 7, 2012, the survey results showed 38.5% bullish, 21.6% neutral, and 39.9% bearish (AAII website, November 12, 2012). Assume these results are based on a sample of 300 AAII members.

a. Over the long term, the proportion of bullish AAII members is .39. Conduct a hypothesis test at the 5% level of significance to see if the current sample results show that bullish sentiment differs from its long term average of .39. What are your findings?

b. Over the long term, the proportion of bearish AAII members is .30. Conduct a hypothesis test at the 1% level of significance to see if the current sample results show that bearish sentiment is above its long term average of .30. What are your findings?

c. Would you feel comfortable extending these results to all investors? Why or why not?

9.6 Hypothesis Testing and Decision Making

In the previous sections of this chapter we have illustrated hypothesis testing applications that are considered significance tests. After formulating the null and alternative hypotheses, we selected a sample and computed the value of a test statistic and the associated *p*-value. We then compared the *p*-value to a controlled probability of a Type I error, α, which is called the level of significance for the test. If *p*-value $\leq \alpha$, we made the conclusion "reject H_0" and declared the results significant; otherwise, we made the conclusion "do not reject H_0." With a significance test, we control the probability of making the Type I error, but not the Type II error. Thus, we recommended the conclusion "do not reject H_0" rather than "accept H_0" because the latter puts us at risk of making the Type II error of accepting H_0 when it is false. With the conclusion "do not reject H_0," the statistical evidence is considered inconclusive and is usually an indication to postpone a decision or action until further research and testing can be undertaken.

However, if the purpose of a hypothesis test is to make a decision when H_0 is true and a different decision when H_a is true, the decision maker may want to, and in some cases be forced to, take action with both the conclusion *do not reject H_0* and the conclusion *reject H_0*. If this situation occurs, statisticians generally recommend controlling the probability of making a Type II error. With the probabilities of both the Type I and Type II error controlled, the conclusion from the hypothesis test is either to *accept H_0* or *reject H_0*. In the first case, H_0 is concluded to be true, while in the second case, H_a is concluded true. Thus, a decision and appropriate action can be taken when either conclusion is reached.

A good illustration of hypothesis testing for decision making is lot-acceptance sampling, a topic we will discuss in more depth in Chapter 20. For example, a quality control manager must decide to accept a shipment of batteries from a supplier or to return the shipment because of poor quality. Assume that design specifications require batteries from the supplier to have a mean useful life of at least 120 hours. To evaluate the quality of an incoming shipment, a sample of 36 batteries will be selected and tested. On the basis of the sample, a decision must be made to accept the shipment of batteries or to return it to the supplier because of poor quality. Let μ denote the mean number of hours of useful life for batteries in the shipment. The null and alternative hypotheses about the population mean follow.

$$H_0: \mu \geq 120$$
$$H_a: \mu < 120$$

If H_0 is rejected, the alternative hypothesis is concluded to be true. This conclusion indicates that the appropriate action is to return the shipment to the supplier. However, if H_0 is not rejected, the decision maker must still determine what action should be taken. Thus, without directly concluding that H_0 is true, but merely by not rejecting it, the decision maker will have made the decision to accept the shipment as being of satisfactory quality.

In such decision-making situations, it is recommended that the hypothesis testing procedure be extended to control the probability of making a Type II error. Because a decision will be made and action taken when we do not reject H_0, knowledge of the probability of making a Type II error will be helpful. In Sections 9.7 and 9.8 we explain how to compute the probability of making a Type II error and how the sample size can be adjusted to help control the probability of making a Type II error.

9.7   Calculating the Probability of Type II Errors

In this section we show how to calculate the probability of making a Type II error for a hypothesis test about a population mean. We illustrate the procedure by using the lot-acceptance example described in Section 9.6. The null and alternative hypotheses about the mean number of hours of useful life for a shipment of batteries are $H_0: \mu \geq 120$ and $H_a: \mu < 120$. If H_0 is rejected, the decision will be to return the shipment to the supplier because the mean hours of useful life are less than the specified 120 hours. If H_0 is not rejected, the decision will be to accept the shipment.

Suppose a level of significance of $\alpha = .05$ is used to conduct the hypothesis test. The test statistic in the σ known case is

$$z = \frac{\bar{x} - \mu_0}{\sigma/\sqrt{n}} = \frac{\bar{x} - 120}{\sigma/\sqrt{n}}$$

Based on the critical value approach and $z_{.05} = 1.645$, the rejection rule for the lower tail test is

Reject H_0 if $z \leq -1.645$

Suppose a sample of 36 batteries will be selected and based upon previous testing the population standard deviation can be assumed known with a value of $\sigma = 12$ hours. The rejection rule indicates that we will reject H_0 if

$$z = \frac{\bar{x} - 120}{12/\sqrt{36}} \leq -1.645$$

Solving for $\bar{x}$ in the preceding expression indicates that we will reject H_0 if

$$\bar{x} \leq 120 - 1.645\left(\frac{12}{\sqrt{36}}\right) = 116.71$$

Rejecting H_0 when $\bar{x} \leq 116.71$ means that we will make the decision to accept the shipment whenever

$$\bar{x} > 116.71$$

With this information, we are ready to compute probabilities associated with making a Type II error. First, recall that we make a Type II error whenever the true shipment mean is less

FIGURE 9.8 PROBABILITY OF A TYPE II ERROR WHEN $\mu = 112$

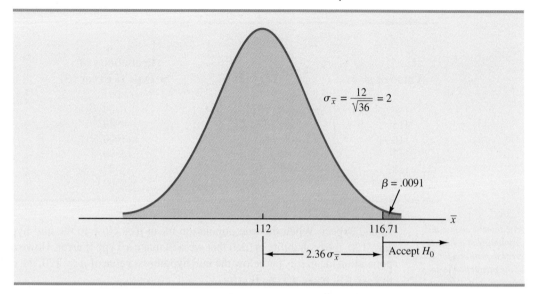

than 120 hours and we make the decision to accept H_0: $\mu \geq 120$. Hence, to compute the probability of making a Type II error, we must select a value of μ less than 120 hours. For example, suppose the shipment is considered to be of poor quality if the batteries have a mean life of $\mu = 112$ hours. If $\mu = 112$ is really true, what is the probability of accepting H_0: $\mu \geq 120$ and hence committing a Type II error? Note that this probability is the probability that the sample mean $\bar{x}$ is greater than 116.71 when $\mu = 112$.

Figure 9.8 shows the sampling distribution of $\bar{x}$ when the mean is $\mu = 112$. The shaded area in the upper tail gives the probability of obtaining $\bar{x} > 116.71$. Using the standard normal distribution, we see that at $\bar{x} = 116.71$

$$z = \frac{\bar{x} - \mu}{\sigma/\sqrt{n}} = \frac{116.71 - 112}{12/\sqrt{36}} = 2.36$$

The standard normal probability table shows that with $z = 2.36$, the area in the upper tail is $1.0000 - .9909 = .0091$. Thus, .0091 is the probability of making a Type II error when $\mu = 112$. Denoting the probability of making a Type II error as β, we see that when $\mu = 112$, $\beta = .0091$. Therefore, we can conclude that if the mean of the population is 112 hours, the probability of making a Type II error is only .0091.

We can repeat these calculations for other values of μ less than 120. Doing so will show a different probability of making a Type II error for each value of μ. For example, suppose the shipment of batteries has a mean useful life of $\mu = 115$ hours. Because we will accept H_0 whenever $\bar{x} > 116.71$, the z value for $\mu = 115$ is given by

$$z = \frac{\bar{x} - \mu}{\sigma/\sqrt{n}} = \frac{116.71 - 115}{12/\sqrt{36}} = .86$$

From the standard normal probability table, we find that the area in the upper tail of the standard normal distribution for $z = .86$ is $1.0000 - .8051 = .1949$. Thus, the probability of making a Type II error is $\beta = .1949$ when the true mean is $\mu = 115$.

In Table 9.5 we show the probability of making a Type II error for a variety of values of μ less than 120. Note that as μ increases toward 120, the probability of making a Type II error increases toward an upper bound of .95. However, as μ decreases to values farther below 120, the probability of making a Type II error diminishes. This pattern is what we

TABLE 9.5   PROBABILITY OF MAKING A TYPE II ERROR FOR THE LOT-ACCEPTANCE HYPOTHESIS TEST

Value of μ	$z = \dfrac{116.71 - \mu}{12/\sqrt{36}}$	Probability of a Type II Error (β)	Power $(1 - \beta)$
112	2.36	.0091	.9909
114	1.36	.0869	.9131
115	.86	.1949	.8051
116.71	.00	.5000	.5000
117	−.15	.5596	.4404
118	−.65	.7422	.2578
119.999	−1.645	.9500	.0500

As Table 9.5 shows, the probability of a Type II error depends on the value of the population mean μ. For values of μ near μ_0, the probability of making the Type II error can be high.

should expect. When the true population mean μ is close to the null hypothesis value of $\mu = 120$, the probability is high that we will make a Type II error. However, when the true population mean μ is far below the null hypothesis value of $\mu = 120$, the probability is low that we will make a Type II error.

The probability of correctly rejecting H_0 when it is false is called the **power** of the test. For any particular value of μ, the power is $1 - \beta$; that is, the probability of correctly rejecting the null hypothesis is 1 minus the probability of making a Type II error. Values of power are also listed in Table 9.5. On the basis of these values, the power associated with each value of μ is shown graphically in Figure 9.9. Such a graph is called a **power curve**. Note that the power curve extends over the values of μ for which the null hypothesis is false. The height of the power curve at any value of μ indicates the probability of correctly rejecting H_0 when H_0 is false.[4]

FIGURE 9.9   POWER CURVE FOR THE LOT-ACCEPTANCE HYPOTHESIS TEST

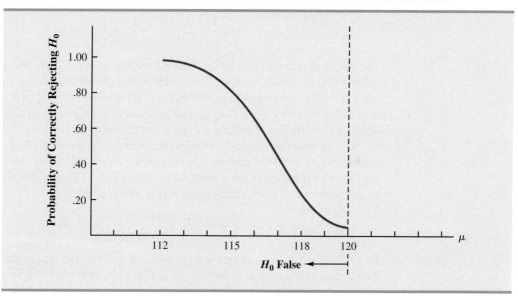

---

[4]Another graph, called the operating characteristic curve, is sometimes used to provide information about the probability of making a Type II error. The operating characteristic curve shows the probability of accepting H_0 and thus provides β for the values of μ where the null hypothesis is false. The probability of making a Type II error can be read directly from this graph.

In summary, the following step-by-step procedure can be used to compute the probability of making a Type II error in hypothesis tests about a population mean.

1. Formulate the null and alternative hypotheses.
2. Use the level of significance α and the critical value approach to determine the critical value and the rejection rule for the test.
3. Use the rejection rule to solve for the value of the sample mean corresponding to the critical value of the test statistic.
4. Use the results from step 3 to state the values of the sample mean that lead to the acceptance of H_0. These values define the acceptance region for the test.
5. Use the sampling distribution of $\bar{x}$ for a value of μ satisfying the alternative hypothesis, and the acceptance region from step 4, to compute the probability that the sample mean will be in the acceptance region. This probability is the probability of making a Type II error at the chosen value of μ.

Exercises

Methods

 SELF*test*

46. Consider the following hypothesis test.

$$H_0: \mu \geq 10$$
$$H_a: \mu < 10$$

The sample size is 120 and the population standard deviation is assumed known with $\sigma = 5$. Use $\alpha = .05$.
   a. If the population mean is 9, what is the probability that the sample mean leads to the conclusion *do not reject* H_0?
   b. What type of error would be made if the actual population mean is 9 and we conclude that $H_0: \mu \geq 10$ is true?
   c. What is the probability of making a Type II error if the actual population mean is 8?

47. Consider the following hypothesis test.

$$H_0: \mu = 20$$
$$H_a: \mu \neq 20$$

A sample of 200 items will be taken and the population standard deviation is $\sigma = 10$. Use $\alpha = .05$. Compute the probability of making a Type II error if the population mean is:
   a. $\mu = 18.0$
   b. $\mu = 22.5$
   c. $\mu = 21.0$

Applications

48. Fowle Marketing Research, Inc., bases charges to a client on the assumption that telephone surveys can be completed within 15 minutes or less. If more time is required, a premium rate is charged. With a sample of 35 surveys, a population standard deviation of 4 minutes, and a level of significance of .01, the sample mean will be used to test the null hypothesis $H_0: \mu \leq 15$.
   a. What is your interpretation of the Type II error for this problem? What is its impact on the firm?
   b. What is the probability of making a Type II error when the actual mean time is $\mu = 17$ minutes?

c.   What is the probability of making a Type II error when the actual mean time is $\mu = 18$ minutes?

d.   Sketch the general shape of the power curve for this test.

 SELFtest

49.   A consumer research group is interested in testing an automobile manufacturer's claim that a new economy model will travel at least 25 miles per gallon of gasoline ($H_0: \mu \geq 25$).

a.   With a .02 level of significance and a sample of 30 cars, what is the rejection rule based on the value of $\bar{x}$ for the test to determine whether the manufacturer's claim should be rejected? Assume that σ is 3 miles per gallon.

b.   What is the probability of committing a Type II error if the actual mileage is 23 miles per gallon?

c.   What is the probability of committing a Type II error if the actual mileage is 24 miles per gallon?

d.   What is the probability of committing a Type II error if the actual mileage is 25.5 miles per gallon?

50.   *Young Adult* magazine states the following hypotheses about the mean age of its subscribers.

$$H_0: \mu = 28$$
$$H_a: \mu \neq 28$$

a.   What would it mean to make a Type II error in this situation?

b.   The population standard deviation is assumed known at $\sigma = 6$ years and the sample size is 100. With $\alpha = .05$, what is the probability of accepting H_0 for μ equal to 26, 27, 29, and 30?

c.   What is the power at $\mu = 26$? What does this result tell you?

51.   A production line operation is tested for filling weight accuracy using the following hypotheses.

Hypothesis	Conclusion and Action
$H_0: \mu = 16$	Filling okay; keep running
$H_a: \mu \neq 16$	Filling off standard; stop and adjust machine

The sample size is 30 and the population standard deviation is $\sigma = .8$. Use $\alpha = .05$.

a.   What would a Type II error mean in this situation?

b.   What is the probability of making a Type II error when the machine is overfilling by .5 ounces?

c.   What is the power of the statistical test when the machine is overfilling by .5 ounces?

d.   Show the power curve for this hypothesis test. What information does it contain for the production manager?

52.   Refer to exercise 48. Assume the firm selects a sample of 50 surveys and repeat parts (b) and (c). What observation can you make about how increasing the sample size affects the probability of making a Type II error?

53.   Sparr Investments, Inc., specializes in tax-deferred investment opportunities for its clients. Recently Sparr offered a payroll deduction investment program for the employees of a particular company. Sparr estimates that the employees are currently averaging $100 or less per month in tax-deferred investments. A sample of 40 employees will be used to test Sparr's hypothesis about the current level of investment activity among the population of employees. Assume the employee monthly tax-deferred investment amounts have a standard deviation of $75 and that a .05 level of significance will be used in the hypothesis test.

a.   What is the Type II error in this situation?

b.   What is the probability of the Type II error if the actual mean employee monthly investment is $120?

c.   What is the probability of the Type II error if the actual mean employee monthly investment is $130?

d.   Assume a sample size of 80 employees is used and repeat parts (b) and (c).

9.8 Determining the Sample Size for a Hypothesis Test About a Population Mean

Assume that a hypothesis test is to be conducted about the value of a population mean. The level of significance specified by the user determines the probability of making a Type I error for the test. By controlling the sample size, the user can also control the probability of making a Type II error. Let us show how a sample size can be determined for the following lower tail test about a population mean.

$$H_0: \mu \geq \mu_0$$
$$H_a: \mu < \mu_0$$

The upper panel of Figure 9.10 is the sampling distribution of $\bar{x}$ when H_0 is true with $\mu = \mu_0$. For a lower tail test, the critical value of the test statistic is denoted $-z_\alpha$. In the upper panel of the figure the vertical line, labeled c, is the corresponding value of $\bar{x}$. Note that, if we reject H_0 when $\bar{x} \leq c$, the probability of a Type I error will be α. With z_α representing the z value corresponding to an area of α in the upper tail of the standard normal distribution, we compute c using the following formula:

$$c = \mu_0 - z_\alpha \frac{\sigma}{\sqrt{n}} \tag{9.5}$$

FIGURE 9.10   DETERMINING THE SAMPLE SIZE FOR SPECIFIED LEVELS OF THE TYPE I (α) AND TYPE II (β) ERRORS

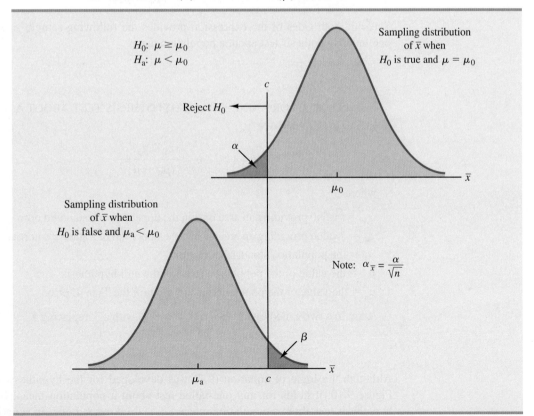

The lower panel of Figure 9.10 is the sampling distribution of $\bar{x}$ when the alternative hypothesis is true with $\mu = \mu_a < \mu_0$. The shaded region shows β, the probability of a Type II error that the decision maker will be exposed to if the null hypothesis is accepted when $\bar{x} > c$. With z_β representing the z value corresponding to an area of β in the upper tail of the standard normal distribution, we compute c using the following formula:

$$c = \mu_a + z_\beta \frac{\sigma}{\sqrt{n}} \tag{9.6}$$

Now what we want to do is to select a value for c so that when we reject H_0 and accept H_a, the probability of a Type I error is equal to the chosen value of α and the probability of a Type II error is equal to the chosen value of β. Therefore, both equations (9.5) and (9.6) must provide the same value for c, and the following equation must be true.

$$\mu_0 - z_\alpha \frac{\sigma}{\sqrt{n}} = \mu_a + z_\beta \frac{\sigma}{\sqrt{n}}$$

To determine the required sample size, we first solve for the $\sqrt{n}$ as follows.

$$\mu_0 - \mu_a = z_\alpha \frac{\sigma}{\sqrt{n}} + z_\beta \frac{\sigma}{\sqrt{n}}$$

$$\mu_0 - \mu_a = \frac{(z_\alpha + z_\beta)\sigma}{\sqrt{n}}$$

and

$$\sqrt{n} = \frac{(z_\alpha + z_\beta)\sigma}{(\mu_0 - \mu_a)}$$

Squaring both sides of the expression provides the following sample size formula for a one-tailed hypothesis test about a population mean.

SAMPLE SIZE FOR A ONE-TAILED HYPOTHESIS TEST ABOUT A POPULATION MEAN

$$n = \frac{(z_\alpha + z_\beta)^2 \sigma^2}{(\mu_0 - \mu_a)^2} \tag{9.7}$$

where

z_α = z value providing an area of α in the upper tail of a standard normal distribution
z_β = z value providing an area of β in the upper tail of a standard normal distribution
σ = the population standard deviation
μ_0 = the value of the population mean in the null hypothesis
μ_a = the value of the population mean used for the Type II error

Note: In a two-tailed hypothesis test, use (9.7) with $z_{\alpha/2}$ replacing z_α.

Although the logic of equation (9.7) was developed for the hypothesis test shown in Figure 9.10, it holds for any one-tailed test about a population mean. In a two-tailed hypothesis test about a population mean, $z_{\alpha/2}$ is used instead of z_α in equation (9.7).

Let us return to the lot-acceptance example from Sections 9.6 and 9.7. The design specification for the shipment of batteries indicated a mean useful life of at least 120 hours for the batteries. Shipments were rejected if $H_0: \mu \geq 120$ was rejected. Let us assume that the quality control manager makes the following statements about the allowable probabilities for the Type I and Type II errors.

Type I error statement: If the mean life of the batteries in the shipment is $\mu = 120$, I am willing to risk an $\alpha = .05$ probability of rejecting the shipment.

Type II error statement: If the mean life of the batteries in the shipment is 5 hours under the specification (i.e., $\mu = 115$), I am willing to risk a $\beta = .10$ probability of accepting the shipment.

These statements are based on the judgment of the manager. Someone else might specify different restrictions on the probabilities. However, statements about the allowable probabilities of both errors must be made before the sample size can be determined.

In the example, $\alpha = .05$ and $\beta = .10$. Using the standard normal probability distribution, we have $z_{.05} = 1.645$ and $z_{.10} = 1.28$. From the statements about the error probabilities, we note that $\mu_0 = 120$ and $\mu_a = 115$. Finally, the population standard deviation was assumed known at $\sigma = 12$. By using equation (9.7), we find that the recommended sample size for the lot-acceptance example is

$$n = \frac{(1.645 + 1.28)^2 (12)^2}{(120 - 115)^2} = 49.3$$

Rounding up, we recommend a sample size of 50.

Because both the Type I and Type II error probabilities have been controlled at allowable levels with $n = 50$, the quality control manager is now justified in using the *accept H_0* and *reject H_0* statements for the hypothesis test. The accompanying inferences are made with allowable probabilities of making Type I and Type II errors.

We can make three observations about the relationship among α, β, and the sample size n.

1. Once two of the three values are known, the other can be computed.
2. For a given level of significance α, increasing the sample size will reduce β.
3. For a given sample size, decreasing α will increase β, whereas increasing α will decrease β.

The third observation should be kept in mind when the probability of a Type II error is not being controlled. It suggests that one should not choose unnecessarily small values for the level of significance α. For a given sample size, choosing a smaller level of significance means more exposure to a Type II error. Inexperienced users of hypothesis testing often think that smaller values of α are always better. They are better if we are concerned only about making a Type I error. However, smaller values of α have the disadvantage of increasing the probability of making a Type II error.

Exercises

Methods

54.   Consider the following hypothesis test.

$$H_0: \mu \geq 10$$
$$H_a: \mu < 10$$

The sample size is 120 and the population standard deviation is 5. Use $\alpha = .05$. If the actual population mean is 9, the probability of a Type II error is .2912. Suppose the researcher wants to reduce the probability of a Type II error to .10 when the actual population mean is 9. What sample size is recommended?

55. Consider the following hypothesis test.

$$H_0: \mu = 20$$
$$H_a: \mu \neq 20$$

The population standard deviation is 10. Use $\alpha = .05$. How large a sample should be taken if the researcher is willing to accept a .05 probability of making a Type II error when the actual population mean is 22?

Applications

56. Suppose the project director for the Hilltop Coffee study (see Section 9.3) asked for a .10 probability of claiming that Hilltop was not in violation when it really was underfilling by 1 ounce ($\mu_a = 2.9375$ pounds). What sample size would have been recommended?

SELF*test*

57. A special industrial battery must have a life of at least 400 hours. A hypothesis test is to be conducted with a .02 level of significance. If the batteries from a particular production run have an actual mean use life of 385 hours, the production manager wants a sampling procedure that only 10% of the time would show erroneously that the batch is acceptable. What sample size is recommended for the hypothesis test? Use 30 hours as an estimate of the population standard deviation.

58. *Young Adult* magazine states the following hypotheses about the mean age of its subscribers.

$$H_0: \mu = 28$$
$$H_a: \mu \neq 28$$

If the manager conducting the test will permit a .15 probability of making a Type II error when the true mean age is 29, what sample size should be selected? Assume $\sigma = 6$ and a .05 level of significance.

59. An automobile mileage study tested the following hypotheses.

Hypothesis	Conclusion
$H_0: \mu \geq 25$ mpg	Manufacturer's claim supported
$H_a: \mu < 25$ mpg	Manufacturer's claim rejected; average mileage per gallon less than stated

For $\sigma = 3$ and a .02 level of significance, what sample size would be recommended if the researcher wants an 80% chance of detecting that μ is less than 25 miles per gallon when it is actually 24?

Summary

Hypothesis testing is a statistical procedure that uses sample data to determine whether a statement about the value of a population parameter should or should not be rejected. The hypotheses are two competing statements about a population parameter. One statement is called the null hypothesis (H_0), and the other statement is called the alternative hypothesis (H_a). In Section 9.1 we provided guidelines for developing hypotheses for situations frequently encountered in practice.

Whenever historical data or other information provides a basis for assuming that the population standard deviation is known, the hypothesis testing procedure for the population mean is based on the standard normal distribution. Whenever σ is unknown, the sample standard deviation s is used to estimate σ and the hypothesis testing procedure is based on the t distribution. In both cases, the quality of results depends on both the form of the population distribution and the sample size. If the population has a normal distribution, both hypothesis testing procedures are applicable, even with small sample sizes. If the population is not normally distributed, larger sample sizes are needed. General guidelines about the sample size were provided in Sections 9.3 and 9.4. In the case of hypothesis tests about a population proportion, the hypothesis testing procedure uses a test statistic based on the standard normal distribution.

In all cases, the value of the test statistic can be used to compute a p-value for the test. A p-value is a probability used to determine whether the null hypothesis should be rejected. If the p-value is less than or equal to the level of significance α, the null hypothesis can be rejected.

Hypothesis testing conclusions can also be made by comparing the value of the test statistic to a critical value. For lower tail tests, the null hypothesis is rejected if the value of the test statistic is less than or equal to the critical value. For upper tail tests, the null hypothesis is rejected if the value of the test statistic is greater than or equal to the critical value. Two-tailed tests consist of two critical values: one in the lower tail of the sampling distribution and one in the upper tail. In this case, the null hypothesis is rejected if the value of the test statistic is less than or equal to the critical value in the lower tail or greater than or equal to the critical value in the upper tail.

Extensions of hypothesis testing procedures to include an analysis of the Type II error were also presented. In Section 9.7 we showed how to compute the probability of making a Type II error. In Section 9.8 we showed how to determine a sample size that will control for the probability of making both a Type I error and a Type II error.

Glossary

Alternative hypothesis The hypothesis concluded to be true if the null hypothesis is rejected.

Critical value A value that is compared with the test statistic to determine whether H_0 should be rejected.

Level of significance The probability of making a Type I error when the null hypothesis is true as an equality.

Null hypothesis The hypothesis tentatively assumed true in the hypothesis testing procedure.

One-tailed test A hypothesis test in which rejection of the null hypothesis occurs for values of the test statistic in one tail of its sampling distribution.

p-value A probability that provides a measure of the evidence against the null hypothesis given by the sample. Smaller p-values indicate more evidence against H_0. For a lower tail test, the p-value is the probability of obtaining a value for the test statistic as small as or smaller than that provided by the sample. For an upper tail test, the p-value is the probability of obtaining a value for the test statistic as large as or larger than that provided by the sample. For a two-tailed test, the p-value is the probability of obtaining a value for the test statistic at least as unlikely as or more unlikely than that provided by the sample.

Power The probability of correctly rejecting H_0 when it is false.

Power curve A graph of the probability of rejecting H_0 for all possible values of the population parameter not satisfying the null hypothesis. The power curve provides the probability of correctly rejecting the null hypothesis.

Test statistic A statistic whose value helps determine whether a null hypothesis should be rejected.

Two-tailed test A hypothesis test in which rejection of the null hypothesis occurs for values of the test statistic in either tail of its sampling distribution.

Type I error The error of rejecting H_0 when it is true.

Type II error The error of accepting H_0 when it is false.

Key Formulas

Test Statistic for Hypothesis Tests About a Population Mean: σ Known

$$z = \frac{\bar{x} - \mu_0}{\sigma/\sqrt{n}} \tag{9.1}$$

Test Statistic for Hypothesis Tests About a Population Mean: σ Unknown

$$t = \frac{\bar{x} - \mu_0}{s/\sqrt{n}} \tag{9.2}$$

Test Statistic for Hypothesis Tests About a Population Proportion

$$z = \frac{\bar{p} - p_0}{\sqrt{\dfrac{p_0(1 - p_0)}{n}}} \tag{9.4}$$

Sample Size for a One-Tailed Hypothesis Test About a Population Mean

$$n = \frac{(z_\alpha + z_\beta)^2 \sigma^2}{(\mu_0 - \mu_a)^2} \tag{9.7}$$

In a two-tailed test, replace z_α with $z_{\alpha/2}$.

Supplementary Exercises

60. A production line operates with a mean filling weight of 16 ounces per container. Overfilling or underfilling presents a serious problem and when detected requires the operator to shut down the production line to readjust the filling mechanism. From past data, a population standard deviation $\sigma = .8$ ounces is assumed. A quality control inspector selects a sample of 30 items every hour and at that time makes the decision of whether to shut down the line for readjustment. The level of significance is $\alpha = .05$.
    a. State the hypothesis test for this quality control application.
    b. If a sample mean of $\bar{x} = 16.32$ ounces were found, what is the p-value? What action would you recommend?
    c. If a sample mean of $\bar{x} = 15.82$ ounces were found, what is the p-value? What action would you recommend?
    d. Use the critical value approach. What is the rejection rule for the preceding hypothesis testing procedure? Repeat parts (b) and (c). Do you reach the same conclusion?

61. At Western University the historical mean of scholarship examination scores for freshman applications is 900. A historical population standard deviation $\sigma = 180$ is assumed known. Each year, the assistant dean uses a sample of applications to determine whether the mean examination score for the new freshman applications has changed.
    a. State the hypotheses.
    b. What is the 95% confidence interval estimate of the population mean examination score if a sample of 200 applications provided a sample mean $\bar{x} = 935$?
    c. Use the confidence interval to conduct a hypothesis test. Using $\alpha = .05$, what is your conclusion?
    d. What is the p-value?

62. Young children in the United States are exposed to an average of 4 hours of background television per day (CNN website, November 13, 2012). Having the television on in the background while children are doing other activities may have adverse consequences on a child's

well-being. You have a research hypothesis that children from low-income families are exposed to more than 4 hours of daily background television. In order to test this hypothesis, you have collected a random sample of 60 children from low-income families and found that these children were exposed to a sample mean of 4.5 hours of daily background television.

a. Develop hypotheses that can be used to test your research hypothesis.

b. Based on a previous study, you are willing to assume that the population standard deviation is $\sigma = 0.5$ hours. What is the p-value based on your sample of 60 children from low-income families?

c. Use $\alpha = .01$ as the level of significance. What is your conclusion?

63. The *Wall Street Journal* reported that bachelor's degree recipients with majors in business received average starting salaries of $53,900 in 2012 (*The Wall Street Journal*, March 17, 2014). The results for a sample of 100 business majors receiving a bachelor's degree in 2013 showed a mean starting salary of $55,144 with a sample standard deviation of $5200. Conduct a hypothesis test to determine whether the mean starting salary for business majors in 2013 is greater than the mean starting salary in 2012. Use $\alpha = .01$ as the level of significance.

BritainMarriages

64. Data from the Office for National Statistics show that the mean age at which men in Great Britain get married is 30.8 years (*The Guardian*, February 15, 2013). A news reporter noted that this represents a continuation of the trend of waiting until a later age to wed. A new sample of 47 recently wed British men provided their age at the time of marriage. These data are contained in the DATAfile BritainMarriages. Do these data indicate that the mean age of British men at the time of marriage exceeds the mean age in 2013? Test this hypothesis at $\alpha = .05$. What is your conclusion?.

WeeklyPay

65. A recent issue of the *AARP Bulletin* reported that the average weekly pay for a woman with a high school school degree is $520 (*AARP Bulletin*, January–February, 2010). Suppose you would like to determine if the average weekly pay for all working women is significantly greater than that for women with a high school degree. Data providing the weekly pay for a sample of 50 working women are available in the file named WeeklyPay. These data are consistent with the findings reported in the AARP article.

a. State the hypotheses that should be used to test whether the mean weekly pay for all women is significantly greater than the mean weekly pay for women with a high school degree.

b. Use the data in the file named WeeklyPay to compute the sample mean, the test statistic, and the p-value.

c. Use $\alpha = .05$. What is your conclusion?

d. Repeat the hypothesis test using the critical value approach.

66. The chamber of commerce of a Florida Gulf Coast community advertises that area residential property is available at a mean cost of $125,000 or less per lot. Suppose a sample of 32 properties provided a sample mean of $130,000 per lot and a sample standard deviation of $12,500. Use a .05 level of significance to test the validity of the advertising claim.

67. In Hamilton County, Ohio, the mean number of days needed to sell a house is 86 days (Cincinnati Multiple Listing Service, April, 2012). Data for the sale of 40 houses in a nearby county showed a sample mean of 80 days with a sample standard deviation of 20 days. Conduct a hypothesis test to determine whether the mean number of days until a house is sold is different than the Hamilton County mean of 86 days in the nearby county. Use $\alpha = .05$ for the level of significance, and state your conclusion.

68. On December 25, 2009, an airline passenger was subdued while attempting to blow up a Northwest Airlines flight headed for Detroit, Michigan. The passenger had smuggled explosives hidden in his underwear past a metal detector at an airport screening facility. As a result, the Transportation Security Administration (TSA) proposed installing full-body scanners to replace the metal detectors at the nation's largest airports. This proposal resulted in strong objections from privacy advocates who considered the scanners an invasion of privacy. On January 5–6, 2010, *USA Today* conducted a poll of 542 adults to learn what proportion of

airline travelers approved of using full-body scanners (*USA Today,* January 11, 2010). The poll results showed that 455 of the respondents felt that full-body scanners would improve airline security and 423 indicated that they approved of using the devices.

   a. Conduct a hypothesis test to determine if the results of the poll justify concluding that over 80% of airline travelers feel that the use of full-body scanners will improve airline security. Use $\alpha = .05$.

   b. Suppose the TSA will go forward with the installation and mandatory use of full-body scanners if over 75% of airline travelers approve of using the devices. You have been told to conduct a statistical analysis using the poll results to determine if the TSA should require mandatory use of the full-body scanners. Because this is viewed as a very sensitive decision, use $\alpha = .01$. What is your recommendation?

69. An airline promotion to business travelers is based on the assumption that two-thirds of business travelers use a laptop computer on overnight business trips.

   a. State the hypotheses that can be used to test the assumption.

   b. What is the sample proportion from an American Express sponsored survey that found 355 of 546 business travelers use a laptop computer on overnight business trips?

   c. What is the *p*-value?

   d. Use $\alpha = .05$. What is your conclusion?

70. Members of the millennial generation are continuing to be dependent on their parents (either living with or otherwise receiving support from parents) into early adulthood (*The Enquirer*, March 16, 2014). A family research organization has claimed that, in past generations, no more than 30% of individuals aged 18 to 32 continued to be dependent on their parents. Suppose that a sample of 400 individuals aged 18 to 32 showed that 136 of them continue to be dependent on their parents.

   a. Develop hypotheses for a test to determine whether the proportion of millennials continuing to be dependent on their parents is higher than for past generations.

   b. What is your point estimate of the proportion of millennials that are continuing to be dependent on their parents?

   c. What is the *p*-value provided by the sample data?

   d. What is your hypothesis testing conclusion? Use $\alpha = .05$ as the level of significance.

71. The unemployment rate for 18- to 34-year-olds was reported to be 10.8% (*The Cincinnati Enquirer*, November 6, 2012). Assume that this report was based on a random sample of four hundred 18- to 34-year-olds.

   a. A political campaign manager wants to know if the sample results can be used to conclude that the unemployment rate for 18- to 34-years-olds is significantly higher than the unemployment rate for all adults. According to the Bureau of Labor Statistics, the unemployment rate for all adults was 7.9%. Develop a hypothesis test that can be used to see if the conclusion that the unemployment rate is higher for 18- to 34-year-olds can be supported.

   b. Use the sample data collected for the 18- to 34-year-olds to compute the *p*-value for the hypothesis test in part (a). Using $\alpha = .05$, what is your conclusion?

   c. Explain to the campaign manager what can be said about the observed level of significance for the hypothesis testing results using the *p*-value.

72. A radio station in Myrtle Beach announced that at least 90% of the hotels and motels would be full for the Memorial Day weekend. The station advised listeners to make reservations in advance if they planned to be in the resort over the weekend. On Saturday night a sample of 58 hotels and motels showed 49 with a no-vacancy sign and 9 with vacancies. What is your reaction to the radio station's claim after seeing the sample evidence? Use $\alpha = .05$ in making the statistical test. What is the *p*-value?

73. In recent years more people have been working past the age of 65. In 2005, 27% of people aged 65–69 worked. A recent report from the Organization for Economic Co-operation and Development (OECD) claimed that the percentage working had increased

(*USA Today*, November 16, 2012). The findings reported by the OECD were consistent with taking a sample of 600 people aged 65–69 and finding that 180 of them were working.

    a.   Develop a point estimate of the proportion of people aged 65–69 who are working.

    b.   Set up a hypothesis test so that the rejection of H_0 will allow you to conclude that the proportion of people aged 65–69 working has increased from 2005.

    c.   Conduct your hypothesis test using $\alpha = .05$. What is your conclusion?

74   Shorney Construction Company bids on projects assuming that the mean idle time per worker is 72 or fewer minutes per day. A sample of 30 construction workers will be used to test this assumption. Assume that the population standard deviation is 20 minutes.

    a.   State the hypotheses to be tested.

    b.   What is the probability of making a Type II error when the population mean idle time is 80 minutes?

    c.   What is the probability of making a Type II error when the population mean idle time is 75 minutes?

    d.   What is the probability of making a Type II error when the population mean idle time is 70 minutes?

    e.   Sketch the power curve for this problem.

75.   A federal funding program is available to low-income neighborhoods. To qualify for the funding, a neighborhood must have a mean household income of less than $15,000 per year. Neighborhoods with mean annual household income of $15,000 or more do not qualify. Funding decisions are based on a sample of residents in the neighborhood. A hypothesis test with a .02 level of significance is conducted. If the funding guidelines call for a maximum probability of .05 of not funding a neighborhood with a mean annual household income of $14,000, what sample size should be used in the funding decision study? Use $\sigma = \$4000$ as a planning value.

76. $H_0: \mu = 120$ and $H_a: \mu \neq 120$ are used to test whether a bath soap production process is meeting the standard output of 120 bars per batch. Use a .05 level of significance for the test and a planning value of 5 for the standard deviation.

    a.   If the mean output drops to 117 bars per batch, the firm wants to have a 98% chance of concluding that the standard production output is not being met. How large a sample should be selected?

    b.   With your sample size from part (a), what is the probability of concluding that the process is operating satisfactorily for each of the following actual mean outputs: 117, 118, 119, 121, 122, and 123 bars per batch? That is, what is the probability of a Type II error in each case?

Case Problem 1   Quality Associates, Inc.

Quality Associates, Inc., a consulting firm, advises its clients about sampling and statistical procedures that can be used to control their manufacturing processes. In one particular application, a client gave Quality Associates a sample of 800 observations taken during a time in which that client's process was operating satisfactorily. The sample standard deviation for these data was .21; hence, with so much data, the population standard deviation was assumed to be .21. Quality Associates then suggested that random samples of size 30 be taken periodically to monitor the process on an ongoing basis. By analyzing the new samples, the client could quickly learn whether the process was operating satisfactorily. When the process was not operating satisfactorily, corrective action could be taken to eliminate the problem. The design specification indicated the mean for the process should be 12. The hypothesis test suggested by Quality Associates follows.

$$H_0: \mu = 12$$
$$H_a: \mu \neq 12$$

Corrective action will be taken any time H_0 is rejected.

The following samples were collected at hourly intervals during the first day of operation of the new statistical process control procedure. These data are available in the data set Quality.

Quality

Sample 1	Sample 2	Sample 3	Sample 4
11.55	11.62	11.91	12.02
11.62	11.69	11.36	12.02
11.52	11.59	11.75	12.05
11.75	11.82	11.95	12.18
11.90	11.97	12.14	12.11
11.64	11.71	11.72	12.07
11.80	11.87	11.61	12.05
12.03	12.10	11.85	11.64
11.94	12.01	12.16	12.39
11.92	11.99	11.91	11.65
12.13	12.20	12.12	12.11
12.09	12.16	11.61	11.90
11.93	12.00	12.21	12.22
12.21	12.28	11.56	11.88
12.32	12.39	11.95	12.03
11.93	12.00	12.01	12.35
11.85	11.92	12.06	12.09
11.76	11.83	11.76	11.77
12.16	12.23	11.82	12.20
11.77	11.84	12.12	11.79
12.00	12.07	11.60	12.30
12.04	12.11	11.95	12.27
11.98	12.05	11.96	12.29
12.30	12.37	12.22	12.47
12.18	12.25	11.75	12.03
11.97	12.04	11.96	12.17
12.17	12.24	11.95	11.94
11.85	11.92	11.89	11.97
12.30	12.37	11.88	12.23
12.15	12.22	11.93	12.25

Managerial Report

1. Conduct a hypothesis test for each sample at the .01 level of significance and determine what action, if any, should be taken. Provide the test statistic and p-value for each test.
2. Compute the standard deviation for each of the four samples. Does the assumption of .21 for the population standard deviation appear reasonable?
3. Compute limits for the sample mean $\bar{x}$ around $\mu = 12$ such that, as long as a new sample mean is within those limits, the process will be considered to be operating satisfactorily. If $\bar{x}$ exceeds the upper limit or if $\bar{x}$ is below the lower limit, corrective action will be taken. These limits are referred to as upper and lower control limits for quality control purposes.
4. Discuss the implications of changing the level of significance to a larger value. What mistake or error could increase if the level of significance is increased?

Case Problem 2 # Ethical Behavior of Business Students at Bayview University

During the global recession of 2008 and 2009, there were many accusations of unethical behavior by Wall Street executives, financial managers, and other corporate officers. At that time, an article appeared that suggested that part of the reason for such unethical business behavior may stem from the fact that cheating has become more prevalent among business students (*Chronicle of Higher Education,* February 10, 2009). The article reported that 56% of business students admitted to cheating at some time during their academic career as compared to 47% of nonbusiness students.

Cheating has been a concern of the dean of the College of Business at Bayview University for several years. Some faculty members in the college believe that cheating is more widespread at Bayview than at other universities, while other faculty members think that cheating is not a major problem in the college. To resolve some of these issues, the dean commissioned a study to assess the current ethical behavior of business students at Bayview. As part of this study, an anonymous exit survey was administered to a sample of 90 business students from this year's graduating class. Responses to the following questions were used to obtain data regarding three types of cheating.

> During your time at Bayview, did you ever present work copied off the Internet as your own?
>
> Yes _____   No _____
>
> During your time at Bayview, did you ever copy answers off another student's exam?
>
> Yes _____   No _____
>
> During your time at Bayview, did you ever collaborate with other students on projects that were supposed to be completed individually?
>
> Yes _____   No _____

Any student who answered Yes to one or more of these questions was considered to have been involved in some type of cheating. A portion of the data collected follows. The complete data set is in the file named Bayview.

DATA *file*

Bayview

Student	Copied from Internet	Copied on Exam	Collaborated on Individual Project	Gender
1	No	No	No	Female
2	No	No	No	Male
3	Yes	No	Yes	Male
4	Yes	Yes	No	Male
5	No	No	Yes	Male
6	Yes	No	No	Female
.	.	.	.	.
.	.	.	.	.
.	.	.	.	.
88	No	No	No	Male
89	No	Yes	Yes	Male
90	No	No	No	Female

Managerial Report

Prepare a report for the dean of the college that summarizes your assessment of the nature of cheating by business students at Bayview University. Be sure to include the following items in your report.

1. Use descriptive statistics to summarize the data and comment on your findings.
2. Develop 95% confidence intervals for the proportion of all students, the proportion of male students, and the proportion of female students who were involved in some type of cheating.
3. Conduct a hypothesis test to determine if the proportion of business students at Bayview University who were involved in some type of cheating is less than that of business students at other institutions as reported by the *Chronicle of Higher Education.*
4. Conduct a hypothesis test to determine if the proportion of business students at Bayview University who were involved in some form of cheating is less than that of nonbusiness students at other institutions as reported by the *Chronicle of Higher Education.*
5. What advice would you give to the dean based upon your analysis of the data?

Appendix 9.1   Hypothesis Testing with Minitab

We describe the use of Minitab to conduct hypothesis tests about a population mean and a population proportion.

Population Mean: σ Known

We illustrate using the MaxFlight golf ball distance example in Section 9.3. The data are in column C1 of the DATAfile GolfTest. The population standard deviation $\sigma = 12$ is assumed known and the level of significance is $\alpha = .05$. The following steps can be used to test the hypothesis $H_0: \mu = 295$ versus $H_a: \mu \neq 295$.

GolfTest

Step 1. Select the **Stat** menu
Step 2. Choose **Basic Statistics**
Step 3. Choose **1-Sample Z**
Step 4. When the One-Sample Z for the Mean dialog box appears:
      Select **One or more samples, each in a column** from the drop-down menu
      Enter C1 in the box just below the drop-down menu
      Enter 12 in the **Known standard deviation** box
      Select **Perform hypothesis test**
      Enter 295 in the **Hypothesized mean** box
      Select **Options**
Step 5. When the One-Sample Z: Options dialog box appears:
      Enter 95 in the **Confidence level** box*
      Select **Mean ≠ hypothesized mean** in the **Alternative hypothesis** box
      Click **OK**
Step 6. Click **OK**

In addition to the hypothesis testing results, Minitab provides a 95% confidence interval for the population mean.

    The procedure can be easily modified for a one-tailed hypothesis test by selecting the **Mean < hypothesized mean** or **Mean > hypothesized mean** option in the **Alternative hypothesis** box in step 5.

---

*Minitab provides both hypothesis testing and interval estimation results simultaneously. The user may select any confidence level for the interval estimate of the population mean: 95% confidence is suggested here.

Population Mean: σ Unknown

AirRating

The ratings that 60 business travelers gave for Heathrow Airport are entered in column C1 of the DATAfile AirRating. The level of significance for the test is $\alpha = .05$, and the population standard deviation σ will be estimated by the sample standard deviation s. The following steps can be used to test the hypothesis H_0: $\mu \leq 7$ against H_a: $\mu > 7$.

Step 1. Select the **Stat** menu

Step 2. Choose **Basic Statistics**

Step 3. Choose **1-Sample t**

Step 4. When the One-Sample t for the Mean dialog box appears:

Select **One or more samples, each in a column** from the drop-down menu

Enter C1 in the box just below the drop-down menu

Select **Perform hypothesis test**

Enter 7 in the **Hypothesized mean** box

Select **Options**

Step 5. When the One-Sample t: Options dialog box appears:

Enter 95 in the **Confidence level** box

Select **Mean > hypothesized mean** in the **Alternative hypothesis** box

Click **OK**

Step 6. Click **OK**

The Heathrow Airport rating study involved a greater than alternative hypothesis. The preceding steps can be easily modified for other hypothesis tests by selecting the **Mean ≠ hypothesized mean** or **Mean < hypothesized mean** option in the **Alternative hypothesis** box in step 5.

Population Proportion

WomenGolf

We illustrate using the Pine Creek golf course example in Section 9.5. The data with responses Female and Male are in column C1 of a the DATAfile WomanGolf. Minitab uses an alphabetical ordering of the responses and selects the *second response* for the population proportion of interest. In this example, Minitab uses the alphabetical ordering Female-Male to provide results for the population proportion of Male responses. Because Female is the response of interest, we change Minitab's ordering as follows: Select any cell in the column and use the sequence: Editor > Column > Value Order. Then choose the option of entering a user-specified order. Enter Male-Female in the **Define-an-order** box and click OK. Minitab's 1 Proportion routine will then provide the hypothesis test results for the population proportion of female golfers. We proceed as follows:

Step 1. Select the **Stat** menu

Step 2. Choose **Basic Statistics**

Step 3. Choose **1 Proportion**

Step 4. When the One-Sample Proportion dialog box appears:

Select **One or more samples, each in a column** from the drop-down menu

Enter C1 in the box just below the drop-down menu

Select **Perform hypothesis test**

Enter .20 in the **Hypothesized proportion** box

Select **Options**

Step 5. When the One-Sample Proportion-Options dialog box appears:

Enter 95 in the **Confidence level** box

Select **Proportion > hypothesized proportion** in the **Alternative hypothesis** box

Select **Normal approximation** in the **Method** box

Click **OK**

Step 6. Click **OK**

You can also select the **Exact** *option from the Method pull-down menu when testing a hypothesis for one proportion. This method uses the binomial distribution for testing a hypothesis for one population proportion.*

Appendix 9.2   Hypothesis Testing with Excel

Excel does not provide built-in routines for the hypothesis tests presented in this chapter. To handle these situations, we present Excel worksheets that we designed to use as templates for testing hypotheses about a population mean and a population proportion. The worksheets are easy to use and can be modified to handle any sample data. The worksheets are available on the website that accompanies this book.

Population Mean: σ Known

We illustrate using the MaxFlight golf ball distance example in Section 9.3. The data are in column A of an Excel worksheet. The population standard deviation $\sigma = 12$ is assumed known and the level of significance is $\alpha = .05$. The following steps can be used to test the hypothesis H_0: $\mu = 295$ versus H_a: $\mu \neq 295$.

DATA *file*

Hyp Sigma Known

Refer to Figure 9.11 as we describe the procedure. The worksheet in the background shows the cell formulas used to compute the results shown in the foreground worksheet. The data are entered into cells A2:A51. The following steps are necessary to use the template for this data set.

Step 1. Enter the data range A2:A51 into the =COUNT cell formula in cell D4
Step 2. Enter the data range A2:A51 into the =AVERAGE cell formula in cell D5
Step 3. Enter the population standard deviation $\sigma = 12$ into cell D7
Step 4. Enter the hypothesized value for the population mean 295 into cell D8

The remaining cell formulas automatically provide the standard error, the value of the test statistic z, and three p-values. Because the alternative hypothesis ($\mu_0 \neq 295$) indicates a two-tailed test, the p-value (Two Tail) in cell D15 is used to make the rejection decision. With p-value $= .1255 > \alpha = .05$, the null hypothesis cannot be rejected. The p-values in cells D13 or D14 would be used if the hypotheses involved a one-tailed test.

This template can be used to make hypothesis testing computations for other applications. For instance, to conduct a hypothesis test for a new data set, enter the new sample data into column A of the worksheet. Modify the formulas in cells D4 and D5 to correspond to the new data range. Enter the population standard deviation into cell D7 and the hypothesized value for the population mean into cell D8 to obtain the results. If the new sample data have already been summarized, the new sample data do not have to be entered into the worksheet. In this case, enter the sample size into cell D4, the sample mean into cell D5, the population standard deviation into cell D7, and the hypothesized value for the population mean into cell D8 to obtain the results. The worksheet in Figure 9.11 is available in the file Hyp Sigma Known on the website that accompanies this book.

Population Mean: σ Unknown

We illustrate using the Heathrow Airport rating example in Section 9.4. The data are in column A of an Excel worksheet. The population standard deviation σ is unknown and will be estimated by the sample standard deviation s. The level of significance is $\alpha = .05$. The following steps can be used to test the hypothesis H_0: $\mu \leq 7$ versus H_a: $\mu > 7$.

DATA *file*

Hyp Sigma Unknown

Refer to Figure 9.12 as we describe the procedure. The background worksheet shows the cell formulas used to compute the results shown in the foreground version of the worksheet. The data are entered into cells A2:A61. The following steps are necessary to use the template for this data set.

Step 1. Enter the data range A2:A61 into the =COUNT cell formula in cell D4
Step 2. Enter the data range A2:A61 into the =AVERAGE cell formula in cell D5
Step 3. Enter the data range A2:A61 into the =STDEV cell formula in cell D6
Step 4. Enter the hypothesized value for the population mean 7 into cell D8

FIGURE 9.11   EXCEL WORKSHEET FOR HYPOTHESIS TESTS ABOUT A POPULATION MEAN WITH σ KNOWN

	A	B	C	D	E
1	**Yards**		**Hypothesis Test About a Population Mean:**		
2	303		σ **Known Case**		
3	282				
4	289		**Sample Size**	=COUNT(A2:A51)	
5	298		**Sample Mean**	=AVERAGE(A2:A51)	
6	283				
7	317		**Population Standard Deviation**	12	
8	297		**Hypothesized Value**	295	
9	308				
10	317		**Standard Error**	=D7/SQRT(D4)	
11	293		**Test Statistic z**	=(D5-D8)/D10	
12	284				
13	290		**p-value (Lower Tail)**	=NORM.S.DIST(D11,TRUE)	
14	304		**p-value (Upper Tail)**	=1-D13	
15	290		**p-value (Two Tail)**	=2*(MIN(D13,D14))	
16	311				
50	301				
51	292				
52					

	A	B	C	D	E
1	**Yards**		**Hypothesis Test About a Population Mean:**		
2	303		σ **Known Case**		
3	282				
4	289		**Sample Size**	50	
5	298		**Sample Mean**	297.6	
6	283				
7	317		**Population Standard Deviation**	12	
8	297		**Hypothesized Value**	295	
9	308				
10	317		**Standard Error**	1.70	
11	293		**Test Statistic z**	1.53	
12	284				
13	290		**p-value (Lower Tail)**	0.9372	
14	304		**p-value (Upper Tail)**	0.0628	
15	290		**p-value (Two Tail)**	0.1255	
16	311				
50	301				
51	292				
52					

Note: Rows 17 to 49 are hidden.

The remaining cell formulas automatically provide the standard error, the value of the test statistic t, the number of degrees of freedom, and three p-values. Because the alternative hypothesis ($\mu > 7$) indicates an upper tail test, the p-value (Upper Tail) in cell D15 is used to make the decision. With p-value $= .0353 < \alpha = .05$, the null hypothesis is rejected. The p-values in cells D14 or D16 would be used if the hypotheses involved a lower tail test or a two-tailed test.

This template can be used to make hypothesis testing computations for other applications. For instance, to conduct a hypothesis test for a new data set, enter the new sample data into column A of the worksheet and modify the formulas in cells D4, D5, and D6 to correspond

FIGURE 9.12   EXCEL WORKSHEET FOR HYPOTHESIS TESTS ABOUT A POPULATION MEAN WITH
σ UNKNOWN

	A	B	C	D	E
1	**Rating**		**Hypothesis Test About a Population Mean**		
2	5		**With σ Unknown**		
3	7				
4	8		**Sample Size**	=COUNT(A2:A61)	
5	7		**Sample Mean**	=AVERAGE(A2:A61)	
6	8		**Sample Std. Deviation**	=STDEV(A2:A61)	
7	8				
8	8		**Hypothesized Value**	7	
9	7				
10	8		**Standard Error**	=D6/SQRT(D4)	
11	10		**Test Statistic** *t*	=(D5-D8)/D10	
12	6		**Degrees of Freedom**	=D4-1	
13	7				
14	8		*p*-**value (Lower Tail)**	=T.DIST(D11,D12,TRUE)	
15	8		*p*-**value (Upper Tail)**	=1-D14	
16	9		*p*-**value (Two Tail)**	=2*(MIN(D14,D15))	
17	7				
59	7				
60	7				
61	8				
62					

	A	B	C	D	E	F
1	**Rating**		**Hypothesis Test About a Population Mean**			
2	5		**With σ Unknown**			
3	7					
4	8		**Sample Size**	60		
5	7		**Sample Mean**	7.25		
6	8		**Sample Std. Deviation**	1.05		
7	8					
8	8		**Hypothesized Value**	7		
9	7					
10	8		**Standard Error**	0.136		
11	10		**Test Statistic** *t*	1.841		
12	6		**Degrees of Freedom**	59		
13	7					
14	8		*p*-**value (Lower Tail)**	0.9647		
15	8		*p*-**value (Upper Tail)**	0.0353		
16	9		*p*-**value (Two Tail)**	0.0706		
17	7					
59	7					
60	7					
61	8					
62						

Note: Rows 18 to 58 are hidden.

to the new data range. Enter the hypothesized value for the population mean into cell D8 to obtain the results. If the new sample data have already been summarized, the new sample data do not have to be entered into the worksheet. In this case, enter the sample size into cell D4, the sample mean into cell D5, the sample standard deviation into cell D6, and the hypothesized value for the population mean into cell D8 to obtain the results. The worksheet in Figure 9.12 is available in the file Hyp Sigma Unknown on the website that accompanies this book.

FIGURE 9.13   EXCEL WORKSHEET FOR HYPOTHESIS TESTS ABOUT A POPULATION PROPORTION

	A	B	C	D	E
1	**Golfer**		**Hypothesis Test About a Population Proportion**		
2	Female				
3	Male		**Sample Size**	=COUNTA(A2:A401)	
4	Female		**Response of Interest**	Female	
5	Male		**Count for Response**	=COUNTIF(A2:A903,D4)	
6	Male		**Sample Proportion**	=D5/D3	
7	Female				
8	Male		**Hypothesized Value**	0.2	
9	Male				
10	Female		**Standard Error**	=SQRT(D8*(1-D8)/D3)	
11	Male		**Test Statistic** z	=(D6-D8)/D10	
12	Male				
13	Male		p-**value (Lower Tail)**	=NORM.S.DIST(D11,TRUE)	
14	Male		p-**value (Upper Tail)**	=1-D13	
15	Male		p-**value (TwoTail)**	=2*MIN(D13,D14)	
16	Female				
400	Male				
401	Male				
402					

Note: Rows 17 to 399 are hidden.

	A	B	C	D	E	F
1	**Golfer**		**Hypothesis Test About a Population Proportion**			
2	Female					
3	Male		**Sample Size**	400		
4	Female		**Response of Interest**	Female		
5	Male		**Count for Response**	100		
6	Male		**Sample Proportion**	0.25		
7	Female					
8	Male		**Hypothesized Value**	0.20		
9	Male					
10	Female		**Standard Error**	0.02		
11	Male		**Test Statistic** z	2.5000		
12	Male					
13	Male		p-**value (Lower Tail)**	0.9938		
14	Male		p-**value (Upper Tail)**	0.0062		
15	Male		p-**value (TwoTail)**	0.0124		
16	Female					
400	Male					
401	Male					
402						

Population Proportion

DATA *file*

Hypothesis p

We illustrate using the Pine Creek golf course survey data presented in Section 9.5. The data of Male or Female golfer are in column A of an Excel worksheet. Refer to Figure 9.13 as we describe the procedure. The background worksheet shows the cell formulas used to compute the results shown in the foreground worksheet. The data are entered into cells A2:A401. The following steps can be used to test the hypothesis H_0: $p \leq .20$ versus H_a: $p > .20$.

> **Step 1.** Enter the data range A2:A401 into the =COUNTA cell formula in cell D3
> **Step 2.** Enter Female as the response of interest in cell D4
> **Step 3.** Enter the data range A2:A401 into the =COUNTIF cell formula in cell D5
> **Step 4.** Enter the hypothesized value for the population proportion .20 into cell D8

The remaining cell formulas automatically provide the standard error, the value of the test statistic z, and three p-values. Because the alternative hypothesis ($p > .20$) indicates an upper tail test, the p-value (Upper Tail) in cell D14 is used to make the decision. With p-value $= .0062 < \alpha = .05$, the null hypothesis is rejected. The p-values in cells D13 or D15 would be used if the hypothesis involved a lower tail test or a two-tailed test.

This template can be used to make hypothesis testing computations for other applications. For instance, to conduct a hypothesis test for a new data set, enter the new sample data into column A of the worksheet. Modify the formulas in cells D3 and D5 to correspond to the new data range. Enter the response of interest into cell D4 and the hypothesized value for the population proportion into cell D8 to obtain the results. If the new sample data have already been summarized, the new sample data do not have to be entered into the worksheet. In this case, enter the sample size into cell D3, the sample proportion into cell D6, and the hypothesized value for the population proportion into cell D8 to obtain the results. The worksheet in Figure 9.13 is available in the file Hypothesis p on the website that accompanies this book.

CHAPTER 14

Simple Linear Regression

CONTENTS

ALLIANCE DATA SYSTEMS*
DALLAS, TEXAS

Alliance Data Systems (ADS) provides transaction processing, credit services, and marketing services for clients in the rapidly growing customer relationship management (CRM) industry. ADS operates through three businesses: LoyaltyOne, Epsilon, and Private Label Services and Credit. The LoyaltyOne business provides customer loyalty services, such as customer analytics, creative services, and mobile solutions. The Epsilon business is focused on marketing programs that utilize transactional data and includes customer database technologies and predictive modeling. The Private Label Services and Credit business provides, among other services, credit card processing, billing/payment processing, and collections services for private label retailers. Formed in 1996 with its headquarters in Plano, Texas, ADS today has 15,000 full-time employees.

As one of its marketing services, ADS designs direct mail campaigns and promotions. With its database containing information on the spending habits of more than 100 million consumers, ADS can target those consumers most likely to benefit from a direct mail promotion. The Analytical Development Group uses regression analysis to build models that measure and predict the responsiveness of consumers to direct market campaigns. Some regression models predict the probability of purchase for individuals receiving a promotion, and others predict the amount spent by those consumers making a purchase.

For one particular campaign, a retail store chain wanted to attract new customers. To predict the effect of the campaign, ADS analysts selected a sample from the consumer database, sent the sampled individuals promotional materials, and then collected transaction data on the consumers' response. Sample data were collected on the amount of purchase made by the consumers responding to the campaign, as well as a variety of consumer-specific variables thought to be useful in predicting sales. The consumer-specific variable that contributed most to predicting the amount purchased was the total amount of

Alliance Data Systems analysts discuss use of a regression model to predict sales for a direct marketing campaign.

credit purchases at related stores over the past 39 months. ADS analysts developed an estimated regression equation relating the amount of purchase to the amount spent at related stores:

$$\hat{y} = 26.7 + 0.00205x$$

where

$\hat{y}$ = amount of purchase
x = amount spent at related stores

Using this equation, we could predict that someone spending $10,000 over the past 39 months at related stores would spend $47.20 when responding to the direct mail promotion. In this chapter, you will learn how to develop this type of estimated regression equation.

The final model developed by ADS analysts also included several other variables that increased the predictive power of the preceding equation. Some of these variables included the absence/presence of a bank credit card, estimated income, and the average amount spent per trip at a selected store. In the following chapter, we will learn how such additional variables can be incorporated into a multiple regression model.

---

*The authors are indebted to Philip Clemance, Director of Analytical Development at Alliance Data Systems, for providing this Statistics in Practice.

Managerial decisions often are based on the relationship between two or more variables. For example, after considering the relationship between advertising expenditures and sales, a marketing manager might attempt to predict sales for a given level of advertising expenditures. In another case, a public utility might use the relationship between the daily high temperature and the demand for electricity to predict electricity usage on the basis of next month's anticipated daily high temperatures. Sometimes a manager will rely on intuition to judge how two variables are related. However, if data can be obtained, a statistical procedure called *regression analysis* can be used to develop an equation showing how the variables are related.

The statistical methods used in studying the relationship between two variables were first employed by Sir Francis Galton (1822–1911). Galton was interested in studying the relationship between a father's height and the son's height. Galton's disciple, Karl Pearson (1857–1936), analyzed the relationship between the father's height and the son's height for 1078 pairs of subjects.

In regression terminology, the variable being predicted is called the **dependent variable**. The variable or variables being used to predict the value of the dependent variable are called the **independent variables**. For example, in analyzing the effect of advertising expenditures on sales, a marketing manager's desire to predict sales would suggest making sales the dependent variable. Advertising expenditure would be the independent variable used to help predict sales. In statistical notation, y denotes the dependent variable and x denotes the independent variable.

In this chapter we consider the simplest type of regression analysis involving one independent variable and one dependent variable in which the relationship between the variables is approximated by a straight line. It is called **simple linear regression**. Regression analysis involving two or more independent variables is called multiple regression analysis; multiple regression and cases involving curvilinear relationships are covered in Chapters 15 and 16.

 14.1 # Simple Linear Regression Model

Armand's Pizza Parlors is a chain of Italian-food restaurants located in a five-state area. Armand's most successful locations are near college campuses. The managers believe that quarterly sales for these restaurants (denoted by y) are related positively to the size of the student population (denoted by x); that is, restaurants near campuses with a large student population tend to generate more sales than those located near campuses with a small student population. Using regression analysis, we can develop an equation showing how the dependent variable y is related to the independent variable x.

Regression Model and Regression Equation

In the Armand's Pizza Parlors example, the population consists of all the Armand's restaurants. For every restaurant in the population, there is a value of x (student population) and a corresponding value of y (quarterly sales). The equation that describes how y is related to x and an error term is called the **regression model**. The regression model used in simple linear regression follows.

SIMPLE LINEAR REGRESSION MODEL

$$y = \beta_0 + \beta_1 x + \epsilon \tag{14.1}$$

β_0 and β_1 are referred to as the parameters of the model, and ϵ (the Greek letter epsilon) is a random variable referred to as the error term. The error term accounts for the variability in y that cannot be explained by the linear relationship between x and y.

The population of all Armand's restaurants can also be viewed as a collection of subpopulations, one for each distinct value of x. For example, one subpopulation consists of all Armand's restaurants located near college campuses with 8000 students; another subpopulation consists of all Armand's restaurants located near college campuses with 9000 students; and so on. Each subpopulation has a corresponding distribution of y values. Thus, a distribution of y values is associated with restaurants located near campuses with 8000 students; a distribution of y values is associated with restaurants located near campuses with 9000 students; and so on. Each distribution of y values has its own mean or expected value. The equation that describes how the expected value of y, denoted $E(y)$, is related to x is called the **regression equation**. The regression equation for simple linear regression follows.

SIMPLE LINEAR REGRESSION EQUATION

$$E(y) = \beta_0 + \beta_1 x \qquad\qquad (14.2)$$

The graph of the simple linear regression equation is a straight line; β_0 is the y-intercept of the regression line, β_1 is the slope, and $E(y)$ is the mean or expected value of y for a given value of x.

Examples of possible regression lines are shown in Figure 14.1. The regression line in Panel A shows that the mean value of y is related positively to x, with larger values of $E(y)$ associated with larger values of x. The regression line in Panel B shows the mean value of y is related negatively to x, with smaller values of $E(y)$ associated with larger values of x. The regression line in Panel C shows the case in which the mean value of y is not related to x; that is, the mean value of y is the same for every value of x.

Estimated Regression Equation

If the values of the population parameters β_0 and β_1 were known, we could use equation (14.2) to compute the mean value of y for a given value of x. In practice, the parameter values are not known and must be estimated using sample data. Sample statistics (denoted b_0 and b_1) are computed as estimates of the population parameters β_0 and β_1. Substituting the values

FIGURE 14.1 POSSIBLE REGRESSION LINES IN SIMPLE LINEAR REGRESSION

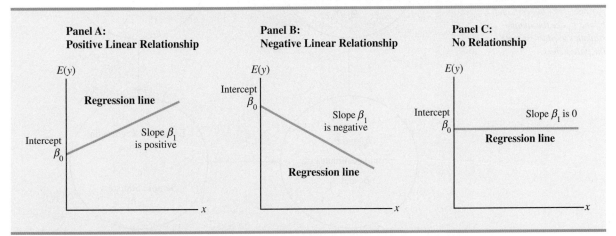

of the sample statistics b_0 and b_1 for β_0 and β_1 in the regression equation, we obtain the **estimated regression equation**. The estimated regression equation for simple linear regression follows.

ESTIMATED SIMPLE LINEAR REGRESSION EQUATION

$$\hat{y} = b_0 + b_1 x \tag{14.3}$$

Figure 14.2 provides a summary of the estimation process for simple linear regression.

The graph of the estimated simple linear regression equation is called the *estimated regression line*; b_0 is the y-intercept and b_1 is the slope. In the next section, we show how the least squares method can be used to compute the values of b_0 and b_1 in the estimated regression equation.

In general, $\hat{y}$ is the point estimator of $E(y)$, the mean value of y for a given value of x. Thus, to estimate the mean or expected value of quarterly sales for all restaurants located near campuses with 10,000 students, Armand's would substitute the value of 10,000 for x in equation (14.3). In some cases, however, Armand's may be more interested in predicting sales for one particular restaurant. For example, suppose Armand's would like to predict quarterly sales for the restaurant they are considering building near Talbot College, a school with 10,000 students. As it turns out, the best predictor of y for a given value of x is also provided by $\hat{y}$. Thus, to predict quarterly sales for the restaurant located near Talbot College, Armand's would also substitute the value of 10,000 for x in equation (14.3).

The value of $\hat{y}$ provides both a point estimate of $E(y)$ for a given value of x and a prediction of an individual value of y for a given value of x.

FIGURE 14.2 THE ESTIMATION PROCESS IN SIMPLE LINEAR REGRESSION

The estimation of β_0 and β_1 is a statistical process much like the estimation of μ discussed in Chapter 7. β_0 and β_1 are the unknown parameters of interest, and b_0 and b_1 are the sample statistics used to estimate the parameters.

NOTES AND COMMENTS

1. Regression analysis cannot be interpreted as a procedure for establishing a cause-and-effect relationship between variables. It can only indicate how or to what extent variables are associated with each other. Any conclusions about cause and effect must be based upon the judgment of those individuals most knowledgeable about the application.

2. The regression equation in simple linear regression is $E(y) = \beta_0 + \beta_1 x$. More advanced texts in regression analysis often write the regression equation as $E(y|x) = \beta_0 + \beta_1 x$ to emphasize that the regression equation provides the mean value of y for a given value of x.

(14.2) Least Squares Method

In simple linear regression, each observation consists of two values: one for the independent variable and one for the dependent variable.

The **least squares method** is a procedure for using sample data to find the estimated regression equation. To illustrate the least squares method, suppose data were collected from a sample of 10 Armand's Pizza Parlor restaurants located near college campuses. For the ith observation or restaurant in the sample, x_i is the size of the student population (in thousands) and y_i is the quarterly sales (in thousands of dollars). The values of x_i and y_i for the 10 restaurants in the sample are summarized in Table 14.1. We see that restaurant 1, with $x_1 = 2$ and $y_1 = 58$, is near a campus with 2000 students and has quarterly sales of $58,000. Restaurant 2, with $x_2 = 6$ and $y_2 = 105$, is near a campus with 6000 students and has quarterly sales of $105,000. The largest sales value is for restaurant 10, which is near a campus with 26,000 students and has quarterly sales of $202,000.

Figure 14.3 is a scatter diagram of the data in Table 14.1. Student population is shown on the horizontal axis and quarterly sales is shown on the vertical axis. **Scatter diagrams** for regression analysis are constructed with the independent variable x on the horizontal axis and the dependent variable y on the vertical axis. The scatter diagram enables us to observe the data graphically and to draw preliminary conclusions about the possible relationship between the variables.

What preliminary conclusions can be drawn from Figure 14.3? Quarterly sales appear to be higher at campuses with larger student populations. In addition, for these data the relationship between the size of the student population and quarterly sales appears to be approximated by a straight line; indeed, a positive linear relationship is indicated between x

TABLE 14.1   STUDENT POPULATION AND QUARTERLY SALES DATA FOR 10 ARMAND'S PIZZA PARLORS

DATA *file*

Armand's

Restaurant i	Student Population (1000s) x_i	Quarterly Sales ($1000s) y_i
1	2	58
2	6	105
3	8	88
4	8	118
5	12	117
6	16	137
7	20	157
8	20	169
9	22	149
10	26	202

FIGURE 14.3   SCATTER DIAGRAM OF STUDENT POPULATION AND QUARTERLY
SALES FOR ARMAND'S PIZZA PARLORS

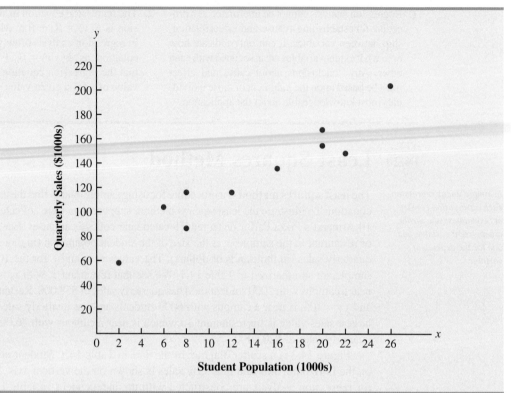

and y. We therefore choose the simple linear regression model to represent the relationship between quarterly sales and student population. Given that choice, our next task is to use the sample data in Table 14.1 to determine the values of b_0 and b_1 in the estimated simple linear regression equation. For the ith restaurant, the estimated regression equation provides

$$\hat{y}_i = b_0 + b_1 x_i \tag{14.4}$$

where

$\hat{y}_i$ = predicted value of quarterly sales ($1000s) for the ith restaurant
b_0 = the y-intercept of the estimated regression line
b_1 = the slope of the estimated regression line
x_i = size of the student population (1000s) for the ith restaurant

With y_i denoting the observed (actual) sales for restaurant i and $\hat{y}_i$ in equation (14.4) representing the predicted value of sales for restaurant i, every restaurant in the sample will have an observed value of sales y_i and a predicted value of sales $\hat{y}_i$. For the estimated regression line to provide a good fit to the data, we want the differences between the observed sales values and the predicted sales values to be small.

The least squares method uses the sample data to provide the values of b_0 and b_1 that minimize the *sum of the squares of the deviations* between the observed values of the dependent variable y_i and the predicted values of the dependent variable $\hat{y}_i$. The criterion for the least squares method is given by expression (14.5).

Carl Friedrich Gauss (1777–1855) proposed the least squares method.

LEAST SQUARES CRITERION

$$\min \Sigma(y_i - \hat{y}_i)^2 \tag{14.5}$$

where

y_i = observed value of the dependent variable for the ith observation

$\hat{y}_i$ = predicted value of the dependent variable for the ith observation

Differential calculus can be used to show (see Appendix 14.1) that the values of b_0 and b_1 that minimize expression (14.5) can be found by using equations (14.6) and (14.7).

SLOPE AND y-INTERCEPT FOR THE ESTIMATED REGRESSION EQUATION[1]

In computing b_1 with a calculator, carry as many significant digits as possible in the intermediate calculations. We recommend carrying at least four significant digits.

$$b_1 = \frac{\Sigma(x_i - \bar{x})(y_i - \bar{y})}{\Sigma(x_i - \bar{x})^2} \tag{14.6}$$

$$b_0 = \bar{y} - b_1\bar{x} \tag{14.7}$$

where

x_i = value of the independent variable for the ith observation

y_i = value of the dependent variable for the ith observation

$\bar{x}$ = mean value for the independent variable

$\bar{y}$ = mean value for the dependent variable

n = total number of observations

Some of the calculations necessary to develop the least squares estimated regression equation for Armand's Pizza Parlors are shown in Table 14.2. With the sample of 10 restaurants, we have $n = 10$ observations. Because equations (14.6) and (14.7) require $\bar{x}$ and $\bar{y}$ we begin the calculations by computing $\bar{x}$ and $\bar{y}$.

$$\bar{x} = \frac{\Sigma x_i}{n} = \frac{140}{10} = 14$$

$$\bar{y} = \frac{\Sigma y_i}{n} = \frac{1300}{10} = 130$$

Using equations (14.6) and (14.7) and the information in Table 14.2, we can compute the slope and intercept of the estimated regression equation for Armand's Pizza Parlors. The calculation of the slope (b_1) proceeds as follows.

---

[1] An alternate formula for b_1 is

$$b_1 = \frac{\Sigma x_i y_i - (\Sigma x_i \Sigma y_i)/n}{\Sigma x_i^2 - (\Sigma x_i)^2/n}$$

This form of equation (14.6) is often recommended when using a calculator to compute b_1.

TABLE 14.2 CALCULATIONS FOR THE LEAST SQUARES ESTIMATED REGRESSION
EQUATION FOR ARMAND'S PIZZA PARLORS

Restaurant i	x_i	y_i	$x_i - \bar{x}$	$y_i - \bar{y}$	$(x_i - \bar{x})(y_i - \bar{y})$	$(x_i - \bar{x})^2$
1	2	58	-12	-72	864	144
2	6	105	-8	-25	200	64
3	8	88	-6	-42	252	36
4	8	118	-6	-12	72	36
5	12	117	-2	-13	26	4
6	16	137	2	7	14	4
7	20	157	6	27	162	36
8	20	169	6	39	234	36
9	22	149	8	19	152	64
10	26	202	12	72	864	144
Totals	140	1300			2840	568
	Σx_i	Σy_i			$\Sigma(x_i - \bar{x})(y_i - \bar{y})$	$\Sigma(x_i - \bar{x})^2$

$$b_1 = \frac{\Sigma(x_i - \bar{x})(y_i - \bar{y})}{\Sigma(x_i - \bar{x})^2}$$
$$= \frac{2840}{568}$$
$$= 5$$

The calculation of the y intercept (b_0) follows.

$$b_0 = \bar{y} - b_1\bar{x}$$
$$= 130 - 5(14)$$
$$= 60$$

Thus, the estimated regression equation is

$$\hat{y} = 60 + 5x$$

Figure 14.4 shows the graph of this equation on the scatter diagram.

The slope of the estimated regression equation ($b_1 = 5$) is positive, implying that as student population increases, sales increase. In fact, we can conclude (based on sales measured in $1000s and student population in 1000s) that an increase in the student population of 1000 is associated with an increase of $5000 in expected sales; that is, quarterly sales are expected to increase by $5 per student.

Using the estimated regression equation to make predictions outside the range of the values of the independent variable should be done with caution because outside that range we cannot be sure that the same relationship is valid.

If we believe the least squares estimated regression equation adequately describes the relationship between x and y, it would seem reasonable to use the estimated regression equation to predict the value of y for a given value of x. For example, if we wanted to predict quarterly sales for a restaurant to be located near a campus with 16,000 students, we would compute

$$\hat{y} = 60 + 5(16) = 140$$

Hence, we would predict quarterly sales of $140,000 for this restaurant. In the following sections we will discuss methods for assessing the appropriateness of using the estimated regression equation for estimation and prediction.

FIGURE 14.4   GRAPH OF THE ESTIMATED REGRESSION EQUATION FOR ARMAND'S
PIZZA PARLORS: $\hat{y} = 60 + 5x$

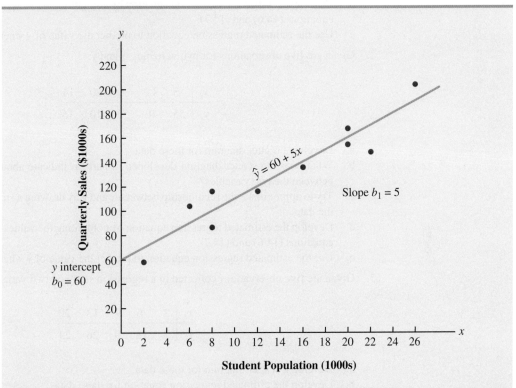

NOTES AND COMMENTS

The least squares method provides an estimated regression equation that minimizes the sum of squared deviations between the observed values of the dependent variable y_i and the predicted values of the dependent variable $\hat{y}_i$. This least squares criterion is used to choose the equation that provides the best fit. If some other criterion were used, such as minimizing the sum of the absolute deviations between y_i and $\hat{y}_i$, a different equation would be obtained. In practice, the least squares method is most widely used.

Exercises

Methods

1. Given are five observations for two variables, x and y.

x_i	1	2	3	4	5
y_i	3	7	5	11	14

    a.   Develop a scatter diagram for these data.

    b.   What does the scatter diagram developed in part (a) indicate about the relationship between the two variables?

c.   Try to approximate the relationship between x and y by drawing a straight line through the data.

d.   Develop the estimated regression equation by computing the values of b_0 and b_1 using equations (14.6) and (14.7).

e.   Use the estimated regression equation to predict the value of y when $x = 4$.

2. Given are five observations for two variables, x and y.

x_i	3	12	6	20	14
y_i	55	40	55	10	15

a.   Develop a scatter diagram for these data.

b.   What does the scatter diagram developed in part (a) indicate about the relationship between the two variables?

c.   Try to approximate the relationship between x and y by drawing a straight line through the data.

d.   Develop the estimated regression equation by computing the values of b_0 and b_1 using equations (14.6) and (14.7).

e.   Use the estimated regression equation to predict the value of y when $x = 10$.

3. Given are five observations collected in a regression study on two variables.

x_i	2	6	9	13	20
y_i	7	18	9	26	23

a.   Develop a scatter diagram for these data.

b.   Develop the estimated regression equation for these data.

c.   Use the estimated regression equation to predict the value of y when $x = 6$.

Applications

 SELF*test*

4. The following data give the percentage of women working in five companies in the retail and trade industry. The percentage of management jobs held by women in each company is also shown.

% Working	67	45	73	54	61
% Management	49	21	65	47	33

a.   Develop a scatter diagram for these data with the percentage of women working in the company as the independent variable.

b.   What does the scatter diagram developed in part (a) indicate about the relationship between the two variables?

c.   Try to approximate the relationship between the percentage of women working in the company and the percentage of management jobs held by women in that company.

d.   Develop the estimated regression equation by computing the values of b_0 and b_1.

e.   Predict the percentage of management jobs held by women in a company that has 60% women employees.

5. Brawdy Plastics, Inc., produces plastic seat belt retainers for General Motors at the Brawdy Plastics plant in Buffalo, New York. After final assembly and painting, the parts are placed on a conveyor belt that moves the parts past a final inspection station. How fast the parts move past the final inspection station depends upon the line speed of the conveyor belt (feet per minute). Although faster line speeds are desirable, management is concerned that

increasing the line speed too much may not provide enough time for inspectors to identify which parts are actually defective. To test this theory, Brawdy Plastics conducted an experiment in which the same batch of parts, with a known number of defective parts, was inspected using a variety of line speeds. The following data were collected.

Line Speed	Number of Defective Parts Found
20	23
20	21
30	19
30	16
40	15
40	17
50	14
50	11

a.   Develop a scatter diagram with the line speed as the independent variable.
b.   What does the scatter diagram developed in part (a) indicate about the relationship between the two variables?
c.   Use the least squares method to develop the estimated regression equation.
d.   Predict the number of defective parts found for a line speed of 25 feet per minute.

6.   The National Football League (NFL) records a variety of performance data for individuals and teams. To investigate the importance of passing on the percentage of games won by a team, the following data show the average number of passing yards per attempt (Yds/Att) and the percentage of games won (WinPct) for a random sample of 10 NFL teams for the 2011 season (NFL website, February 12, 2012).

NFLPassing

Team	Yds/Att	WinPct
Arizona Cardinals	6.5	50
Atlanta Falcons	7.1	63
Carolina Panthers	7.4	38
Chicago Bears	6.4	50
Dallas Cowboys	7.4	50
New England Patriots	8.3	81
Philadelphia Eagles	7.4	50
Seattle Seahawks	6.1	44
St. Louis Rams	5.2	13
Tampa Bay Buccaneers	6.2	25

a.   Develop a scatter diagram with the number of passing yards per attempt on the horizontal axis and the percentage of games won on the vertical axis.
b.   What does the scatter diagram developed in part (a) indicate about the relationship between the two variables?
c.   Develop the estimated regression equation that could be used to predict the percentage of games won given the average number of passing yards per attempt.
d.   Provide an interpretation for the slope of the estimated regression equation.
e.   For the 2011 season, the average number of passing yards per attempt for the Kansas City Chiefs was 6.2. Use the estimated regression equation developed in part (c) to predict the percentage of games won by the Kansas City Chiefs. (*Note:* For the 2011

season the Kansas City Chiefs record was 7 wins and 9 losses.) Compare your prediction to the actual percentage of games won by the Kansas City Chiefs.

7.   A sales manager collected the following data on annual sales for new customer accounts
     and the number of years of experience for a sample of 10 salespersons.

Sales

Salesperson	Years of Experience	Annual Sales ($1000s)
1	1	80
2	3	97
3	4	92
4	4	102
5	6	103
6	8	111
7	10	119
8	10	123
9	11	117
10	13	136

a.   Develop a scatter diagram for these data with years of experience as the independent
     variable.
b.   Develop an estimated regression equation that can be used to predict annual sales
     given the years of experience.
c.   Use the estimated regression equation to predict annual sales for a salesperson with
     9 years of experience.

8.   The American Association of Individual Investors (AAII) On-Line Discount Broker Survey
     polls members on their experiences with discount brokers. As part of the survey, members
     were asked to rate the quality of the speed of execution with their broker as well as provide an
     overall satisfaction rating for electronic trades. Possible responses (scores) were no opinion
     (0), unsatisfied (1), somewhat satisfied (2), satisfied (3), and very satisfied (4). For each bro-
     ker summary scores were computed by calculating a weighted average of the scores provided
     by each respondent. A portion of the survey results follow (AAII website, February 7, 2012).

BrokerRatings

Brokerage	Speed	Satisfaction
Scottrade, Inc.	3.4	3.5
Charles Schwab	3.3	3.4
Fidelity Brokerage Services	3.4	3.9
TD Ameritrade	3.6	3.7
E*Trade Financial	3.2	2.9
Vanguard Brokerage Services	3.8	2.8
USAA Brokerage Services	3.8	3.6
Thinkorswim	2.6	2.6
Wells Fargo Investments	2.7	2.3
Interactive Brokers	4.0	4.0
Zecco.com	2.5	2.5

a.   Develop a scatter diagram for these data with the speed of execution as the independ-
     ent variable.
b.   What does the scatter diagram developed in part (a) indicate about the relationship
     between the two variables?
c.   Develop the least squares estimated regression equation.
d.   Provide an interpretation for the slope of the estimated regression equation.
e.   Suppose Zecco.com developed new software to increase their speed of execution rating.
     If the new software is able to increase their speed of execution rating from the current

value of 2.5 to the average speed of execution rating for the other 10 brokerage firms that were surveyed, what value would you predict for the overall satisfaction rating?

9. Companies in the U.S. car rental market vary greatly in terms of the size of the fleet, the number of locations, and annual revenue. In 2011 Hertz had 320,000 cars in service and annual revenue of approximately $4.2 billion. The following data show the number of cars in service (1000s) and the annual revenue ($ millions) for six smaller car rental companies (*Auto Rental News* website, August 7, 2012).

Company	Cars (1000s)	Revenue ($ millions)
U-Save Auto Rental System, Inc.	11.5	118
Payless Car Rental System, Inc.	10.0	135
ACE Rent A Car	9.0	100
Rent-A-Wreck of America	5.5	37
Triangle Rent-A-Car	4.2	40
Affordable/Sensible	3.3	32

a. Develop a scatter diagram with the number of cars in service as the independent variable.
b. What does the scatter diagram developed in part (a) indicate about the relationship between the two variables?
c. Use the least squares method to develop the estimated regression equation.
d. For every additional car placed in service, estimate how much annual revenue will change.
e. Fox Rent A Car has 11,000 cars in service. Use the estimated regression equation developed in part (c) to predict annual revenue for Fox Rent A Car.

10. On March 31, 2009, Ford Motor Company's shares were trading at a 26-year low of $2.63. Ford's board of directors gave the CEO a grant of options and restricted shares with an estimated value of $16 million. On April 26, 2011, the price of a share of Ford had increased to $15.58, and the CEO's grant was worth $202.8 million, a gain in value of $186.8 million. The following table shows the share price in 2009 and 2011 for 10 companies, the stock-option and share grants to the CEOs in late 2008 and 2009, and the value of the options and grants in 2011. Also shown are the percentage increases in the stock price and the percentage gains in the options values (*The Wall Street Journal,* April 27, 2011).

DATA *file*

CEOGrants

Company	Stock Price 2009 ($)	Stock Price 2011 ($)	% Increase in Stock Price	Options and Grants Value 2009 ($ millions)	Options and Grants Value 2011 ($ millions)	% Gain in Options Value
Ford Motor	2.63	15.58	492	16.0	202.8	1168
Abercrombie & Fitch	23.80	70.47	196	46.2	196.1	324
Nabors Industries	9.99	32.06	221	37.2	132.2	255
Starbucks	9.99	32.06	221	12.4	75.9	512
Salesforce.com	32.73	137.61	320	7.8	67.0	759
Starwood Hotels	12.70	60.28	375	5.8	57.1	884
Caterpillar	27.96	111.94	300	4.0	47.5	1088
Oracle	18.07	34.97	94	61.9	97.5	58
Capital One	12.24	54.61	346	6.0	40.6	577
Dow Chemical	8.43	39.97	374	5.0	38.8	676

a. Develop a scatter diagram for these data with the percentage increase in the stock price as the independent variable.
b. What does the scatter diagram developed in part (a) indicate about the relationship between the two variables?

    c. Develop the least squares estimated regression equation.
    d. Provide an interpretation for the slope of the estimated regression equation.
    e. Do the rewards for the CEO appear to be based on performance increases as measured by the stock price?

11. To help consumers in purchasing a laptop computer, *Consumer Reports* calculates an overall test score for each computer tested based upon rating factors such as ergonomics, portability, performance, display, and battery life. Higher overall scores indicate better test results. The following data show the average retail price and the overall score for ten 13-inch models (*Consumer Reports* website, October 25, 2012).

Computer

Brand & Model	Price ($)	Overall Score
Samsung Ultrabook NP900X3C-A01US	1250	83
Apple MacBook Air MC965LL/A	1300	83
Apple MacBook Air MD231LL/A	1200	82
HP ENVY 13-2050nr Spectre XT	950	79
Sony VAIO SVS13112FXB	800	77
Acer Aspire S5-391-9880 Ultrabook	1200	74
Apple MacBook Pro MD101LL/A	1200	74
Apple MacBook Pro MD313LL/A	1000	73
Dell Inspiron I13Z-6591SLV	700	67
Samsung NP535U3C-A01US	600	63

    a. Develop a scatter diagram with price as the independent variable.
    b. What does the scatter diagram developed in part (a) indicate about the relationship between the two variables?
    c. Use the least squares method to develop the estimated regression equation.
    d. Provide an interpretation of the slope of the estimated regression equation.
    e. Another laptop that *Consumer Reports* tested is the Acer Aspire S3-951-6646 Ultrabook; the price for this laptop was $700. Predict the overall score for this laptop using the estimated regression equation developed in part (c).

12. Concur Technologies, Inc., is a large expense-management company located in Redmond, Washington. *The Wall Street Journal* asked Concur to examine the data from 8.3 million expense reports to provide insights regarding business travel expenses. Their analysis of the data showed that New York was the most expensive city, with an average daily hotel room rate of $198 and an average amount spent on entertainment, including group meals and tickets for shows, sports, and other events, of $172. In comparison, the U.S. averages for these two categories were $89 for the room rate and $99 for entertainment. The following table shows the average daily hotel room rate and the amount spent on entertainment for a random sample of 9 of the 25 most visited U.S. cities (*The Wall Street Journal*, August 18, 2011).

BusinessTravel

City	Room Rate ($)	Entertainment ($)
Boston	148	161
Denver	96	105
Nashville	91	101
New Orleans	110	142
Phoenix	90	100
San Diego	102	120
San Francisco	136	167
San Jose	90	140
Tampa	82	98

a. Develop a scatter diagram for these data with the room rate as the independent variable.
b. What does the scatter diagram developed in part (a) indicate about the relationship between the two variables?
c. Develop the least squares estimated regression equation.
d. Provide an interpretation for the slope of the estimated regression equation.
e. The average room rate in Chicago is $128, considerably higher than the U.S. average. Predict the entertainment expense per day for Chicago.

13. To the Internal Revenue Service, the reasonableness of total itemized deductions depends on the taxpayer's adjusted gross income. Large deductions, which include charity and medical deductions, are more reasonable for taxpayers with large adjusted gross incomes. If a taxpayer claims larger than average itemized deductions for a given level of income, the chances of an IRS audit are increased. Data (in thousands of dollars) on adjusted gross income and the average or reasonable amount of itemized deductions follow.

Adjusted Gross Income ($1000s)	Reasonable Amount of Itemized Deductions ($1000s)
22	9.6
27	9.6
32	10.1
48	11.1
65	13.5
85	17.7
120	25.5

a. Develop a scatter diagram for these data with adjusted gross income as the independent variable.
b. Use the least squares method to develop the estimated regression equation.
c. Predict the reasonable level of total itemized deductions for a taxpayer with an adjusted gross income of $52,500. If this taxpayer claimed itemized deductions of $20,400, would the IRS agent's request for an audit appear justified? Explain.

14. A large city hospital conducted a study to investigate the relationship between the number of unauthorized days that employees are absent per year and the distance (miles) between home and work for the employees. A sample of 10 employees was selected and the following data were collected.

Distance to Work (miles)	Number of Days Absent
1	8
3	5
4	8
6	7
8	6
10	3
12	5
14	2
14	4
18	2

a. Develop a scatter diagram for these data. Does a linear relationship appear reasonable? Explain.
b. Develop the least squares estimated regression equation that relates the distance to work to the number of days absent.
c. Predict the number of days absent for an employee who lives 5 miles from the hospital.

(14.3) Coefficient of Determination

For the Armand's Pizza Parlors example, we developed the estimated regression equation $\hat{y} = 60 + 5x$ to approximate the linear relationship between the size of the student population x and quarterly sales y. A question now is: How well does the estimated regression equation fit the data? In this section, we show that the **coefficient of determination** provides a measure of the goodness of fit for the estimated regression equation.

For the ith observation, the difference between the observed value of the dependent variable, y_i, and the predicted value of the dependent variable, $\hat{y}_i$, is called the **ith residual**. The ith residual represents the error in using $\hat{y}_i$ to estimate y_i. Thus, for the ith observation, the residual is $y_i - \hat{y}_i$. The sum of squares of these residuals or errors is the quantity that is minimized by the least squares method. This quantity, also known as the *sum of squares due to error,* is denoted by SSE.

SUM OF SQUARES DUE TO ERROR

$$SSE = \Sigma(y_i - \hat{y}_i)^2 \tag{14.8}$$

The value of SSE is a measure of the error in using the estimated regression equation to predict the values of the dependent variable in the sample.

In Table 14.3 we show the calculations required to compute the sum of squares due to error for the Armand's Pizza Parlors example. For instance, for restaurant 1 the values of the independent and dependent variables are $x_1 = 2$ and $y_1 = 58$. Using the estimated regression equation, we find that the predicted value of quarterly sales for restaurant 1 is $\hat{y}_1 = 60 + 5(2) = 70$. Thus, the error in using $\hat{y}_1$ to predict y_1 for restaurant 1 is $y_1 - \hat{y}_1 = 58 - 70 = -12$. The squared error, $(-12)^2 = 144$, is shown in the last column of Table 14.3. After computing and squaring the residuals for each restaurant in the sample, we sum them to obtain SSE = 1530. Thus, SSE = 1530 measures the error in using the estimated regression equation $\hat{y} = 60 + 5x$ to predict sales.

Now suppose we are asked to develop an estimate of quarterly sales without knowledge of the size of the student population. Without knowledge of any related variables, we would

TABLE 14.3 CALCULATION OF SSE FOR ARMAND'S PIZZA PARLORS

Restaurant i	x_i = Student Population (1000s)	y_i = Quarterly Sales ($1000s)	Predicted Sales $\hat{y}_i = 60 + 5x_i$	Error $y_i - \hat{y}_i$	Squared Error $(y_i - \hat{y}_i)^2$
1	2	58	70	−12	144
2	6	105	90	15	225
3	8	88	100	−12	144
4	8	118	100	18	324
5	12	117	120	−3	9
6	16	137	140	−3	9
7	20	157	160	−3	9
8	20	169	160	9	81
9	22	149	170	−21	441
10	26	202	190	12	144
					SSE = 1530

TABLE 14.4   COMPUTATION OF THE TOTAL SUM OF SQUARES FOR ARMAND'S PIZZA PARLORS

Restaurant i	x_i = Student Population (1000s)	y_i = Quarterly Sales ($1000s)	Deviation $y_i - \bar{y}$	Squared Deviation $(y_i - \bar{y})^2$
1	2	58	-72	5184
2	6	105	-25	625
3	8	88	-42	1764
4	8	118	-12	144
5	12	117	-13	169
6	16	137	7	49
7	20	157	27	729
8	20	169	39	1521
9	22	149	19	361
10	26	202	72	5184
				SST = 15,730

use the sample mean as an estimate of quarterly sales at any given restaurant. Table 14.2 showed that for the sales data, $\Sigma y_i = 1300$. Hence, the mean value of quarterly sales for the sample of 10 Armand's restaurants is $\bar{y} = \Sigma y_i/n = 1300/10 = 130$. In Table 14.4 we show the sum of squared deviations obtained by using the sample mean $\bar{y} = 130$ to predict the value of quarterly sales for each restaurant in the sample. For the ith restaurant in the sample, the difference $y_i - \bar{y}$ provides a measure of the error involved in using $\bar{y}$ to predict sales. The corresponding sum of squares, called the *total sum of squares*, is denoted SST.

TOTAL SUM OF SQUARES

$$\text{SST} = \Sigma(y_i - \bar{y})^2 \tag{14.9}$$

The sum at the bottom of the last column in Table 14.4 is the total sum of squares for Armand's Pizza Parlors; it is SST = 15,730.

With SST = 15,730 and SSE = 1530, the estimated regression line provides a much better fit to the data than the line y = ȳ.

In Figure 14.5 we show the estimated regression line $\hat{y} = 60 + 5x$ and the line corresponding to $\bar{y} = 130$. Note that the points cluster more closely around the estimated regression line than they do about the line $\bar{y} = 130$. For example, for the 10th restaurant in the sample we see that the error is much larger when $\bar{y} = 130$ is used to predict y_{10} than when $\hat{y}_{10} = 60 + 5(26) = 190$ is used. We can think of SST as a measure of how well the observations cluster about the $\bar{y}$ line and SSE as a measure of how well the observations cluster about the $\hat{y}$ line.

To measure how much the $\hat{y}$ values on the estimated regression line deviate from $\bar{y}$, another sum of squares is computed. This sum of squares, called the *sum of squares due to regression,* is denoted SSR.

SUM OF SQUARES DUE TO REGRESSION

$$\text{SSR} = \Sigma(\hat{y}_i - \bar{y})^2 \tag{14.10}$$

FIGURE 14.5   DEVIATIONS ABOUT THE ESTIMATED REGRESSION LINE AND THE LINE $y = \bar{y}$ FOR ARMAND'S PIZZA PARLORS

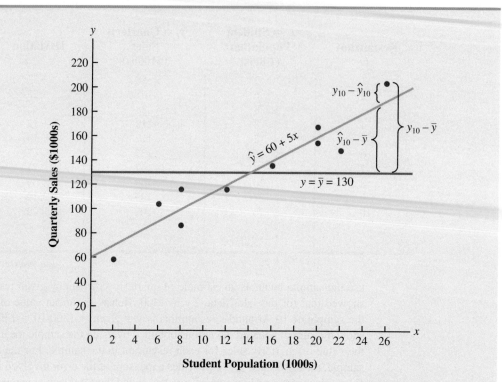

From the preceding discussion, we should expect that SST, SSR, and SSE are related. Indeed, the relationship among these three sums of squares provides one of the most important results in statistics.

SSR can be thought of as the explained portion of SST, and SSE can be thought of as the unexplained portion of SST.

RELATIONSHIP AMONG SST, SSR, AND SSE

$$SST = SSR + SSE \tag{14.11}$$

where

SST = total sum of squares
SSR = sum of squares due to regression
SSE = sum of squares due to error

Equation (14.11) shows that the total sum of squares can be partitioned into two components, the sum of squares due to regression and the sum of squares due to error. Hence, if the values of any two of these sum of squares are known, the third sum of squares can be computed easily. For instance, in the Armand's Pizza Parlors example, we already know that SSE = 1530 and SST = 15,730; therefore, solving for SSR in equation (14.11), we find that the sum of squares due to regression is

$$SSR = SST - SSE = 15{,}730 - 1530 = 14{,}200$$

Now let us see how the three sums of squares, SST, SSR, and SSE, can be used to provide a measure of the goodness of fit for the estimated regression equation. The estimated regression equation would provide a perfect fit if every value of the dependent variable y_i happened to lie on the estimated regression line. In this case, $y_i - \hat{y}_i$ would be zero for each observation, resulting in SSE = 0. Because SST = SSR + SSE, we see that for a perfect fit SSR must equal SST, and the ratio (SSR/SST) must equal one. Poorer fits will result in larger values for SSE. Solving for SSE in equation (14.11), we see that SSE = SST − SSR. Hence, the largest value for SSE (and hence the poorest fit) occurs when SSR = 0 and SSE = SST.

The ratio SSR/SST, which will take values between zero and one, is used to evaluate the goodness of fit for the estimated regression equation. This ratio is called the *coefficient of determination* and is denoted by r^2.

COEFFICIENT OF DETERMINATION

$$r^2 = \frac{SSR}{SST} \tag{14.12}$$

For the Armand's Pizza Parlors example, the value of the coefficient of determination is

$$r^2 = \frac{SSR}{SST} = \frac{14{,}200}{15{,}730} = .9027$$

When we express the coefficient of determination as a percentage, r^2 can be interpreted as the percentage of the total sum of squares that can be explained by using the estimated regression equation. For Armand's Pizza Parlors, we can conclude that 90.27% of the total sum of squares can be explained by using the estimated regression equation $\hat{y} = 60 + 5x$ to predict quarterly sales. In other words, 90.27% of the variability in sales can be explained by the linear relationship between the size of the student population and sales. We should be pleased to find such a good fit for the estimated regression equation.

Correlation Coefficient

In Chapter 3 we introduced the **correlation coefficient** as a descriptive measure of the strength of linear association between two variables, x and y. Values of the correlation coefficient are always between −1 and +1. A value of +1 indicates that the two variables x and y are perfectly related in a positive linear sense. That is, all data points are on a straight line that has a positive slope. A value of −1 indicates that x and y are perfectly related in a negative linear sense, with all data points on a straight line that has a negative slope. Values of the correlation coefficient close to zero indicate that x and y are not linearly related.

In Section 3.5 we presented the equation for computing the sample correlation coefficient. If a regression analysis has already been performed and the coefficient of determination r^2 computed, the sample correlation coefficient can be computed as follows:

SAMPLE CORRELATION COEFFICIENT

$$r_{xy} = (\text{sign of } b_1)\sqrt{\text{Coefficient of determination}}$$
$$= (\text{sign of } b_1)\sqrt{r^2} \tag{14.13}$$

where

$$b_1 = \text{the slope of the estimated regression equation } \hat{y} = b_0 + b_1 x$$

The sign for the sample correlation coefficient is positive if the estimated regression equation has a positive slope ($b_1 > 0$) and negative if the estimated regression equation has a negative slope ($b_1 < 0$).

For the Armand's Pizza Parlor example, the value of the coefficient of determination corresponding to the estimated regression equation $\hat{y} = 60 + 5x$ is .9027. Because the slope of the estimated regression equation is positive, equation (14.13) shows that the sample correlation coefficient is $+\sqrt{.9027} = +.9501$. With a sample correlation coefficient of $r_{xy} = +.9501$, we would conclude that a strong positive linear association exists between x and y.

In the case of a linear relationship between two variables, both the coefficient of determination and the sample correlation coefficient provide measures of the strength of the relationship. The coefficient of determination provides a measure between zero and one, whereas the sample correlation coefficient provides a measure between -1 and $+1$. Although the sample correlation coefficient is restricted to a linear relationship between two variables, the coefficient of determination can be used for nonlinear relationships and for relationships that have two or more independent variables. Thus, the coefficient of determination provides a wider range of applicability.

NOTES AND COMMENTS

1. In developing the least squares estimated regression equation and computing the coefficient of determination, we made no probabilistic assumptions about the error term ϵ, and no statistical tests for significance of the relationship between x and y were conducted. Larger values of r^2 imply that the least squares line provides a better fit to the data; that is, the observations are more closely grouped about the least squares line. But, using only r^2, we can draw no conclusion about whether the relationship between x and y is statistically significant. Such a conclusion must be based on considerations that involve the sample size and the properties of the appropriate sampling distributions of the least squares estimators.

2. As a practical matter, for typical data found in the social sciences, values of r^2 as low as .25 are often considered useful. For data in the physical and life sciences, r^2 values of .60 or greater are often found; in fact, in some cases, r^2 values greater than .90 can be found. In business applications, r^2 values vary greatly, depending on the unique characteristics of each application.

Exercises

Methods

SELF*test*

15. The data from exercise 1 follow.

x_i	1	2	3	4	5
y_i	3	7	5	11	14

The estimated regression equation for these data is $\hat{y} = .20 + 2.60x$.
a. Compute SSE, SST, and SSR using equations (14.8), (14.9), and (14.10).
b. Compute the coefficient of determination r^2. Comment on the goodness of fit.
c. Compute the sample correlation coefficient.

16. The data from exercise 2 follow.

x_i	3	12	6	20	14
y_i	55	40	55	10	15

The estimated regression equation for these data is $\hat{y} = 68 - 3x$.
a. Compute SSE, SST, and SSR.
b. Compute the coefficient of determination r^2. Comment on the goodness of fit.
c. Compute the sample correlation coefficient.

17. The data from exercise 3 follow.

x_i	2	6	9	13	20
y_i	7	18	9	26	23

The estimated regression equation for these data is $\hat{y} = 7.6 + .9x$. What percentage of the total sum of squares can be accounted for by the estimated regression equation? What is the value of the sample correlation coefficient?

Applications

18. The following data show the brand, price ($), and the overall score for six stereo headphones that were tested by *Consumer Reports* (*Consumer Reports* website, March 5, 2012). The overall score is based on sound quality and effectiveness of ambient noise reduction. Scores range from 0 (lowest) to 100 (highest). The estimated regression equation for these data is $\hat{y} = 23.194 + .318x$, where x = price ($) and y = overall score.

Brand	Price ($)	Score
Bose	180	76
Skullcandy	150	71
Koss	95	61
Phillips/O'Neill	70	56
Denon	70	40
JVC	35	26

a. Compute SST, SSR, and SSE.
b. Compute the coefficient of determination r^2. Comment on the goodness of fit.
c. What is the value of the sample correlation coefficient?

19. In exercise 7 a sales manager collected the following data on x = annual sales and y = years of experience. The estimated regression equation for these data is $\hat{y} = 80 + 4x$.

Salesperson	Years of Experience	Annual Sales ($1000s)
1	1	80
2	3	97
3	4	92
4	4	102
5	6	103
6	8	111
7	10	119
8	10	123
9	11	117
10	13	136

a. Compute SST, SSR, and SSE.
b. Compute the coefficient of determination r^2. Comment on the goodness of fit.
c. What is the value of the sample correlation coefficient?

20. *Bicycling,* the world's leading cycling magazine, reviews hundreds of bicycles throughout the year. Their "Road-Race" category contains reviews of bikes used by riders primarily

interested in racing. One of the most important factors in selecting a bike for racing is the weight of the bike. The following data show the weight (pounds) and price ($) for 10 racing bikes reviewed by the magazine (*Bicycling* website, March 8, 2012).

DATA *file*

RacingBicycles

Brand	Weight	Price ($)
FELT F5	17.8	2100
PINARELLO Paris	16.1	6250
ORBEA Orca GDR	14.9	8370
EDDY MERCKX EMX-7	15.9	6200
BH RC1 Ultegra	17.2	4000
BH Ultralight 386	13.1	8600
CERVELO S5 Team	16.2	6000
GIANT TCR Advanced 2	17.1	2580
WILIER TRIESTINA Gran Turismo	17.6	3400
SPECIALIZED S-Works Amira SL4	14.1	8000

a.   Use the data to develop an estimated regression equation that could be used to estimate the price for a bike given the weight.
b.   Compute r^2. Did the estimated regression equation provide a good fit?
c.   Predict the price for a bike that weighs 15 pounds.

21.   An important application of regression analysis in accounting is in the estimation of cost. By collecting data on volume and cost and using the least squares method to develop an estimated regression equation relating volume and cost, an accountant can estimate the cost associated with a particular manufacturing volume. Consider the following sample of production volumes and total cost data for a manufacturing operation.

Production Volume (units)	Total Cost ($)
400	4000
450	5000
550	5400
600	5900
700	6400
750	7000

a.   Use these data to develop an estimated regression equation that could be used to predict the total cost for a given production volume.
b.   What is the variable cost per unit produced?
c.   Compute the coefficient of determination. What percentage of the variation in total cost can be explained by production volume?
d.   The company's production schedule shows 500 units must be produced next month. Predict the total cost for this operation?

22.   Refer to exercise 9, where the following data were used to investigate the relationship between the number of cars in service (1000s) and the annual revenue ($millions) for six smaller car rental companies (*Auto Rental News* website, August 7, 2012).

Company	Cars (1000s)	Revenue ($ millions)
U-Save Auto Rental System, Inc.	11.5	118
Payless Car Rental System, Inc.	10.0	135
ACE Rent A Car	9.0	100
Rent-A-Wreck of America	5.5	37
Triangle Rent-A-Car	4.2	40
Affordable/Sensible	3.3	32

With x = cars in service (1000s) and y = annual revenue (\$ millions), the estimated regression equation is $\hat{y} = -17.005 + 12.966x$. For these data SSE = 1043.03.

a. Compute the coefficient of determination r^2.

b. Did the estimated regression equation provide a good fit? Explain.

c. What is the value of the sample correlation coefficient? Does it reflect a strong or weak relationship between the number of cars in service and the annual revenue?

(14.4) # Model Assumptions

In conducting a regression analysis, we begin by making an assumption about the appropriate model for the relationship between the dependent and independent variable(s). For the case of simple linear regression, the assumed regression model is

$$y = \beta_0 + \beta_1 x + \epsilon$$

Then the least squares method is used to develop values for b_0 and b_1, the estimates of the model parameters β_0 and β_1, respectively. The resulting estimated regression equation is

$$\hat{y} = b_0 + b_1 x$$

We saw that the value of the coefficient of determination (r^2) is a measure of the goodness of fit of the estimated regression equation. However, even with a large value of r^2, the estimated regression equation should not be used until further analysis of the appropriateness of the assumed model has been conducted. An important step in determining whether the assumed model is appropriate involves testing for the significance of the relationship. The tests of significance in regression analysis are based on the following assumptions about the error term ϵ.

ASSUMPTIONS ABOUT THE ERROR TERM ϵ IN THE REGRESSION MODEL

$$y = \beta_0 + \beta_1 x + \epsilon$$

1. The error term ϵ is a random variable with a mean or expected value of zero; that is, $E(\epsilon) = 0$.
    Implication: β_0 and β_1 are constants, therefore $E(\beta_0) = \beta_0$ and $E(\beta_1) = \beta_1$; thus, for a given value of x, the expected value of y is

    $$E(y) = \beta_0 + \beta_1 x \qquad\qquad (14.14)$$

    As we indicated previously, equation (14.14) is referred to as the regression equation.

2. The variance of ϵ, denoted by σ^2, is the same for all values of x.
    Implication: The variance of y about the regression line equals σ^2 and is the same for all values of x.

3. The values of ϵ are independent.
    Implication: The value of ϵ for a particular value of x is not related to the value of ϵ for any other value of x; thus, the value of y for a particular value of x is not related to the value of y for any other value of x.

4. The error term ϵ is a normally distributed random variable for all values of x.
    Implication: Because y is a linear function of ϵ, y is also a normally distributed random variable for all values of x.

FIGURE 14.6   ASSUMPTIONS FOR THE REGRESSION MODEL

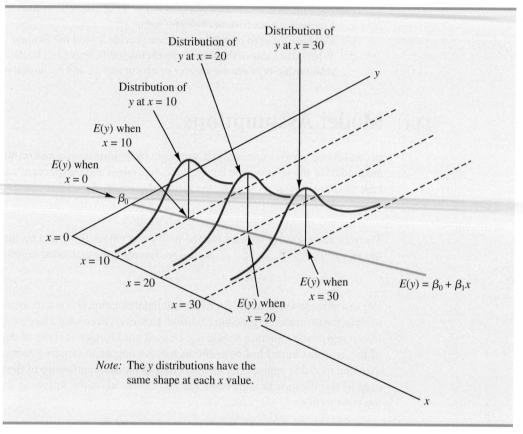

Figure 14.6 illustrates the model assumptions and their implications; note that in this graphical interpretation, the value of $E(y)$ changes according to the specific value of x considered. However, regardless of the x value, the probability distribution of ϵ and hence the probability distributions of y are normally distributed, each with the same variance. The specific value of the error ϵ at any particular point depends on whether the actual value of y is greater than or less than $E(y)$.

At this point, we must keep in mind that we are also making an assumption or hypothesis about the form of the relationship between x and y. That is, we assume that a straight line represented by $\beta_0 + \beta_1 x$ is the basis for the relationship between the variables. We must not lose sight of the fact that some other model, for instance $y = \beta_0 + \beta_1 x^2 + \epsilon$, may turn out to be a better model for the underlying relationship.

14.5 Testing for Significance

In a simple linear regression equation, the mean or expected value of y is a linear function of x: $E(y) = \beta_0 + \beta_1 x$. If the value of β_1 is zero, $E(y) = \beta_0 + (0)x = \beta_0$. In this case, the mean value of y does not depend on the value of x and hence we would conclude that x and y are not linearly related. Alternatively, if the value of β_1 is not equal to zero, we would conclude that the two variables are related. Thus, to test for a significant regression relationship, we must conduct a hypothesis test to determine whether the value of β_1 is zero. Two tests are commonly used. Both require an estimate of σ^2, the variance of ϵ in the regression model.

Estimate of σ^2

From the regression model and its assumptions we can conclude that σ^2, the variance of ϵ, also represents the variance of the y values about the regression line. Recall that the deviations of the y values about the estimated regression line are called residuals. Thus, SSE, the sum of squared residuals, is a measure of the variability of the actual observations about the estimated regression line. The **mean square error** (MSE) provides the estimate of σ^2; it is SSE divided by its degrees of freedom.

With $\hat{y}_i = b_0 + b_1x_i$, SSE can be written as

$$\text{SSE} = \Sigma(y_i - \hat{y}_i)^2 = \Sigma(y_i - b_0 - b_1x_i)^2$$

Every sum of squares has associated with it a number called its degrees of freedom. Statisticians have shown that SSE has $n - 2$ degrees of freedom because two parameters (β_0 and β_1) must be estimated to compute SSE. Thus, the mean square error is computed by dividing SSE by $n - 2$. MSE provides an unbiased estimator of σ^2. Because the value of MSE provides an estimate of σ^2, the notation s^2 is also used.

MEAN SQUARE ERROR (ESTIMATE OF σ^2)

$$s^2 = \text{MSE} = \frac{\text{SSE}}{n - 2} \qquad \text{(14.15)}$$

In Section 14.3 we showed that for the Armand's Pizza Parlors example, SSE = 1530; hence,

$$s^2 = \text{MSE} = \frac{1530}{8} = 191.25$$

provides an unbiased estimate of σ^2.

To estimate σ we take the square root of s^2. The resulting value, s, is referred to as the **standard error of the estimate**.

STANDARD ERROR OF THE ESTIMATE

$$s = \sqrt{\text{MSE}} = \sqrt{\frac{\text{SSE}}{n - 2}} \qquad \text{(14.16)}$$

For the Armand's Pizza Parlors example, $s = \sqrt{\text{MSE}} = \sqrt{191.25} = 13.829$. In the following discussion, we use the standard error of the estimate in the tests for a significant relationship between x and y.

t Test

The simple linear regression model is $y = \beta_0 + \beta_1x + \epsilon$. If x and y are linearly related, we must have $\beta_1 \neq 0$. The purpose of the t test is to see whether we can conclude that $\beta_1 \neq 0$. We will use the sample data to test the following hypotheses about the parameter β_1.

$$H_0: \beta_1 = 0$$
$$H_a: \beta_1 \neq 0$$

If H_0 is rejected, we will conclude that $\beta_1 \neq 0$ and that a statistically significant relationship exists between the two variables. However, if H_0 cannot be rejected, we will have insufficient evidence to conclude that a significant relationship exists. The properties of the sampling distribution of b_1, the least squares estimator of β_1, provide the basis for the hypothesis test.

First, let us consider what would happen if we used a different random sample for the same regression study. For example, suppose that Armand's Pizza Parlors used the sales records of a different sample of 10 restaurants. A regression analysis of this new sample might result in an estimated regression equation similar to our previous estimated regression equation $\hat{y} = 60 + 5x$. However, it is doubtful that we would obtain exactly the same equation (with an intercept of exactly 60 and a slope of exactly 5). Indeed, b_0 and b_1, the least squares estimators, are sample statistics with their own sampling distributions. The properties of the sampling distribution of b_1 follow.

SAMPLING DISTRIBUTION OF b_1

Expected Value
$$E(b_1) = \beta_1$$

Standard Deviation
$$\sigma_{b_1} = \frac{\sigma}{\sqrt{\Sigma(x_i - \bar{x})^2}} \qquad (14.17)$$

Distribution Form
Normal

Note that the expected value of b_1 is equal to β_1, so b_1 is an unbiased estimator of β_1.

Because we do not know the value of σ, we develop an estimate of σ_{b_1}, denoted s_{b_1}, by estimating σ with s in equation (14.17). Thus, we obtain the following estimate of σ_{b_1}.

The standard deviation of b_1 is also referred to as the standard error of b_1. Thus, s_{b_1} provides an estimate of the standard error of b_1.

ESTIMATED STANDARD DEVIATION OF b_1

$$s_{b_1} = \frac{s}{\sqrt{\Sigma(x_i - \bar{x})^2}} \qquad (14.18)$$

For Armand's Pizza Parlors, $s = 13.829$. Hence, using $\Sigma(x_i - \bar{x})^2 = 568$ as shown in Table 14.2, we have

$$s_{b_1} = \frac{13.829}{\sqrt{568}} = .5803$$

as the estimated standard deviation of b_1.

The t test for a significant relationship is based on the fact that the test statistic

$$\frac{b_1 - \beta_1}{s_{b_1}}$$

follows a t distribution with $n - 2$ degrees of freedom. If the null hypothesis is true, then $\beta_1 = 0$ and $t = b_1/s_{b_1}$.

Let us conduct this test of significance for Armand's Pizza Parlors at the $\alpha = .01$ level of significance. The test statistic is

$$t = \frac{b_1}{s_{b_1}} = \frac{5}{.5803} = 8.62$$

Appendixes 14.3 and 14.4 show how Minitab and Excel can be used to compute the p-value.

The t distribution table (Table 2 of Appendix D) shows that with $n - 2 = 10 - 2 = 8$ degrees of freedom, $t = 3.355$ provides an area of .005 in the upper tail. Thus, the area in the upper tail of the t distribution corresponding to the test statistic $t = 8.62$ must be less than .005. Because this test is a two-tailed test, we double this value to conclude that the p-value associated with $t = 8.62$ must be less than $2(.005) = .01$. Excel or Minitab show the p-value $= .000$. Because the p-value is less than $\alpha = .01$, we reject H_0 and conclude that β_1 is not equal to zero. This evidence is sufficient to conclude that a significant relationship exists between student population and quarterly sales. A summary of the t test for significance in simple linear regression follows.

---

t TEST FOR SIGNIFICANCE IN SIMPLE LINEAR REGRESSION

$$H_0\colon \beta_1 = 0$$
$$H_a\colon \beta_1 \neq 0$$

TEST STATISTIC

$$t = \frac{b_1}{s_{b_1}} \tag{14.19}$$

REJECTION RULE

p-value approach: Reject H_0 if p-value $\leq \alpha$

Critical value approach: Reject H_0 if $t \leq -t_{\alpha/2}$ or if $t \geq t_{\alpha/2}$

where $t_{\alpha/2}$ is based on a t distribution with $n - 2$ degrees of freedom.

Confidence Interval for β_1

The form of a confidence interval for β_1 is as follows:

$$b_1 \pm t_{\alpha/2} s_{b_1}$$

The point estimator is b_1 and the margin of error is $t_{\alpha/2} s_{b_1}$. The confidence coefficient associated with this interval is $1 - \alpha$, and $t_{\alpha/2}$ is the t value providing an area of $\alpha/2$ in the upper tail of a t distribution with $n - 2$ degrees of freedom. For example, suppose that we wanted to develop a 99% confidence interval estimate of β_1 for Armand's Pizza Parlors. From Table 2 of Appendix B we find that the t value corresponding to $\alpha = .01$ and $n - 2 = 10 - 2 = 8$ degrees of freedom is $t_{.005} = 3.355$. Thus, the 99% confidence interval estimate of β_1 is

$$b_1 \pm t_{\alpha/2} s_{b_1} = 5 \pm 3.355(.5803) = 5 \pm 1.95$$

or 3.05 to 6.95.

In using the t test for significance, the hypotheses tested were

$$H_0\colon \beta_1 = 0$$
$$H_a\colon \beta_1 \neq 0$$

At the $\alpha = .01$ level of significance, we can use the 99% confidence interval as an alternative for drawing the hypothesis testing conclusion for the Armand's data. Because 0, the hypothesized value of β_1, is not included in the confidence interval (3.05 to 6.95), we can reject H_0 and conclude that a significant statistical relationship exists between the size of the student population and quarterly sales. In general, a confidence interval can be used to test any two-sided hypothesis about β_1. If the hypothesized value of β_1 is contained in the confidence interval, do not reject H_0. Otherwise, reject H_0.

F **Test**

An F test, based on the F probability distribution, can also be used to test for significance in regression. With only one independent variable, the F test will provide the same conclusion as the t test; that is, if the t test indicates $\beta_1 \neq 0$ and hence a significant relationship, the F test will also indicate a significant relationship. But with more than one independent variable, only the F test can be used to test for an overall significant relationship.

The logic behind the use of the F test for determining whether the regression relationship is statistically significant is based on the development of two independent estimates of σ^2. We explained how MSE provides an estimate of σ^2. If the null hypothesis H_0: $\beta_1 = 0$ is true, the sum of squares due to regression, SSR, divided by its degrees of freedom provides another independent estimate of σ^2. This estimate is called the *mean square due to regression,* or simply the *mean square regression,* and is denoted MSR. In general,

$$\text{MSR} = \frac{\text{SSR}}{\text{Regression degrees of freedom}}$$

For the models we consider in this text, the regression degrees of freedom is always equal to the number of independent variables in the model:

$$\text{MSR} = \frac{\text{SSR}}{\text{Number of independent variables}} \qquad \text{(14.20)}$$

Because we consider only regression models with one independent variable in this chapter, we have MSR = SSR/1 = SSR. Hence, for Armand's Pizza Parlors, MSR = SSR = 14,200.

If the null hypothesis (H_0: $\beta_1 = 0$) is true, MSR and MSE are two independent estimates of σ^2 and the sampling distribution of MSR/MSE follows an F distribution with numerator degrees of freedom equal to one and denominator degrees of freedom equal to $n - 2$. Therefore, when $\beta_1 = 0$, the value of MSR/MSE should be close to one. However, if the null hypothesis is false ($\beta_1 \neq 0$), MSR will overestimate σ^2 and the value of MSR/MSE will be inflated; thus, large values of MSR/MSE lead to the rejection of H_0 and the conclusion that the relationship between x and y is statistically significant.

Let us conduct the F test for the Armand's Pizza Parlors example. The test statistic is

$$F = \frac{\text{MSR}}{\text{MSE}} = \frac{14,200}{191.25} = 74.25$$

The F test and the t test provide identical results for simple linear regression.

The F distribution table (Table 4 of Appendix B) shows that with one degree of freedom in the numerator and $n - 2 = 10 - 2 = 8$ degrees of freedom in the denominator, $F = 11.26$ provides an area of .01 in the upper tail. Thus, the area in the upper tail of the F distribution corresponding to the test statistic $F = 74.25$ must be less than .01. Thus, we conclude that the p-value must be less than .01. Excel or Minitab show the p-value = .000. Because the p-value is less than $\alpha = .01$, we reject H_0 and conclude that a significant relationship exists between the size of the student population and quarterly sales. A summary of the F test for significance in simple linear regression follows.

If H_0 is false, MSE still provides an unbiased estimate of σ^2 and MSR overestimates σ^2. If H_0 is true, both MSE and MSR provide unbiased estimates of σ^2; in this case the value of MSR/MSE should be close to 1.

F TEST FOR SIGNIFICANCE IN SIMPLE LINEAR REGRESSION

$$H_0: \beta_1 = 0$$
$$H_a: \beta_1 \neq 0$$

TEST STATISTIC

$$F = \frac{\text{MSR}}{\text{MSE}} \tag{14.21}$$

REJECTION RULE

p-value approach: Reject H_0 if p-value $\leq \alpha$

Critical value approach: Reject H_0 if $F \geq F_\alpha$

where F_α is based on an F distribution with 1 degree of freedom in the numerator and $n - 2$ degrees of freedom in the denominator.

In Chapter 13 we covered analysis of variance (ANOVA) and showed how an **ANOVA table** could be used to provide a convenient summary of the computational aspects of analysis of variance. A similar ANOVA table can be used to summarize the results of the F test for significance in regression. Table 14.5 is the general form of the ANOVA table for simple linear regression. Table 14.6 is the ANOVA table with the F test computations performed for Armand's Pizza Parlors. Regression, Error, and Total are the labels for the three sources of variation, with SSR, SSE, and SST appearing as the corresponding sum of squares in column 2. The degrees of freedom, 1 for SSR, $n - 2$ for SSE, and $n - 1$ for

TABLE 14.5   GENERAL FORM OF THE ANOVA TABLE FOR SIMPLE LINEAR REGRESSION

In every analysis of variance table the total sum of squares is the sum of the regression sum of squares and the error sum of squares; in addition, the total degrees of freedom is the sum of the regression degrees of freedom and the error degrees of freedom.

Source of Variation	Sum of Squares	Degrees of Freedom	Mean Square	F	p-value
Regression	SSR	1	$\text{MSR} = \dfrac{\text{SSR}}{1}$	$F = \dfrac{\text{MSR}}{\text{MSE}}$	
Error	SSE	$n - 2$	$\text{MSE} = \dfrac{\text{SSE}}{n - 2}$		
Total	SST	$n - 1$			

TABLE 14.6   ANOVA TABLE FOR THE ARMAND'S PIZZA PARLORS PROBLEM

Source of Variation	Sum of Squares	Degrees of Freedom	Mean Square	F	p-value
Regression	14,200	1	$\dfrac{14{,}200}{1} = 14{,}200$	$\dfrac{14{,}200}{191.25} = 74.25$	.000
Error	1530	8	$\dfrac{1530}{8} = 191.25$		
Total	15,730	9			

SST, are shown in column 3. Column 4 contains the values of MSR and MSE, column 5 contains the value of $F = $ MSR/MSE, and column 6 contains the p-value corresponding to the F value in column 5. Almost all computer printouts of regression analysis include an ANOVA table summary of the F test for significance.

Some Cautions About the Interpretation of Significance Tests

Regression analysis, which can be used to identify how variables are associated with one another, cannot be used as evidence of a cause-and-effect relationship.

Rejecting the null hypothesis $H_0: \beta_1 = 0$ and concluding that the relationship between x and y is significant does not enable us to conclude that a cause-and-effect relationship is present between x and y. Concluding a cause-and-effect relationship is warranted only if the analyst can provide some type of theoretical justification that the relationship is in fact causal. In the Armand's Pizza Parlors example, we can conclude that there is a significant relationship between the size of the student population x and quarterly sales y; moreover, the estimated regression equation $\hat{y} = 60 + 5x$ provides the least squares estimate of the relationship. We cannot, however, conclude that changes in student population x *cause* changes in quarterly sales y just because we identified a statistically significant relationship. The appropriateness of such a cause-and-effect conclusion is left to supporting theoretical justification and to good judgment on the part of the analyst. Armand's managers felt that increases in the student population were a likely cause of increased quarterly sales. Thus, the result of the significance test enabled them to conclude that a cause-and-effect relationship was present.

In addition, just because we are able to reject $H_0: \beta_1 = 0$ and demonstrate statistical significance does not enable us to conclude that the relationship between x and y is linear. We can state only that x and y are related and that a linear relationship explains a significant portion of the variability in y over the range of values for x observed in the sample. Figure 14.7 illustrates this situation. The test for significance calls for the rejection of the null hypothesis $H_0: \beta_1 = 0$ and leads to the conclusion that x and y are significantly related, but the figure shows that the actual relationship between x and y is not linear. Although the

FIGURE 14.7   EXAMPLE OF A LINEAR APPROXIMATION OF A NONLINEAR RELATIONSHIP

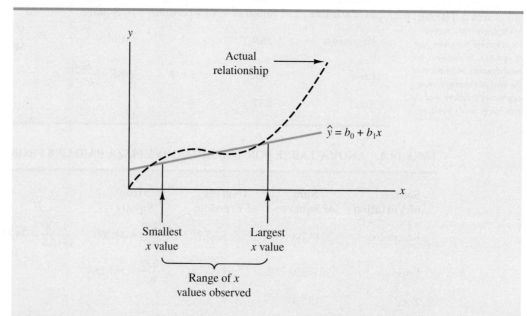

linear approximation provided by $\hat{y} = b_0 + b_1 x$ is good over the range of x values observed in the sample, it becomes poor for x values outside that range.

Given a significant relationship, we should feel confident in using the estimated regression equation for predictions corresponding to x values within the range of the x values observed in the sample. For Armand's Pizza Parlors, this range corresponds to values of x between 2 and 26. Unless other reasons indicate that the model is valid beyond this range, predictions outside the range of the independent variable should be made with caution. For Armand's Pizza Parlors, because the regression relationship has been found significant at the .01 level, we should feel confident using it to predict sales for restaurants where the associated student population is between 2000 and 26,000.

NOTES AND COMMENTS

1. The assumptions made about the error term (Section 14.4) are what allow the tests of statistical significance in this section. The properties of the sampling distribution of b_1 and the subsequent t and F tests follow directly from these assumptions.
2. Do not confuse statistical significance with practical significance. With very large sample sizes, statistically significant results can be obtained for small values of b_1; in such cases, one must exercise care in concluding that the relationship has practical significance.
3. A test of significance for a linear relationship between x and y can also be performed by using the sample correlation coefficient r_{xy}. With ρ_{xy}

denoting the population correlation coefficient, the hypotheses are as follows.

$$H_0: \rho_{xy} = 0$$
$$H_a: \rho_{xy} \neq 0$$

A significant relationship can be concluded if H_0 is rejected. The details of this test are provided in Appendix 14.2. However, the t and F tests presented previously in this section give the same result as the test for significance using the correlation coefficient. Conducting a test for significance using the correlation coefficient therefore is not necessary if a t or F test has already been conducted.

Exercises

Methods

SELFtest

23. The data from exercise 1 follow.

x_i	1	2	3	4	5
y_i	3	7	5	11	14

a. Compute the mean square error using equation (14.15).
b. Compute the standard error of the estimate using equation (14.16).
c. Compute the estimated standard deviation of b_1 using equation (14.18).
d. Use the t test to test the following hypotheses ($\alpha = .05$):

$$H_0: \beta_1 = 0$$
$$H_a: \beta_1 \neq 0$$

e. Use the F test to test the hypotheses in part (d) at a .05 level of significance. Present the results in the analysis of variance table format.

24. The data from exercise 2 follow.

x_i	3	12	6	20	14
y_i	55	40	55	10	15

a. Compute the mean square error using equation (14.15).
b. Compute the standard error of the estimate using equation (14.16).
c. Compute the estimated standard deviation of b_1 using equation (14.18).
d. Use the t test to test the following hypotheses ($\alpha = .05$):

$$H_0: \beta_1 = 0$$
$$H_a: \beta_1 \neq 0$$

e. Use the F test to test the hypotheses in part (d) at a .05 level of significance. Present the results in the analysis of variance table format.

25. The data from exercise 3 follow.

x_i	2	6	9	13	20
y_i	7	18	9	26	23

a. What is the value of the standard error of the estimate?
b. Test for a significant relationship by using the t test. Use $\alpha = .05$.
c. Use the F test to test for a significant relationship. Use $\alpha = .05$. What is your conclusion?

Applications

 SELF*test*

26. In exercise 18 the data on price ($) and the overall score for six stereo headphones tested by *Consumer Reports* were as follows (*Consumer Reports* website, March 5, 2012).

Brand	Price ($)	Score
Bose	180	76
Skullcandy	150	71
Koss	95	61
Phillips/O'Neill	70	56
Denon	70	40
JVC	35	26

a. Does the t test indicate a significant relationship between price and the overall score? What is your conclusion? Use $\alpha = .05$.
b. Test for a significant relationship using the F test. What is your conclusion? Use $\alpha = .05$.
c. Show the ANOVA table for these data.

27. To identify high-paying jobs for people who do not like stress, the following data were collected showing the average annual salary ($1000s) and the stress tolerance for a variety of occupations (Business Insider, November 8, 2013).

DATA *file*

SalaryStress

Job	Average Annual Salary ($1000s)	Stress Tolerance
Art directors	81	69.0
Astronomers	96	62.0
Audiologists	70	67.5
Dental hygienists	70	71.3
Economists	92	63.3
Engineers	92	69.5
Law teachers	100	62.8
Optometrists	98	65.5
Political scientists	102	60.1
Urban and regional planners	65	69.0

The stress tolerance for each job is rated on a scale from 0 to 100, where a lower rating indicates less stress.

a. Develop a scatter diagram for these data with average annual salary as the independent variable. What does the scatter diagram indicate about the relationship between the two variables?

b. Use these data to develop an estimated regression equation that can be used to predict stress tolerance given the average annual salary.

c. At the .05 level of significance, does there appear to be a significant statistical relationship between the two variables?

d. Would you feel comfortable in predicting the stress tolerance for a different occupation given the average annual salary for the occupation? Explain.

e. Does the relationship between average annual salary and stress tolerance for these data seem reasonable to you? Explain.

BrokerRatings

28. In exercise 8 ratings data on $x =$ the quality of the speed of execution and $y =$ overall satisfaction with electronic trades provided the estimated regression equation $\hat{y} = .2046 + .9077x$. At the .05 level of significance, test whether speed of execution and overall satisfaction are related. Show the ANOVA table. What is your conclusion?

29. Refer to exercise 21, where data on production volume and cost were used to develop an estimated regression equation relating production volume and cost for a particular manufacturing operation. Use $\alpha = .05$ to test whether the production volume is significantly related to the total cost. Show the ANOVA table. What is your conclusion?

30. Refer to exercise 9, where the following data were used to investigate the relationship between the number of cars in service (1000s) and the annual revenue ($ millions) for six smaller car rental companies (*Auto Rental News* website, August 7, 2012).

Company	Cars (1000s)	Revenue ($ millions)
U-Save Auto Rental System, Inc.	11.5	118
Payless Car Rental System, Inc.	10.0	135
ACE Rent A Car	9.0	100
Rent-A-Wreck of America	5.5	37
Triangle Rent-A-Car	4.2	40
Affordable/Sensible	3.3	32

With $x =$ cars in service (1000s) and $y =$ annual revenue ($ millions), the estimated regression equation is $\hat{y} = -17.005 + 12.966x$. For these data SSE $= 1043.03$ and SST $= 10,568$. Do these results indicate a significant relationship between the number of cars in service and the annual revenue?

RacingBicycles

31. In exercise 20, data on $x =$ weight (pounds) and $y =$ price ($) for 10 road-racing bikes provided the estimated regression equation $\hat{y} = 28,574 - 1439x$. (*Bicycling* website, March 8, 2012). For these data SSE $= 7,102,922.54$ and SST $= 52,120,800$. Use the F test to determine whether the weight for a bike and the price are related at the .05 level of significance.

(14.6) Using the Estimated Regression Equation for Estimation and Prediction

When using the simple linear regression model, we are making an assumption about the relationship between x and y. We then use the least squares method to obtain the estimated simple linear regression equation. If a significant relationship exists between x and y and the coefficient of determination shows that the fit is good, the estimated regression equation should be useful for estimation and prediction.

For the Armand's Pizza Parlors example, the estimated regression equation is $\hat{y} = 60 + 5x$. At the end of Section 14.1 we stated that $\hat{y}$ can be used as a *point estimator* of $E(y)$, the mean or expected value of y for a given value of x, and as a predictor of an individual value of y. For example, suppose Armand's managers want to estimate the mean quarterly sales for *all* restaurants located near college campuses with 10,000 students. Using the estimated regression equation $\hat{y} = 60 + 5x$, we see that for $x = 10$ (10,000 students), $\hat{y} = 60 + 5(10) = 110$. Thus, a *point estimate* of the mean quarterly sales for all restaurant locations near campuses with 10,000 students is $110,000. In this case we are using $\hat{y}$ as the point estimator of the mean value of y when $x = 10$.

We can also use the estimated regression equation to *predict* an individual value of y for a given value of x. For example, to predict quarterly sales for a new restaurant Armand's is considering building near Talbot College, a campus with 10,000 students, we would compute $\hat{y} = 60 + 5(10) = 110$. Hence, we would predict quarterly sales of $110,000 for such a new restaurant. In this case, we are using $\hat{y}$ as the *predictor* of y for a new observation when $x = 10$.

When we are using the estimated regression equation to estimate the mean value of y or to predict an individual value of y, it is clear that the estimate or prediction depends on the given value of x. For this reason, as we discuss in more depth the issues concerning estimation and prediction, the following notation will help clarify matters.

$x^* = $ the given value of the independent variable x

$y^* = $ the random variable denoting the possible values of the dependent variable y when $x = x^*$

$E(y^*) = $ the mean or expected value of the dependent variable y when $x = x^*$

$\hat{y}^* = b_0 + b_1 x^* = $ the point estimator of $E(y^*)$ and the predictor of an individual value of y^* when $x = x^*$

To illustrate the use of this notation, suppose we want to estimate the mean value of quarterly sales for *all* Armand's restaurants located near a campus with 10,000 students. For this case, $x^* = 10$ and $E(y^*)$ denotes the unknown mean value of quarterly sales for all restaurants where $x^* = 10$. Thus, the point estimate of $E(y^*)$ is provided by $\hat{y}^* = 60 + 5(10) = 110$, or $110,000. But, using this notation, $\hat{y}^* = 110$ is also the predictor of quarterly sales for the new restaurant located near Talbot College, a school with 10,000 students.

Interval Estimation

Confidence intervals and prediction intervals show the precision of the regression results. Narrower intervals provide a higher degree of precision.

Point estimators and predictors do not provide any information about the precision associated with the estimate and/or prediction. For that we must develop confidence intervals and prediction intervals. A **confidence interval** is an interval estimate of the *mean value of y* for a given value of x. A **prediction interval** is used whenever we want to *predict an individual value of y* for a new observation corresponding to a given value of x. Although the predictor of y for a given value of x is the same as the point estimator of the mean value of y for a given value of x, the interval estimates we obtain for the two cases are different. As we will show, the margin of error is larger for a prediction interval. We begin by showing how to develop an interval estimate of the mean value of y.

Confidence Interval for the Mean Value of y

In general, we cannot expect $\hat{y}^*$ to equal $E(y^*)$ exactly. If we want to make an inference about how close $\hat{y}^*$ is to the true mean value $E(y^*)$, we will have to estimate the variance of $\hat{y}^*$. The formula for estimating the variance of $\hat{y}^*$, denoted by $s_{\hat{y}^*}^2$, is

$$s_{\hat{y}^*}^2 = s^2 \left[\frac{1}{n} + \frac{(x^* - \bar{x})^2}{\Sigma(x_i - \bar{x})^2} \right] \tag{14.22}$$

The estimate of the standard deviation of $\hat{y}^*$ is given by the square root of equation (14.22).

$$s_{\hat{y}^*} = s \sqrt{\frac{1}{n} + \frac{(x^* - \bar{x})^2}{\Sigma(x_i - \bar{x})^2}} \tag{14.23}$$

The computational results for Armand's Pizza Parlors in Section 14.5 provided $s = 13.829$. With $x^* = 10$, $\bar{x} = 14$, and $\Sigma(x_i - \bar{x})^2 = 568$, we can use equation (14.23) to obtain

$$s_{\hat{y}^*} = 13.829 \sqrt{\frac{1}{10} + \frac{(10 - 14)^2}{568}}$$

$$= 13.829 \sqrt{.1282} = 4.95$$

The general expression for a confidence interval follows.

The margin of error associated with this confidence interval is $t_{\alpha/2} s_{\hat{y}^*}$.

CONFIDENCE INTERVAL FOR $E(y^*)$

$$\hat{y}^* \pm t_{\alpha/2} s_{\hat{y}^*} \tag{14.24}$$

where the confidence coefficient is $1 - \alpha$ and $t_{\alpha/2}$ is based on the t distribution with $n - 2$ degrees of freedom.

Using expression (14.24) to develop a 95% confidence interval of the mean quarterly sales for all Armand's restaurants located near campuses with 10,000 students, we need the value of t for $\alpha/2 = .025$ and $n - 2 = 10 - 2 = 8$ degrees of freedom. Using Table 2 of Appendix B, we have $t_{.025} = 2.306$. Thus, with $\hat{y}^* = 110$ and a margin of error of $t_{\alpha/2} s_{\hat{y}^*} = 2.306(4.95) = 11.415$, the 95% confidence interval estimate is

$$110 \pm 11.415$$

In dollars, the 95% confidence interval for the mean quarterly sales of all restaurants near campuses with 10,000 students is $110,000 \pm $11,415. Therefore, the 95% confidence interval for the mean quarterly sales when the student population is 10,000 is $98,585 to $121,415.

Note that the estimated standard deviation of $\hat{y}^*$ given by equation (14.23) is smallest when $x^* - \bar{x} = 0$. In this case the estimated standard deviation of $\hat{y}^*$ becomes

$$s_{\hat{y}^*} = s \sqrt{\frac{1}{n} + \frac{(\bar{x} - \bar{x})^2}{\Sigma(x_i - \bar{x})^2}} = s \sqrt{\frac{1}{n}}$$

This result implies that we can make the best or most precise estimate of the mean value of y whenever $x^* = \bar{x}$. In fact, the further x^* is from $\bar{x}$, the larger $x^* - \bar{x}$ becomes. As a result, the confidence interval for the mean value of y will become wider as x^* deviates more from $\bar{x}$. This pattern is shown graphically in Figure 14.8.

FIGURE 14.8   CONFIDENCE INTERVALS FOR THE MEAN SALES y AT GIVEN VALUES OF STUDENT
POPULATION x

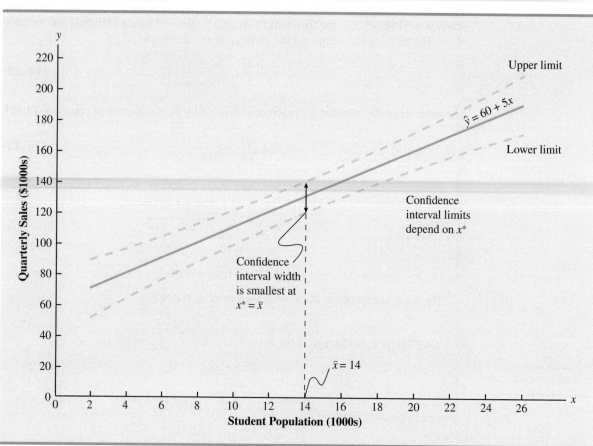

Prediction Interval for an Individual Value of y

Instead of estimating the mean value of quarterly sales for all Armand's restaurants located near campuses with 10,000 students, suppose we want to predict quarterly sales for a new restaurant Armand's is considering building near Talbot College, a campus with 10,000 students. As noted previously, the predictor of y^*, the value of y corresponding to the given x^*, is $\hat{y}^* = b_0 + b_1 x^*$. For the new restaurant located near Talbot College, $x^* = 10$ and the prediction of quarterly sales is $\hat{y}^* = 60 + 5(10) = 110$, or \$110,000. Note that the prediction of quarterly sales for the new Armand's restaurant near Talbot College is the same as the point estimate of the mean sales for all Armand's restaurants located near campuses with 10,000 students.

To develop a prediction interval, let us first determine the variance associated with using $\hat{y}^*$ as a predictor of y when $x = x^*$. This variance is made up of the sum of the following two components.

1. The variance of the y^* values about the mean $E(y^*)$, an estimate of which is given by s^2

2. The variance associated with using $\hat{y}^*$ to estimate $E(y^*)$, an estimate of which is given by $s_{\hat{y}^*}^2$

The formula for estimating the variance corresponding to the prediction of the value of y when $x = x^*$, denoted s^2_{pred}, is

$$s^2_{pred} = s^2 + s^2_{\hat{y}*}$$

$$= s^2 + s^2 \left[\frac{1}{n} + \frac{(x^* - \bar{x})^2}{\Sigma(x_i - \bar{x})^2} \right]$$

$$= s^2 \left[1 + \frac{1}{n} + \frac{(x^* - \bar{x})^2}{\Sigma(x_i - \bar{x})^2} \right] \qquad (14.25)$$

Hence, an estimate of the standard deviation corresponding to the prediction of the value of $y*$ is

$$s_{pred} = s \sqrt{1 + \frac{1}{n} + \frac{(x^* - \bar{x})^2}{\Sigma(x_i - \bar{x})^2}} \qquad (14.26)$$

For Armand's Pizza Parlors, the estimated standard deviation corresponding to the prediction of quarterly sales for a new restaurant located near Talbot College, a campus with 10,000 students, is computed as follows.

$$s_{pred} = 13.829 \sqrt{1 + \frac{1}{10} + \frac{(10 - 14)^2}{568}}$$

$$= 13.829 \sqrt{1.282}$$

$$= 14.69$$

The general expression for a prediction interval follows.

PREDICTION INTERVAL FOR $y*$

The margin of error associated with this prediction interval is $t_{\alpha/2} s_{pred}$.

$$\hat{y}* \pm t_{\alpha/2} s_{pred} \qquad (14.27)$$

where the confidence coefficient is $1 - \alpha$ and $t_{\alpha/2}$ is based on a t distribution with $n - 2$ degrees of freedom.

The 95% prediction interval for quarterly sales for the new Armand's restaurant located near Talbot College can be found using $t_{\alpha/2} = t_{.025} = 2.306$ and $s_{pred} = 14.69$. Thus, with $\hat{y}* = 110$ and a margin of error of $t_{.025} s_{pred} = 2.306(14.69) = 33.875$, the 95% prediction interval is

$$110 \pm 33.875$$

In dollars, this prediction interval is $\$110,000 \pm \$33,875$ or $\$76,125$ to $\$143,875$. Note that the prediction interval for the new restaurant located near Talbot College, a campus with 10,000 students, is wider than the confidence interval for the mean quarterly sales of all restaurants located near campuses with 10,000 students. The difference reflects the fact that we are able to estimate the mean value of y more precisely than we can predict an individual value of y.

FIGURE 14.9 CONFIDENCE AND PREDICTION INTERVALS FOR SALES y AT GIVEN VALUES OF STUDENT POPULATION x

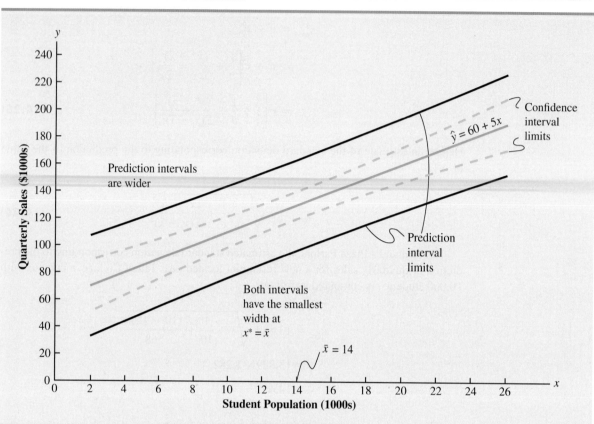

In general, the lines for the confidence interval limits and the prediction interval limits both have curvature.

Confidence intervals and prediction intervals are both more precise when the value of the independent variable x^* is closer to $\bar{x}$. The general shapes of confidence intervals and the wider prediction intervals are shown together in Figure 14.9.

A prediction interval is used to predict the value of the dependent variable y for a *new observation*. As an illustration, we showed how to develop a prediction interval of quarterly sales for a new restaurant that Armand's is considering building near Talbot College, a campus with 10,000 students. The fact that the value of $x = 10$ is not one of the values of student population for the Armand's sample data in Table 14.1 is not meant to imply that prediction intervals cannot be developed for values of x in the sample data. But, for the ten restaurants that make up the data in Table 14.1, developing a prediction interval for quarterly sales for *one of these restaurants* does not make any sense because we already know the value of quarterly sales for each of these restaurants. In other words, a prediction interval only has meaning for something new, in this case a new observation corresponding to a particular value of x that may or may not equal one of the values of x in the sample.

Exercises

Methods

SELF*test*

32.   The data from exercise 1 follow.

x_i	1	2	3	4	5
y_i	3	7	5	11	14

   a.   Use equation (14.23) to estimate the standard deviation of $\hat{y}^*$ when $x = 4$.
   b.   Use expression (14.24) to develop a 95% confidence interval for the expected value of y when $x = 4$.
   c.   Use equation (14.26) to estimate the standard deviation of an individual value of y when $x = 4$.
   d.   Use expression (14.27) to develop a 95% prediction interval for y when $x = 4$.

33.   The data from exercise 2 follow.

x_i	3	12	6	20	14
y_i	55	40	55	10	15

   a.   Estimate the standard deviation of $\hat{y}^*$ when $x = 8$.
   b.   Develop a 95% confidence interval for the expected value of y when $x = 8$.
   c.   Estimate the standard deviation of an individual value of y when $x = 8$.
   d.   Develop a 95% prediction interval for y when $x = 8$.

34.   The data from exercise 3 follow.

x_i	2	6	9	13	20
y_i	7	18	9	26	23

Develop the 95% confidence and prediction intervals when $x = 12$. Explain why these two intervals are different.

Applications

SELF*test*

35.   The following data are the monthly salaries y and the grade point averages x for students who obtained a bachelor's degree in business administration.

GPA	Monthly Salary ($)
2.6	3600
3.4	3900
3.6	4300
3.2	3800
3.5	4200
2.9	3900

The estimated regression equation for these data is $\hat{y} = 2090.5 + 581.1x$ and MSE = 21,284.
   a.   Develop a point estimate of the starting salary for a student with a GPA of 3.0.
   b.   Develop a 95% confidence interval for the mean starting salary for all students with a 3.0 GPA.
   c.   Develop a 95% prediction interval for Ryan Dailey, a student with a GPA of 3.0.
   d.   Discuss the differences in your answers to parts (b) and (c).

36. In exercise 7, the data on y = annual sales ($1000s) for new customer accounts and x = number of years of experience for a sample of 10 salespersons provided the estimated regression equation $\hat{y} = 80 + 4x$. For these data $\bar{x} = 7$, $\Sigma(x_i - \bar{x})^2 = 142$, and $s = 4.6098$.
   a. Develop a 95% confidence interval for the mean annual sales for all salespersons with nine years of experience.
   b. The company is considering hiring Tom Smart, a salesperson with nine years of experience. Develop a 95% prediction interval of annual sales for Tom Smart.
   c. Discuss the differences in your answers to parts (a) and (b).

37. In exercise 13, data were given on the adjusted gross income x and the amount of itemized deductions taken by taxpayers. Data were reported in thousands of dollars. With the estimated regression equation $\hat{y} = 4.68 + .16x$, the point estimate of a reasonable level of total itemized deductions for a taxpayer with an adjusted gross income of $52,500 is $13,080.
   a. Develop a 95% confidence interval for the mean amount of total itemized deductions for all taxpayers with an adjusted gross income of $52,500.
   b. Develop a 95% prediction interval estimate for the amount of total itemized deductions for a particular taxpayer with an adjusted gross income of $52,500.
   c. If the particular taxpayer referred to in part (b) claimed total itemized deductions of $20,400, would the IRS agent's request for an audit appear to be justified?
   d. Use your answer to part (b) to give the IRS agent a guideline as to the amount of total itemized deductions a taxpayer with an adjusted gross income of $52,500 should claim before an audit is recommended.

38. Refer to exercise 21, where data on the production volume x and total cost y for a particular manufacturing operation were used to develop the estimated regression equation $\hat{y} = 1246.67 + 7.6x$.
   a. The company's production schedule shows that 500 units must be produced next month. What is the point estimate of the total cost for next month?
   b. Develop a 99% prediction interval for the total cost for next month.
   c. If an accounting cost report at the end of next month shows that the actual production cost during the month was $6000, should managers be concerned about incurring such a high total cost for the month? Discuss.

39. In exercise 12, the following data on x = average daily hotel room rate and y = amount spent on entertainment (*The Wall Street Journal*, August 18, 2011) lead to the estimated regression equation $\hat{y} = 17.49 + 1.0334x$. For these data SSE = 1541.4.

City	Room Rate ($)	Entertainment ($)
Boston	148	161
Denver	96	105
Nashville	91	101
New Orleans	110	142
Phoenix	90	100
San Diego	102	120
San Francisco	136	167
San Jose	90	140
Tampa	82	98

   a. Predict the amount spent on entertainment for a particular city that has a daily room rate of $89.
   b. Develop a 95% confidence interval for the mean amount spent on entertainment for all cities that have a daily room rate of $89.
   c. The average room rate in Chicago is $128. Develop a 95% prediction interval for the amount spent on entertainment in Chicago.

(14.7) Computer Solution

Performing the regression analysis computations without the help of a computer can be quite time consuming. In this section we discuss how the computational burden can be minimized by using a computer software package such as Minitab.

We entered Armand's student population and sales data into a Minitab worksheet. The independent variable was named Population and the dependent variable was named Sales to assist with interpretation of the computer output. Using Minitab, we obtained the printout for Armand's Pizza Parlors shown in Figure 14.10.[2]

We have highlighted the portions of the output that are topics we have previously discussed in this chapter (the portions of the output not highlighted are beyond the scope of this text, but can be found in more advanced statistics texts).

FIGURE 14.10 MINITAB OUTPUT FOR THE ARMAND'S PIZZA PARLORS PROBLEM

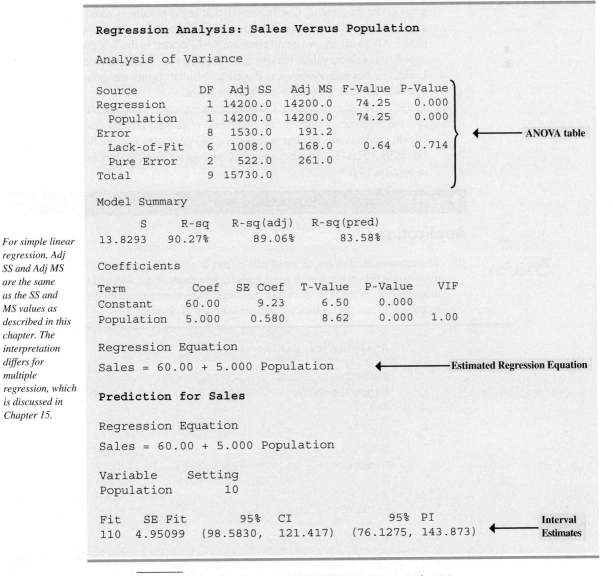

For simple linear regression, Adj SS and Adj MS are the same as the SS and MS values as described in this chapter. The interpretation differs for multiple regression, which is discussed in Chapter 15.

```
Regression Analysis: Sales Versus Population

Analysis of Variance

Source         DF   Adj SS   Adj MS  F-Value  P-Value
Regression      1  14200.0  14200.0    74.25    0.000
  Population     1  14200.0  14200.0    74.25    0.000
Error           8   1530.0    191.2
  Lack-of-Fit   6   1008.0    168.0     0.64    0.714
  Pure Error    2    522.0    261.0
Total           9  15730.0                              ◄── ANOVA table

Model Summary

      S     R-sq   R-sq(adj)   R-sq(pred)
13.8293   90.27%     89.06%       83.58%

Coefficients

Term          Coef  SE Coef  T-Value  P-Value   VIF
Constant     60.00     9.23     6.50    0.000
Population    5.000    0.580     8.62    0.000  1.00

Regression Equation

Sales = 60.00 + 5.000 Population         ◄──── Estimated Regression Equation

Prediction for Sales

Regression Equation

Sales = 60.00 + 5.000 Population


Variable    Setting
Population        10


Fit    SE Fit        95%  CI            95%  PI          Interval
110   4.95099  (98.5830,  121.417)  (76.1275, 143.873)  ◄── Estimates
```

The interpretation of the highlighted portion of the printout follows.

1. The ANOVA table is printed below the heading Analysis of Variance. Minitab uses the label Error for the error source of variation. Note that DF is an abbreviation for degrees of freedom and that MSR is given in the Regression row under the column Adj MS as 14,200 and MSE is given in the Error row under Adj MS as 191.2. The ratio of these two values provides the F value of 74.25 and the corresponding p-value of 0.000. Because the p-value is zero (to three decimal places), the relationship between Sales and Population is judged statistically significant.

2. Under the heading Model Summary, Minitab prints the standard error of the estimate, $s = 13.8293$, as well as information about the goodness of fit. Note that "R-sq = 90.27%" is the coefficient of determination expressed as a percentage. The value "R-Sq(adj) = 89.06%" is discussed in Chapter 15.

3. A table is printed that shows the values of the coefficients b_0 and b_1, the standard deviation of each coefficient, the t value obtained by dividing each coefficient value by its standard deviation, and the p-value associated with the t test. This appears under the heading Coefficients. Because the p-value is zero (to three decimal places), the sample results indicate that the null hypothesis ($H_0: \beta_1 = 0$) should be rejected. Alternatively, we could compare 8.62 (located in the T-Value column) to the appropriate critical value. This procedure for the t test was described in Section 14.5.

4. Under the heading Regression Equation, Minitab prints the estimated regression equation as Sales = 60.00 + 5.000 Population.

5. The 95% confidence interval estimate of the expected sales and the 95% prediction interval estimate of sales for an individual restaurant located near a campus with 10,000 students are printed below the ANOVA table. The confidence interval is (98.5830, 121.4417) and the prediction interval is (76.1275, 143.873) as we showed in Section 14.6.

Exercises

Applications

SELF*test*

40. The commercial division of a real estate firm is conducting a regression analysis of the relationship between x, annual gross rents (in thousands of dollars), and y, selling price (in thousands of dollars) for apartment buildings. Data were collected on several properties recently sold and the following computer output was obtained.

```
Analysis of Variance

SOURCE          DF      Adj SS
Regression       1      41587.3
Error            7
Total            8      51984.1

Predictor       Coef     SE Coef     T-Value
Constant      20.000      3.2213        6.21
X              7.210      1.3626        5.29

Regression Equation

Y = 20.0 + 7.21 X
```

a. How many apartment buildings were in the sample?
b. Write the estimated regression equation.

 c. What is the value of s_{b_1}?

 d. Use the F statistic to test the significance of the relationship at a .05 level of significance.

 e. Predict the selling price of an apartment building with gross annual rents of $50,000.

41. Following is a portion of the computer output for a regression analysis relating y = maintenance expense (dollars per month) to x = usage (hours per week) of a particular brand of computer terminal.

```
Analysis of Variance

SOURCE          DF      Adj SS      Adj MS
Regression       1     1575.76     1575.76
Error            8      349.14       43.64
Total            9     1924.90


Predictor      Coef     SE Coef
Constant     6.1092      0.9361
X            0.8951      0.1490


Regression Equation

Y = 6.1092 + .8951 X
```

 a. Write the estimated regression equation.

 b. Use a t test to determine whether monthly maintenance expense is related to usage at the .05 level of significance.

 c. Use the estimated regression equation to predict monthly maintenance expense for any terminal that is used 25 hours per week.

42. A regression model relating x, number of salespersons at a branch office, to y, annual sales at the office (in thousands of dollars) provided the following computer output from a regression analysis of the data.

```
Analysis of Variance

SOURCE          DF      Adj SS      Adj MS
Regression       1      6828.6      6828.6
Error           28      2298.8       82.1
Total           29      9127.4


Predictor      Coef     SE Coef        T
Constant      80.0      11.333      7.06
X             50.0       5.482      9.12


Regression Equation

Y = 80.0 + 50.00 X
```

 a. Write the estimated regression equation.

 b. How many branch offices were involved in the study?

c. Compute the F statistic and test the significance of the relationship at a .05 level of significance.

d. Predict the annual sales at the Memphis branch office. This branch employs 12 salespersons.

43. A 2012 suvey conducted by Idea Works provided data showing the percentage of seats available when customers try to redeem points or miles for free travel. For each airline listed, the column labeled 2011 Percentage shows the percentage of seats available in 2011 and the column labeled 2012 shows the correponding percentage in 2012 (*The Wall Street Journal*, May 17, 2012).

DATA file

AirlineSeats

Airline	2011 Percentage	2012 Percentage
AirBerlin	96.4	100.0
Air Canada	82.1	78.6
Air France, KLM	65.0	55.7
AirTran Airways	47.1	87.1
Alaska Airlines	64.3	59.3
American Airlines	62.9	45.7
British Airways	61.4	79.3
Cathay Pacific	66.4	70.7
Delta Air Lines	27.1	27.1
Emirates	35.7	32.9
GOL Airlines (Brazil)	100.0	97.1
Iberia	70.7	63.6
JetBlue	79.3	86.4
Lan (Chile)	75.7	78.6
Lufthansa, Swiss, Austrian	85.0	92.1
Qantas	75.0	78.6
SAS Scandinavian	52.9	57.9
Singapore Airlines	90.7	90.7
Southwest	99.3	100.0
Turkish Airways	49.3	38.6
United Airlines	71.4	87.1
US Airways	25.7	33.6
Virgin Australia	91.4	90.0

a. Develop a scatter diagram with 2011 Percentage as the independent variable.

b. What does the scatter diagram developed in part (a) indicate about the relationship between the two variables?

c. Develop the estimated regression equation.

d. Test for a significant relationship. Use $\alpha = .05$.

e. Did the estimated regression equation provide a good fit?

44. Automobile racing, high-performance driving schools, and driver education programs run by automobile clubs continue to grow in popularity. All these activities require the participant to wear a helmet that is certified by the Snell Memorial Foundation, a not-for-profit organization dedicated to research, education, testing, and development of helmet safety standards. Snell "SA" (Sports Application)-rated professional helmets are designed for auto racing and provide extreme impact resistance and high fire protection. One of the key factors in selecting a helmet is weight, since lower weight helmets tend to place less stress on the neck. Consider the following data showing the weight and price for 18 SA helmets.

Weight (oz)	Price ($)
64	248
64	278
64	200
64	200
58	300
47	700
49	900
59	340
66	199
58	299
58	299
52	479
52	479
63	369
62	369
54	559
63	250
63	280

DATA *file*

RaceHelmets

a. Develop a scatter diagram with weight as the independent variable.
b. Does there appear to be any relationship between these two variables?
c. Develop the estimated regression equation that could be used to predict the price given the weight.
d. Test for the significance of the relationship at the .05 level of significance.
e. Did the estimated regression equation provide a good fit? Explain.

(14.8) Residual Analysis: Validating Model Assumptions

Residual analysis is the primary tool for determining whether the assumed regression model is appropriate.

As we noted previously, the *residual* for observation i is the difference between the observed value of the dependent variable (y_i) and the predicted value of the dependent variable ($\hat{y}_i$).

RESIDUAL FOR OBSERVATION i

$$y_i - \hat{y}_i \qquad (14.28)$$

where

y_i is the observed value of the dependent variable
$\hat{y}_i$ is the predicted value of the dependent variable

In other words, the ith residual is the error resulting from using the estimated regression equation to predict the value of the dependent variable. The residuals for the Armand's Pizza Parlors example are computed in Table 14.7. The observed values of the dependent variable are in the second column and the predicted values of the dependent variable, obtained using the estimated regression equation $\hat{y} = 60 + 5x$, are in the third column. An analysis of the corresponding residuals in the fourth column will help determine whether the assumptions made about the regression model are appropriate.

TABLE 14.7   RESIDUALS FOR ARMAND'S PIZZA PARLORS

Student Population x_i	Sales y_i	Predicted Sales $\hat{y}_i = 60 + 5x_i$	Residuals $y_i - \hat{y}_i$
2	58	70	−12
6	105	90	15
8	88	100	−12
8	118	100	18
12	117	120	−3
16	137	140	−3
20	157	160	−3
20	169	160	9
22	149	170	−21
26	202	190	12

Let us now review the regression assumptions for the Armand's Pizza Parlors example. A simple linear regression model was assumed.

$$y = \beta_0 + \beta_1 x + \epsilon \tag{14.29}$$

This model indicates that we assumed quarterly sales (y) to be a linear function of the size of the student population (x) plus an error term ϵ. In Section 14.4 we made the following assumptions about the error term ϵ.

1. $E(\epsilon) = 0$.
2. The variance of ϵ, denoted by σ^2, is the same for all values of x.
3. The values of ϵ are independent.
4. The error term ϵ has a normal distribution.

These assumptions provide the theoretical basis for the t test and the F test used to determine whether the relationship between x and y is significant, and for the confidence and prediction interval estimates presented in Section 14.6. If the assumptions about the error term ϵ appear questionable, the hypothesis tests about the significance of the regression relationship and the interval estimation results may not be valid.

The residuals provide the best information about ϵ; hence an analysis of the residuals is an important step in determining whether the assumptions for ϵ are appropriate. Much of residual analysis is based on an examination of graphical plots. In this section, we discuss the following residual plots.

1. A plot of the residuals against values of the independent variable x
2. A plot of residuals against the predicted values of the dependent variable y
3. A standardized residual plot
4. A normal probability plot

Residual Plot Against x

A **residual plot** against the independent variable x is a graph in which the values of the independent variable are represented by the horizontal axis and the corresponding residual values are represented by the vertical axis. A point is plotted for each residual. The first coordinate for each point is given by the value of x_i and the second coordinate is given by the corresponding value of the residual $y_i - \hat{y}_i$. For a residual plot against x with the Armand's Pizza Parlors data from Table 14.7, the coordinates of the first point are $(2, -12)$, corresponding to $x_1 = 2$ and $y_1 - \hat{y}_1 = -12$; the coordinates of the second point are $(6, 15)$, corresponding to $x_2 = 6$ and $y_2 - \hat{y}_2 = 15$; and so on. Figure 14.11 shows the resulting residual plot.

FIGURE 14.11 PLOT OF THE RESIDUALS AGAINST THE INDEPENDENT VARIABLE x FOR ARMAND'S PIZZA PARLORS

Before interpreting the results for this residual plot, let us consider some general patterns that might be observed in any residual plot. Three examples appear in Figure 14.12. If the assumption that the variance of ϵ is the same for all values of x and the assumed regression model is an adequate representation of the relationship between the variables, the residual plot should give an overall impression of a horizontal band of points such as the one in Panel A of Figure 14.12. However, if the variance of ϵ is not the same for all values of x—for example, if variability about the regression line is greater for larger values of x—a pattern such as the one in Panel B of Figure 14.12 could be observed. In this case, the assumption of a constant variance of ϵ is violated. Another possible residual plot is shown in Panel C. In this case, we would conclude that the assumed regression model is not an adequate representation of the relationship between the variables. A curvilinear regression model or multiple regression model should be considered.

Now let us return to the residual plot for Armand's Pizza Parlors shown in Figure 14.11. The residuals appear to approximate the horizontal pattern in Panel A of Figure 14.12. Hence, we conclude that the residual plot does not provide evidence that the assumptions made for Armand's regression model should be challenged. At this point, we are confident in the conclusion that Armand's simple linear regression model is valid.

Experience and good judgment are always factors in the effective interpretation of residual plots. Seldom does a residual plot conform precisely to one of the patterns in Figure 14.12. Yet analysts who frequently conduct regression studies and frequently review residual plots become adept at understanding the differences between patterns that are reasonable and patterns that indicate the assumptions of the model should be questioned. A residual plot provides one technique to assess the validity of the assumptions for a regression model.

Residual Plot Against $\hat{y}$

Another residual plot represents the predicted value of the dependent variable $\hat{y}$ on the horizontal axis and the residual values on the vertical axis. A point is plotted for each residual.

FIGURE 14.12   RESIDUAL PLOTS FROM THREE REGRESSION STUDIES

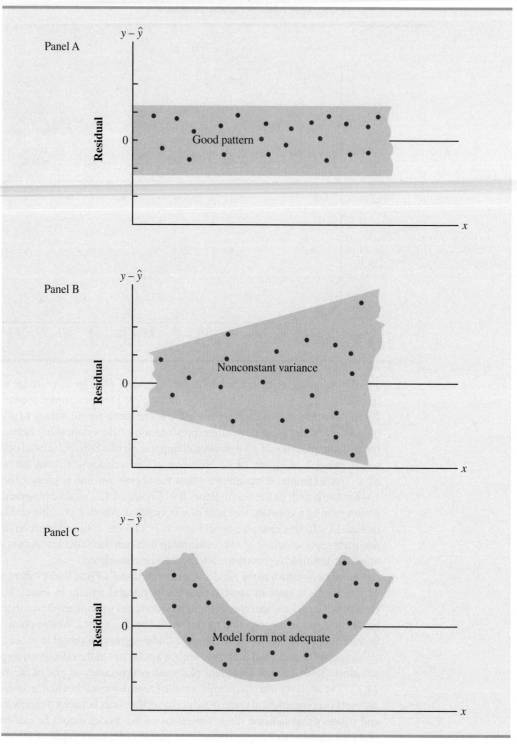

FIGURE 14.13   PLOT OF THE RESIDUALS AGAINST THE PREDICTED VALUES y FOR ARMAND'S PIZZA PARLORS

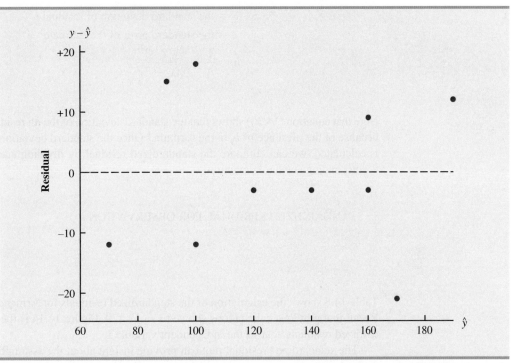

The first coordinate for each point is given by $\hat{y}_i$ and the second coordinate is given by the corresponding value of the ith residual $y_i - \hat{y}_i$. With the Armand's data from Table 14.7, the coordinates of the first point are $(70, -12)$, corresponding to $\hat{y}_1 = 70$ and $y_1 - \hat{y}_1 = -12$; the coordinates of the second point are $(90, 15)$; and so on. Figure 14.13 provides the residual plot. Note that the pattern of this residual plot is the same as the pattern of the residual plot against the independent variable x. It is not a pattern that would lead us to question the model assumptions. For simple linear regression, both the residual plot against x and the residual plot against $\hat{y}$ provide the same pattern. For multiple regression analysis, the residual plot against $\hat{y}$ is more widely used because of the presence of more than one independent variable.

Standardized Residuals

Many of the residual plots provided by computer software packages use a standardized version of the residuals. As demonstrated in preceding chapters, a random variable is standardized by subtracting its mean and dividing the result by its standard deviation. With the least squares method, the mean of the residuals is zero. Thus, simply dividing each residual by its standard deviation provides the **standardized residual**.

It can be shown that the standard deviation of residual i depends on the standard error of the estimate s and the corresponding value of the independent variable x_i.

STANDARD DEVIATION OF THE ith RESIDUAL[3]

$$s_{y_i - \hat{y}_i} = s\sqrt{1 - h_i} \qquad (14.30)$$

---

[3]This equation actually provides an estimate of the standard deviation of the ith residual, because s is used instead of σ.

where

$$s_{y_i - \hat{y}_i} = \text{the standard deviation of residual } i$$
$$s = \text{the standard error of the estimate}$$
$$h_i = \frac{1}{n} + \frac{(x_i - \bar{x})^2}{\Sigma(x_i - \bar{x})^2} \qquad (14.31)$$

Note that equation (14.30) shows that the standard deviation of the ith residual depends on x_i because of the presence of h_i in the formula.[4] Once the standard deviation of each residual is calculated, we can compute the standardized residual by dividing each residual by its corresponding standard deviation.

STANDARDIZED RESIDUAL FOR OBSERVATION i

$$\frac{y_i - \hat{y}_i}{s_{y_i - \hat{y}_i}} \qquad (14.32)$$

Table 14.8 shows the calculation of the standardized residuals for Armand's Pizza Parlors. Recall that previous calculations showed $s = 13.829$. Figure 14.14 is the plot of the standardized residuals against the independent variable x.

Small departures from normality do not have a great effect on the statistical tests used in regression analysis.

The standardized residual plot can provide insight about the assumption that the error term ϵ has a normal distribution. If this assumption is satisfied, the distribution of the standardized residuals should appear to come from a standard normal probability distribution.[5] Thus, when looking at a standardized residual plot, we should expect to see approximately 95% of the standardized residuals between -2 and $+2$. We see in Figure 14.14 that for the

TABLE 14.8   COMPUTATION OF STANDARDIZED RESIDUALS FOR ARMAND'S PIZZA PARLORS

Restaurant i	x_i	$x_i - \bar{x}$	$(x_i - \bar{x})^2$	$\dfrac{(x_i - \bar{x})^2}{S(x_i - \bar{x})^2}$	h_i	$s_{y_i - \hat{y}_i}$	$y_i - \hat{y}_i$	Standardized Residual
1	2	−12	144	.2535	.3535	11.1193	−12	−1.0792
2	6	−8	64	.1127	.2127	12.2709	15	1.2224
3	8	−6	36	.0634	.1634	12.6493	−12	−.9487
4	8	−6	36	.0634	.1634	12.6493	18	1.4230
5	12	−2	4	.0070	.1070	13.0682	−3	−.2296
6	16	2	4	.0070	.1070	13.0682	−3	−.2296
7	20	6	36	.0634	.1634	12.6493	−3	−.2372
8	20	6	36	.0634	.1634	12.6493	9	.7115
9	22	8	64	.1127	.2127	12.2709	−21	−1.7114
10	26	12	144	.2535	.3535	11.1193	12	1.0792
		Total	568					

Note: The values of the residuals were computed in Table 14.7.

---

[4] h_i is referred to as the *leverage* of observation i. Leverage will be discussed further when we consider influential observations in Section 14.9.

[5] Because s is used instead of σ in equation (14.30), the probability distribution of the standardized residuals is not technically normal. However, in most regression studies, the sample size is large enough that a normal approximation is very good.

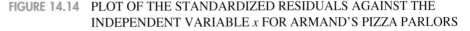

FIGURE 14.14   PLOT OF THE STANDARDIZED RESIDUALS AGAINST THE
INDEPENDENT VARIABLE *x* FOR ARMAND'S PIZZA PARLORS

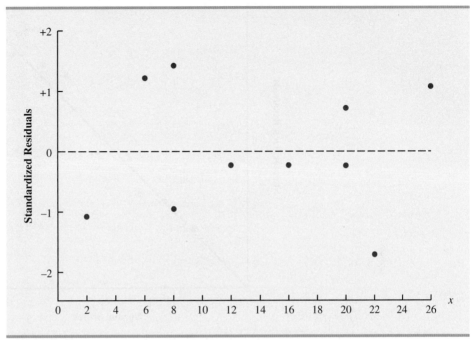

TABLE 14.9

NORMAL SCORES
FOR $n = 10$

Order Statistic	Normal Score
1	−1.55
2	−1.00
3	−.65
4	−.37
5	−.12
6	.12
7	.37
8	.65
9	1.00
10	1.55

TABLE 14.10

NORMAL SCORES
AND ORDERED
STANDARDIZED
RESIDUALS FOR
ARMAND'S PIZZA
PARLORS

Normal Scores	Ordered Standardized Residuals
−1.55	−1.7114
−1.00	−1.0792
−.65	−.9487
−.37	−.2372
−.12	−.2296
.12	−.2296
.37	.7115
.65	1.0792
1.00	1.2224
1.55	1.4230

Armand's example all standardized residuals are between −2 and +2. Therefore, on the basis of the standardized residuals, this plot gives us no reason to question the assumption that ϵ has a normal distribution.

Because of the effort required to compute the estimated values of $\hat{y}$, the residuals, and the standardized residuals, most statistical packages provide these values as optional regression output. Hence, residual plots can be easily obtained. For large problems computer packages are the only practical means for developing the residual plots discussed in this section.

Normal Probability Plot

Another approach for determining the validity of the assumption that the error term has a normal distribution is the **normal probability plot**. To show how a normal probability plot is developed, we introduce the concept of *normal scores*.

Suppose 10 values are selected randomly from a normal probability distribution with a mean of zero and a standard deviation of one, and that the sampling process is repeated over and over with the values in each sample of 10 ordered from smallest to largest. For now, let us consider only the smallest value in each sample. The random variable representing the smallest value obtained in repeated sampling is called the first-order statistic.

Statisticians show that for samples of size 10 from a standard normal probability distribution, the expected value of the first-order statistic is −1.55. This expected value is called a normal score. For the case with a sample of size $n = 10$, there are 10 order statistics and 10 normal scores (see Table 14.9). In general, a data set consisting of n observations will have n order statistics and hence n normal scores.

Let us now show how the 10 normal scores can be used to determine whether the standardized residuals for Armand's Pizza Parlors appear to come from a standard normal probability distribution. We begin by ordering the 10 standardized residuals from Table 14.8. The 10 normal scores and the ordered standardized residuals are shown together in Table 14.10. If the normality assumption is satisfied, the smallest standardized residual should be close to the

FIGURE 14.15 NORMAL PROBABILITY PLOT FOR ARMAND'S PIZZA PARLORS

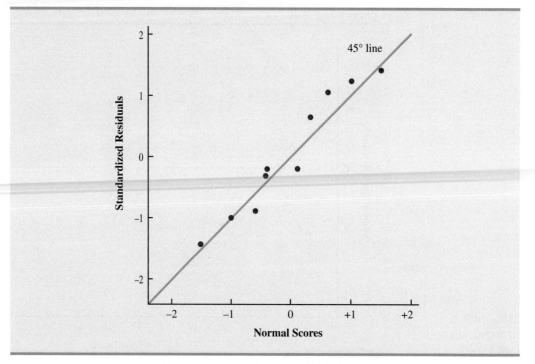

smallest normal score, the next smallest standardized residual should be close to the next small-est normal score, and so on. If we were to develop a plot with the normal scores on the horizontal axis and the corresponding standardized residuals on the vertical axis, the plotted points should cluster closely around a 45-degree line passing through the origin if the standardized residuals are approximately normally distributed. Such a plot is referred to as a *normal probability plot*.

Figure 14.15 is the normal probability plot for the Armand's Pizza Parlors example. Judgment is used to determine whether the pattern observed deviates from the line enough to conclude that the standardized residuals are not from a standard normal probability distribution. In Figure 14.15, we see that the points are grouped closely about the line. We therefore conclude that the assumption of the error term having a normal probability distribution is reasonable. In general, the more closely the points are clustered about the 45-degree line, the stronger the evidence supporting the normality assumption. Any sub-stantial curvature in the normal probability plot is evidence that the residuals have not come from a normal distribution. Normal scores and the associated normal probability plot can be obtained easily from statistical packages such as Minitab.

NOTES AND COMMENTS

1. We use residual and normal probability plots to validate the assumptions of a regression model. If our review indicates that one or more assumptions are questionable, a different regression model or a transformation of the data should be considered. The appropriate corrective action when the assumptions are violated must be based on good judgment; recommendations from an experienced statistician can be valuable.

2. Analysis of residuals is the primary method statisticians use to verify that the assumptions associated with a regression model are valid. Even if no violations are found, it does not necessarily follow that the model will yield good predictions. However, if additional statistical tests support the conclusion of significance and the coefficient of determination is large, we should be able to develop good estimates and predictions using the estimated regression equation.

Exercises

Methods

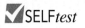

45. Given are data for two variables, x and y.

x_i	6	11	15	18	20
y_i	6	8	12	20	30

a. Develop an estimated regression equation for these data.
b. Compute the residuals.
c. Develop a plot of the residuals against the independent variable x. Do the assumptions about the error terms seem to be satisfied?
d. Compute the standardized residuals.
e. Develop a plot of the standardized residuals against $\hat{y}$. What conclusions can you draw from this plot?

46. The following data were used in a regression study.

Observation	x_i	y_i	Observation	x_i	y_i
1	2	4	6	7	6
2	3	5	7	7	9
3	4	4	8	8	5
4	5	6	9	9	11
5	7	4			

a. Develop an estimated regression equation for these data.
b. Construct a plot of the residuals. Do the assumptions about the error term seem to be satisfied?

Applications

47. Data on advertising expenditures and revenue (in thousands of dollars) for the Four Seasons Restaurant follow.

Advertising Expenditures	Revenue
1	19
2	32
4	44
6	40
10	52
14	53
20	54

a. Let x equal advertising expenditures and y equal revenue. Use the method of least squares to develop a straight line approximation of the relationship between the two variables.
b. Test whether revenue and advertising expenditures are related at a .05 level of significance.
c. Prepare a residual plot of $y - \hat{y}$ versus $\hat{y}$. Use the result from part (a) to obtain the values of $\hat{y}$.
d. What conclusions can you draw from residual analysis? Should this model be used, or should we look for a better one?

48. Refer to exercise 7, where an estimated regression equation relating years of experience and annual sales was developed.
    a. Compute the residuals and construct a residual plot for this problem.
    b. Do the assumptions about the error terms seem reasonable in light of the residual plot?

49. In 2011 home prices and mortgage rates dropped so low that in a number of cities the monthly cost of owning a home was less expensive than renting. The following data show the average asking rent for 10 markets and the monthly mortgage on the median priced home (including taxes and insurance) for 10 cities where the average monthly mortgage payment was less than the average asking rent (*The Wall Street Journal*, November 26–27, 2011).

DATA *file*

RentMortgage

City	Rent ($)	Mortgage ($)
Atlanta	840	539
Chicago	1062	1002
Detroit	823	626
Jacksonville, Fla.	779	711
Las Vegas	796	655
Miami	1071	977
Minneapolis	953	776
Orlando, Fla.	851	695
Phoenix	762	651
St. Louis	723	654

a. Develop the estimated regression equation that can be used to predict the monthly mortgage given the average asking rent.
b. Construct a residual plot against the independent variable.
c. Do the assumptions about the error term and model form seem reasonable in light of the residual plot?

(14.9) Residual Analysis: Outliers and Influential Observations

In Section 14.8 we showed how residual analysis could be used to determine when violations of assumptions about the regression model occur. In this section, we discuss how residual analysis can be used to identify observations that can be classified as outliers or as being especially influential in determining the estimated regression equation. Some steps that should be taken when such observations occur are discussed.

Detecting Outliers

Figure 14.16 is a scatter diagram for a data set that contains an **outlier**, a data point (observation) that does not fit the trend shown by the remaining data. Outliers represent observations that are suspect and warrant careful examination. They may represent erroneous data; if so, the data should be corrected. They may signal a violation of model assumptions; if so, another model should be considered. Finally, they may simply be unusual values that occurred by chance. In this case, they should be retained.

To illustrate the process of detecting outliers, consider the data set in Table 14.11; Figure 14.17 is a scatter diagram. Except for observation 4 ($x_4 = 3$, $y_4 = 75$), a pattern suggesting a negative linear relationship is apparent. Indeed, given the pattern of the rest of the data, we would expect y_4 to be much smaller and hence would identify the corresponding

FIGURE 14.16   DATA SET WITH AN OUTLIER

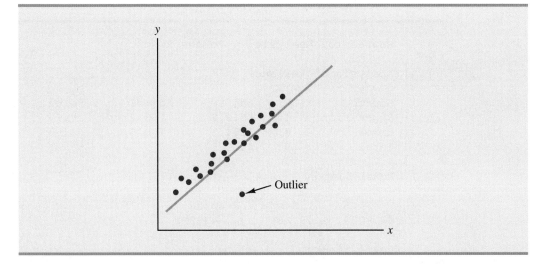

TABLE 14.11	

DATA SET
ILLUSTRATING
THE EFFECT
OF AN OUTLIER

x_i	y_i
1	45
1	55
2	50
3	75
3	40
3	45
4	30
4	35
5	25
6	15

observation as an outlier. For the case of simple linear regression, one can often detect outliers by simply examining the scatter diagram.

The standardized residuals can also be used to identify outliers. If an observation deviates greatly from the pattern of the rest of the data (e.g., the outlier in Figure 14.16), the corresponding standardized residual will be large in absolute value. Many computer packages automatically identify observations with standardized residuals that are large in absolute value. In Figure 14.18 we show a portion of the Minitab output from a regression analysis of the data in Table 14.11. The highlighted portion of the output shows that the standardized residual for observation 4 is 2.67. Minitab provides a list of each observation with a standardized residual of less than −2 or greater than +2 in the Unusual Observation section of the output; in such cases, the observation is printed on a separate line with an R next to the standardized residual, as shown in Figure 14.18. With normally distributed errors, standardized residuals should be outside these limits approximately 5% of the time.

FIGURE 14.17   SCATTER DIAGRAM FOR OUTLIER DATA SET

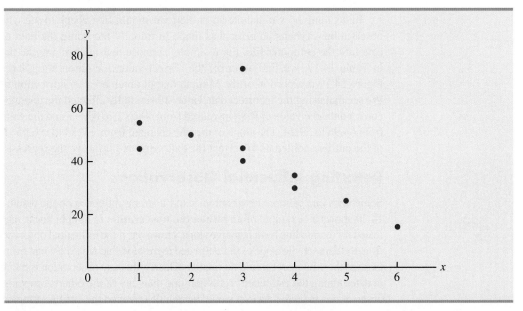

FIGURE 14.18 MINITAB OUTPUT FOR REGRESSION ANALYSIS OF THE OUTLIER DATA SET

```
Regression Analysis: y Versus x

Analysis of Variance

Source        DF    Adj SS    Adj MS    F-Value    P-Value
Regression     1    1268.2    1268.2       7.90      0.023
Error          8    1284.3     160.5
Total          9    2552.5

Model Summary

       S      R-sq    R-sq(adj)
 12.6704    49.68%       43.39%

Coefficients

Term          Coef    SE Coef    T-Value    P-Value
Constant     64.96       9.26       7.02      0.000
x            -7.33       2.61      -2.81      0.023

Regression Equation

y = 64.96 - 7.33 x

Fits and Diagnostics for Unusual Observations

                          Std
Obs       y      Fit    Resid      Resid
  4   75.00    42.97    32.03     2.67  R

R  Large residual
```

In deciding how to handle an outlier, we should first check to see whether it is a valid observation. Perhaps an error was made in initially recording the data or in entering the data into the computer file. For example, suppose that in checking the data for the outlier in Table 14.17, we find an error; the correct value for observation 4 is $x_4 = 3$, $y_4 = 30$. Figure 14.19 is a portion of the Minitab output obtained after correction of the value of y_4. We see that using the incorrect data value substantially affected the goodness of fit. With the correct data, the value of R-sq increased from 49.68% to 83.8% and the value of b_0 decreased from 64.96 to 59.24. The slope of the line changed from -7.33 to -6.95. The identification of the outlier enabled us to correct the data error and improve the regression results.

Detecting Influential Observations

Sometimes one or more observations exert a strong influence on the results obtained. Figure 14.20 shows an example of an **influential observation** in simple linear regression. The estimated regression line has a negative slope. However, if the influential observation were dropped from the data set, the slope of the estimated regression line would change from negative to positive and the y-intercept would be smaller. Clearly, this one observation is much more influential in determining the estimated regression line than any of the others; dropping one of the other observations from the data set would have little effect on the estimated regression equation.

FIGURE 14.19   MINITAB OUTPUT FOR THE REVISED OUTLIER DATA SET

```
Regression Analysis: y Versus x

Analysis of Variance

Source          DF    Adj SS    Adj MS    F-Value   P-Value
Regression       1   1139.66   1139.66     41.38     0.000
Error            8    220.34     27.54
Total            9   1360.00

Model Summary

       S     R-sq    R-sq(adj)
 5.24808   83.80%      81.77%

Coefficients

Term          Coef   SE Coef   T-Value   P-Value
Constant     59.24      3.83     15.45     0.000
x            -6.95      1.08     -6.43     0.000

Regression Equation

y = 59.24 - 6.95 x
```

Influential observations can be identified from a scatter diagram when only one independent variable is present. An influential observation may be an outlier (an observation with a y value that deviates substantially from the trend), it may correspond to an x value far away from its mean (e.g., see Figure 14.20), or it may be caused by a combination of the two (a somewhat off-trend y value and a somewhat extreme x value).

Because influential observations may have such a dramatic effect on the estimated regression equation, they must be examined carefully. We should first check to make sure that no error was made in collecting or recording the data. If an error occurred, it can be corrected and a new estimated regression equation can be developed. If the observation is

FIGURE 14.20   DATA SET WITH AN INFLUENTIAL OBSERVATION

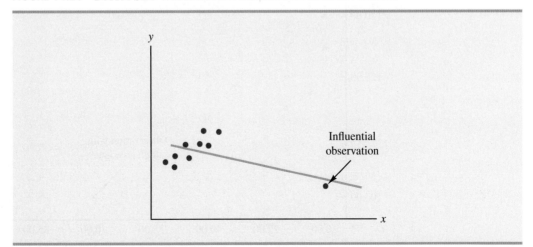

TABLE 14.12

DATA SET WITH A
HIGH LEVERAGE
OBSERVATION

x_i	y_i
10	125
10	130
15	120
20	115
20	120
25	110
70	100

valid, we might consider ourselves fortunate to have it. Such a point, if valid, can contribute to a better understanding of the appropriate model and can lead to a better estimated regression equation. The presence of the influential observation in Figure 14.20, if valid, would suggest trying to obtain data on intermediate values of x to understand better the relationship between x and y.

Observations with extreme values for the independent variables are called **high leverage points**. The influential observation in Figure 14.20 is a point with high leverage. The leverage of an observation is determined by how far the values of the independent variables are from their mean values. For the single-independent-variable case, the leverage of the ith observation, denoted h_i, can be computed by using equation (14.33).

LEVERAGE OF OBSERVATION i

$$h_i = \frac{1}{n} + \frac{(x_i - \bar{x})^2}{\Sigma(x_i - \bar{x})^2} \qquad (14.33)$$

From the formula, it is clear that the farther x_i is from its mean $\bar{x}$, the higher the leverage of observation i.

Many statistical packages automatically identify observations with high leverage as part of the standard regression output. As an illustration of how the Minitab statistical package identifies points with high leverage, let us consider the data set in Table 14.12.

From Figure 14.21, a scatter diagram for the data set in Table 14.12, it is clear that observation 7 ($x = 70$, $y = 100$) is an observation with an extreme value of x. Hence, we would expect it to be identified as a point with high leverage. For this observation, the leverage is computed by using equation (14.33) as follows.

$$h_7 = \frac{1}{n} + \frac{(x_7 - \bar{x})^2}{\Sigma(x_i - \bar{x})^2} = \frac{1}{7} + \frac{(70 - 24.286)^2}{2621.43} = .94$$

FIGURE 14.21   SCATTER DIAGRAM FOR THE DATA SET WITH A HIGH LEVERAGE OBSERVATION

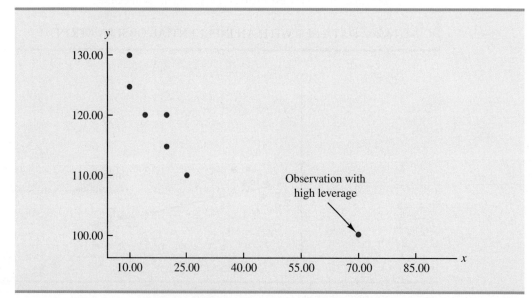

FIGURE 14.22   MINITAB OUTPUT FOR THE DATA SET WITH A HIGH LEVERAGE OBSERVATION

```
Regression Analysis: y Versus x

Analysis of Variance

Source         DF    Adj SS    Adj MS   F-Value   P-Value
Regression      1    473.65    473.65     19.87     0.007
Error           5    119.21     23.84
Total           6    592.86

Model Summary

       S     R-sq    R-sq(adj)
 4.88282   79.89%       75.87%

Coefficients

Term          Coef    SE Coef   T-Value   P-Value
Constant    127.47       2.96     43.04     0.000
x           -0.4251     0.0954     -4.46     0.007

Regression Equation

y = 127.47 - 0.4251 x

Fits and Diagnostics for Unusual Observations

                                     Std
Obs         y      Fit    Resid    Resid
  7    100.00    97.71     2.29     1.91 X

X Unusual X
```

For the case of simple linear regression, Minitab identifies observations as having high leverage if $h_i > 6/n$ or .99, whichever is smaller. For the data set in Table 14.12, $6/n = 6/7 = .86$. Because $h_7 = .94 > .86$, Minitab will identify observation 7 as an observation whose x value gives it large influence. Figure 14.22 shows a portion of the Minitab output for a regression analysis of this data set. Observation 7 ($x = 70$, $y = 100$) is identified as an unusual observation with an unusual x value it is printed on a separate line at the bottom, with an X in the right margin.

Computer software packages are essential for performing the computations to identify influential observations. Minitab's selection rule is discussed here.

Influential observations that are caused by an interaction of large residuals and high leverage can be difficult to detect. Diagnostic procedures are available that take both into account in determining when an observation is influential. One such measure, called Cook's D statistic, will be discussed in Chapter 15.

NOTES AND COMMENTS

Once an observation is identified as potentially influential because of a large residual or high leverage, its impact on the estimated regression equation should be evaluated. More advanced texts discuss diagnostics for doing so. However, if one is not familiar with the more advanced material, a simple procedure is to run the regression analysis with and without the observation. This approach will reveal the influence of the observation on the results.

Exercises

Methods

 SELF*test*

50. Consider the following data for two variables, x and y.

x_i	135	110	130	145	175	160	120
y_i	145	100	120	120	130	130	110

    a. Compute the standardized residuals for these data. Do the data include any outliers? Explain.
    b. Plot the standardized residuals against $\hat{y}$. Does this plot reveal any outliers?
    c. Develop a scatter diagram for these data. Does the scatter diagram indicate any outliers in the data? In general, what implications does this finding have for simple linear regression?

51. Consider the following data for two variables, x and y.

x_i	4	5	7	8	10	12	12	22
y_i	12	14	16	15	18	20	24	19

    a. Compute the standardized residuals for these data. Do the data include any outliers? Explain.
    b. Compute the leverage values for these data. Do there appear to be any influential observations in these data? Explain.
    c. Develop a scatter diagram for these data. Does the scatter diagram indicate any influential observations? Explain.

Applications

52. Charity Navigator is America's leading independent charity evaluator. The following data show the total expenses ($), the percentage of the total budget spent on administrative expenses, the percentage spent on fundraising, and the percentage spent on program expenses for 10 supersized charities (Charity Navigator website, April 12, 2012). Administrative expenses include overhead, administrative staff and associated costs, and organizational meetings. Fundraising expenses are what a charity spends to raise money, and program expenses are what the charity spends on the programs and services it exists to deliver. The sum of the three percentages does not add to 100% because of rounding.

DATA *file*

Charities

Charity	Total Expenses ($)	Administrative Expenses (%)	Fundraising Expenses (%)	Program Expenses (%)
American Red Cross	3,354,177,445	3.9	3.8	92.1
World Vision	1,205,887,020	4.0	7.5	88.3
Smithsonian Institution	1,080,995,083	23.5	2.6	73.7
Food For The Poor	1,050,829,851	.7	2.4	96.8
American Cancer Society	1,003,781,897	6.1	22.2	71.6
Volunteers of America	929,158,968	8.6	1.9	89.4
Dana-Farber Cancer Institute	877,321,613	13.1	1.6	85.2
AmeriCares	854,604,824	.4	.7	98.8
ALSAC—St. Jude Children's Research Hospital	829,662,076	9.6	16.9	73.4
City of Hope	736,176,619	13.7	3.0	83.1

a.   Develop a scatter diagram with fundraising expenses (%) on the horizontal axis and program expenses (%) on the vertical axis. Looking at the data, do there appear to be any outliers and/or influential observations?

b.   Develop an estimated regression equation that could be used to predict program expenses (%) given fundraising expenses (%).

c.   Does the value for the slope of the estimated regression equation make sense in the context of this problem situation?

d.   Use residual analysis to determine whether any outliers and/or influential observations are present. Briefly summarize your findings and conclusions.

53.   Many countries, especially those in Europe, have significant gold holdings. But, many of these countries also have massive debts. The following data show the total value of gold holdings in billions of U.S. dollars and the debt as a percentage of the gross domestic product for nine countries (WordPress and Trading Economics websites, February 24, 2012).

DATA *file*

GoldHoldings

Country	Gold Value ($ billions)	Debt (% of GDP)
China	63	17.7
France	146	81.7
Germany	203	83.2
Indonesia	33	69.2
Italy	147	119.0
Netherlands	36	63.7
Russia	50	9.9
Switzerland	62	55.0
United States	487	93.2

a.   Develop a scatter diagram for the total value of a country's gold holdings ($ billions) as the independent variable.

b.   What does the scatter diagram developed in part (a) indicate about the relationship between the two variables? Do there appear to be any outliers and/or influential observations? Explain.

c.   Using the entire data set, develop the estimated regression equation that can be used to predict the debt of a country given the total value of its gold holdings.

d.   Use residual analysis to determine whether any outliers or influential observations are present.

e.   Suppose that after looking at the scatter diagram in part (a) that you were able to visually identify what appears to be an influential observation. Drop this observation from the data set and fit an estimated regression equation to the remaining data. Compare the estimated slope for the new estimated regression equation to the estimated slope obtained in part (c). Does this approach confirm the conclusion you reached in part (d)? Explain.

54.   The following data show the annual revenue ($ millions) and the estimated team value ($ millions) for the 30 Major League Baseball teams (*Forbes* website, January 16, 2014).

DATA *file*

MLBValues

Team	Revenue ($ millions)	Value ($ millions)
Arizona Diamondbacks	195	584
Atlanta Braves	225	629
Baltimore Orioles	206	618
Boston Red Sox	336	1312
Chicago Cubs	274	1000

(*continued*)

Team	Revenue ($ millions)	Value ($ millions)
Chicago White Sox	216	692
Cincinnati Reds	202	546
Cleveland Indians	186	559
Colorado Rockies	199	537
Detroit Tigers	238	643
Houston Astros	196	626
Kansas City Royals	169	457
Los Angeles Angels of Anaheim	239	718
Los Angeles Dodgers	245	1615
Miami Marlins	195	520
Milwaukee Brewers	201	562
Minnesota Twins	214	578
New York Mets	232	811
New York Yankees	471	2300
Oakland Athletics	173	468
Philadelphia Phillies	279	893
Pittsburgh Pirates	178	479
San Diego Padres	189	600
San Francisco Giants	262	786
Seattle Mariners	215	644
St. Louis Cardinals	239	716
Tampa Bay Rays	167	451
Texas Rangers	239	764
Toronto Blue Jays	203	568
Washington Nationals	225	631

a. Develop a scatter diagram with Revenue on the horizontal axis and Value on the vertical axis. Looking at the scatter diagram, does it appear that there are any outliers and/or influential observations in the data?

b. Develop the estimated regression equation that can be used to predict team value given the annual revenue.

c. Use residual analysis to determine whether any outliers and/or influential observations are present. Briefly summarize your findings and conclusions.

Summary

In this chapter we showed how regression analysis can be used to determine how a dependent variable y is related to an independent variable x. In simple linear regression, the regression model is $y = \beta_0 + \beta_1 x + \epsilon$. The simple linear regression equation $E(y) = \beta_0 + \beta_1 x$ describes how the mean or expected value of y is related to x. We used sample data and the least squares method to develop the estimated regression equation $\hat{y} = b_0 + b_1 x$. In effect, b_0 and b_1 are the sample statistics used to estimate the unknown model parameters β_0 and β_1.

The coefficient of determination was presented as a measure of the goodness of fit for the estimated regression equation; it can be interpreted as the proportion of the variation in the dependent variable y that can be explained by the estimated regression equation. We reviewed correlation as a descriptive measure of the strength of a linear relationship between two variables.

The assumptions about the regression model and its associated error term ϵ were discussed, and t and F tests, based on those assumptions, were presented as a means for determining whether the relationship between two variables is statistically significant. We showed how to use the estimated regression equation to develop confidence interval estimates of the mean value of y and prediction interval estimates of individual values of y.

The chapter concluded with a section on the computer solution of regression problems and two sections on the use of residual analysis to validate the model assumptions and to identify outliers and influential observations.

Glossary

ANOVA table The analysis of variance table used to summarize the computations associated with the F test for significance.

Coefficient of determination A measure of the goodness of fit of the estimated regression equation. It can be interpreted as the proportion of the variability in the dependent variable y that is explained by the estimated regression equation.

Confidence interval The interval estimate of the mean value of y for a given value of x.

Correlation coefficient A measure of the strength of the linear relationship between two variables (previously discussed in Chapter 3).

Dependent variable The variable that is being predicted or explained. It is denoted by y.

Estimated regression equation The estimate of the regression equation developed from sample data by using the least squares method. For simple linear regression, the estimated regression equation is $\hat{y} = b_0 + b_1x$.

High leverage points Observations with extreme values for the independent variables.

Independent variable The variable that is doing the predicting or explaining. It is denoted by x.

Influential observation An observation that has a strong influence or effect on the regression results.

ith residual The difference between the observed value of the dependent variable and the value predicted using the estimated regression equation; for the ith observation the ith residual is $y_i - \hat{y}_i$.

Least squares method A procedure used to develop the estimated regression equation. The objective is to minimize $\Sigma(y_i - \hat{y}_i)^2$.

Mean square error The unbiased estimate of the variance of the error term σ^2. It is denoted by MSE or s^2.

Normal probability plot A graph of the standardized residuals plotted against values of the normal scores. This plot helps determine whether the assumption that the error term has a normal probability distribution appears to be valid.

Outlier A data point or observation that does not fit the trend shown by the remaining data.

Prediction interval The interval estimate of an individual value of y for a given value of x.

Regression equation The equation that describes how the mean or expected value of the dependent variable is related to the independent variable; in simple linear regression, $E(y) = \beta_0 + \beta_1x$.

Regression model The equation that describes how y is related to x and an error term; in simple linear regression, the regression model is $y = \beta_0 + \beta_1x + \epsilon$.

Residual analysis The analysis of the residuals used to determine whether the assumptions made about the regression model appear to be valid. Residual analysis is also used to identify outliers and influential observations.

Residual plot Graphical representation of the residuals that can be used to determine whether the assumptions made about the regression model appear to be valid.

Scatter diagram A graph of bivariate data in which the independent variable is on the horizontal axis and the dependent variable is on the vertical axis.

Simple linear regression Regression analysis involving one independent variable and one dependent variable in which the relationship between the variables is approximated by a straight line.

Standard error of the estimate The square root of the mean square error, denoted by s. It is the estimate of σ, the standard deviation of the error term ϵ.

Standardized residual The value obtained by dividing a residual by its standard deviation.

Key Formulas

Simple Linear Regression Model

$$y = \beta_0 + \beta_1 x + \epsilon \tag{14.1}$$

Simple Linear Regression Equation

$$E(y) = \beta_0 + \beta_1 x \tag{14.2}$$

Estimated Simple Linear Regression Equation

$$\hat{y} = b_0 + b_1 x \tag{14.3}$$

Least Squares Criterion

$$\min \Sigma(y_i - \hat{y}_i)^2 \tag{14.5}$$

Slope and y-Intercept for the Estimated Regression Equation

$$b_1 = \frac{\Sigma(x_i - \bar{x})(y_i - \bar{y})}{\Sigma(x_i - \bar{x})^2} \tag{14.6}$$

$$b_0 = \bar{y} - b_1\bar{x} \tag{14.7}$$

Sum of Squares Due to Error

$$SSE = \Sigma(y_i - \bar{y}_i)^2 \tag{14.8}$$

Total Sum of Squares

$$SST = \Sigma(y_i - \bar{y})^2 \tag{14.9}$$

Sum of Squares Due to Regression

$$SSR = \Sigma(\hat{y}_i - \bar{y})^2 \tag{14.10}$$

Relationship Among SST, SSR, and SSE

$$SST = SSR + SSE \tag{14.11}$$

Coefficient of Determination

$$r^2 = \frac{SSR}{SST} \tag{14.12}$$

Sample Correlation Coefficient

$$r_{xy} = (\text{sign of } b_1)\sqrt{\text{Coefficient of determination}}$$
$$= (\text{sign of } b_1)\sqrt{r^2} \tag{14.13}$$

Mean Square Error (Estimate of σ^2)

$$s^2 = MSE = \frac{SSE}{n - 2} \tag{14.15}$$

Standard Error of the Estimate

$$s = \sqrt{\text{MSE}} = \sqrt{\frac{\text{SSE}}{n-2}} \qquad \textbf{(14.16)}$$

Standard Deviation of b_1

$$\sigma_{b_1} = \frac{\sigma}{\sqrt{\Sigma(x_i - \bar{x})^2}} \qquad \textbf{(14.17)}$$

Estimated Standard Deviation of b_1

$$s_{b_1} = \frac{s}{\sqrt{\Sigma(x_i - \bar{x})^2}} \qquad \textbf{(14.18)}$$

t Test Statistic

$$t = \frac{b_1}{s_{b_1}} \qquad \textbf{(14.19)}$$

Mean Square Regression

$$\text{MSR} = \frac{\text{SSR}}{\text{Number of independent variables}} \qquad \textbf{(14.20)}$$

F Test Statistic

$$F = \frac{\text{MSR}}{\text{MSE}} \qquad \textbf{(14.21)}$$

Estimated Standard Deviation of $\hat{y}^*$

$$s_{\hat{y}^*} = s\sqrt{\frac{1}{n} + \frac{(x^* - \bar{x})^2}{\Sigma(x_i - \bar{x})^2}} \qquad \textbf{(14.23)}$$

Confidence Interval for $E(y^*)$

$$\hat{y}^* \pm t_{\alpha/2} s_{\hat{y}^*} \qquad \textbf{(14.24)}$$

Estimated Standard Deviation of an Individual Value

$$s_{\text{pred}} = s\sqrt{1 + \frac{1}{n} + \frac{(x^* - \bar{x})^2}{\Sigma(x_i - \bar{x})^2}} \qquad \textbf{(14.26)}$$

Prediction Interval for y^*

$$\hat{y}^* \pm t_{\alpha/2} s_{\text{pred}} \qquad \textbf{(14.27)}$$

Residual for Observation i

$$y_i - \hat{y}_i \qquad \textbf{(14.28)}$$

Standard Deviation of the ith Residual

$$s_{y_i - \hat{y}_i} = s\sqrt{1 - h_i} \qquad (14.30)$$

Standardized Residual for Observation i

$$\frac{y_i - \hat{y}_i}{s_{y_i - \hat{y}_i}} \qquad (14.32)$$

Leverage of Observation i

$$h_i = \frac{1}{n} + \frac{(x_i - \bar{x})^2}{\Sigma(x_i - \bar{x})^2} \qquad (14.33)$$

Supplementary Exercises

55. Does a high value of r^2 imply that two variables are causally related? Explain.

56. In your own words, explain the difference between an interval estimate of the mean value of y for a given x and an interval estimate for an individual value of y for a given x.

57. What is the purpose of testing whether $\beta_1 = 0$? If we reject $\beta_1 = 0$, does it imply a good fit?

58. The Dow Jones Industrial Average (DJIA) and the Standard & Poor's 500 (S&P 500) indexes are used as measures of overall movement in the stock market. The DJIA is based on the price movements of 30 large companies; the S&P 500 is an index composed of 500 stocks. Some say the S&P 500 is a better measure of stock market performance because it is broader based. The closing price for the DJIA and the S&P 500 for 15 weeks, beginning with January 6, 2012, follow (*Barron*'s website, April 17, 2012).

DATA *file*

DJIAS&P500

Date	DJIA	S&P
January 6	12,360	1278
January 13	12,422	1289
January 20	12,720	1315
January 27	12,660	1316
February 3	12,862	1345
February 10	12,801	1343
February 17	12,950	1362
February 24	12,983	1366
March 2	12,978	1370
March 9	12,922	1371
March 16	13,233	1404
March 23	13,081	1397
March 30	13,212	1408
April 5	13,060	1398
April 13	12,850	1370

a. Develop a scatter diagram with DJIA as the independent variable.
b. Develop the estimated regression equation.
c. Test for a significant relationship. Use $\alpha = .05$.
d. Did the estimated regression equation provide a good fit? Explain.
e. Suppose that the closing price for the DJIA is 13,500. Predict the closing price for the S&P 500.
f. Should we be concerned that the DJIA value of 13,500 used to predict the S&P 500 value in part (e) is beyond the range of the data used to develop the estimated regression equation?

59. Is the number of square feet of living space a good predictor of a house's selling price? The following data show the square footage and selling price for fifteen houses in Winston Salem, North Carolina (*Zillow.com*, April 5, 2015).

DATA *file*

WSHouses

Size (1000s sq. ft)	Selling Price ($1000s)
1.26	117.5
3.02	299.9
1.99	139.0
0.91	45.6
1.87	129.9
2.63	274.9
2.60	259.9
2.27	177.0
2.30	175.0
2.08	189.9
1.12	95.0
1.38	82.1
1.80	169.0
1.57	96.5
1.45	114.9

a. Develop a scatter diagram with square feet of living space as the independent variable and selling price as the dependent variable. What does the scatter diagram indicate about the relationship between the size of a house and the selling price?

b. Develop the estimated regression equation that could be used to predict the selling price given the number of square feet of living space.

c. At the .05 level, is there a significant relationship between the two variables?

d. Use the estimated regression equation to predict the selling price of a 2000 square foot house in Winston Salem, North Carolina.

e. Do you believe the estimated regression equation developed in part (b) will provide a good prediction of selling price of a particular house in Winston Salem, North Carolina? Explain.

f. Would you be comfortable using the estimated regression equation developed in part (b) to predict the selling price of a particular house in Seattle, Washington? Why or why not?

60. One of the biggest changes in higher education in recent years has been the growth of online universities. The Online Education Database is an independent organization whose mission is to build a comprehensive list of the top accredited online colleges. The following table shows the retention rate (%) and the graduation rate (%) for 29 online colleges.

DATA *file*

OnlineEdu

Retention Rate (%)	Graduation Rate (%)
7	25
51	25
4	28
29	32
33	33

(*continued*)

Retention Rate (%)	Graduation Rate (%)
47	33
63	34
45	36
60	36
62	36
67	36
65	37
78	37
75	38
54	39
45	41
38	44
51	45
69	46
60	47
37	48
63	50
73	51
78	52
48	53
95	55
68	56
100	57
100	61

a. Develop a scatter diagram with retention rate as the independent variable. What does the scatter diagram indicate about the relationship between the two variables?
b. Develop the estimated regression equation.
c. Test for a significant relationship. Use $\alpha = .05$.
d. Did the estimated regression equation provide a good fit?
e. Suppose you were the president of South University. After reviewing the results, would you have any concerns about the performance of your university as compared to other online universities?
f. Suppose you were the president of the University of Phoenix. After reviewing the results, would you have any concerns about the performance of your university as compared to other online universities?

61. Jensen Tire & Auto is in the process of deciding whether to purchase a maintenance contract for its new computer wheel alignment and balancing machine. Managers feel that maintenance expense should be related to usage, and they collected the following information on weekly usage (hours) and annual maintenance expense (in hundreds of dollars).

DATA *file*

Jensen

Weekly Usage (hours)	Annual Maintenance Expense
13	17.0
10	22.0
20	30.0
28	37.0
32	47.0
17	30.5

Weekly Usage (hours)	Annual Maintenance Expense
24	32.5
31	39.0
40	51.5
38	40.0

a. Develop the estimated regression equation that relates annual maintenance expense to weekly usage.
b. Test the significance of the relationship in part (a) at a .05 level of significance.
c. Jensen expects to use the new machine 30 hours per week. Develop a 95% prediction interval for the company's annual maintenance expense.
d. If the maintenance contract costs $3000 per year, would you recommend purchasing it? Why or why not?

62. In a manufacturing process the assembly line speed (feet per minute) was thought to affect the number of defective parts found during the inspection process. To test this theory, managers devised a situation in which the same batch of parts was inspected visually at a variety of line speeds. They collected the following data.

Line Speed	Number of Defective Parts Found
20	21
20	19
40	15
30	16
60	14
40	17

a. Develop the estimated regression equation that relates line speed to the number of defective parts found.
b. At a .05 level of significance, determine whether line speed and number of defective parts found are related.
c. Did the estimated regression equation provide a good fit to the data?
d. Develop a 95% confidence interval to predict the mean number of defective parts for a line speed of 50 feet per minute.

63. A sociologist was hired by a large city hospital to investigate the relationship between the number of unauthorized days that employees are absent per year and the distance (miles) between home and work for the employees. A sample of 10 employees was chosen, and the following data were collected.

DATA *file*

Absent

Distance to Work (miles)	Number of Days Absent
1	8
3	5
4	8
6	7
8	6
10	3
12	5
14	2
14	4
18	2

a. Develop a scatter diagram for these data. Does a linear relationship appear reasonable? Explain.
b. Develop the least squares estimated regression equation.
c. Is there a significant relationship between the two variables? Use $\alpha = .05$.
d. Did the estimated regression equation provide a good fit? Explain.
e. Use the estimated regression equation developed in part (b) to develop a 95% confidence interval for the expected number of days absent for employees living 5 miles from the company.

64. The regional transit authority for a major metropolitan area wants to determine whether there is any relationship between the age of a bus and the annual maintenance cost. A sample of 10 buses resulted in the following data.

DATA *file*

AgeCost

Age of Bus (years)	Maintenance Cost ($)
1	350
2	370
2	480
2	520
2	590
3	550
4	750
4	800
5	790
5	950

a. Develop the least squares estimated regression equation.
b. Test to see whether the two variables are significantly related with $\alpha = .05$.
c. Did the least squares line provide a good fit to the observed data? Explain.
d. Develop a 95% prediction interval for the maintenance cost for a specific bus that is 4 years old.

65. A marketing professor at Givens College is interested in the relationship between hours spent studying and total points earned in a course. Data collected on 10 students who took the course last quarter follow.

DATA *file*

HoursPts

Hours Spent Studying	Total Points Earned
45	40
30	35
90	75
60	65
105	90
65	50
90	90
80	80
55	45
75	65

a. Develop an estimated regression equation showing how total points earned is related to hours spent studying.
b. Test the significance of the model with $\alpha = .05$.
c. Predict the total points earned by Mark Sweeney. He spent 95 hours studying.
d. Develop a 95% prediction interval for the total points earned by Mark Sweeney.

66. Market betas for individual stocks are determined by simple linear regression. For each stock, the dependent variable is its quarterly percentage return (capital appreciation plus dividends) minus the percentage return that could be obtained from a risk-free investment (the Treasury

Bill rate is used as the risk-free rate). The independent variable is the quarterly percentage return (capital appreciation plus dividends) for the stock market (S&P 500) minus the percentage return from a risk-free investment. An estimated regression equation is developed with quarterly data; the market beta for the stock is the slope of the estimated regression equation (b_1). The value of the market beta is often interpreted as a measure of the risk associated with the stock. Market betas greater than 1 indicate that the stock is more volatile than the market average; market betas less than 1 indicate that the stock is less volatile than the market average. Suppose that the following figures are the differences between the percentage return and the risk-free return for 10 quarters for the S&P 500 and Horizon Technology.

S&P 500	Horizon
1.2	−.7
−2.5	−2.0
−3.0	−5.5
2.0	4.7
5.0	1.8
1.2	4.1
3.0	2.6
−1.0	2.0
.5	−1.3
2.5	5.5

MktBeta

a. Develop an estimated regression equation that can be used to predict the market beta for Horizon Technology. What is Horizon Technology's market beta?
b. Test for a significant relationship at the .05 level of significance.
c. Did the estimated regression equation provide a good fit? Explain.
d. Use the market betas of Xerox and Horizon Technology to compare the risk associated with the two stocks.

67. The Transactional Records Access Clearinghouse at Syracuse University reported data showing the odds of an Internal Revenue Service audit. The following table shows the average adjusted gross income reported and the percent of the returns that were audited for 20 selected IRS districts.

IRSAudit

District	Adjusted Gross Income ($)	Percent Audited
Los Angeles	36,664	1.3
Sacramento	38,845	1.1
Atlanta	34,886	1.1
Boise	32,512	1.1
Dallas	34,531	1.0
Providence	35,995	1.0
San Jose	37,799	0.9
Cheyenne	33,876	0.9
Fargo	30,513	0.9
New Orleans	30,174	0.9
Oklahoma City	30,060	0.8
Houston	37,153	0.8
Portland	34,918	0.7
Phoenix	33,291	0.7
Augusta	31,504	0.7
Albuquerque	29,199	0.6
Greensboro	33,072	0.6
Columbia	30,859	0.5
Nashville	32,566	0.5
Buffalo	34,296	0.5

a. Develop the estimated regression equation that could be used to predict the percent audited given the average adjusted gross income reported.
b. At the .05 level of significance, determine whether the adjusted gross income and the percent audited are related.
c. Did the estimated regression equation provide a good fit? Explain.
d. Use the estimated regression equation developed in part (a) to calculate a 95% confidence interval for the expected percent audited for districts with an average adjusted gross income of $35,000.

68. The Toyota Camry is one of the best-selling cars in North America. The cost of a previously owned Camry depends upon many factors, including the model year, mileage, and condition. To investigate the relationship between the car's mileage and the sales price for a 2007 model year Camry, the following data show the mileage and sale price for 19 sales (PriceHub website, February 24, 2012).

DATA *file*

Camry

Miles (1000s)	Price ($1000s)
22	16.2
29	16.0
36	13.8
47	11.5
63	12.5
77	12.9
73	11.2
87	13.0
92	11.8
101	10.8
110	8.3
28	12.5
59	11.1
68	15.0
68	12.2
91	13.0
42	15.6
65	12.7
110	8.3

a. Develop a scatter diagram with the car mileage on the horizontal axis and the price on the vertical axis.
b. What does the scatter diagram developed in part (a) indicate about the relationship between the two variables?
c. Develop the estimated regression equation that could be used to predict the price ($1000s) given the miles (1000s).
d. Test for a significant relationship at the .05 level of significance.
e. Did the estimated regression equation provide a good fit? Explain.
f. Provide an interpretation for the slope of the estimated regression equation.
g. Suppose that you are considering purchasing a previously owned 2007 Camry that has been driven 60,000 miles. Using the estimated regression equation developed in part (c), predict the price for this car. Is this the price you would offer the seller?

Case Problem 1   Measuring Stock Market Risk

One measure of the risk or volatility of an individual stock is the standard deviation of the total return (capital appreciation plus dividends) over several periods of time. Although the standard deviation is easy to compute, it does not take into account the extent to which the price of a given stock varies as a function of a standard market index, such as the S&P 500. As a result, many financial analysts prefer to use another measure of risk referred to as *beta*.

Beta

Betas for individual stocks are determined by simple linear regression. The dependent variable is the total return for the stock and the independent variable is the total return for the stock market.* For this case problem we will use the S&P 500 index as the measure of the total return for the stock market, and an estimated regression equation will be developed using monthly data. The beta for the stock is the slope of the estimated regression equation (b_1). The data contained in the file named Beta provides the total return (capital appreciation plus dividends) over 36 months for eight widely traded common stocks and the S&P 500.

The value of beta for the stock market will always be 1; thus, stocks that tend to rise and fall with the stock market will also have a beta close to 1. Betas greater than 1 indicate that the stock is more volatile than the market, and betas less than 1 indicate that the stock is less volatile than the market. For instance, if a stock has a beta of 1.4, it is 40% *more* volatile than the market, and if a stock has a beta of .4, it is 60% *less* volatile than the market.

Managerial Report

You have been assigned to analyze the risk characteristics of these stocks. Prepare a report that includes but is not limited to the following items.
   a. Compute descriptive statistics for each stock and the S&P 500. Comment on your results. Which stocks are the most volatile?
   b. Compute the value of beta for each stock. Which of these stocks would you expect to perform best in an up market? Which would you expect to hold their value best in a down market?
   c. Comment on how much of the return for the individual stocks is explained by the market.

Case Problem 2   U.S. Department of Transportation

As part of a study on transportation safety, the U.S. Department of Transportation collected data on the number of fatal accidents per 1000 licenses and the percentage of licensed drivers under the age of 21 in a sample of 42 cities. Data collected over a one-year period follow. These data are contained in the file named Safety.

Safety

Percent Under 21	Fatal Accidents per 1000 Licenses	Percent Under 21	Fatal Accidents per 1000 Licenses
13	2.962	17	4.100
12	0.708	8	2.190
8	0.885	16	3.623
12	1.652	15	2.623
11	2.091	9	0.835
17	2.627	8	0.820
18	3.830	14	2.890
8	0.368	8	1.267
13	1.142	15	3.224
8	0.645	10	1.014
9	1.028	10	0.493

(continued)

---

*Various sources use different approaches for computing betas. For instance, some sources subtract the return that could be obtained from a risk-free investment (e.g., T-bills) from the dependent variable and the independent variable before computing the estimated regression equation. Some also use different indexes for the total return of the stock market; for instance, Value Line computes betas using the New York Stock Exchange composite index.

Percent Under 21	Fatal Accidents per 1000 Licenses	Percent Under 21	Fatal Accidents per 1000 Licenses
16	2.801	14	1.443
12	1.405	18	3.614
9	1.433	10	1.926
10	0.039	14	1.643
9	0.338	16	2.943
11	1.849	12	1.913
12	2.246	15	2.814
14	2.855	13	2.634
14	2.352	9	0.926
11	1.294	17	3.256

Managerial Report

1. Develop numerical and graphical summaries of the data.
2. Use regression analysis to investigate the relationship between the number of fatal accidents and the percentage of drivers under the age of 21. Discuss your findings.
3. What conclusion and recommendations can you derive from your analysis?

Case Problem 3   # Selecting a Point-and-Shoot Digital Camera

Consumer Reports tested 166 different point-and-shoot digital cameras. Based upon factors such as the number of megapixels, weight (oz.), image quality, and ease of use, they developed an overall score for each camera tested. The overall score ranges from 0 to 100, with higher scores indicating better overall test results. Selecting a camera with many options can be a difficult process, and price is certainly a key issue for most consumers. By spending more, will a consumer really get a superior camera? And, do cameras that have more megapixels, a factor often considered to be a good measure of picture quality, cost more than cameras with fewer megapixels? Table 14.13 shows the brand, average retail price ($), number of megapixels, weight (oz.), and the overall score for 13 Canon and 15 Nikon subcompact cameras tested by *Consumer Reports* (*Consumer Reports* website, February 7, 2012).

Managerial Report

1. Develop numerical summaries of the data.
2. Using overall score as the dependent variable, develop three scatter diagrams, one using price as the independent variable, one using the number of megapixels as the independent variable, and one using weight as the independent variable. Which of the three independent variables appears to be the best predictor of overall score?
3. Using simple linear regression, develop an estimated regression equation that could be used to predict the overall score given the price of the camera. For this estimated regression equation, perform an analysis of the residuals and discuss your findings and conclusions.
4. Analyze the data using only the observations for the Canon cameras. Discuss the appropriateness of using simple linear regression and make any recommendations regarding the prediction of overall score using just the price of the camera.

TABLE 14.13   DATA FOR 28 POINT-AND-SHOOT DIGITAL CAMERAS

Observation	Brand	Price ($)	Megapixels	Weight (oz.)	Score
1	Canon	330	10	7	66
2	Canon	200	12	5	66
3	Canon	300	12	7	65
4	Canon	200	10	6	62
5	Canon	180	12	5	62
6	Canon	200	12	7	61
7	Canon	200	14	5	60
8	Canon	130	10	7	60
9	Canon	130	12	5	59
10	Canon	110	16	5	55
11	Canon	90	14	5	52
12	Canon	100	10	6	51
13	Canon	90	12	7	46
14	Nikon	270	16	5	65
15	Nikon	300	16	7	63
16	Nikon	200	14	6	61
17	Nikon	400	14	7	59
18	Nikon	120	14	5	57
19	Nikon	170	16	6	56
20	Nikon	150	12	5	56
21	Nikon	230	14	6	55
22	Nikon	180	12	6	53
23	Nikon	130	12	6	53
24	Nikon	80	12	7	52
25	Nikon	80	14	7	50
26	Nikon	100	12	4	46
27	Nikon	110	12	5	45
28	Nikon	130	14	4	42

DATA *file*

Cameras

Case Problem 4   Finding the Best Car Value

When trying to decide what car to buy, real value is not necessarily determined by how much you spend on the initial purchase. Instead, cars that are reliable and don't cost much to own often represent the best values. But, no matter how reliable or inexpensive a car may cost to own, it must also perform well.

To measure value, *Consumer Reports* developed a statistic referred to as a value score. The value score is based upon five-year owner costs, overall road-test scores, and predicted reliability ratings. Five-year owner costs are based on the expenses incurred in the first five years of ownership, including depreciation, fuel, maintenance and repairs, and so on. Using a national average of 12,000 miles per year, an average cost per mile driven is used as the measure of five-year owner costs. Road-test scores are the results of more than 50 tests and evaluations and are based upon a 100-point scale, with higher scores indicating better performance, comfort, convenience, and fuel economy. The highest road-test score obtained in the tests conducted by *Consumer Reports* was a 99 for a Lexus LS 460L. Predicted-reliability ratings (1 = Poor, 2 = Fair, 3 = Good, 4 = Very Good, and 5 = Excellent) are based on data from *Consumer Reports'* Annual Auto Survey.

A car with a value score of 1.0 is considered to be "average-value." A car with a value score of 2.0 is considered to be twice as good a value as a car with a value score of 1.0; a car with a value score of 0.5 is considered half as good as average; and so on. The data for 20 family sedans, including the price ($) of each car tested, follow.

FamilySedans

Car	Price ($)	Cost/Mile	Road-Test Score	Predicted Reliability	Value Score
Nissan Altima 2.5 S (4-cyl.)	23,970	0.59	91	4	1.75
Kia Optima LX (2.4)	21,885	0.58	81	4	1.73
Subaru Legacy 2.5i Premium	23,830	0.59	83	4	1.73
Ford Fusion Hybrid	32,360	0.63	84	5	1.70
Honda Accord LX-P (4-cyl.)	23,730	0.56	80	4	1.62
Mazda6 i Sport (4-cyl.)	22,035	0.58	73	4	1.60
Hyundai Sonata GLS (2.4)	21,800	0.56	89	3	1.58
Ford Fusion SE (4-cyl.)	23,625	0.57	76	4	1.55
Chevrolet Malibu LT (4-cyl.)	24,115	0.57	74	3	1.48
Kia Optima SX (2.0T)	29,050	0.72	84	4	1.43
Ford Fusion SEL (V6)	28,400	0.67	80	4	1.42
Nissan Altima 3.5 SR (V6)	30,335	0.69	93	4	1.42
Hyundai Sonata Limited (2.0T)	28,090	0.66	89	3	1.39
Honda Accord EX-L (V6)	28,695	0.67	90	3	1.36
Mazda6 s Grand Touring (V6)	30,790	0.74	81	4	1.34
Ford Fusion SEL (V6, AWD)	30,055	0.71	75	4	1.32
Subaru Legacy 3.6R Limited	30,094	0.71	88	3	1.29
Chevrolet Malibu LTZ (V6)	28,045	0.67	83	3	1.20
Chrysler 200 Limited (V6)	27,825	0.70	52	5	1.20
Chevrolet Impala LT (3.6)	28,995	0.67	63	3	1.05

Managerial Report

1. Develop numerical summaries of the data.
2. Use regression analysis to develop an estimated regression equation that could be used to predict the value score given the price of the car.
3. Use regression analysis to develop an estimated regression equation that could be used to predict the value score given the five-year owner costs (cost/mile).
4. Use regression analysis to develop an estimated regression equation that could be used to predict the value score given the road-test score.
5. Use regression analysis to develop an estimated regression equation that could be used to predict the value score given the predicted-reliability.
6. What conclusions can you derive from your analysis?

Case Problem 5   Buckeye Creek Amusement Park

Buckeye Creek Amusement Park is open from the beginning of May to the end of October. Buckeye Creek relies heavily on the sale of season passes. The sale of season passes brings in significant revenue prior to the park opening each season, and season pass holders contribute a substantial portion of the food, beverage, and novelty sales in the park. Greg Ross, director of marketing at Buckeye Creek, has been asked to develop a targeted marketing campaign to increase season pass sales.

BuckeyeCreek

Greg has data for last season that show the number of season pass holders for each zip code within 50 miles of Buckeye Creek. He has also obtained the total population of each zip code from the U.S. Census bureau website. Greg thinks it may be possible to use regression analysis to predict the number of season pass holders in a zip code given the total population of a zip code. If this is possible, he could then conduct a direct mail campaign that would target zip codes that have fewer than the expected number of season pass holders.

Managerial Report

1. Compute descriptive statistics and construct a scatter diagram for the data. Discuss your findings.
2. Using simple linear regression, develop an estimated regression equation that could be used to predict the number of season pass holders in a zip code given the total population of the zip code.
3. Test for a significant relationship at the .05 level of significance.
4. Did the estimated regression equation provide a good fit?
5. Use residual analysis to determine whether the assumed regression model is appropriate.
6. Discuss if/how the estimated regression equation should be used to guide the marketing campaign.
7. What other data might be useful to predict the number of season pass holders in a zip code?

Appendix 14.1   Calculus-Based Derivation of Least Squares Formulas

As mentioned in the chapter, the least squares method is a procedure for determining the values of b_0 and b_1 that minimize the sum of squared residuals. The sum of squared residuals is given by

$$\Sigma(y_i - \hat{y}_i)^2$$

Substituting $\hat{y}_i = b_0 + b_1x_i$, we get

$$\Sigma(y_i - b_0 - b_1x_i)^2 \qquad (14.34)$$

as the expression that must be minimized.

To minimize expression (14.34), we must take the partial derivatives with respect to b_0 and b_1, set them equal to zero, and solve. Doing so, we get

$$\frac{\partial\Sigma(y_i - b_0 - b_1x_i)^2}{\partial b_0} = -2\Sigma(y_i - b_0 - b_1x_i) = 0 \qquad (14.35)$$

$$\frac{\partial\Sigma(y_i - b_0 - b_1x_i)^2}{\partial b_1} = -2\Sigma x_i(y_i - b_0 - b_1x_i) = 0 \qquad (14.36)$$

Dividing equation (14.35) by two and summing each term individually yields

$$-\Sigma y_i + \Sigma b_0 + \Sigma b_1x_i = 0$$

Bringing Σy_i to the other side of the equal sign and noting that $\Sigma b_0 = nb_0$, we obtain

$$nb_0 + (\Sigma x_i)b_1 = \Sigma y_i \qquad (14.37)$$

Similar algebraic simplification applied to equation (14.36) yields

$$(\Sigma x_i)b_0 + (\Sigma x_i^2)b_1 = \Sigma x_iy_i \qquad (14.38)$$

Equations (14.37) and (14.38) are known as the *normal equations*. Solving equation (14.37) for b_0 yields

$$b_0 = \frac{\Sigma y_i}{n} - b_1 \frac{\Sigma x_i}{n} \qquad (14.39)$$

Using equation (14.39) to substitute for b_0 in equation (14.38) provides

$$\frac{\Sigma x_i \Sigma y_i}{n} - \frac{(\Sigma x_i)^2}{n} b_1 + (\Sigma x_i^2) b_1 = \Sigma x_i y_i \qquad (14.40)$$

By rearranging the terms in equation (14.40), we obtain

$$b_1 = \frac{\Sigma x_i y_i - (\Sigma x_i \Sigma y_i)/n}{\Sigma x_i^2 - (\Sigma x_i)^2/n} = \frac{\Sigma(x_i - \bar{x})(y_i - \bar{y})}{\Sigma(x_i - \bar{x})^2} \qquad (14.41)$$

Because $\bar{y} = \Sigma y_i/n$ and $\bar{x} = \Sigma x_i/n$, we can rewrite equation (14.39) as

$$b_0 = \bar{y} - b_1 \bar{x} \qquad (14.42)$$

Equations (14.41) and (14.42) are the formulas (14.6) and (14.7) we used in the chapter to compute the coefficients in the estimated regression equation.

Appendix 14.2 A Test for Significance Using Correlation

Using the sample correlation coefficient r_{xy}, we can determine whether the linear relationship between x and y is significant by testing the following hypotheses about the population correlation coefficient ρ_{xy}.

$$H_0: \rho_{xy} = 0$$
$$H_a: \rho_{xy} \neq 0$$

If H_0 is rejected, we can conclude that the population correlation coefficient is not equal to zero and that the linear relationship between the two variables is significant. This test for significance follows.

A TEST FOR SIGNIFICANCE USING CORRELATION

$$H_0: \rho_{xy} = 0$$
$$H_a: \rho_{xy} \neq 0$$

TEST STATISTIC

$$t = r_{xy} \sqrt{\frac{n-2}{1 - r_{xy}^2}} \qquad (14.43)$$

REJECTION RULE

p-value approach: Reject H_0 if p-value $\leq \alpha$

Critical value approach: Reject H_0 if $t \leq -t_{\alpha/2}$ or if $t \geq t_{\alpha/2}$

where $t_{\alpha/2}$ is based on a t distribution with $n - 2$ degrees of freedom.

In Section 14.3, we found that the sample with $n = 10$ provided the sample correlation coefficient for student population and quarterly sales of $r_{xy} = .9501$. The test statistic is

$$t = r_{xy} \sqrt{\frac{n - 2}{1 - r_{xy}^2}} = .9501 \sqrt{\frac{10 - 2}{1 - (.9501)^2}} = 8.61$$

The t distribution table shows that with $n - 2 = 10 - 2 = 8$ degrees of freedom, $t = 3.355$ provides an area of .005 in the upper tail. Thus, the area in the upper tail of the t distribution corresponding to the test statistic $t = 8.61$ must be less than .005. Because this test is a two-tailed test, we double this value to conclude that the p-value associated with $t = 8.61$ must be less than $2(.005) = .01$. Excel or Minitab show the p-value $= .000$. Because the p-value is less than $\alpha = .01$, we reject H_0 and conclude that ρ_{xy} is not equal to zero. This evidence is sufficient to conclude that a significant linear relationship exists between student population and quarterly sales.

Note that except for rounding, the test statistic t and the conclusion of a significant relationship are identical to the results obtained in Section 14.5 for the t test conducted using Armand's estimated regression equation $\hat{y} = 60 + 5x$. Performing regression analysis provides the conclusion of a significant relationship between x and y and in addition provides the equation showing how the variables are related. Most analysts therefore use modern computer packages to perform regression analysis and find that using correlation as a test of significance is unnecessary.

Appendix 14.3 Regression Analysis with Minitab

Armand's

In Section 14.7 we discussed the computer solution of regression problems by showing Minitab's output for the Armand's Pizza Parlors problem. In this appendix, we describe the steps required to generate the Minitab computer solution. First, the data must be entered in a Minitab worksheet. As shown in Table 14.1, restaurant, student population, and sales data are entered in columns C1, C2, and C3. The variable names Restaurant, Population, and Sales are entered as the column headings on the worksheet. In subsequent steps, we refer to the data by using the variable names Population and Sales or the column indicators C1, C2, and C3. The following steps describe how to use Minitab to produce the regression results shown in Figure 14.10.

Step 1. Select the **Stat** menu
Step 2. Select the **Regression** menu
Step 3. Choose **Regression**
Step 4. Choose **Fit Regression Model**
Step 5. When the Regression dialog box appears:
  Enter Sales in the Responses box
  Enter Population in the Continuous predictors box
  Click **OK**

The Minitab regression dialog box provides additional capabilities that can be obtained by selecting the desired options. For instance, to obtain a residual plot that shows the predicted value of the dependent variable $\hat{y}$ on the horizontal axis and the standardized residual values on the vertical axis, step 5 would be as follows:

Step 5. When the Regression dialog box appears:
  Enter Sales in the Responses box
  Enter Population in the Continuous predictors box
  Click the **Graphs** button

When the Regression-Graphs dialog box appears:

Select **Standardized** under Residuals for Plots

Select **Residuals versus fits** under Residual Plots

Click **OK**

When the Regression dialog box reappears:

Click **OK**

After a regression model has been estimated, the following steps may be used to obtain confidence intervals and prediction intervals as discussed in Section 14.6.

Step 1. Select the **Stat** menu

Step 2. Select the **Regression** menu

Step 3. Choose **Regression**

Step 4. Choose **Predict**

Step 5. When the Predict dialog box appears:

Select Sales from the drop-down menu in the Response box

Select Enter individual values from the drop-down menu in the next box

Enter 10 in the first box under Population

Click **OK**

Appendix 14.4 Regression Analysis with Excel

DATA *file*

Armand's

In this appendix we will illustrate how Excel's Regression tool can be used to perform the regression analysis computations for the Armand's Pizza Parlors problem. Refer to Figure 14.23 as we describe the steps involved. The labels Restaurant, Population, and Sales

FIGURE 14.23 EXCEL SOLUTION TO THE ARMAND'S PIZZA PARLORS PROBLEM

	A	B	C	D	E	F	G	H	I	J
			fx	Restaurant						
1	**Restaurant**	**Population**	**Sales**							
2	1	2	58							
3	2	6	105							
4	3	8	88							
5	4	8	118							
6	5	12	117							
7	6	16	137							
8	7	20	157							
9	8	20	169							
10	9	22	149							
11	10	26	202							
12										
13	SUMMARY OUTPUT									
14										
15	*Regression Statistics*									
16	Multiple R	0.9501								
17	R Square	0.9027								
18	Adjusted R Square	0.8906								
19	Standard Error	13.8293								
20	Observations	10								
21										
22	ANOVA									
23		*df*	*SS*	*MS*	*F*	*Significance F*				
24	Regression	1	14200	14200	74.2484	2.55E-05				
25	Residual	8	1530	191.25						
26	Total	9	15730							
27										
28		*Coefficients*	*Standard Error*	*t Stat*	*P-value*	*Lower 95%*	*Upper 95%*	*Lower 99.0%*	*Upper 99.0%*	
29	Intercept	60	9.2260	6.5033	0.0002	38.7247	81.2753	29.0431	90.9569	
30	Population	5	0.5803	8.6167	2.55E-05	3.6619	6.3381	3.0530	6.9470	
31										

are entered into cells A1:C1 of the worksheet. To identify each of the 10 observations, we entered the numbers 1 through 10 into cells A2:A11. The sample data are entered into cells B2:C11. The following steps describe how to use Excel to produce the regression results.

Step 1. Click the **Data** tab on the Ribbon
Step 2. In the **Analysis** group, click **Data Analysis**
Step 3. Choose **Regression** from the list of Analysis Tools
Step 4. Click **OK**
Step 5. When the Regression dialog box appears:
   Enter C1:C11 in the **Input Y Range** box
   Enter B1:B11 in the **Input X Range** box
   Select **Labels**
   Select **Confidence Level**
   Enter 99 in the **Confidence Level** box
   Select **Output Range**
   Enter A13 in the **Output Range** box
      (Any upper left-hand corner cell indicating where the output is to begin may be entered here.)
   Click **OK**

The first section of the output, entitled *Regression Statistics*, contains summary statistics such as the coefficient of determination (R Square). The second section of the output, titled ANOVA, contains the analysis of variance table. The last section of the output, which is not titled, contains the estimated regression coefficients and related information. We will begin our discussion of the interpretation of the regression output with the information contained in cells A28:I30.

Interpretation of Estimated Regression Equation Output

The y-intercept of the estimated regression line, $b_0 = 60$, is shown in cell B29, and the slope of the estimated regression line, $b_1 = 5$, is shown in cell B30. The label Intercept in cell A29 and the label Population in cell A30 are used to identify these two values.

In Section 14.5 we showed that the estimated standard deviation of b_1 is $s_{b_1} = .5803$. Note that the value in cell C30 is .5803. The label Standard Error in cell C28 is Excel's way of indicating that the value in cell C30 is the standard error, or standard deviation, of b_1. Recall that the t test for a significant relationship required the computation of the t statistic, $t = b_1/s_{b_1}$. For the Armand's data, the value of t that we computed was $t = 5/.5803 = 8.62$. The label in cell D28, t *Stat*, reminds us that cell D30 contains the value of the t test statistic.

The value in cell E30 is the p-value associated with the t test for significance. Excel has displayed the p-value in cell E30 using scientific notation. To obtain the decimal value, we move the decimal point 5 places to the left, obtaining a value of .0000255. Because the p-value $= .0000255 < \alpha = .01$, we can reject H_0 and conclude that we have a significant relationship between student population and quarterly sales.

The information in cells F28:I30 can be used to develop confidence interval estimates of the y-intercept and slope of the estimated regression equation. Excel always provides the lower and upper limits for a 95% confidence interval. Recall that in step 4 we selected Confidence Level and entered 99 in the Confidence Level box. As a result, Excel's Regression tool also provides the lower and upper limits for a 99% confidence interval. The value in cell H30 is the lower limit for the 99% confidence interval estimate of β_1 and the value in cell I30 is the upper limit. Thus, after rounding, the 99% confidence interval estimate of β_1 is 3.05 to 6.95. The values in cells F30 and G30 provide the lower and upper limits for the 95% confidence interval. Thus, the 95% confidence interval is 3.66 to 6.34.

Interpretation of ANOVA Output

The information in cells A22:F26 is a summary of the analysis of variance computations. The three sources of variation are labeled Regression, Residual, and Total. The label *df* in cell B23 stands for degrees of freedom, the label *SS* in cell C23 stands for sum of squares, and the label *MS* in cell D23 stands for mean square.

In Section 14.5 we stated that the mean square error, obtained by dividing the error or residual sum of squares by its degrees of freedom, provides an estimate of σ^2. The value in cell D25, 191.25, is the mean square error for the Armand's regression output. In Section 14.5 we showed that an *F* test could also be used to test for significance in regression. The value in cell F24, .0000255, is the *p*-value associated with the *F* test for significance. Because the *p*-value = .0000255 < α = .01, we can reject H_0 and conclude that we have a significant relationship between student population and quarterly sales. The label Excel uses to identify the *p*-value for the *F* test for significance, shown in cell F23, is *Significance F*.

The label Significance F may be more meaningful if you think of the value in cell F24 as the observed level of significance for the F test.

Interpretation of Regression Statistics Output

The coefficient of determination, .9027, appears in cell B17; the corresponding label, R Square, is shown in cell A17. The square root of the coefficient of determination provides the sample correlation coefficient of .9501 shown in cell B16. Note that Excel uses the label Multiple R (cell A16) to identify this value. In cell A19, the label Standard Error is used to identify the value of the standard error of the estimate shown in cell B19. Thus, the standard error of the estimate is 13.8293. We caution the reader to keep in mind that in the Excel output, the label Standard Error appears in two different places. In the Regression Statistics section of the output, the label Standard Error refers to the estimate of σ. In the Estimated Regression Equation section of the output, the label *Standard Error* refers to s_{b_1}, the standard deviation of the sampling distribution of b_1.

APPENDIXES

Appendix A: References and Bibliography

General

Freedman, D., R. Pisani, and R. Purves. *Statistics*, 4th ed. W. W. Norton, 2007.

Hogg R. V., E. A. Tanis, and D. L. Zimmerman. *Probability and Statistical Inference*, 9th ed. Prentice Hall, 2015.

McKean, J. W., R. V. Hogg, and A. T. Craig. *Introduction to Mathematical Statistics*, 7th ed. Prentice Hall, 2012.

Miller, I., and M. Miller. *John E. Freund's Mathematical Statistics*, 7th ed. Pearson Prentice Hall, 2014.

Moore, D. S., G. P. McCabe, and B. Craig. *Introduction to the Practice of Statistics*, 7th ed. Freeman, 2010.

Wackerly, D. D., W. Mendenhall, and R. L. Scheaffer. *Mathematical Statistics with Applications*, 7th ed. Cengage Learning, 2007.

Experimental Design

Cochran, W. G., and G. M. Cox. *Experimental Designs*, 2nd ed. Wiley, 1992.

Hicks, C. R., and K. V. Turner. *Fundamental Concepts in the Design of Experiments*, 5th ed. Oxford University Press, 1999.

Montgomery, D. C. *Design and Analysis of Experiments*, 8th ed. Wiley, 2012.

Winer, B. J., K. M. Michels, and D. R. Brown. *Statistical Principles in Experimental Design*, 3rd ed. McGraw-Hill, 1991.

Wu, C. F. Jeff, and M. Hamada. *Experiments: Planning, Analysis, and Optimization*, 2nd ed. Wiley, 2009.

Time Series and Forecasting

Bowerman, B. L., R. T. O'Connell, and A. Koehler. *Forecasting and Time Series: An Applied Approach*, 4th ed. Thomson Learning, 2004.

Box, G. E. P., G. M. Jenkins, and G. C. Reinsel. *Time Series Analysis: Forecasting and Control*, 4th ed. Wiley, 2008.

Makridakis, S. G., S. C. Wheelwright, and R. J. Hyndman. *Forecasting Methods and Applications*, 3rd ed. Wiley, 1997.

Wilson, J. H., B. Keating, and John Galt Solutions, Inc. *Business Forecasting with Accompanying Excel-Based Forecast X^{TM}*, 5th ed. McGraw-Hill/Irwin, 2007.

Index Numbers

U.S. Department of Commerce. *Survey of Current Business.*

U.S. Department of Labor, Bureau of Labor Statistics. *CPI Detailed Report.*

U.S. Department of Labor. *Producer Price Indexes.*

Nonparametric Methods

Conover, W. J. *Practical Nonparametric Statistics*, 3rd ed. Wiley, 1999.

Corder, G. W., and D. I. Foreman. *Nonparametric Statistics: A Step-by-Step Approach*, 2nd ed. Wiley, 2014.

Gibbons, J. D., and S. Chakraborti. *Nonparametric Statistical Inference*, 5th ed. CRC Press, 2010.

Higgins, J. J. *Introduction to Modern Nonparametric Statistics*. Thomson-Brooks/Cole, 2004.

Hollander, M., D. A. Wolfe, and E. Chicken. *Non-Parametric Statistical Methods*, 3rd ed. Wiley, 2013.

Jureckova, J., P. K. Sen, and J. Picek. *Methodology in Robust and Nonparametric Statistics*, 7th ed. CRC Press, 2012.

Probability

Hogg R. V., E. A. Tanis, and D. L. Zimmerman. *Probability and Statistical Inference*, 9th ed. Prentice Hall, 2015.

Ross, S. M. *Introduction to Probability Models*, 11th ed. Academic Press, 2014.

Wackerly, D. D., W. Mendenhall, and R. L. Scheaffer. *Mathematical Statistics with Applications*, 7th ed. Cengage Learning, 2007.

Quality Control

DeFeo, J. A., and J. M. Juran, *Juran's Quality Handbook*, 6th ed. McGraw-Hill, 2010.

Evans, J. R., and W. M. Lindsay. *The Management and Control of Quality*, 6th ed. South-Western, 2006.

Montgomery, D. C. *Introduction to Statistical Quality Control*, 6th ed. Wiley, 2008.

Regression Analysis

Chatterjee, S., and A. S. Hadi. *Regression Analysis by Example*, 5th ed. Wiley, 2012.

Draper, N. R., and H. Smith. *Applied Regression Analysis*, 3rd ed. Wiley, 1998.

Graybill, F. A., and H. K. Iyer. *Regression Analysis: Concepts and Applications*. Wadsworth, 1994.

Hosmer, D. W., and S. Lemeshow. *Applied Logistic Regression*, 2nd ed. Wiley, 2000.

Kleinbaum, D. G., L. L. Kupper, and K. E. Muller. *Applied Regression Analysis and Multivariate Methods*, 4th ed. Cengage Learning, 2007.

Neter, J., W. Wasserman, M. H. Kutner, and C. Nashtsheim. *Applied Linear Statistical Models*, 5th ed. McGraw-Hill, 2004.

Mendenhall, M., T. Sincich., and T. R. Dye. *A Second Course in Statistics: Regression Analysis*, 7th ed. Prentice Hall, 2011.

Decision Analysis

Clemen, R. T., and T. Reilly. *Making Hard Decisions with Decision Tools*, 3rd ed. Cengage Learning, 2014.

Goodwin, P., and G. Wright. *Decision Analysis for Management Judgment*, 5th ed. Wiley, 2014.

Pratt, J. W., H. Raiffa, and R. Schlaifer. *Introduction to Statistical Decision Theory*. MIT Press, 1995.

Sampling

Cochran, W. G. *Sampling Techniques*, 3rd ed. Wiley, 1977.

Hansen, M. H., W. N. Hurwitz, W. G. Madow, and M. N. Hanson. *Sample Survey Methods and Theory*. Wiley, 1993.

Kish, L. *Survey Sampling*. Wiley, 2008.

Levy, P. S., and S. Lemeshow. *Sampling of Populations: Methods and Applications*, 4th ed. Wiley, 2009.

Scheaffer, R. L., W. Mendenhall, and L. Ott. *Elementary Survey Sampling*, 7th ed. Duxbury Press, 2011.

Data Visualization

Cleveland, W. S. *Visualizing Data*. Hobart Press, 1993.

Cleveland, W. S. *The Elements of Graphing Data*, 2nd ed. Hobart Press, 1994.

Few, S. *Show Me the Numbers: Designing Tables and Graphs to Enlighten*, 2nd ed. Analytics Press, 2012.

Few, S. *Information Dashboard Design: The Effective Visual Communication of Data*, 2nd ed. O'Reilly Media, 2012.

Few, S. *Now You See It: Simple Visualization Techniques for Quantitative Analysis*. Analytics Press, 2009.

Fry, B. *Visualizing Data: Exploring and Explaining Data with the Processing Environment*. O'Reilly Media, 2008.

Robbins, N. B. *Creating More Effective Graphs*. Chart House, 2013.

Telea, A. C. *Data Visualization Principles and Practice*. A.K. Peters Ltd., 2008.

Tufte, E. R. *Envisioning Information*. Graphics Press, 1990.

Tufte, E. R. *The Visual Display of Quantitative Information*, 2nd ed. Graphics Press, 1990.

Tufte, E. R. *Visual Explanations: Images and Quantities, Evidence and Narrative*. Graphics Press, 1997.

Tufte, E. R. *Visual and Statistical Thinking: Displays of Evidence for Making Decisions*. Graphics Press, 1997.

Tufte, E. R. *Beautiful Evidence*. Graphics Press, 2006.

Wong, D. M. *The Wall Street Journal Guide to Information Graphics*. W. W. Norton & Company, 2010.

Young, F. W., P. M. Valero-Mora, and M. Friendly. *Visual Statistics: Seeing Data with Dynamic Interactive Graphics*. Wiley, 2006.

Business Analytics

Camm, J. D., J. J. Cochran, M. J. Fry, J. W. Ohlmann, D. R. Anderson, D. J. Sweeney, and T. A. Anderson, *Essentials of Business Analytics*, 1st ed. Cengage Learning, 2014.

Appendix B: Tables

TABLE 1 CUMULATIVE PROBABILITIES FOR THE STANDARD NORMAL DISTRIBUTION

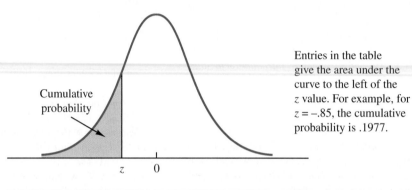

Cumulative probability

Entries in the table give the area under the curve to the left of the z value. For example, for $z = -.85$, the cumulative probability is .1977.

z	.00	.01	.02	.03	.04	.05	.06	.07	.08	.09
−3.0	.0013	.0013	.0013	.0012	.0012	.0011	.0011	.0011	.0010	.0010
−2.9	.0019	.0018	.0018	.0017	.0016	.0016	.0015	.0015	.0014	.0014
−2.8	.0026	.0025	.0024	.0023	.0023	.0022	.0021	.0021	.0020	.0019
−2.7	.0035	.0034	.0033	.0032	.0031	.0030	.0029	.0028	.0027	.0026
−2.6	.0047	.0045	.0044	.0043	.0041	.0040	.0039	.0038	.0037	.0036
−2.5	.0062	.0060	.0059	.0057	.0055	.0054	.0052	.0051	.0049	.0048
−2.4	.0082	.0080	.0078	.0075	.0073	.0071	.0069	.0068	.0066	.0064
−2.3	.0107	.0104	.0102	.0099	.0096	.0094	.0091	.0089	.0087	.0084
−2.2	.0139	.0136	.0132	.0129	.0125	.0122	.0119	.0116	.0113	.0110
−2.1	.0179	.0174	.0170	.0166	.0162	.0158	.0154	.0150	.0146	.0143
−2.0	.0228	.0222	.0217	.0212	.0207	.0202	.0197	.0192	.0188	.0183
−1.9	.0287	.0281	.0274	.0268	.0262	.0256	.0250	.0244	.0239	.0233
−1.8	.0359	.0351	.0344	.0336	.0329	.0322	.0314	.0307	.0301	.0294
−1.7	.0446	.0436	.0427	.0418	.0409	.0401	.0392	.0384	.0375	.0367
−1.6	.0548	.0537	.0526	.0516	.0505	.0495	.0485	.0475	.0465	.0455
−1.5	.0668	.0655	.0643	.0630	.0618	.0606	.0594	.0582	.0571	.0559
−1.4	.0808	.0793	.0778	.0764	.0749	.0735	.0721	.0708	.0694	.0681
−1.3	.0968	.0951	.0934	.0918	.0901	.0885	.0869	.0853	.0838	.0823
−1.2	.1151	.1131	.1112	.1093	.1075	.1056	.1038	.1020	.1003	.0985
−1.1	.1357	.1335	.1314	.1292	.1271	.1251	.1230	.1210	.1190	.1170
−1.0	.1587	.1562	.1539	.1515	.1492	.1469	.1446	.1423	.1401	.1379
−.9	.1841	.1814	.1788	.1762	.1736	.1711	.1685	.1660	.1635	.1611
−.8	.2119	.2090	.2061	.2033	.2005	.1977	.1949	.1922	.1894	.1867
−.7	.2420	.2389	.2358	.2327	.2296	.2266	.2236	.2206	.2177	.2148
−.6	.2743	.2709	.2676	.2643	.2611	.2578	.2546	.2514	.2483	.2451
−.5	.3085	.3050	.3015	.2981	.2946	.2912	.2877	.2843	.2810	.2776
−.4	.3446	.3409	.3372	.3336	.3300	.3264	.3228	.3192	.3156	.3121
−.3	.3821	.3783	.3745	.3707	.3669	.3632	.3594	.3557	.3520	.3483
−.2	.4207	.4168	.4129	.4090	.4052	.4013	.3974	.3936	.3897	.3859
−.1	.4602	.4562	.4522	.4483	.4443	.4404	.4364	.4325	.4286	.4247
−.0	.5000	.4960	.4920	.4880	.4840	.4801	.4761	.4721	.4681	.4641

TABLE 1   CUMULATIVE PROBABILITIES FOR THE STANDARD NORMAL
             DISTRIBUTION (*Continued*)

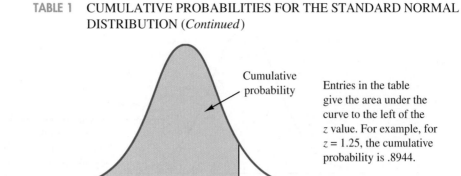

Cumulative
probability

Entries in the table
give the area under the
curve to the left of the
z value. For example, for
z = 1.25, the cumulative
probability is .8944.

z	.00	.01	.02	.03	.04	.05	.06	.07	.08	.09
.0	.5000	.5040	.5080	.5120	.5160	.5199	.5239	.5279	.5319	.5359
.1	.5398	.5438	.5478	.5517	.5557	.5596	.5636	.5675	.5714	.5753
.2	.5793	.5832	.5871	.5910	.5948	.5987	.6026	.6064	.6103	.6141
.3	.6179	.6217	.6255	.6293	.6331	.6368	.6406	.6443	.6480	.6517
.4	.6554	.6591	.6628	.6664	.6700	.6736	.6772	.6808	.6844	.6879
.5	.6915	.6950	.6985	.7019	.7054	.7088	.7123	.7157	.7190	.7224
.6	.7257	.7291	.7324	.7357	.7389	.7422	.7454	.7486	.7517	.7549
.7	.7580	.7611	.7642	.7673	.7704	.7734	.7764	.7794	.7823	.7852
.8	.7881	.7910	.7939	.7967	.7995	.8023	.8051	.8078	.8106	.8133
.9	.8159	.8186	.8212	.8238	.8264	.8289	.8315	.8340	.8365	.8389
1.0	.8413	.8438	.8461	.8485	.8508	.8531	.8554	.8577	.8599	.8621
1.1	.8643	.8665	.8686	.8708	.8729	.8749	.8770	.8790	.8810	.8830
1.2	.8849	.8869	.8888	.8907	.8925	.8944	.8962	.8980	.8997	.9015
1.3	.9032	.9049	.9066	.9082	.9099	.9115	.9131	.9147	.9162	.9177
1.4	.9192	.9207	.9222	.9236	.9251	.9265	.9279	.9292	.9306	.9319
1.5	.9332	.9345	.9357	.9370	.9382	.9394	.9406	.9418	.9429	.9441
1.6	.9452	.9463	.9474	.9484	.9495	.9505	.9515	.9525	.9535	.9545
1.7	.9554	.9564	.9573	.9582	.9591	.9599	.9608	.9616	.9625	.9633
1.8	.9641	.9649	.9656	.9664	.9671	.9678	.9686	.9693	.9699	.9706
1.9	.9713	.9719	.9726	.9732	.9738	.9744	.9750	.9756	.9761	.9767
2.0	.9772	.9778	.9783	.9788	.9793	.9798	.9803	.9808	.9812	.9817
2.1	.9821	.9826	.9830	.9834	.9838	.9842	.9846	.9850	.9854	.9857
2.2	.9861	.9864	.9868	.9871	.9875	.9878	.9881	.9884	.9887	.9890
2.3	.9893	.9896	.9898	.9901	.9904	.9906	.9909	.9911	.9913	.9916
2.4	.9918	.9920	.9922	.9925	.9927	.9929	.9931	.9932	.9934	.9936
2.5	.9938	.9940	.9941	.9943	.9945	.9946	.9948	.9949	.9951	.9952
2.6	.9953	.9955	.9956	.9957	.9959	.9960	.9961	.9962	.9963	.9964
2.7	.9965	.9966	.9967	.9968	.9969	.9970	.9971	.9972	.9973	.9974
2.8	.9974	.9975	.9976	.9977	.9977	.9978	.9979	.9979	.9980	.9981
2.9	.9981	.9982	.9982	.9983	.9984	.9984	.9985	.9985	.9986	.9986
3.0	.9987	.9987	.9987	.9988	.9988	.9989	.9989	.9989	.9990	.9990

TABLE 2   *t* DISTRIBUTION

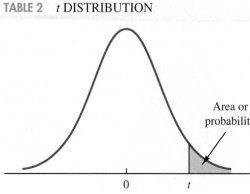

Area or probability Entries in the table give *t* values for an area or probability in the upper tail of the *t* distribution. For example, with 10 degrees of freedom and a .05 area in the upper tail, $t_{.05} = 1.812$.

Degrees of Freedom	Area in Upper Tail					
	.20	.10	.05	.025	.01	.005
1	1.376	3.078	6.314	12.706	31.821	63.656
2	1.061	1.886	2.920	4.303	6.965	9.925
3	.978	1.638	2.353	3.182	4.541	5.841
4	.941	1.533	2.132	2.776	3.747	4.604
5	.920	1.476	2.015	2.571	3.365	4.032
6	.906	1.440	1.943	2.447	3.143	3.707
7	.896	1.415	1.895	2.365	2.998	3.499
8	.889	1.397	1.860	2.306	2.896	3.355
9	.883	1.383	1.833	2.262	2.821	3.250
10	.879	1.372	1.812	2.228	2.764	3.169
11	.876	1.363	1.796	2.201	2.718	3.106
12	.873	1.356	1.782	2.179	2.681	3.055
13	.870	1.350	1.771	2.160	2.650	3.012
14	.868	1.345	1.761	2.145	2.624	2.977
15	.866	1.341	1.753	2.131	2.602	2.947
16	.865	1.337	1.746	2.120	2.583	2.921
17	.863	1.333	1.740	2.110	2.567	2.898
18	.862	1.330	1.734	2.101	2.552	2.878
19	.861	1.328	1.729	2.093	2.539	2.861
20	.860	1.325	1.725	2.086	2.528	2.845
21	.859	1.323	1.721	2.080	2.518	2.831
22	.858	1.321	1.717	2.074	2.508	2.819
23	.858	1.319	1.714	2.069	2.500	2.807
24	.857	1.318	1.711	2.064	2.492	2.797
25	.856	1.316	1.708	2.060	2.485	2.787
26	.856	1.315	1.706	2.056	2.479	2.779
27	.855	1.314	1.703	2.052	2.473	2.771
28	.855	1.313	1.701	2.048	2.467	2.763
29	.854	1.311	1.699	2.045	2.462	2.756
30	.854	1.310	1.697	2.042	2.457	2.750
31	.853	1.309	1.696	2.040	2.453	2.744
32	.853	1.309	1.694	2.037	2.449	2.738
33	.853	1.308	1.692	2.035	2.445	2.733
34	.852	1.307	1.691	2.032	2.441	2.728

TABLE 2   *t* DISTRIBUTION (*Continued*)

Degrees of Freedom	Area in Upper Tail					
	.20	.10	.05	.025	.01	.005
35	.852	1.306	1.690	2.030	2.438	2.724
36	.852	1.306	1.688	2.028	2.434	2.719
37	.851	1.305	1.687	2.026	2.431	2.715
38	.851	1.304	1.686	2.024	2.429	2.712
39	.851	1.304	1.685	2.023	2.426	2.708
40	.851	1.303	1.684	2.021	2.423	2.704
41	.850	1.303	1.683	2.020	2.421	2.701
42	.850	1.302	1.682	2.018	2.418	2.698
43	.850	1.302	1.681	2.017	2.416	2.695
44	.850	1.301	1.680	2.015	2.414	2.692
45	.850	1.301	1.679	2.014	2.412	2.690
46	.850	1.300	1.679	2.013	2.410	2.687
47	.849	1.300	1.678	2.012	2.408	2.685
48	.849	1.299	1.677	2.011	2.407	2.682
49	.849	1.299	1.677	2.010	2.405	2.680
50	.849	1.299	1.676	2.009	2.403	2.678
51	.849	1.298	1.675	2.008	2.402	2.676
52	.849	1.298	1.675	2.007	2.400	2.674
53	.848	1.298	1.674	2.006	2.399	2.672
54	.848	1.297	1.674	2.005	2.397	2.670
55	.848	1.297	1.673	2.004	2.396	2.668
56	.848	1.297	1.673	2.003	2.395	2.667
57	.848	1.297	1.672	2.002	2.394	2.665
58	.848	1.296	1.672	2.002	2.392	2.663
59	.848	1.296	1.671	2.001	2.391	2.662
60	.848	1.296	1.671	2.000	2.390	2.660
61	.848	1.296	1.670	2.000	2.389	2.659
62	.847	1.295	1.670	1.999	2.388	2.657
63	.847	1.295	1.669	1.998	2.387	2.656
64	.847	1.295	1.669	1.998	2.386	2.655
65	.847	1.295	1.669	1.997	2.385	2.654
66	.847	1.295	1.668	1.997	2.384	2.652
67	.847	1.294	1.668	1.996	2.383	2.651
68	.847	1.294	1.668	1.995	2.382	2.650
69	.847	1.294	1.667	1.995	2.382	2.649
70	.847	1.294	1.667	1.994	2.381	2.648
71	.847	1.294	1.667	1.994	2.380	2.647
72	.847	1.293	1.666	1.993	2.379	2.646
73	.847	1.293	1.666	1.993	2.379	2.645
74	.847	1.293	1.666	1.993	2.378	2.644
75	.846	1.293	1.665	1.992	2.377	2.643
76	.846	1.293	1.665	1.992	2.376	2.642
77	.846	1.293	1.665	1.991	2.376	2.641
78	.846	1.292	1.665	1.991	2.375	2.640
79	.846	1.292	1.664	1.990	2.374	2.639

TABLE 2 *t* DISTRIBUTION (*Continued*)

Degrees of Freedom	Area in Upper Tail					
	.20	.10	.05	.025	.01	.005
80	.846	1.292	1.664	1.990	2.374	2.639
81	.846	1.292	1.664	1.990	2.373	2.638
82	.846	1.292	1.664	1.989	2.373	2.637
83	.846	1.292	1.663	1.989	2.372	2.636
84	.846	1.292	1.663	1.989	2.372	2.636
85	.846	1.292	1.663	1.988	2.371	2.635
86	.846	1.291	1.663	1.988	2.370	2.634
87	.846	1.291	1.663	1.988	2.370	2.634
88	.846	1.291	1.662	1.987	2.369	2.633
89	.846	1.291	1.662	1.987	2.369	2.632
90	.846	1.291	1.662	1.987	2.368	2.632
91	.846	1.291	1.662	1.986	2.368	2.631
92	.846	1.291	1.662	1.986	2.368	2.630
93	.846	1.291	1.661	1.986	2.367	2.630
94	.845	1.291	1.661	1.986	2.367	2.629
95	.845	1.291	1.661	1.985	2.366	2.629
96	.845	1.290	1.661	1.985	2.366	2.628
97	.845	1.290	1.661	1.985	2.365	2.627
98	.845	1.290	1.661	1.984	2.365	2.627
99	.845	1.290	1.660	1.984	2.364	2.626
100	.845	1.290	1.660	1.984	2.364	2.626
∞	.842	1.282	1.645	1.960	2.326	2.576

TABLE 3   CHI-SQUARE DISTRIBUTION

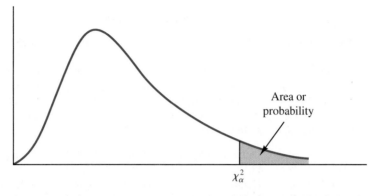

Entries in the table give χ_α^2 values, where α is the area or probability in the upper tail of the chi-square distribution. For example, with 10 degrees of freedom and a .01 area in the upper tail, $\chi_{.01}^2 = 23.209$.

Degrees of Freedom	Area in Upper Tail									
	.995	.99	.975	.95	.90	.10	.05	.025	.01	.005
1	.000	.000	.001	.004	.016	2.706	3.841	5.024	6.635	7.879
2	.010	.020	.051	.103	.211	4.605	5.991	7.378	9.210	10.597
3	.072	.115	.216	.352	.584	6.251	7.815	9.348	11.345	12.838
4	.207	.297	.484	.711	1.064	7.779	9.488	11.143	13.277	14.860
5	.412	.554	.831	1.145	1.610	9.236	11.070	12.832	15.086	16.750
6	.676	.872	1.237	1.635	2.204	10.645	12.592	14.449	16.812	18.548
7	.989	1.239	1.690	2.167	2.833	12.017	14.067	16.013	18.475	20.278
8	1.344	1.647	2.180	2.733	3.490	13.362	15.507	17.535	20.090	21.955
9	1.735	2.088	2.700	3.325	4.168	14.684	16.919	19.023	21.666	23.589
10	2.156	2.558	3.247	3.940	4.865	15.987	18.307	20.483	23.209	25.188
11	2.603	3.053	3.816	4.575	5.578	17.275	19.675	21.920	24.725	26.757
12	3.074	3.571	4.404	5.226	6.304	18.549	21.026	23.337	26.217	28.300
13	3.565	4.107	5.009	5.892	7.041	19.812	22.362	24.736	27.688	29.819
14	4.075	4.660	5.629	6.571	7.790	21.064	23.685	26.119	29.141	31.319
15	4.601	5.229	6.262	7.261	8.547	22.307	24.996	27.488	30.578	32.801
16	5.142	5.812	6.908	7.962	9.312	23.542	26.296	28.845	32.000	34.267
17	5.697	6.408	7.564	8.672	10.085	24.769	27.587	30.191	33.409	35.718
18	6.265	7.015	8.231	9.390	10.865	25.989	28.869	31.526	34.805	37.156
19	6.844	7.633	8.907	10.117	11.651	27.204	30.144	32.852	36.191	38.582
20	7.434	8.260	9.591	10.851	12.443	28.412	31.410	34.170	37.566	39.997
21	8.034	8.897	10.283	11.591	13.240	29.615	32.671	35.479	38.932	41.401
22	8.643	9.542	10.982	12.338	14.041	30.813	33.924	36.781	40.289	42.796
23	9.260	10.196	11.689	13.091	14.848	32.007	35.172	38.076	41.638	44.181
24	9.886	10.856	12.401	13.848	15.659	33.196	36.415	39.364	42.980	45.558
25	10.520	11.524	13.120	14.611	16.473	34.382	37.652	40.646	44.314	46.928
26	11.160	12.198	13.844	15.379	17.292	35.563	38.885	41.923	45.642	48.290
27	11.808	12.878	14.573	16.151	18.114	36.741	40.113	43.195	46.963	49.645
28	12.461	13.565	15.308	16.928	18.939	37.916	41.337	44.461	48.278	50.994
29	13.121	14.256	16.047	17.708	19.768	39.087	42.557	45.722	49.588	52.335

TABLE 3   CHI-SQUARE DISTRIBUTION (*Continued*)

Degrees of Freedom	Area in Upper Tail									
	.995	**.99**	**.975**	**.95**	**.90**	**.10**	**.05**	**.025**	**.01**	**.005**
30	13.787	14.953	16.791	18.493	20.599	40.256	43.773	46.979	50.892	53.672
35	17.192	18.509	20.569	22.465	24.797	46.059	49.802	53.203	57.342	60.275
40	20.707	22.164	24.433	26.509	29.051	51.805	55.758	59.342	63.691	66.766
45	24.311	25.901	28.366	30.612	33.350	57.505	61.656	65.410	69.957	73.166
50	27.991	29.707	32.357	34.764	37.689	63.167	67.505	71.420	76.154	79.490
55	31.735	33.571	36.398	38.958	42.060	68.796	73.311	77.380	82.292	85.749
60	35.534	37.485	40.482	43.188	46.459	74.397	79.082	83.298	88.379	91.952
65	39.383	41.444	44.603	47.450	50.883	79.973	84.821	89.177	94.422	98.105
70	43.275	45.442	48.758	51.739	55.329	85.527	90.531	95.023	100.425	104.215
75	47.206	49.475	52.942	56.054	59.795	91.061	96.217	100.839	106.393	110.285
80	51.172	53.540	57.153	60.391	64.278	96.578	101.879	106.629	112.329	116.321
85	55.170	57.634	61.389	64.749	68.777	102.079	107.522	112.393	118.236	122.324
90	59.196	61.754	65.647	69.126	73.291	107.565	113.145	118.136	124.116	128.299
95	63.250	65.898	69.925	73.520	77.818	113.038	118.752	123.858	129.973	134.247
100	67.328	70.065	74.222	77.929	82.358	118.498	124.342	129.561	135.807	140.170

TABLE 4 *F* DISTRIBUTION

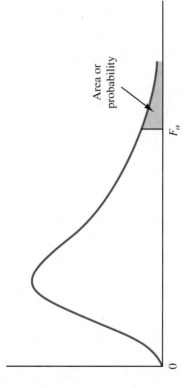

Area or probability

F_α

0

Entries in the table give F_α values, where α is the area or probability in the upper tail of the F distribution. For example, with 4 numerator degrees of freedom, 8 denominator degrees of freedom, and a .05 area in the upper tail, $F_{.05} = 3.84$.

Denominator Degrees of Freedom	Area in Upper Tail	Numerator Degrees of Freedom																	
		1	2	3	4	5	6	7	8	9	10	15	20	25	30	40	60	100	1000
1	.10	39.86	49.50	53.59	55.83	57.24	58.20	58.91	59.44	59.86	60.19	61.22	61.74	62.05	62.26	62.53	62.79	63.01	63.30
	.05	161.45	199.50	215.71	224.58	230.16	233.99	236.77	238.88	240.54	241.88	245.95	248.02	249.26	250.10	251.14	252.20	253.04	254.19
	.025	647.79	799.48	864.15	899.60	921.83	937.11	948.20	956.64	963.28	968.63	984.87	993.08	998.09	1001.40	1005.60	1009.79	1013.16	1017.76
	.01	4052.18	4999.34	5403.53	5624.26	5763.96	5858.95	5928.33	5980.95	6022.40	6055.93	6156.97	6208.66	6239.86	6260.35	6286.43	6312.97	6333.92	6362.80
2	.10	8.53	9.00	9.16	9.24	9.29	9.33	9.35	9.37	9.38	9.39	9.42	9.44	9.45	9.46	9.47	9.47	9.48	9.49
	.05	18.51	19.00	19.16	19.25	19.30	19.33	19.35	19.37	19.38	19.40	19.43	19.45	19.46	19.46	19.47	19.48	19.49	19.49
	.025	38.51	39.00	39.17	39.25	39.30	39.33	39.36	39.37	39.39	39.40	39.43	39.45	39.46	39.46	39.47	39.48	39.49	39.50
	.01	98.50	99.00	99.16	99.25	99.30	99.33	99.36	99.38	99.39	99.40	99.43	99.45	99.46	99.47	99.48	99.48	99.49	99.50
3	.10	5.54	5.46	5.39	5.34	5.31	5.28	5.27	5.25	5.24	5.23	5.20	5.18	5.17	5.17	5.16	5.15	5.14	5.13
	.05	10.13	9.55	9.28	9.12	9.01	8.94	8.89	8.85	8.81	8.79	8.70	8.66	8.63	8.62	8.59	8.57	8.55	8.53
	.025	17.44	16.04	15.44	15.10	14.88	14.73	14.62	14.54	14.47	14.42	14.25	14.17	14.12	14.08	14.04	13.99	13.96	13.91
	.01	34.12	30.82	29.46	28.71	28.24	27.91	27.67	27.49	27.34	27.23	26.87	26.69	26.58	26.50	26.41	26.32	26.24	26.14
4	.10	4.54	4.32	4.19	4.11	4.05	4.01	3.98	3.95	3.94	3.92	3.87	3.84	3.83	3.82	3.80	3.79	3.78	3.76
	.05	7.71	6.94	6.59	6.39	6.26	6.16	6.09	6.04	6.00	5.96	5.86	5.80	5.77	5.75	5.72	5.69	5.66	5.63
	.025	12.22	10.65	9.98	9.60	9.36	9.20	9.07	8.98	8.90	8.84	8.66	8.56	8.50	8.46	8.41	8.36	8.32	8.26
	.01	21.20	18.00	16.69	15.98	15.52	15.21	14.98	14.80	14.66	14.55	14.20	14.02	13.91	13.84	13.75	13.65	13.58	13.47
5	.10	4.06	3.78	3.62	3.52	3.45	3.40	3.37	3.34	3.32	3.30	3.324	3.21	3.19	3.17	3.16	3.14	3.13	3.11
	.05	6.61.	5.79	5.41	5.19	5.05	4.95	4.88	4.82	4.77	4.74	4.62	4.56	4.52	4.50	4.46	4.43	4.41	4.37
	.025	10.01	8.43	7.76	7.39	7.15	6.98	6.85	6.76	6.68	6.62	6.43	6.33	6.27	6.23	6.18	6.12	6.08	6.02
	.01	16.26	13.27	12.06	11.39	10.97	10.67	10.46	10.29	10.16	10.05	9.72	9.55	9.45	9.38	9.29	9.20	9.13	9.03

TABLE 4 *F* DISTRIBUTION (*Continued*)

Denominator Degrees of Freedom	Area in Upper Tail	Numerator Degrees of Freedom																	
		1	2	3	4	5	6	7	8	9	10	15	20	25	30	40	60	100	1000
6	.10	3.78	3.46	3.29	3.18	3.11	3.05	3.01	2.98	2.96	2.94	2.87	2.84	2.81	2.80	2.78	2.76	2.75	2.72
	.05	5.99	5.14	4.76	4.53	4.39	4.28	4.21	4.15	4.10	4.06	3.94	3.87	3.83	3.81	3.77	3.74	3.71	3.67
	.025	8.81	7.26	6.60	6.23	5.99	5.82	5.70	5.60	5.52	5.46	5.27	5.17	5.11	5.07	5.01	4.96	4.92	4.86
	.01	13.75	10.92	9.78	9.15	8.75	8.47	8.26	8.10	7.98	7.87	7.56	7.40	7.30	7.23	7.14	7.06	6.99	6.89
7	.10	3.59	3.26	3.07	2.96	2.88	2.83	2.78	2.75	2.72	2.70	2.63	2.59	2.57	2.56	2.54	2.51	2.50	2.47
	.05	5.59	4.74	4.35	4.12	3.97	3.87	3.79	3.73	3.68	3.64	3.51	3.44	3.40	3.38	3.34	3.30	3.27	3.23
	.025	8.07	6.54	5.89	5.52	5.29	5.12	4.99	4.90	4.82	4.76	4.57	4.47	4.40	4.36	4.31	4.25	4.21	4.15
	.01	12.25	9.55	8.45	7.85	7.46	7.19	6.99	6.84	6.72	6.62	6.31	6.16	6.06	5.99	5.91	5.82	5.75	5.66
8	.10	3.46	3.11	2.92	2.81	2.73	2.67	2.62	2.59	2.56	2.54	2.46	2.42	2.40	2.38	2.36	2.34	2.32	2.30
	.05	5.32	4.46	4.07	3.84	3.69	3.58	3.50	3.44	3.39	3.35	3.22	3.15	3.11	3.08	3.04	3.01	2.97	2.93
	.025	7.57	6.06	5.42	5.05	4.82	4.65	4.53	4.43	4.36	4.30	4.10	4.00	3.94	3.89	3.84	3.78	3.74	3.68
	.01	11.26	8.65	7.59	7.01	6.63	6.37	6.18	6.03	5.91	5.81	5.52	5.36	5.26	5.20	5.12	5.03	4.96	4.87
9	.10	3.36	3.01	2.81	2.69	2.61	2.55	2.51	2.47	2.44	2.42	2.34	2.30	2.27	2.25	2.23	2.21	2.19	2.16
	.05	5.12	4.26	3.86	3.63	3.48	3.37	3.29	3.23	3.18	3.14	3.01	2.94	2.89	2.86	2.83	2.79	2.76	2.71
	.025	7.21	5.71	5.08	4.72	4.48	4.32	4.20	4.10	4.03	3.96	3.77	3.67	3.60	3.56	3.51	3.45	3.40	3.34
	.01	10.56	8.02	6.99	6.42	6.06	5.80	5.61	5.47	5.35	5.26	4.96	4.81	4.71	4.65	4.57	4.48	4.41	4.32
10	.10	3.29	2.92	2.73	2.61	2.52	2.46	2.41	2.38	2.35	2.32	2.24	2.20	2.17	2.16	2.13	2.11	2.09	2.06
	.05	4.96	4.10	3.71	3.48	3.33	3.22	3.14	3.07	3.02	2.98	2.85	2.77	2.73	2.70	2.66	2.62	2.59	2.54
	.025	6.94	5.46	4.83	4.47	4.24	4.07	3.95	3.85	3.78	3.72	3.52	3.42	3.35	3.31	3.26	3.20	3.15	3.09
	.01	10.04	7.56	6.55	5.99	5.64	5.39	5.20	5.06	4.94	4.85	4.56	4.41	4.31	4.25	4.17	4.08	4.01	3.92
11	.10	3.23	2.86	2.66	2.54	2.45	2.39	2.34	2.30	2.27	2.25	2.17	2.12	2.10	2.08	2.05	2.03	2.01	1.98
	.05	4.84	3.98	3.59	3.36	3.20	3.09	3.01	2.95	2.90	2.85	2.72	2.65	2.60	2.57	2.53	2.49	2.46	2.41
	.025	6.72	5.26	4.63	4.28	4.04	3.88	3.76	3.66	3.59	3.53	3.33	3.23	3.16	3.12	3.06	3.00	2.96	2.89
	.01	9.65	7.21	6.22	5.67	5.32	5.07	4.89	4.74	4.63	4.54	4.25	4.10	4.01	3.94	3.86	3.78	3.71	3.61
12	.10	3.18	2.81	2.61	2.48	2.39	2.33	2.28	2.24	2.21	2.19	2.10	2.06	2.03	2.01	1.99	1.96	1.94	1.91
	.05	4.75	3.89	3.49	3.26	3.11	3.00	2.91	2.85	2.80	2.75	2.62	2.54	2.50	2.47	2.43	2.38	2.35	2.30
	.025	6.55	5.10	4.47	4.12	3.89	3.73	3.61	3.51	3.44	3.37	3.18	3.07	3.01	2.96	2.91	2.85	2.80	2.73
	.01	9.33	6.93	5.95	5.41	5.06	4.82	4.64	4.50	4.39	4.30	4.01	3.86	3.76	3.70	3.62	3.54	3.47	3.37
13	.10	3.14	2.76	2.56	2.43	2.35	2.28	2.23	2.20	2.16	2.14	2.05	2.01	1.98	1.96	1.93	1.90	1.88	1.85
	.05	4.67	3.81	3.41	3.18	3.03	2.92	2.83	2.77	2.71	2.67	2.53	2.46	2.41	2.38	2.34	2.30	2.26	2.21
	.025	6.41	4.97	4.35	4.00	3.77	3.60	3.48	3.39	3.31	3.25	3.05	2.95	2.88	2.84	2.78	2.72	2.67	2.60
	.01	9.07	6.70	5.74	5.21	4.86	4.62	4.44	4.30	4.19	4.10	3.82	3.66	3.57	3.51	3.43	3.34	3.27	3.18
14	.10	3.10	2.73	2.52	2.39	2.31	2.24	2.19	2.15	2.12	2.10	2.01	1.96	1.93	1.91	1.89	1.86	1.83	1.80
	.05	4.60	3.74	3.34	3.11	2.96	2.85	2.76	2.70	2.65	2.60	2.46	2.39	2.34	2.31	2.27	2.22	2.19	2.14
	.025	6.30	4.86	4.24	3.89	3.66	3.50	3.38	3.29	3.21	3.15	2.95	2.84	2.78	2.73	2.67	2.61	2.56	2.50
	.01	8.86	6.51	5.56	5.04	4.69	4.46	4.28	4.14	4.03	3.94	3.66	3.51	3.41	3.35	3.27	3.18	3.11	3.02
15	.10	3.07	2.70	2.49	2.36	2.27	2.21	2.16	2.12	2.09	2.06	1.97	1.92	1.89	1.87	1.85	1.82	1.79	1.76
	.05	4.54	3.68	3.29	3.06	2.90	2.79	2.71	2.64	2.59	2.54	2.40	2.33	2.28	2.25	2.20	2.16	2.12	2.07
	.025	6.20	4.77	4.15	3.80	3.58	3.41	3.29	3.20	3.12	3.06	2.86	2.76	2.69	2.64	2.59	2.52	2.47	2.40
	.01	8.68	6.36	5.42	4.89	4.56	4.32	4.14	4.00	3.89	3.80	3.52	3.37	3.28	3.21	3.13	3.05	2.98	2.88

Denominator Degrees of Freedom	Area in Upper Tail	Numerator Degrees of Freedom																	
		1	2	3	4	5	6	7	8	9	10	15	20	25	30	40	60	100	1000
16	.10	3.05	2.67	2.46	2.33	2.24	2.18	2.13	2.09	2.06	2.03	1.94	1.89	1.86	1.84	1.81	1.78	1.76	1.72
	.05	4.49	3.63	3.24	3.01	2.85	2.74	2.66	2.59	2.54	2.49	2.35	2.28	2.23	2.19	2.15	2.11	2.07	2.02
	.025	6.12	4.69	4.08	3.73	3.50	3.34	3.22	3.12	3.05	2.99	2.79	2.68	2.61	2.57	2.51	2.45	2.40	2.32
	.01	8.53	6.23	5.29	4.77	4.44	4.20	4.03	3.89	3.78	3.69	3.41	3.26	3.16	3.10	3.02	2.93	2.86	2.76
17	.10	3.03	2.64	2.44	2.31	2.22	2.15	2.10	2.06	2.03	2.00	1.91	1.86	1.83	1.81	1.78	1.75	1.73	1.69
	.05	4.45	3.59	3.20	2.96	2.81	2.70	2.61	2.55	2.49	2.45	2.31	2.23	2.18	2.15	2.10	2.06	2.02	1.97
	.025	6.04	4.62	4.01	3.66	3.44	3.28	3.16	3.06	2.98	2.92	2.72	2.62	2.55	2.50	2.44	2.38	2.33	2.26
	.01	8.40	6.11	5.19	4.67	4.34	4.10	3.93	3.79	3.68	3.59	3.31	3.16	3.07	3.00	2.92	2.83	2.76	2.66
18	.10	3.01	2.62	2.42	2.29	2.20	2.13	2.08	2.04	2.00	1.98	1.89	1.84	1.80	1.78	1.75	1.72	1.70	1.66
	.05	4.41	3.55	3.16	2.93	2.77	2.66	2.58	2.51	2.46	2.41	2.27	2.19	2.14	2.11	2.06	2.02	1.98	1.92
	.025	5.98	4.56	3.95	3.61	3.38	3.22	3.10	3.01	2.93	2.87	2.67	2.56	2.49	2.44	2.38	2.32	2.27	2.20
	.01	8.29	6.01	5.09	4.58	4.25	4.01	3.84	3.71	3.60	3.51	3.23	3.08	2.98	2.92	2.84	2.75	2.68	2.58
19	.10	2.99	2.61	2.40	2.27	2.18	2.11	2.06	2.02	1.98	1.96	1.86	1.81	1.78	1.76	1.73	1.70	1.67	1.64
	.05	4.38	3.52	3.13	2.90	2.74	2.63	2.54	2.48	2.42	2.38	2.23	2.16	2.11	2.07	2.03	1.98	1.94	1.88
	.025	5.92	4.51	3.90	3.56	3.33	3.17	3.05	2.96	2.88	2.82	2.62	2.51	2.44	2.39	2.33	2.27	2.22	2.14
	.01	8.18	5.93	5.01	4.50	4.17	3.94	3.77	3.63	3.52	3.43	3.15	3.00	2.91	2.84	2.76	2.67	2.60	2.50
20	.10	2.97	2.59	2.38	2.25	2.16	2.09	2.04	2.00	1.96	1.94	1.84	1.79	1.76	1.74	1.71	1.68	1.65	1.61
	.05	4.35	3.49	3.10	2.87	2.71	2.60	2.51	2.45	2.39	2.35	2.20	2.12	2.07	2.04	1.99	1.95	1.91	1.85
	.025	5.87	4.46	3.86	3.51	3.29	3.13	3.01	2.91	2.84	2.77	2.57	2.46	2.40	2.35	2.29	2.22	2.17	2.09
	.01	8.10	5.85	4.94	4.43	4.10	3.87	3.70	3.56	3.46	3.37	3.09	2.94	2.84	2.78	2.69	2.61	2.54	2.43
21	.10	2.96	2.57	2.36	2.23	2.14	2.08	2.02	1.98	1.95	1.92	1.83	1.78	1.74	1.72	1.69	1.66	1.63	1.59
	.05	4.32	3.47	3.07	2.84	2.68	2.57	2.49	2.42	2.37	2.32	2.18	2.10	2.05	2.01	1.96	1.92	1.88	1.82
	.025	5.83	4.42	3.82	3.48	3.25	3.09	2.97	2.87	2.80	2.73	2.53	2.42	2.36	2.31	2.25	2.18	2.13	2.05
	.01	8.02	5.78	4.87	4.37	4.04	3.81	3.64	3.51	3.40	3.31	3.03	2.88	2.79	2.72	2.64	2.55	2.48	2.37
22	.10	2.95	2.56	2.35	2.22	2.13	2.06	2.01	1.97	1.93	1.90	1.81	1.76	1.73	1.70	1.67	1.64	1.61	1.57
	.05	4.30	3.44	3.05	2.82	2.66	2.55	2.46	2.40	2.34	2.30	2.15	2.07	2.02	1.98	1.94	1.89	1.85	1.79
	.025	5.79	4.38	3.78	3.44	3.22	3.05	2.93	2.84	2.76	2.70	2.50	2.39	2.32	2.27	2.21	2.14	2.09	2.01
	.01	7.95	5.72	4.82	4.31	3.99	3.76	3.59	3.45	3.35	3.26	2.98	2.83	2.73	2.67	2.58	2.50	2.42	2.32
23	.10	2.94	2.55	2.34	2.21	2.11	2.05	1.99	1.95	1.92	1.89	1.80	1.74	1.71	1.69	1.66	1.62	1.59	1.55
	.05	4.28	3.42	3.03	2.80	2.64	2.53	2.44	2.37	2.32	2.27	2.13	2.05	2.00	1.96	1.91	1.86	1.82	1.76
	.025	5.75	4.35	3.75	3.41	3.18	3.02	2.90	2.81	2.73	2.67	2.47	2.36	2.29	2.24	2.18	2.11	2.06	1.98
	.01	7.88	5.66	4.76	4.26	3.94	3.71	3.54	3.41	3.30	3.21	2.93	2.78	2.69	2.62	2.54	2.45	2.37	2.27
24	.10	2.93	2.54	2.33	2.19	2.10	2.04	1.98	1.94	1.91	1.88	1.78	1.73	1.70	1.67	1.64	1.61	1.58	1.54
	.05	4.26	3.40	3.01	2.78	2.62	2.51	2.42	2.36	2.30	2.25	2.11	2.03	1.97	1.94	1.89	1.84	1.80	1.74
	.025	5.72	4.32	3.72	3.38	3.15	2.99	2.87	2.78	2.70	2.64	2.44	2.33	2.26	2.21	2.15	2.08	2.02	1.94
	.01	7.82	5.61	4.72	4.22	3.90	3.67	3.50	3.36	3.26	3.17	2.89	2.74	2.64	2.58	2.49	2.40	2.33	2.22

TABLE 4 F DISTRIBUTION (*Continued*)

Denominator Degrees of Freedom	Area in Upper Tail	1	2	3	4	5	6	7	8	9	10	15	20	25	30	40	60	100	1000
25	.10	2.92	2.53	2.32	2.18	2.09	2.02	1.97	1.93	1.89	1.87	1.77	1.72	1.68	1.66	1.63	1.59	1.56	1.52
	.05	4.24	3.39	2.99	2.76	2.60	2.49	2.40	2.34	2.28	2.24	2.09	2.01	1.96	1.92	1.87	1.82	1.78	1.72
	.025	5.69	4.29	3.69	3.35	3.13	2.97	2.85	2.75	2.68	2.61	2.41	2.30	2.23	2.18	2.12	2.05	2.00	1.91
	.01	7.77	5.57	4.68	4.18	3.85	3.63	3.46	3.32	3.22	3.13	2.85	2.70	2.60	2.54	2.45	2.36	2.29	2.18
26	.10	2.91	2.52	2.31	2.17	2.08	2.01	1.96	1.92	1.88	1.86	1.76	1.71	1.67	1.65	1.61	1.58	1.55	1.51
	.05	4.23	3.37	2.98	2.74	2.59	2.47	2.39	2.32	2.27	2.22	2.07	1.99	1.94	1.90	1.85	1.80	1.76	1.70
	.025	5.66	4.27	3.67	3.33	3.10	2.94	2.82	2.73	2.65	2.59	2.39	2.28	2.21	2.16	2.09	2.03	1.97	1.89
	.01	7.72	5.53	4.64	4.14	3.82	3.59	3.42	3.29	3.18	3.09	2.81	2.66	2.57	2.50	2.42	2.33	2.25	2.14
27	.10	2.90	2.51	2.30	2.17	2.07	2.00	1.95	1.91	1.87	1.85	1.75	1.70	1.66	1.64	1.60	1.57	1.54	1.50
	.05	4.21	3.35	2.96	2.73	2.57	2.46	2.37	2.31	2.25	2.20	2.06	1.97	1.92	1.88	1.84	1.79	1.74	1.68
	.025	5.63	4.24	3.65	3.31	3.08	2.92	2.80	2.71	2.63	2.57	2.36	2.25	2.18	2.13	2.07	2.00	1.94	1.86
	.01	7.68	5.49	4.60	4.11	3.78	3.56	3.39	3.26	3.15	3.06	2.78	2.63	2.54	2.47	2.38	2.29	2.22	2.11
28	.10	2.89	2.50	2.29	2.16	2.06	2.00	1.94	1.90	1.87	1.84	1.74	1.69	1.65	1.63	1.59	1.56	1.53	1.48
	.05	4.20	3.34	2.95	2.71	2.56	2.45	2.36	2.29	2.24	2.19	2.04	1.96	1.91	1.87	1.82	1.77	1.73	1.66
	.025	5.61	4.22	3.63	3.29	3.06	2.90	2.78	2.69	2.61	2.55	2.34	2.23	2.16	2.11	2.05	1.98	1.92	1.84
	.01	7.64	5.45	4.57	4.07	3.75	3.53	3.36	3.23	3.12	3.03	2.75	2.60	2.51	2.44	2.35	2.26	2.19	2.08
29	.10	2.89	2.50	2.28	2.15	2.06	1.99	1.93	1.89	1.86	1.83	1.73	1.68	1.64	1.62	1.58	1.55	1.52	1.47
	.05	4.18	3.33	2.93	2.70	2.55	2.43	2.35	2.28	2.22	2.18	2.03	1.94	1.89	1.85	1.81	1.75	1.71	1.65
	.025	5.59	4.20	3.61	3.27	3.04	2.88	2.76	2.67	2.59	2.53	2.32	2.21	2.14	2.09	2.03	1.96	1.90	1.82
	.01	7.60	5.42	4.54	4.04	3.73	3.50	3.33	3.20	3.09	3.00	2.73	2.57	2.48	2.41	2.33	2.23	2.16	2.05
30	.10	2.88	2.49	2.28	2.14	2.05	1.98	1.93	1.88	1.85	1.82	1.72	1.67	1.63	1.61	1.57	1.54	1.51	1.46
	.05	4.17	3.32	2.92	2.69	2.53	2.42	2.33	2.27	2.21	2.16	2.01	1.93	1.88	1.84	1.79	1.74	1.70	1.63
	.025	5.57	4.18	3.59	3.25	3.03	2.87	2.75	2.65	2.57	2.51	2.31	2.20	2.12	2.07	2.01	1.94	1.88	1.80
	.01	7.56	5.39	4.51	4.02	3.70	3.47	3.30	3.17	3.07	2.98	2.70	2.55	2.45	2.39	2.30	2.21	2.13	2.02
40	.10	2.84	2.44	2.23	2.09	2.00	1.93	1.87	1.83	1.79	1.76	1.66	1.61	1.57	1.54	1.51	1.47	1.43	1.38
	.05	4.08	3.23	2.84	2.61	2.45	2.34	2.25	2.18	2.12	2.08	1.92	1.84	1.78	1.74	1.69	1.64	1.59	1.52
	.025	5.42	4.05	3.46	3.13	2.90	2.74	2.62	2.53	2.45	2.39	2.18	2.07	1.99	1.94	1.88	1.80	1.74	1.65
	.01	7.31	5.18	4.31	3.83	3.51	3.29	3.12	2.99	2.89	2.80	2.52	2.37	2.27	2.20	2.11	2.02	1.94	1.82
60	.10	2.79	2.39	2.18	2.04	1.95	1.87	1.82	1.77	1.74	1.71	1.60	1.54	1.50	1.48	1.44	1.40	1.36	1.30
	.05	4.00	3.15	2.76	2.53	2.37	2.25	2.17	2.10	2.04	1.99	1.84	1.75	1.69	1.65	1.59	1.53	1.48	1.40
	.025	5.29	3.93	3.34	3.01	2.79	2.63	2.51	2.41	2.33	2.27	2.06	1.94	1.87	1.82	1.74	1.67	1.60	1.49
	.01	7.08	4.98	4.13	3.65	3.34	3.12	2.95	2.82	2.72	2.63	2.35	2.20	2.10	2.03	1.94	1.84	1.75	1.62
100	.10	2.76	2.36	2.14	2.00	1.91	1.83	1.78	1.73	1.69	1.66	1.56	1.49	1.45	1.42	1.38	1.34	1.29	1.22
	.05	3.94	3.09	2.70	2.46	2.31	2.19	2.10	2.03	1.97	1.93	1.77	1.68	1.62	1.57	1.52	1.45	1.39	1.30
	.025	5.18	3.83	3.25	2.92	2.70	2.54	2.42	2.32	2.24	2.18	1.97	1.85	1.77	1.71	1.64	1.56	1.48	1.36
	.01	6.90	4.82	3.98	3.51	3.21	2.99	2.82	2.69	2.59	2.50	2.22	2.07	1.97	1.89	1.80	1.69	1.60	1.45
1000	.10	2.71	2.31	2.09	1.95	1.85	1.78	1.72	1.68	1.64	1.61	1.49	1.43	1.38	1.35	1.30	1.25	1.20	1.08
	.05	3.85	3.00	2.61	2.38	2.22	2.11	2.02	1.95	1.89	1.84	1.68	1.58	1.52	1.47	1.41	1.33	1.26	1.11
	.025	5.04	3.70	3.13	2.80	2.58	2.42	2.30	2.20	2.13	2.06	1.85	1.72	1.64	1.58	1.50	1.41	1.32	1.13
	.01	6.66	4.63	3.80	3.34	3.04	2.82	2.66	2.53	2.43	2.34	2.06	1.90	1.79	1.72	1.61	1.50	1.38	1.16

Numerator Degrees of Freedom

TABLE 5   BINOMIAL PROBABILITIES

Entries in the table give the probability of x successes in n trials of a binomial experiment, where p is the probability of a success on one trial. For example, with six trials and $p = .05$, the probability of two successes is .0305.

						p				
n	x	.01	.02	.03	.04	.05	.06	.07	.08	.09
2	0	.9801	.9604	.9409	.9216	.9025	.8836	.8649	.8464	.8281
	1	.0198	.0392	.0582	.0768	.0950	.1128	.1302	.1472	.1638
	2	.0001	.0004	.0009	.0016	.0025	.0036	.0049	.0064	.0081
3	0	.9703	.9412	.9127	.8847	.8574	.8306	.8044	.7787	.7536
	1	.0294	.0576	.0847	.1106	.1354	.1590	.1816	.2031	.2236
	2	.0003	.0012	.0026	.0046	.0071	.0102	.0137	.0177	.0221
	3	.0000	.0000	.0000	.0001	.0001	.0002	.0003	.0005	.0007
4	0	.9606	.9224	.8853	.8493	.8145	.7807	.7481	.7164	.6857
	1	.0388	.0753	.1095	.1416	.1715	.1993	.2252	.2492	.2713
	2	.0006	.0023	.0051	.0088	.0135	.0191	.0254	.0325	.0402
	3	.0000	.0000	.0001	.0002	.0005	.0008	.0013	.0019	.0027
	4	.0000	.0000	.0000	.0000	.0000	.0000	.0000	.0000	.0001
5	0	.9510	.9039	.8587	.8154	.7738	.7339	.6957	.6591	.6240
	1	.0480	.0922	.1328	.1699	.2036	.2342	.2618	.2866	.3086
	2	.0010	.0038	.0082	.0142	.0214	.0299	.0394	.0498	.0610
	3	.0000	.0001	.0003	.0006	.0011	.0019	.0030	.0043	.0060
	4	.0000	.0000	.0000	.0000	.0000	.0001	.0001	.0002	.0003
	5	.0000	.0000	.0000	.0000	.0000	.0000	.0000	.0000	.0000
6	0	.9415	.8858	.8330	.7828	.7351	.6899	.6470	.6064	.5679
	1	.0571	.1085	.1546	.1957	.2321	.2642	.2922	.3164	.3370
	2	.0014	.0055	.0120	.0204	.0305	.0422	.0550	.0688	.0833
	3	.0000	.0002	.0005	.0011	.0021	.0036	.0055	.0080	.0110
	4	.0000	.0000	.0000	.0000	.0001	.0002	.0003	.0005	.0008
	5	.0000	.0000	.0000	.0000	.0000	.0000	.0000	.0000	.0000
	6	.0000	.0000	.0000	.0000	.0000	.0000	.0000	.0000	.0000
7	0	.9321	.8681	.8080	.7514	.6983	.6485	.6017	.5578	.5168
	1	.0659	.1240	.1749	.2192	.2573	.2897	.3170	.3396	.3578
	2	.0020	.0076	.0162	.0274	.0406	.0555	.0716	.0886	.1061
	3	.0000	.0003	.0008	.0019	.0036	.0059	.0090	.0128	.0175
	4	.0000	.0000	.0000	.0001	.0002	.0004	.0007	.0011	.0017
	5	.0000	.0000	.0000	.0000	.0000	.0000	.0000	.0001	.0001
	6	.0000	.0000	.0000	.0000	.0000	.0000	.0000	.0000	.0000
	7	.0000	.0000	.0000	.0000	.0000	.0000	.0000	.0000	.0000
8	0	.9227	.8508	.7837	.7214	.6634	.6096	.5596	.5132	.4703
	1	.0746	.1389	.1939	.2405	.2793	.3113	.3370	.3570	.3721
	2	.0026	.0099	.0210	.0351	.0515	.0695	.0888	.1087	.1288
	3	.0001	.0004	.0013	.0029	.0054	.0089	.0134	.0189	.0255
	4	.0000	.0000	.0001	.0002	.0004	.0007	.0013	.0021	.0031
	5	.0000	.0000	.0000	.0000	.0000	.0000	.0001	.0001	.0002
	6	.0000	.0000	.0000	.0000	.0000	.0000	.0000	.0000	.0000
	7	.0000	.0000	.0000	.0000	.0000	.0000	.0000	.0000	.0000
	8	.0000	.0000	.0000	.0000	.0000	.0000	.0000	.0000	.0000

TABLE 5   BINOMIAL PROBABILITIES (*Continued*)

						p				
n	x	.01	.02	.03	.04	.05	.06	.07	.08	.09
9	0	.9135	.8337	.7602	.6925	.6302	.5730	.5204	.4722	.4279
	1	.0830	.1531	.2116	.2597	.2985	.3292	.3525	.3695	.3809
	2	.0034	.0125	.0262	.0433	.0629	.0840	.1061	.1285	.1507
	3	.0001	.0006	.0019	.0042	.0077	.0125	.0186	.0261	.0348
	4	.0000	.0000	.0001	.0003	.0006	.0012	.0021	.0034	.0052
	5	.0000	.0000	.0000	.0000	.0000	.0001	.0002	.0003	.0005
	6	.0000	.0000	.0000	.0000	.0000	.0000	.0000	.0000	.0000
	7	.0000	.0000	.0000	.0000	.0000	.0000	.0000	.0000	.0000
	8	.0000	.0000	.0000	.0000	.0000	.0000	.0000	.0000	.0000
	9	.0000	.0000	.0000	.0000	.0000	.0000	.0000	.0000	.0000
10	0	.9044	.8171	.7374	.6648	.5987	.5386	.4840	.4344	.3894
	1	.0914	.1667	.2281	.2770	.3151	.3438	.3643	.3777	.3851
	2	.0042	.0153	.0317	.0519	.0746	.0988	.1234	.1478	.1714
	3	.0001	.0008	.0026	.0058	.0105	.0168	.0248	.0343	.0452
	4	.0000	.0000	.0001	.0004	.0010	.0019	.0033	.0052	.0078
	5	.0000	.0000	.0000	.0000	.0001	.0001	.0003	.0005	.0009
	6	.0000	.0000	.0000	.0000	.0000	.0000	.0000	.0000	.0001
	7	.0000	.0000	.0000	.0000	.0000	.0000	.0000	.0000	.0000
	8	.0000	.0000	.0000	.0000	.0000	.0000	.0000	.0000	.0000
	9	.0000	.0000	.0000	.0000	.0000	.0000	.0000	.0000	.0000
	10	.0000	.0000	.0000	.0000	.0000	.0000	.0000	.0000	.0000
12	0	.8864	.7847	.6938	.6127	.5404	.4759	.4186	.3677	.3225
	1	.1074	.1922	.2575	.3064	.3413	.3645	.3781	.3837	.3827
	2	.0060	.0216	.0438	.0702	.0988	.1280	.1565	.1835	.2082
	3	.0002	.0015	.0045	.0098	.0173	.0272	.0393	.0532	.0686
	4	.0000	.0001	.0003	.0009	.0021	.0039	.0067	.0104	.0153
	5	.0000	.0000	.0000	.0001	.0002	.0004	.0008	.0014	.0024
	6	.0000	.0000	.0000	.0000	.0000	.0000	.0001	.0001	.0003
	7	.0000	.0000	.0000	.0000	.0000	.0000	.0000	.0000	.0000
	8	.0000	.0000	.0000	.0000	.0000	.0000	.0000	.0000	.0000
	9	.0000	.0000	.0000	.0000	.0000	.0000	.0000	.0000	.0000
	10	.0000	.0000	.0000	.0000	.0000	.0000	.0000	.0000	.0000
	11	.0000	.0000	.0000	.0000	.0000	.0000	.0000	.0000	.0000
	12	.0000	.0000	.0000	.0000	.0000	.0000	.0000	.0000	.0000
15	0	.8601	.7386	.6333	.5421	.4633	.3953	.3367	.2863	.2430
	1	.1303	.2261	.2938	.3388	.3658	.3785	.3801	.3734	.3605
	2	.0092	.0323	.0636	.0988	.1348	.1691	.2003	.2273	.2496
	3	.0004	.0029	.0085	.0178	.0307	.0468	.0653	.0857	.1070
	4	.0000	.0002	.0008	.0022	.0049	.0090	.0148	.0223	.0317
	5	.0000	.0000	.0001	.0002	.0006	.0013	.0024	.0043	.0069
	6	.0000	.0000	.0000	.0000	.0000	.0001	.0003	.0006	.0011
	7	.0000	.0000	.0000	.0000	.0000	.0000	.0000	.0001	.0001
	8	.0000	.0000	.0000	.0000	.0000	.0000	.0000	.0000	.0000
	9	.0000	.0000	.0000	.0000	.0000	.0000	.0000	.0000	.0000
	10	.0000	.0000	.0000	.0000	.0000	.0000	.0000	.0000	.0000
	11	.0000	.0000	.0000	.0000	.0000	.0000	.0000	.0000	.0000
	12	.0000	.0000	.0000	.0000	.0000	.0000	.0000	.0000	.0000
	13	.0000	.0000	.0000	.0000	.0000	.0000	.0000	.0000	.0000
	14	.0000	.0000	.0000	.0000	.0000	.0000	.0000	.0000	.0000
	15	.0000	.0000	.0000	.0000	.0000	.0000	.0000	.0000	.0000

TABLE 5   BINOMIAL PROBABILITIES (*Continued*)

n	x	.01	.02	.03	.04	.05	.06	.07	.08	.09
18	0	.8345	.6951	.5780	.4796	.3972	.3283	.2708	.2229	.1831
	1	.1517	.2554	.3217	.3597	.3763	.3772	.3669	.3489	.3260
	2	.0130	.0443	.0846	.1274	.1683	.2047	.2348	.2579	.2741
	3	.0007	.0048	.0140	.0283	.0473	.0697	.0942	.1196	.1446
	4	.0000	.0004	.0016	.0044	.0093	.0167	.0266	.0390	.0536
	5	.0000	.0000	.0001	.0005	.0014	.0030	.0056	.0095	.0148
	6	.0000	.0000	.0000	.0000	.0002	.0004	.0009	.0018	.0032
	7	.0000	.0000	.0000	.0000	.0000	.0000	.0001	.0003	.0005
	8	.0000	.0000	.0000	.0000	.0000	.0000	.0000	.0000	.0001
	9	.0000	.0000	.0000	.0000	.0000	.0000	.0000	.0000	.0000
	10	.0000	.0000	.0000	.0000	.0000	.0000	.0000	.0000	.0000
	11	.0000	.0000	.0000	.0000	.0000	.0000	.0000	.0000	.0000
	12	.0000	.0000	.0000	.0000	.0000	.0000	.0000	.0000	.0000
	13	.0000	.0000	.0000	.0000	.0000	.0000	.0000	.0000	.0000
	14	.0000	.0000	.0000	.0000	.0000	.0000	.0000	.0000	.0000
	15	.0000	.0000	.0000	.0000	.0000	.0000	.0000	.0000	.0000
	16	.0000	.0000	.0000	.0000	.0000	.0000	.0000	.0000	.0000
	17	.0000	.0000	.0000	.0000	.0000	.0000	.0000	.0000	.0000
	18	.0000	.0000	.0000	.0000	.0000	.0000	.0000	.0000	.0000
20	0	.8179	.6676	.5438	.4420	.3585	.2901	.2342	.1887	.1516
	1	.1652	.2725	.3364	.3683	.3774	.3703	.3526	.3282	.3000
	2	.0159	.0528	.0988	.1458	.1887	.2246	.2521	.2711	.2818
	3	.0010	.0065	.0183	.0364	.0596	.0860	.1139	.1414	.1672
	4	.0000	.0006	.0024	.0065	.0133	.0233	.0364	.0523	.0703
	5	.0000	.0000	.0002	.0009	.0022	.0048	.0088	.0145	.0222
	6	.0000	.0000	.0000	.0001	.0003	.0008	.0017	.0032	.0055
	7	.0000	.0000	.0000	.0000	.0000	.0001	.0002	.0005	.0011
	8	.0000	.0000	.0000	.0000	.0000	.0000	.0000	.0001	.0002
	9	.0000	.0000	.0000	.0000	.0000	.0000	.0000	.0000	.0000
	10	.0000	.0000	.0000	.0000	.0000	.0000	.0000	.0000	.0000
	11	.0000	.0000	.0000	.0000	.0000	.0000	.0000	.0000	.0000
	12	.0000	.0000	.0000	.0000	.0000	.0000	.0000	.0000	.0000
	13	.0000	.0000	.0000	.0000	.0000	.0000	.0000	.0000	.0000
	14	.0000	.0000	.0000	.0000	.0000	.0000	.0000	.0000	.0000
	15	.0000	.0000	.0000	.0000	.0000	.0000	.0000	.0000	.0000
	16	.0000	.0000	.0000	.0000	.0000	.0000	.0000	.0000	.0000
	17	.0000	.0000	.0000	.0000	.0000	.0000	.0000	.0000	.0000
	18	.0000	.0000	.0000	.0000	.0000	.0000	.0000	.0000	.0000
	19	.0000	.0000	.0000	.0000	.0000	.0000	.0000	.0000	.0000
	20	.0000	.0000	.0000	.0000	.0000	.0000	.0000	.0000	.0000

TABLE 5   BINOMIAL PROBABILITIES (*Continued*)

n	x	.10	.15	.20	.25	.30	.35	.40	.45	.50
						p				
2	0	.8100	.7225	.6400	.5625	.4900	.4225	.3600	.3025	.2500
	1	.1800	.2550	.3200	.3750	.4200	.4550	.4800	.4950	.5000
	2	.0100	.0225	.0400	.0625	.0900	.1225	.1600	.2025	.2500
3	0	.7290	.6141	.5120	.4219	.3430	.2746	.2160	.1664	.1250
	1	.2430	.3251	.3840	.4219	.4410	.4436	.4320	.4084	.3750
	2	.0270	.0574	.0960	.1406	.1890	.2389	.2880	.3341	.3750
	3	.0010	.0034	.0080	.0156	.0270	.0429	.0640	.0911	.1250
4	0	.6561	.5220	.4096	.3164	.2401	.1785	.1296	.0915	.0625
	1	.2916	.3685	.4096	.4219	.4116	.3845	.3456	.2995	.2500
	2	.0486	.0975	.1536	.2109	.2646	.3105	.3456	.3675	.3750
	3	.0036	.0115	.0256	.0469	.0756	.1115	.1536	.2005	.2500
	4	.0001	.0005	.0016	.0039	.0081	.0150	.0256	.0410	.0625
5	0	.5905	.4437	.3277	.2373	.1681	.1160	.0778	.0503	.0312
	1	.3280	.3915	.4096	.3955	.3602	.3124	.2592	.2059	.1562
	2	.0729	.1382	.2048	.2637	.3087	.3364	.3456	.3369	.3125
	3	.0081	.0244	.0512	.0879	.1323	.1811	.2304	.2757	.3125
	4	.0004	.0022	.0064	.0146	.0284	.0488	.0768	.1128	.1562
	5	.0000	.0001	.0003	.0010	.0024	.0053	.0102	.0185	.0312
6	0	.5314	.3771	.2621	.1780	.1176	.0754	.0467	.0277	.0156
	1	.3543	.3993	.3932	.3560	.3025	.2437	.1866	.1359	.0938
	2	.0984	.1762	.2458	.2966	.3241	.3280	.3110	.2780	.2344
	3	.0146	.0415	.0819	.1318	.1852	.2355	.2765	.3032	.3125
	4	.0012	.0055	.0154	.0330	.0595	.0951	.1382	.1861	.2344
	5	.0001	.0004	.0015	.0044	.0102	.0205	.0369	.0609	.0938
	6	.0000	.0000	.0001	.0002	.0007	.0018	.0041	.0083	.0156
7	0	.4783	.3206	.2097	.1335	.0824	.0490	.0280	.0152	.0078
	1	.3720	.3960	.3670	.3115	.2471	.1848	.1306	.0872	.0547
	2	.1240	.2097	.2753	.3115	.3177	.2985	.2613	.2140	.1641
	3	.0230	.0617	.1147	.1730	.2269	.2679	.2903	.2918	.2734
	4	.0026	.0109	.0287	.0577	.0972	.1442	.1935	.2388	.2734
	5	.0002	.0012	.0043	.0115	.0250	.0466	.0774	.1172	.1641
	6	.0000	.0001	.0004	.0013	.0036	.0084	.0172	.0320	.0547
	7	.0000	.0000	.0000	.0001	.0002	.0006	.0016	.0037	.0078
8	0	.4305	.2725	.1678	.1001	.0576	.0319	.0168	.0084	.0039
	1	.3826	.3847	.3355	.2670	.1977	.1373	.0896	.0548	.0312
	2	.1488	.2376	.2936	.3115	.2965	.2587	.2090	.1569	.1094
	3	.0331	.0839	.1468	.2076	.2541	.2786	.2787	.2568	.2188
	4	.0046	.0185	.0459	.0865	.1361	.1875	.2322	.2627	.2734
	5	.0004	.0026	.0092	.0231	.0467	.0808	.1239	.1719	.2188
	6	.0000	.0002	.0011	.0038	.0100	.0217	.0413	.0703	.1094
	7	.0000	.0000	.0001	.0004	.0012	.0033	.0079	.0164	.0313
	8	.0000	.0000	.0000	.0000	.0001	.0002	.0007	.0017	.0039

TABLE 5   BINOMIAL PROBABILITIES (*Continued*)

n	x	.10	.15	.20	.25	.30	.35	.40	.45	.50
9	0	.3874	.2316	.1342	.0751	.0404	.0207	.0101	.0046	.0020
	1	.3874	.3679	.3020	.2253	.1556	.1004	.0605	.0339	.0176
	2	.1722	.2597	.3020	.3003	.2668	.2162	.1612	.1110	.0703
	3	.0446	.1069	.1762	.2336	.2668	.2716	.2508	.2119	.1641
	4	.0074	.0283	.0661	.1168	.1715	.2194	.2508	.2600	.2461
	5	.0008	.0050	.0165	.0389	.0735	.1181	.1672	.2128	.2461
	6	.0001	.0006	.0028	.0087	.0210	.0424	.0743	.1160	.1641
	7	.0000	.0000	.0003	.0012	.0039	.0098	.0212	.0407	.0703
	8	.0000	.0000	.0000	.0001	.0004	.0013	.0035	.0083	.0176
	9	.0000	.0000	.0000	.0000	.0000	.0001	.0003	.0008	.0020
10	0	.3487	.1969	.1074	.0563	.0282	.0135	.0060	.0025	.0010
	1	.3874	.3474	.2684	.1877	.1211	.0725	.0403	.0207	.0098
	2	.1937	.2759	.3020	.2816	.2335	.1757	.1209	.0763	.0439
	3	.0574	.1298	.2013	.2503	.2668	.2522	.2150	.1665	.1172
	4	.0112	.0401	.0881	.1460	.2001	.2377	.2508	.2384	.2051
	5	.0015	.0085	.0264	.0584	.1029	.1536	.2007	.2340	.2461
	6	.0001	.0012	.0055	.0162	.0368	.0689	.1115	.1596	.2051
	7	.0000	.0001	.0008	.0031	.0090	.0212	.0425	.0746	.1172
	8	.0000	.0000	.0001	.0004	.0014	.0043	.0106	.0229	.0439
	9	.0000	.0000	.0000	.0000	.0001	.0005	.0016	.0042	.0098
	10	.0000	.0000	.0000	.0000	.0000	.0000	.0001	.0003	.0010
12	0	.2824	.1422	.0687	.0317	.0138	.0057	.0022	.0008	.0002
	1	.3766	.3012	.2062	.1267	.0712	.0368	.0174	.0075	.0029
	2	.2301	.2924	.2835	.2323	.1678	.1088	.0639	.0339	.0161
	3	.0853	.1720	.2362	.2581	.2397	.1954	.1419	.0923	.0537
	4	.0213	.0683	.1329	.1936	.2311	.2367	.2128	.1700	.1208
	5	.0038	.0193	.0532	.1032	.1585	.2039	.2270	.2225	.1934
	6	.0005	.0040	.0155	.0401	.0792	.1281	.1766	.2124	.2256
	7	.0000	.0006	.0033	.0115	.0291	.0591	.1009	.1489	.1934
	8	.0000	.0001	.0005	.0024	.0078	.0199	.0420	.0762	.1208
	9	.0000	.0000	.0001	.0004	.0015	.0048	.0125	.0277	.0537
	10	.0000	.0000	.0000	.0000	.0002	.0008	.0025	.0068	.0161
	11	.0000	.0000	.0000	.0000	.0000	.0001	.0003	.0010	.0029
	12	.0000	.0000	.0000	.0000	.0000	.0000	.0000	.0001	.0002
15	0	.2059	.0874	.0352	.0134	.0047	.0016	.0005	.0001	.0000
	1	.3432	.2312	.1319	.0668	.0305	.0126	.0047	.0016	.0005
	2	.2669	.2856	.2309	.1559	.0916	.0476	.0219	.0090	.0032
	3	.1285	.2184	.2501	.2252	.1700	.1110	.0634	.0318	.0139
	4	.0428	.1156	.1876	.2252	.2186	.1792	.1268	.0780	.0417
	5	.0105	.0449	.1032	.1651	.2061	.2123	.1859	.1404	.0916
	6	.0019	.0132	.0430	.0917	.1472	.1906	.2066	.1914	.1527
	7	.0003	.0030	.0138	.0393	.0811	.1319	.1771	.2013	.1964
	8	.0000	.0005	.0035	.0131	.0348	.0710	.1181	.1647	.1964
	9	.0000	.0001	.0007	.0034	.0016	.0298	.0612	.1048	.1527
	10	.0000	.0000	.0001	.0007	.0030	.0096	.0245	.0515	.0916
	11	.0000	.0000	.0000	.0001	.0006	.0024	.0074	.0191	.0417
	12	.0000	.0000	.0000	.0000	.0001	.0004	.0016	.0052	.0139
	13	.0000	.0000	.0000	.0000	.0000	.0001	.0003	.0010	.0032
	14	.0000	.0000	.0000	.0000	.0000	.0000	.0000	.0001	.0005
	15	.0000	.0000	.0000	.0000	.0000	.0000	.0000	.0000	.0000

TABLE 5   BINOMIAL PROBABILITIES (*Continued*)

n	x	.10	.15	.20	.25	.30	.35	.40	.45	.50
						p				
18	0	.1501	.0536	.0180	.0056	.0016	.0004	.0001	.0000	.0000
	1	.3002	.1704	.0811	.0338	.0126	.0042	.0012	.0003	.0001
	2	.2835	.2556	.1723	.0958	.0458	.0190	.0069	.0022	.0006
	3	.1680	.2406	.2297	.1704	.1046	.0547	.0246	.0095	.0031
	4	.0700	.1592	.2153	.2130	.1681	.1104	.0614	.0291	.0117
	5	.0218	.0787	.1507	.1988	.2017	.1664	.1146	.0666	.0327
	6	.0052	.0301	.0816	.1436	.1873	.1941	.1655	.1181	.0708
	7	.0010	.0091	.0350	.0820	.1376	.1792	.1892	.1657	.1214
	8	.0002	.0022	.0120	.0376	.0811	.1327	.1734	.1864	.1669
	9	.0000	.0004	.0033	.0139	.0386	.0794	.1284	.1694	.1855
	10	.0000	.0001	.0008	.0042	.0149	.0385	.0771	.1248	.1669
	11	.0000	.0000	.0001	.0010	.0046	.0151	.0374	.0742	.1214
	12	.0000	.0000	.0000	.0002	.0012	.0047	.0145	.0354	.0708
	13	.0000	.0000	.0000	.0000	.0002	.0012	.0045	.0134	.0327
	14	.0000	.0000	.0000	.0000	.0000	.0002	.0011	.0039	.0117
	15	.0000	.0000	.0000	.0000	.0000	.0000	.0002	.0009	.0031
	16	.0000	.0000	.0000	.0000	.0000	.0000	.0000	.0001	.0006
	17	.0000	.0000	.0000	.0000	.0000	.0000	.0000	.0000	.0001
	18	.0000	.0000	.0000	.0000	.0000	.0000	.0000	.0000	.0000
20	0	.1216	.0388	.0115	.0032	.0008	.0002	.0000	.0000	.0000
	1	.2702	.1368	.0576	.0211	.0068	.0020	.0005	.0001	.0000
	2	.2852	.2293	.1369	.0669	.0278	.0100	.0031	.0008	.0002
	3	.1901	.2428	.2054	.1339	.0716	.0323	.0123	.0040	.0011
	4	.0898	.1821	.2182	.1897	.1304	.0738	.0350	.0139	.0046
	5	.0319	.1028	.1746	.2023	.1789	.1272	.0746	.0365	.0148
	6	.0089	.0454	.1091	.1686	.1916	.1712	.1244	.0746	.0370
	7	.0020	.0160	.0545	.1124	.1643	.1844	.1659	.1221	.0739
	8	.0004	.0046	.0222	.0609	.1144	.1614	.1797	.1623	.1201
	9	.0001	.0011	.0074	.0271	.0654	.1158	.1597	.1771	.1602
	10	.0000	.0002	.0020	.0099	.0308	.0686	.1171	.1593	.1762
	11	.0000	.0000	.0005	.0030	.0120	.0336	.0710	.1185	.1602
	12	.0000	.0000	.0001	.0008	.0039	.0136	.0355	.0727	.1201
	13	.0000	.0000	.0000	.0002	.0010	.0045	.0146	.0366	.0739
	14	.0000	.0000	.0000	.0000	.0002	.0012	.0049	.0150	.0370
	15	.0000	.0000	.0000	.0000	.0000	.0003	.0013	.0049	.0148
	16	.0000	.0000	.0000	.0000	.0000	.0000	.0003	.0013	.0046
	17	.0000	.0000	.0000	.0000	.0000	.0000	.0000	.0002	.0011
	18	.0000	.0000	.0000	.0000	.0000	.0000	.0000	.0000	.0002
	19	.0000	.0000	.0000	.0000	.0000	.0000	.0000	.0000	.0000
	20	.0000	.0000	.0000	.0000	.0000	.0000	.0000	.0000	.0000

TABLE 5   BINOMIAL PROBABILITIES (*Continued*)

						p				
n	*x*	.55	.60	.65	.70	.75	.80	.85	.90	.95
2	0	.2025	.1600	.1225	.0900	.0625	.0400	.0225	.0100	.0025
	1	.4950	.4800	.4550	.4200	.3750	.3200	.2550	.1800	.0950
	2	.3025	.3600	.4225	.4900	.5625	.6400	.7225	.8100	.9025
3	0	.0911	.0640	.0429	.0270	.0156	.0080	.0034	.0010	.0001
	1	.3341	.2880	.2389	.1890	.1406	.0960	.0574	.0270	.0071
	2	.4084	.4320	.4436	.4410	.4219	.3840	.3251	.2430	.1354
	3	.1664	.2160	.2746	.3430	.4219	.5120	.6141	.7290	.8574
4	0	.0410	.0256	.0150	.0081	.0039	.0016	.0005	.0001	.0000
	1	.2005	.1536	.1115	.0756	.0469	.0256	.0115	.0036	.0005
	2	.3675	.3456	.3105	.2646	.2109	.1536	.0975	.0486	.0135
	3	.2995	.3456	.3845	.4116	.4219	.4096	.3685	.2916	.1715
	4	.0915	.1296	.1785	.2401	.3164	.4096	.5220	.6561	.8145
5	0	.0185	.0102	.0053	.0024	.0010	.0003	.0001	.0000	.0000
	1	.1128	.0768	.0488	.0284	.0146	.0064	.0022	.0005	.0000
	2	.2757	.2304	.1811	.1323	.0879	.0512	.0244	.0081	.0011
	3	.3369	.3456	.3364	.3087	.2637	.2048	.1382	.0729	.0214
	4	.2059	.2592	.3124	.3601	.3955	.4096	.3915	.3281	.2036
	5	.0503	.0778	.1160	.1681	.2373	.3277	.4437	.5905	.7738
6	0	.0083	.0041	.0018	.0007	.0002	.0001	.0000	.0000	.0000
	1	.0609	.0369	.0205	.0102	.0044	.0015	.0004	.0001	.0000
	2	.1861	.1382	.0951	.0595	.0330	.0154	.0055	.0012	.0001
	3	.3032	.2765	.2355	.1852	.1318	.0819	.0415	.0146	.0021
	4	.2780	.3110	.3280	.3241	.2966	.2458	.1762	.0984	.0305
	5	.1359	.1866	.2437	.3025	.3560	.3932	.3993	.3543	.2321
	6	.0277	.0467	.0754	.1176	.1780	.2621	.3771	.5314	.7351
7	0	.0037	.0016	.0006	.0002	.0001	.0000	.0000	.0000	.0000
	1	.0320	.0172	.0084	.0036	.0013	.0004	.0001	.0000	.0000
	2	.1172	.0774	.0466	.0250	.0115	.0043	.0012	.0002	.0000
	3	.2388	.1935	.1442	.0972	.0577	.0287	.0109	.0026	.0002
	4	.2918	.2903	.2679	.2269	.1730	.1147	.0617	.0230	.0036
	5	.2140	.2613	.2985	.3177	.3115	.2753	.2097	.1240	.0406
	6	.0872	.1306	.1848	.2471	.3115	.3670	.3960	.3720	.2573
	7	.0152	.0280	.0490	.0824	.1335	.2097	.3206	.4783	.6983
8	0	.0017	.0007	.0002	.0001	.0000	.0000	.0000	.0000	.0000
	1	.0164	.0079	.0033	.0012	.0004	.0001	.0000	.0000	.0000
	2	.0703	.0413	.0217	.0100	.0038	.0011	.0002	.0000	.0000
	3	.1719	.1239	.0808	.0467	.0231	.0092	.0026	.0004	.0000
	4	.2627	.2322	.1875	.1361	.0865	.0459	.0185	.0046	.0004
	5	.2568	.2787	.2786	.2541	.2076	.1468	.0839	.0331	.0054
	6	.1569	.2090	.2587	.2965	.3115	.2936	.2376	.1488	.0515
	7	.0548	.0896	.1373	.1977	.2670	.3355	.3847	.3826	.2793
	8	.0084	.0168	.0319	.0576	.1001	.1678	.2725	.4305	.6634

TABLE 5   BINOMIAL PROBABILITIES (*Continued*)

n	x	.55	.60	.65	.70	.75	.80	.85	.90	.95
9	0	.0008	.0003	.0001	.0000	.0000	.0000	.0000	.0000	.0000
	1	.0083	.0035	.0013	.0004	.0001	.0000	.0000	.0000	.0000
	2	.0407	.0212	.0098	.0039	.0012	.0003	.0000	.0000	.0000
	3	.1160	.0743	.0424	.0210	.0087	.0028	.0006	.0001	.0000
	4	.2128	.1672	.1181	.0735	.0389	.0165	.0050	.0008	.0000
	5	.2600	.2508	.2194	.1715	.1168	.0661	.0283	.0074	.0006
	6	.2119	.2508	.2716	.2668	.2336	.1762	.1069	.0446	.0077
	7	.1110	.1612	.2162	.2668	.3003	.3020	.2597	.1722	.0629
	8	.0339	.0605	.1004	.1556	.2253	.3020	.3679	.3874	.2985
	9	.0046	.0101	.0207	.0404	.0751	.1342	.2316	.3874	.6302
10	0	.0003	.0001	.0000	.0000	.0000	.0000	.0000	.0000	.0000
	1	.0042	.0016	.0005	.0001	.0000	.0000	.0000	.0000	.0000
	2	.0229	.0106	.0043	.0014	.0004	.0001	.0000	.0000	.0000
	3	.0746	.0425	.0212	.0090	.0031	.0008	.0001	.0000	.0000
	4	.1596	.1115	.0689	.0368	.0162	.0055	.0012	.0001	.0000
	5	.2340	.2007	.1536	.1029	.0584	.0264	.0085	.0015	.0001
	6	.2384	.2508	.2377	.2001	.1460	.0881	.0401	.0112	.0010
	7	.1665	.2150	.2522	.2668	.2503	.2013	.1298	.0574	.0105
	8	.0763	.1209	.1757	.2335	.2816	.3020	.2759	.1937	.0746
	9	.0207	.0403	.0725	.1211	.1877	.2684	.3474	.3874	.3151
	10	.0025	.0060	.0135	.0282	.0563	.1074	.1969	.3487	.5987
12	0	.0001	.0000	.0000	.0000	.0000	.0000	.0000	.0000	.0000
	1	.0010	.0003	.0001	.0000	.0000	.0000	.0000	.0000	.0000
	2	.0068	.0025	.0008	.0002	.0000	.0000	.0000	.0000	.0000
	3	.0277	.0125	.0048	.0015	.0004	.0001	.0000	.0000	.0000
	4	.0762	.0420	.0199	.0078	.0024	.0005	.0001	.0000	.0000
	5	.1489	.1009	.0591	.0291	.0115	.0033	.0006	.0000	.0000
	6	.2124	.1766	.1281	.0792	.0401	.0155	.0040	.0005	.0000
	7	.2225	.2270	.2039	.1585	.1032	.0532	.0193	.0038	.0002
	8	.1700	.2128	.2367	.2311	.1936	.1329	.0683	.0213	.0021
	9	.0923	.1419	.1954	.2397	.2581	.2362	.1720	.0852	.0173
	10	.0339	.0639	.1088	.1678	.2323	.2835	.2924	.2301	.0988
	11	.0075	.0174	.0368	.0712	.1267	.2062	.3012	.3766	.3413
	12	.0008	.0022	.0057	.0138	.0317	.0687	.1422	.2824	.5404
15	0	.0000	.0000	.0000	.0000	.0000	.0000	.0000	.0000	.0000
	1	.0001	.0000	.0000	.0000	.0000	.0000	.0000	.0000	.0000
	2	.0010	.0003	.0001	.0000	.0000	.0000	.0000	.0000	.0000
	3	.0052	.0016	.0004	.0001	.0000	.0000	.0000	.0000	.0000
	4	.0191	.0074	.0024	.0006	.0001	.0000	.0000	.0000	.0000
	5	.0515	.0245	.0096	.0030	.0007	.0001	.0000	.0000	.0000
	6	.1048	.0612	.0298	.0116	.0034	.0007	.0001	.0000	.0000
	7	.1647	.1181	.0710	.0348	.0131	.0035	.0005	.0000	.0000
	8	.2013	.1771	.1319	.0811	.0393	.0138	.0030	.0003	.0000
	9	.1914	.2066	.1906	.1472	.0917	.0430	.0132	.0019	.0000
	10	.1404	.1859	.2123	.2061	.1651	.1032	.0449	.0105	.0006
	11	.0780	.1268	.1792	.2186	.2252	.1876	.1156	.0428	.0049

TABLE 5   BINOMIAL PROBABILITIES (*Continued*)

n	x	.55	.60	.65	.70	.75	.80	.85	.90	.95
						p				
	12	.0318	.0634	.1110	.1700	.2252	.2501	.2184	.1285	.0307
	13	.0090	.0219	.0476	.0916	.1559	.2309	.2856	.2669	.1348
	14	.0016	.0047	.0126	.0305	.0668	.1319	.2312	.3432	.3658
	15	.0001	.0005	.0016	.0047	.0134	.0352	.0874	.2059	.4633
18	0	.0000	.0000	.0000	.0000	.0000	.0000	.0000	.0000	.0000
	1	.0000	.0000	.0000	.0000	.0000	.0000	.0000	.0000	.0000
	2	.0001	.0000	.0000	.0000	.0000	.0000	.0000	.0000	.0000
	3	.0009	.0002	.0000	.0000	.0000	.0000	.0000	.0000	.0000
	4	.0039	.0011	.0002	.0000	.0000	.0000	.0000	.0000	.0000
	5	.0134	.0045	.0012	.0002	.0000	.0000	.0000	.0000	.0000
	6	.0354	.0145	.0047	.0012	.0002	.0000	.0000	.0000	.0000
	7	.0742	.0374	.0151	.0046	.0010	.0001	.0000	.0000	.0000
	8	.1248	.0771	.0385	.0149	.0042	.0008	.0001	.0000	.0000
	9	.1694	.1284	.0794	.0386	.0139	.0033	.0004	.0000	.0000
	10	.1864	.1734	.1327	.0811	.0376	.0120	.0022	.0002	.0000
	11	.1657	.1892	.1792	.1376	.0820	.0350	.0091	.0010	.0000
	12	.1181	.1655	.1941	.1873	.1436	.0816	.0301	.0052	.0002
	13	.0666	.1146	.1664	.2017	.1988	.1507	.0787	.0218	.0014
	14	.0291	.0614	.1104	.1681	.2130	.2153	.1592	.0700	.0093
	15	.0095	.0246	.0547	.1046	.1704	.2297	.2406	.1680	.0473
	16	.0022	.0069	.0190	.0458	.0958	.1723	.2556	.2835	.1683
	17	.0003	.0012	.0042	.0126	.0338	.0811	.1704	.3002	.3763
	18	.0000	.0001	.0004	.0016	.0056	.0180	.0536	.1501	.3972
20	0	.0000	.0000	.0000	.0000	.0000	.0000	.0000	.0000	.0000
	1	.0000	.0000	.0000	.0000	.0000	.0000	.0000	.0000	.0000
	2	.0000	.0000	.0000	.0000	.0000	.0000	.0000	.0000	.0000
	3	.0002	.0000	.0000	.0000	.0000	.0000	.0000	.0000	.0000
	4	.0013	.0003	.0000	.0000	.0000	.0000	.0000	.0000	.0000
	5	.0049	.0013	.0003	.0000	.0000	.0000	.0000	.0000	.0000
	6	.0150	.0049	.0012	.0002	.0000	.0000	.0000	.0000	.0000
	7	.0366	.0146	.0045	.0010	.0002	.0000	.0000	.0000	.0000
	8	.0727	.0355	.0136	.0039	.0008	.0001	.0000	.0000	.0000
	9	.1185	.0710	.0336	.0120	.0030	.0005	.0000	.0000	.0000
	10	.1593	.1171	.0686	.0308	.0099	.0020	.0002	.0000	.0000
	11	.1771	.1597	.1158	.0654	.0271	.0074	.0011	.0001	.0000
	12	.1623	.1797	.1614	.1144	.0609	.0222	.0046	.0004	.0000
	13	.1221	.1659	.1844	.1643	.1124	.0545	.0160	.0020	.0000
	14	.0746	.1244	.1712	.1916	.1686	.1091	.0454	.0089	.0003
	15	.0365	.0746	.1272	.1789	.2023	.1746	.1028	.0319	.0022
	16	.0139	.0350	.0738	.1304	.1897	.2182	.1821	.0898	.0133
	17	.0040	.0123	.0323	.0716	.1339	.2054	.2428	.1901	.0596
	18	.0008	.0031	.0100	.0278	.0669	.1369	.2293	.2852	.1887
	19	.0001	.0005	.0020	.0068	.0211	.0576	.1368	.2702	.3774
	20	.0000	.0000	.0002	.0008	.0032	.0115	.0388	.1216	.3585

TABLE 6   VALUES OF $e^{-\mu}$

μ	$e^{-\mu}$	μ	$e^{-\mu}$	μ	$e^{-\mu}$
.00	1.0000	2.00	.1353	4.00	.0183
.05	.9512	2.05	.1287	4.05	.0174
.10	.9048	2.10	.1225	4.10	.0166
.15	.8607	2.15	.1165	4.15	.0158
.20	.8187	2.20	.1108	4.20	.0150
.25	.7788	2.25	.1054	4.25	.0143
.30	.7408	2.30	.1003	4.30	.0136
.35	.7047	2.35	.0954	4.35	.0129
.40	.6703	2.40	.0907	4.40	.0123
.45	.6376	2.45	.0863	4.45	.0117
.50	.6065	2.50	.0821	4.50	.0111
.55	.5769	2.55	.0781	4.55	.0106
.60	.5488	2.60	.0743	4.60	.0101
.65	.5220	2.65	.0707	4.65	.0096
.70	.4966	2.70	.0672	4.70	.0091
.75	.4724	2.75	.0639	4.75	.0087
.80	.4493	2.80	.0608	4.80	.0082
.85	.4274	2.85	.0578	4.85	.0078
.90	.4066	2.90	.0550	4.90	.0074
.95	.3867	2.95	.0523	4.95	.0071
1.00	.3679	3.00	.0498	5.00	.0067
1.05	.3499	3.05	.0474	6.00	.0025
1.10	.3329	3.10	.0450	7.00	.0009
1.15	.3166	3.15	.0429	8.00	.000335
1.20	.3012	3.20	.0408	9.00	.000123
				10.00	.000045
1.25	.2865	3.25	.0388		
1.30	.2725	3.30	.0369		
1.35	.2592	3.35	.0351		
1.40	.2466	3.40	.0334		
1.45	.2346	3.45	.0317		
1.50	.2231	3.50	.0302		
1.55	.2122	3.55	.0287		
1.60	.2019	3.60	.0273		
1.65	.1920	3.65	.0260		
1.70	.1827	3.70	.0247		
1.75	.1738	3.75	.0235		
1.80	.1653	3.80	.0224		
1.85	.1572	3.85	.0213		
1.90	.1496	3.90	.0202		
1.95	.1423	3.95	.0193		

TABLE 7   POISSON PROBABILITIES

Entries in the table give the probability of x occurrences for a Poisson process with a mean μ. For example, when $\mu = 2.5$, the probability of four occurrences is .1336.

| | μ | | | | | | | | | |
x	0.1	0.2	0.3	0.4	0.5	0.6	0.7	0.8	0.9	1.0
0	.9048	.8187	.7408	.6703	.6065	.5488	.4966	.4493	.4066	.3679
1	.0905	.1637	.2222	.2681	.3033	.3293	.3476	.3595	.3659	.3679
2	.0045	.0164	.0333	.0536	.0758	.0988	.1217	.1438	.1647	.1839
3	.0002	.0011	.0033	.0072	.0126	.0198	.0284	.0383	.0494	.0613
4	.0000	.0001	.0002	.0007	.0016	.0030	.0050	.0077	.0111	.0153
5	.0000	.0000	.0000	.0001	.0002	.0004	.0007	.0012	.0020	.0031
6	.0000	.0000	.0000	.0000	.0000	.0000	.0001	.0002	.0003	.0005
7	.0000	.0000	.0000	.0000	.0000	.0000	.0000	.0000	.0000	.0001

| | μ | | | | | | | | | |
x	1.1	1.2	1.3	1.4	1.5	1.6	1.7	1.8	1.9	2.0
0	.3329	.3012	.2725	.2466	.2231	.2019	.1827	.1653	.1496	.1353
1	.3662	.3614	.3543	.3452	.3347	.3230	.3106	.2975	.2842	.2707
2	.2014	.2169	.2303	.2417	.2510	.2584	.2640	.2678	.2700	.2707
3	.0738	.0867	.0998	.1128	.1255	.1378	.1496	.1607	.1710	.1804
4	.0203	.0260	.0324	.0395	.0471	.0551	.0636	.0723	.0812	.0902
5	.0045	.0062	.0084	.0111	.0141	.0176	.0216	.0260	.0309	.0361
6	.0008	.0012	.0018	.0026	.0035	.0047	.0061	.0078	.0098	.0120
7	.0001	.0002	.0003	.0005	.0008	.0011	.0015	.0020	.0027	.0034
8	.0000	.0000	.0001	.0001	.0001	.0002	.0003	.0005	.0006	.0009
9	.0000	.0000	.0000	.0000	.0000	.0000	.0001	.0001	.0001	.0002

| | μ | | | | | | | | | |
x	2.1	2.2	2.3	2.4	2.5	2.6	2.7	2.8	2.9	3.0
0	.1225	.1108	.1003	.0907	.0821	.0743	.0672	.0608	.0550	.0498
1	.2572	.2438	.2306	.2177	.2052	.1931	.1815	.1703	.1596	.1494
2	.2700	.2681	.2652	.2613	.2565	.2510	.2450	.2384	.2314	.2240
3	.1890	.1966	.2033	.2090	.2138	.2176	.2205	.2225	.2237	.2240
4	.0992	.1082	.1169	.1254	.1336	.1414	.1488	.1557	.1622	.1680
5	.0417	.0476	.0538	.0602	.0668	.0735	.0804	.0872	.0940	.1008
6	.0146	.0174	.0206	.0241	.0278	.0319	.0362	.0407	.0455	.0504
7	.0044	.0055	.0068	.0083	.0099	.0118	.0139	.0163	.0188	.0216
8	.0011	.0015	.0019	.0025	.0031	.0038	.0047	.0057	.0068	.0081
9	.0003	.0004	.0005	.0007	.0009	.0011	.0014	.0018	.0022	.0027
10	.0001	.0001	.0001	.0002	.0002	.0003	.0004	.0005	.0006	.0008
11	.0000	.0000	.0000	.0000	.0000	.0001	.0001	.0001	.0002	.0002
12	.0000	.0000	.0000	.0000	.0000	.0000	.0000	.0000	.0000	.0001

TABLE 7   POISSON PROBABILITIES (*Continued*)

x	μ 3.1	3.2	3.3	3.4	3.5	3.6	3.7	3.8	3.9	4.0
0	.0450	.0408	.0369	.0344	.0302	.0273	.0247	.0224	.0202	.0183
1	.1397	.1304	.1217	.1135	.1057	.0984	.0915	.0850	.0789	.0733
2	.2165	.2087	.2008	.1929	.1850	.1771	.1692	.1615	.1539	.1465
3	.2237	.2226	.2209	.2186	.2158	.2125	.2087	.2046	.2001	.1954
4	.1734	.1781	.1823	.1858	.1888	.1912	.1931	.1944	.1951	.1954
5	.1075	.1140	.1203	.1264	.1322	.1377	.1429	.1477	.1522	.1563
6	.0555	.0608	.0662	.0716	.0771	.0826	.0881	.0936	.0989	.1042
7	.0246	.0278	.0312	.0348	.0385	.0425	.0466	.0508	.0551	.0595
8	.0095	.0111	.0129	.0148	.0169	.0191	.0215	.0241	.0269	.0298
9	.0033	.0040	.0047	.0056	.0066	.0076	.0089	.0102	.0116	.0132
10	.0010	.0013	.0016	.0019	.0023	.0028	.0033	.0039	.0045	.0053
11	.0003	.0004	.0005	.0006	.0007	.0009	.0011	.0013	.0016	.0019
12	.0001	.0001	.0001	.0002	.0002	.0003	.0003	.0004	.0005	.0006
13	.0000	.0000	.0000	.0000	.0001	.0001	.0001	.0001	.0002	.0002
14	.0000	.0000	.0000	.0000	.0000	.0000	.0000	.0000	.0000	.0001

x	μ 4.1	4.2	4.3	4.4	4.5	4.6	4.7	4.8	4.9	5.0
0	.0166	.0150	.0136	.0123	.0111	.0101	.0091	.0082	.0074	.0067
1	.0679	.0630	.0583	.0540	.0500	.0462	.0427	.0395	.0365	.0337
2	.1393	.1323	.1254	.1188	.1125	.1063	.1005	.0948	.0894	.0842
3	.1904	.1852	.1798	.1743	.1687	.1631	.1574	.1517	.1460	.1404
4	.1951	.1944	.1933	.1917	.1898	.1875	.1849	.1820	.1789	.1755
5	.1600	.1633	.1662	.1687	.1708	.1725	.1738	.1747	.1753	.1755
6	.1093	.1143	.1191	.1237	.1281	.1323	.1362	.1398	.1432	.1462
7	.0640	.0686	.0732	.0778	.0824	.0869	.0914	.0959	.1002	.1044
8	.0328	.0360	.0393	.0428	.0463	.0500	.0537	.0575	.0614	.0653
9	.0150	.0168	.0188	.0209	.0232	.0255	.0280	.0307	.0334	.0363
10	.0061	.0071	.0081	.0092	.0104	.0118	.0132	.0147	.0164	.0181
11	.0023	.0027	.0032	.0037	.0043	.0049	.0056	.0064	.0073	.0082
12	.0008	.0009	.0011	.0014	.0016	.0019	.0022	.0026	.0030	.0034
13	.0002	.0003	.0004	.0005	.0006	.0007	.0008	.0009	.0011	.0013
14	.0001	.0001	.0001	.0001	.0002	.0002	.0003	.0003	.0004	.0005
15	.0000	.0000	.0000	.0000	.0001	.0001	.0001	.0001	.0001	.0002

x	μ 5.1	5.2	5.3	5.4	5.5	5.6	5.7	5.8	5.9	6.0
0	.0061	.0055	.0050	.0045	.0041	.0037	.0033	.0030	.0027	.0025
1	.0311	.0287	.0265	.0244	.0225	.0207	.0191	.0176	.0162	.0149
2	.0793	.0746	.0701	.0659	.0618	.0580	.0544	.0509	.0477	.0446
3	.1348	.1293	.1239	.1185	.1133	.1082	.1033	.0985	.0938	.0892
4	.1719	.1681	.1641	.1600	.1558	.1515	.1472	.1428	.1383	.1339

TABLE 7   POISSON PROBABILITIES (*Continued*)

					μ					
x	**5.1**	**5.2**	**5.3**	**5.4**	**5.5**	**5.6**	**5.7**	**5.8**	**5.9**	**6.0**
5	.1753	.1748	.1740	.1728	.1714	.1697	.1678	.1656	.1632	.1606
6	.1490	.1515	.1537	.1555	.1571	.1587	.1594	.1601	.1605	.1606
7	.1086	.1125	.1163	.1200	.1234	.1267	.1298	.1326	.1353	.1377
8	.0692	.0731	.0771	.0810	.0849	.0887	.0925	.0962	.0998	.1033
9	.0392	.0423	.0454	.0486	.0519	.0552	.0586	.0620	.0654	.0688
10	.0200	.0220	.0241	.0262	.0285	.0309	.0334	.0359	.0386	.0413
11	.0093	.0104	.0116	.0129	.0143	.0157	.0173	.0190	.0207	.0225
12	.0039	.0045	.0051	.0058	.0065	.0073	.0082	.0092	.0102	.0113
13	.0015	.0018	.0021	.0024	.0028	.0032	.0036	.0041	.0046	.0052
14	.0006	.0007	.0008	.0009	.0011	.0013	.0015	.0017	.0019	.0022
15	.0002	.0002	.0003	.0003	.0004	.0005	.0006	.0007	.0008	.0009
16	.0001	.0001	.0001	.0001	.0001	.0002	.0002	.0002	.0003	.0003
17	.0000	.0000	.0000	.0000	.0000	.0001	.0001	.0001	.0001	.0001

					μ					
x	**6.1**	**6.2**	**6.3**	**6.4**	**6.5**	**6.6**	**6.7**	**6.8**	**6.9**	**7.0**
0	.0022	.0020	.0018	.0017	.0015	.0014	.0012	.0011	.0010	.0009
1	.0137	.0126	.0116	.0106	.0098	.0090	.0082	.0076	.0070	.0064
2	.0417	.0390	.0364	.0340	.0318	.0296	.0276	.0258	.0240	.0223
3	.0848	.0806	.0765	.0726	.0688	.0652	.0617	.0584	.0552	.0521
4	.1294	.1249	.1205	.1162	.1118	.1076	.1034	.0992	.0952	.0912
5	.1579	.1549	.1519	.1487	.1454	.1420	.1385	.1349	.1314	.1277
6	.1605	.1601	.1595	.1586	.1575	.1562	.1546	.1529	.1511	.1490
7	.1399	.1418	.1435	.1450	.1462	.1472	.1480	.1486	.1489	.1490
8	.1066	.1099	.1130	.1160	.1188	.1215	.1240	.1263	.1284	.1304
9	.0723	.0757	.0791	.0825	.0858	.0891	.0923	.0954	.0985	.1014
10	.0441	.0469	.0498	.0528	.0558	.0588	.0618	.0649	.0679	.0710
11	.0245	.0265	.0285	.0307	.0330	.0353	.0377	.0401	.0426	.0452
12	.0124	.0137	.0150	.0164	.0179	.0194	.0210	.0227	.0245	.0264
13	.0058	.0065	.0073	.0081	.0089	.0098	.0108	.0119	.0130	.0142
14	.0025	.0029	.0033	.0037	.0041	.0046	.0052	.0058	.0064	.0071
15	.0010	.0012	.0014	.0016	.0018	.0020	.0023	.0026	.0029	.0033
16	.0004	.0005	.0005	.0006	.0007	.0008	.0010	.0011	.0013	.0014
17	.0001	.0002	.0002	.0002	.0003	.0003	.0004	.0004	.0005	.0006
18	.0000	.0001	.0001	.0001	.0001	.0001	.0001	.0002	.0002	.0002
19	.0000	.0000	.0000	.0000	.0000	.0000	.0000	.0001	.0001	.0001

					μ					
x	**7.1**	**7.2**	**7.3**	**7.4**	**7.5**	**7.6**	**7.7**	**7.8**	**7.9**	**8.0**
0	.0008	.0007	.0007	.0006	.0006	.0005	.0005	.0004	.0004	.0003
1	.0059	.0054	.0049	.0045	.0041	.0038	.0035	.0032	.0029	.0027
2	.0208	.0194	.0180	.0167	.0156	.0145	.0134	.0125	.0116	.0107
3	.0492	.0464	.0438	.0413	.0389	.0366	.0345	.0324	.0305	.0286
4	.0874	.0836	.0799	.0764	.0729	.0696	.0663	.0632	.0602	.0573

TABLE 7   POISSON PROBABILITIES (*Continued*)

					μ					
x	7.1	7.2	7.3	7.4	7.5	7.6	7.7	7.8	7.9	8.0
5	.1241	.1204	.1167	.1130	.1094	.1057	.1021	.0986	.0951	.0916
6	.1468	.1445	.1420	.1394	.1367	.1339	.1311	.1282	.1252	.1221
7	.1489	.1486	.1481	.1474	.1465	.1454	.1442	.1428	.1413	.1396
8	.1321	.1337	.1351	.1363	.1373	.1382	.1388	.1392	.1395	.1396
9	.1042	.1070	.1096	.1121	.1144	.1167	.1187	.1207	.1224	.1241
10	.0740	.0770	.0800	.0829	.0858	.0887	.0914	.0941	.0967	.0993
11	.0478	.0504	.0531	.0558	.0585	.0613	.0640	.0667	.0695	.0722
12	.0283	.0303	.0323	.0344	.0366	.0388	.0411	.0434	.0457	.0481
13	.0154	.0168	.0181	.0196	.0211	.0227	.0243	.0260	.0278	.0296
14	.0078	.0086	.0095	.0104	.0113	.0123	.0134	.0145	.0157	.0169
15	.0037	.0041	.0046	.0051	.0057	.0062	.0069	.0075	.0083	.0090
16	.0016	.0019	.0021	.0024	.0026	.0030	.0033	.0037	.0041	.0045
17	.0007	.0008	.0009	.0010	.0012	.0013	.0015	.0017	.0019	.0021
18	.0003	.0003	.0004	.0004	.0005	.0006	.0006	.0007	.0008	.0009
19	.0001	.0001	.0001	.0002	.0002	.0002	.0003	.0003	.0003	.0004
20	.0000	.0000	.0001	.0001	.0001	.0001	.0001	.0001	.0001	.0002
21	.0000	.0000	.0000	.0000	.0000	.0000	.0000	.0000	.0001	.0001

					μ					
x	8.1	8.2	8.3	8.4	8.5	8.6	8.7	8.8	8.9	9.0
0	.0003	.0003	.0002	.0002	.0002	.0002	.0002	.0002	.0001	.0001
1	.0025	.0023	.0021	.0019	.0017	.0016	.0014	.0013	.0012	.0011
2	.0100	.0092	.0086	.0079	.0074	.0068	.0063	.0058	.0054	.0050
3	.0269	.0252	.0237	.0222	.0208	.0195	.0183	.0171	.0160	.0150
4	.0544	.0517	.0491	.0466	.0443	.0420	.0398	.0377	.0357	.0337
5	.0882	.0849	.0816	.0784	.0752	.0722	.0692	.0663	.0635	.0607
6	.1191	.1160	.1128	.1097	.1066	.1034	.1003	.0972	.0941	.0911
7	.1378	.1358	.1338	.1317	.1294	.1271	.1247	.1222	.1197	.1171
8	.1395	.1392	.1388	.1382	.1375	.1366	.1356	.1344	.1332	.1318
9	.1256	.1269	.1280	.1290	.1299	.1306	.1311	.1315	.1317	.1318
10	.1017	.1040	.1063	.1084	.1104	.1123	.1140	.1157	.1172	.1186
11	.0749	.0776	.0802	.0828	.0853	.0878	.0902	.0925	.0948	.0970
12	.0505	.0530	.0555	.0579	.0604	.0629	.0654	.0679	.0703	.0728
13	.0315	.0334	.0354	.0374	.0395	.0416	.0438	.0459	.0481	.0504
14	.0182	.0196	.0210	.0225	.0240	.0256	.0272	.0289	.0306	.0324
15	.0098	.0107	.0116	.0126	.0136	.0147	.0158	.0169	.0182	.1094
16	.0050	.0055	.0060	.0066	.0072	.0079	.0086	.0093	.0101	.0109
17	.0024	.0026	.0029	.0033	.0036	.0040	.0044	.0048	.0053	.0058
18	.0011	.0012	.0014	.0015	.0017	.0019	.0021	.0024	.0026	.0029
19	.0005	.0005	.0006	.0007	.0008	.0009	.0010	.0011	.0012	.0014
20	.0002	.0002	.0002	.0003	.0003	.0004	.0004	.0005	.0005	.0006
21	.0001	.0001	.0001	.0001	.0001	.0002	.0002	.0002	.0002	.0003
22	.0000	.0000	.0000	.0000	.0001	.0001	.0001	.0001	.0001	.0001

TABLE 7   POISSON PROBABILITIES (*Continued*)

					μ					
x	9.1	9.2	9.3	9.4	9.5	9.6	9.7	9.8	9.9	10
0	.0001	.0001	.0001	.0001	.0001	.0001	.0001	.0001	.0001	.0000
1	.0010	.0009	.0009	.0008	.0007	.0007	.0006	.0005	.0005	.0005
2	.0046	.0043	.0040	.0037	.0034	.0031	.0029	.0027	.0025	.0023
3	.0140	.0131	.0123	.0115	.0107	.0100	.0093	.0087	.0081	.0076
4	.0319	.0302	.0285	.0269	.0254	.0240	.0226	.0213	.0201	.0189
5	.0581	.0555	.0530	.0506	.0483	.0460	.0439	.0418	.0398	.0378
6	.0881	.0851	.0822	.0793	.0764	.0736	.0709	.0682	.0656	.0631
7	.1145	.1118	.1091	.1064	.1037	.1010	.0982	.0955	.0928	.0901
8	.1302	.1286	.1269	.1251	.1232	.1212	.1191	.1170	.1148	.1126
9	.1317	.1315	.1311	.1306	.1300	.1293	.1284	.1274	.1263	.1251
10	.1198	.1210	.1219	.1228	.1235	.1241	.1245	.1249	.1250	.1251
11	.0991	.1012	.1031	.1049	.1067	.1083	.1098	.1112	.1125	.1137
12	.0752	.0776	.0799	.0822	.0844	.0866	.0888	.0908	.0928	.0948
13	.0526	.0549	.0572	.0594	.0617	.0640	.0662	.0685	.0707	.0729
14	.0342	.0361	.0380	.0399	.0419	.0439	.0459	.0479	.0500	.0521
15	.0208	.0221	.0235	.0250	.0265	.0281	.0297	.0313	.0330	.0347
16	.0118	.0127	.0137	.0147	.0157	.0168	.0180	.0192	.0204	.0217
17	.0063	.0069	.0075	.0081	.0088	.0095	.0103	.0111	.0119	.0128
18	.0032	.0035	.0039	.0042	.0046	.0051	.0055	.0060	.0065	.0071
19	.0015	.0017	.0019	.0021	.0023	.0026	.0028	.0031	.0034	.0037
20	.0007	.0008	.0009	.0010	.0011	.0012	.0014	.0015	.0017	.0019
21	.0003	.0003	.0004	.0004	.0005	.0006	.0006	.0007	.0008	.0009
22	.0001	.0001	.0002	.0002	.0002	.0002	.0003	.0003	.0004	.0004
23	.0000	.0001	.0001	.0001	.0001	.0001	.0001	.0001	.0002	.0002
24	.0000	.0000	.0000	.0000	.0000	.0000	.0000	.0001	.0001	.0001

					μ					
x	11	12	13	14	15	16	17	18	19	20
0	.0000	.0000	.0000	.0000	.0000	.0000	.0000	.0000	.0000	.0000
1	.0002	.0001	.0000	.0000	.0000	.0000	.0000	.0000	.0000	.0000
2	.0010	.0004	.0002	.0001	.0000	.0000	.0000	.0000	.0000	.0000
3	.0037	.0018	.0008	.0004	.0002	.0001	.0000	.0000	.0000	.0000
4	.0102	.0053	.0027	.0013	.0006	.0003	.0001	.0001	.0000	.0000
5	.0224	.0127	.0070	.0037	.0019	.0010	.0005	.0002	.0001	.0001
6	.0411	.0255	.0152	.0087	.0048	.0026	.0014	.0007	.0004	.0002
7	.0646	.0437	.0281	.0174	.0104	.0060	.0034	.0018	.0010	.0005
8	.0888	.0655	.0457	.0304	.0194	.0120	.0072	.0042	.0024	.0013
9	.1085	.0874	.0661	.0473	.0324	.0213	.0135	.0083	.0050	.0029
10	.1194	.1048	.0859	.0663	.0486	.0341	.0230	.0150	.0095	.0058
11	.1194	.1144	.1015	.0844	.0663	.0496	.0355	.0245	.0164	.0106
12	.1094	.1144	.1099	.0984	.0829	.0661	.0504	.0368	.0259	.0176
13	.0926	.1056	.1099	.1060	.0956	.0814	.0658	.0509	.0378	.0271
14	.0728	.0905	.1021	.1060	.1024	.0930	.0800	.0655	.0514	.0387

TABLE 7   POISSON PROBABILITIES (*Continued*)

x	11	12	13	14	15	16	17	18	19	20
					μ					
15	.0534	.0724	.0885	.0989	.1024	.0992	.0906	.0786	.0650	.0516
16	.0367	.0543	.0719	.0866	.0960	.0992	.0963	.0884	.0772	.0646
17	.0237	.0383	.0550	.0713	.0847	.0934	.0963	.0936	.0863	.0760
18	.0145	.0256	.0397	.0554	.0706	.0830	.0909	.0936	.0911	.0844
19	.0084	.0161	.0272	.0409	.0557	.0699	.0814	.0887	.0911	.0888
20	.0046	.0097	.0177	.0286	.0418	.0559	.0692	.0798	.0866	.0888
21	.0024	.0055	.0109	.0191	.0299	.0426	.0560	.0684	.0783	.0846
22	.0012	.0030	.0065	.0121	.0204	.0310	.0433	.0560	.0676	.0769
23	.0006	.0016	.0037	.0074	.0133	.0216	.0320	.0438	.0559	.0669
24	.0003	.0008	.0020	.0043	.0083	.0144	.0226	.0328	.0442	.0557
25	.0001	.0004	.0010	.0024	.0050	.0092	.0154	.0237	.0336	.0446
26	.0000	.0002	.0005	.0013	.0029	.0057	.0101	.0164	.0246	.0343
27	.0000	.0001	.0002	.0007	.0016	.0034	.0063	.0109	.0173	.0254
28	.0000	.0000	.0001	.0003	.0009	.0019	.0038	.0070	.0117	.0181
29	.0000	.0000	.0001	.0002	.0004	.0011	.0023	.0044	.0077	.0125
30	.0000	.0000	.0000	.0001	.0002	.0006	.0013	.0026	.0049	.0083
31	.0000	.0000	.0000	.0000	.0001	.0003	.0007	.0015	.0030	.0054
32	.0000	.0000	.0000	.0000	.0001	.0001	.0004	.0009	.0018	.0034
33	.0000	.0000	.0000	.0000	.0000	.0001	.0002	.0005	.0010	.0020
34	.0000	.0000	.0000	.0000	.0000	.0000	.0001	.0002	.0006	.0012
35	.0000	.0000	.0000	.0000	.0000	.0000	.0000	.0001	.0003	.0007
36	.0000	.0000	.0000	.0000	.0000	.0000	.0000	.0001	.0002	.0004
37	.0000	.0000	.0000	.0000	.0000	.0000	.0000	.0000	.0001	.0002
38	.0000	.0000	.0000	.0000	.0000	.0000	.0000	.0000	.0000	.0001
39	.0000	.0000	.0000	.0000	.0000	.0000	.0000	.0000	.0000	.0001

Summations

Definition

$$\sum_{i=1}^{n} x_i = x_1 + x_2 + \cdots + x_n \tag{C.1}$$

Example for $x_1 = 5$, $x_2 = 8$, $x_3 = 14$:

$$\sum_{i=1}^{3} x_i = x_1 + x_2 + x_3$$
$$= 5 + 8 + 14$$
$$= 27$$

Result 1

For a constant c:

$$\sum_{i=1}^{n} c = \underbrace{(c + c + \cdots + c)}_{n \text{ times}} = nc \tag{C.2}$$

Example for $c = 5$, $n = 10$:

$$\sum_{i=1}^{10} 5 = 10(5) = 50$$

Example for $c = \bar{x}$:

$$\sum_{i=1}^{n} \bar{x} = n\bar{x}$$

Result 2

$$\sum_{i=1}^{n} cx_i = cx_1 + cx_2 + \cdots + cx_n$$
$$= c(x_1 + x_2 + \cdots + x_n) = c \sum_{i=1}^{n} x_i \tag{C.3}$$

Example for $x_1 = 5$, $x_2 = 8$, $x_3 = 14$, $c = 2$:

$$\sum_{i=1}^{3} 2x_i = 2 \sum_{i=1}^{3} x_i = 2(27) = 54$$

Result 3

$$\sum_{i=1}^{n} (ax_i + by_i) = a \sum_{i=1}^{n} x_i + b \sum_{i=1}^{n} y_i \tag{C.4}$$

Example for $x_1 = 5$, $x_2 = 8$, $x_3 = 14$, $a = 2$, $y_1 = 7$, $y_2 = 3$, $y_3 = 8$, $b = 4$:

$$\sum_{i=1}^{3} (2x_i + 4y_i) = 2 \sum_{i=1}^{3} x_i + 4 \sum_{i=1}^{3} y_i$$
$$= 2(27) + 4(18)$$
$$= 54 + 72$$
$$= 126$$

Double Summations

Consider the following data involving the variable x_{ij}, where i is the subscript denoting the row position and j is the subscript denoting the column position:

		Column		
		1	**2**	**3**
Row	**1**	$x_{11} = 10$	$x_{12} = 8$	$x_{13} = 6$
	2	$x_{21} = 7$	$x_{22} = 4$	$x_{23} = 12$

Definition

$$\sum_{i=1}^{n} \sum_{j=1}^{m} x_{ij} = (x_{11} + x_{12} + \cdots + x_{1m}) + (x_{21} + x_{22} + \cdots + x_{2m})$$
$$+ (x_{31} + x_{32} + \cdots + x_{3m}) + \cdots + (x_{n1} + x_{n2} + \cdots + x_{nm}) \qquad \text{(C.5)}$$

Example:

$$\sum_{i=1}^{2} \sum_{j=1}^{3} x_{ij} = x_{11} + x_{12} + x_{13} + x_{21} + x_{22} + x_{23}$$
$$= 10 + 8 + 6 + 7 + 4 + 12$$
$$= 47$$

Definition

$$\sum_{i=1}^{n} x_{ij} = x_{1j} + x_{2j} + \cdots + x_{nj} \qquad \text{(C.6)}$$

Example:

$$\sum_{i=1}^{2} x_{i2} = x_{12} + x_{22}$$
$$= 8 + 4$$
$$= 12$$

Shorthand Notation

Sometimes when a summation is for all values of the subscript, we use the following shorthand notations:

$$\sum_{i=1}^{n} x_i = \sum_i x_i \qquad \text{(C.7)}$$

$$\sum_{i=1}^{n} \sum_{j=1}^{m} x_{ij} = \sum \sum x_{ij} \qquad \text{(C.8)}$$

$$\sum_{i=1}^{n} x_{ij} = \sum_i x_{ij} \qquad \text{(C.9)}$$

Chapter 1

2. a. Ten elements
  b. 5 variables: Cost ($), Operating System, Display Size (inches), Battery Life (hours), CPU Manufacturer
  c. Categorical variables: Operating System and CPU Manufacturer Quantitative variables: Cost ($), Display Size (inches), and Battery Life (hours)
  d. Cost, Display Size, Battery Life – ratio, Operating System, COU Manufacturing -nominal

3. a. $582.90
  b. Windows operating: $723.20, Android operating system: $428.5
  c. 20%
  d. 40%

4. a. Eight elements
  b. Categorical variables: Voice Quality and Handset on Base; Quantitative variables: Price, Overall Score, and Talk Time
  c. Price – ratio, Overall Score – interval, Voice Quality – ordinal, Handset on Base – nominal, Talk Time – ratio

6. a. Categorical
  b. Quantitative
  c. Categorical
  d. Quantitative
  e. Quantitative

8. a. 762
  b. Categorical
  c. Percentages
  d. .67(762) = 510.54, 510 or 511 respondents said they want the amendment to pass.

10. a. Categorical
  b. Percentages
  c. 15%
  d. Support against

12. a. All visitors to Hawaii
  b. Yes
  c. First and fourth questions provide quantitative data Second and third questions provide categorical data

13. a. Google revenue in billions of dollars
  b. Quantitative
  c. Time series
  d. Google revenue is increasing over time.

14. a. Graph with time series line for each company
  b. Hertz leader in 2007–2008; Avis increasing and now similar to Hertz; Dollar declining
  c. A bar chart of cross-sectional data Bar heights: Hertz 290, Dollar 108, Avis 270

16. The answer to this exercise depends on updating the time series of the average price per gallon of conventional regular gasoline as shown in Figure 1.1.

18. a. 67%
  b. 612
  c. Categorical

20. a. 43% of managers were bullish or very bullish, and 21% of managers expected health care to be the leading industry over the next 12 months
  b. The average 12-month return estimate is 11.2% for the population of investment managers
  c. The sample average of 2.5 years is an estimate of how long the population of investment managers think it will take to resume sustainable growth

22. a. The population consists of all customers of the chain stores in Charlotte, North Carolina
  b. Some of the ways the grocery store chain could use to collect the data are
  • Customers entering or leaving the store could be surveyed
  • A survey could be mailed to customers who have a shopper's club card
  • Customers could be given a printed survey when they check out
  • Customers could be given a coupon that asks them to complete a brief online survey; if they do, they will receive a 5% discount on their next shopping trip

24. a. Correct
  b. Incorrect
  c. Correct
  d. Incorrect
  e. Incorrect

Chapter 2

2. a. .20
  b. 40
  c/d.

Class	Frequency	Percent Frequency
A	44	22
B	36	18
C	80	40
D	40	20
Total	200	100

3. a. $360° \times 58/120 = 174°$
  b. $360° \times 42/120 = 126°$

c.

d.

4. a. These data are categorical

b.

Show	Relative Frequency	Percent Frequency
Jep	10	20
JJ	8	16
OWS	7	14
THM	12	24
WoF	13	26
Total	50	100

c.

d. The largest viewing audience is for *Wheel of Fortune* and the second largest is for *Two and a Half Men*

6. a.

Network	Relative Frequency	Percent Frequency
ABC	6	24
CBS	9	36
FOX	1	4
NBC	9	36
Total	25	100

b. For these data, NBC and CBS tie for the number of to-prated shows; each has 9 (36%) of the top 25; ABC is third with 6 (24%) and the much younger FOX network has 1 (4%)

7. a.

Rating	Frequency	Percent Frequency
Excellent	20	40
Very Good	23	46
Good	4	8
Fair	1	2
Poor	2	4
Total	50	100

Management should be very pleased; 86% of the ratings are very good or excellent.

b. Review explanations from the three with Fair or Poor ratings to identify reasons for the low ratings

8. a.

Position	Frequency	Relative Frequency
P	17	.309
H	4	.073
1	5	.091
2	4	.073
3	2	.036
S	5	.091
L	6	.109
C	5	.091
R	7	.127
Totals	55	1.000

b. Pitcher
c. 3rd base
d. Right field
e. Infielders 16 to outfielders 18

10. a/b.

Rating	Frequency	Percent Frequency
Excellent	187	29
Very Good	252	39
Average	107	16
Poor	62	10
Terrible	41	6
Total	649	100

c.

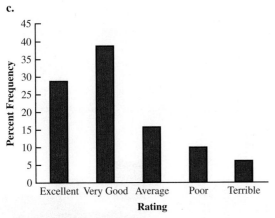

d. 29% + 39% = 68% of the guests at the Sheraton Anaheim Hotel rated the hotel as Excellent or Very Good. But, 10% + 6% = 16% of the guests rated the hotel as poor or terrible.

e. The percent frequency distribution for Disney's Grand Californian follows: Excellent (48%), Very Good (31%), and Average (12%).

48% + 31% = 79% of the guests at the Sheraton Anaheim Hotel rated the hotel as Excellent or Very Good. And, 6% + 3% = 9% of the guests rated the hotel as poor or terrible.

12.

Class	Cumulative Frequency	Cumulative Relative Frequency
≤19	10	.20
≤29	24	.48
≤39	41	.82
≤49	48	.96
≤59	50	1.00

14. b/c.

Class	Frequency	Percent Frequency
6.0–7.9	4	20
8.0–9.9	2	10
10.0–11.9	8	40
12.0–13.9	3	15
14.0–15.9	3	15
Totals	20	100

15. Leaf unit = .1

```
 6 | 3
 7 | 5  5  7
 8 | 1  3  4  8
 9 | 3  6
10 | 0  4  5
11 | 3
```

16. Leaf unit = 10

```
11 | 6
12 | 0  2
13 | 0  6  7
14 | 2  2  7
15 | 5
16 | 0  2  8
17 | 0  2  3
```

17. a/b.

Waiting Time	Frequency	Relative Frequency
0–4	4	.20
5–9	8	.40
10–14	5	.25
15–19	2	.10
20–24	1	.05
Totals	20	1.00

c/d.

Waiting Time	Cumulative Frequency	Cumulative Relative Frequency
≤4	4	.20
≤9	12	.60
≤14	17	.85
≤19	19	.95
≤24	20	1.00

e. 12/20 = .60

18. a.

PPG	Frequency
10–12	1
12–14	3
14–16	7
16–18	19
18–20	9
20–22	4
22–24	2
24–26	0
26–28	3
28–30	2
Total	50

b.

PPG	Relative Frequency
10–12	0.02
12–14	0.06
14–16	0.14
16–18	0.38
18–20	0.18
20–22	0.08
22–24	0.04
24–26	0.00
26–28	0.06
28–30	0.04
Total	1.00

c.

PPG	Cumulative Percent Frequency
less than 12	2
less than 14	8
less than 16	22
less than 18	60
less than 20	78
less than 22	86
less than 24	90
less than 26	90
less than 28	96
less than 30	100

d.

e. There is skewness to the right.
f. (11/50)(100) = 22%

20. a. Lowest = 12, Highest = 23
b.

Hours in Meetings per Week	Frequency	Percent Frequency
11–12	1	4
13–14	2	8
15–16	6	24
17–18	3	12
19–20	5	20
21–22	4	16
23–24	4	16
	25	100

c.

d. The distribution is slightly skewed to the left

22. a.

# U.S. Locations	Frequency	Percent Frequency
0–4999	10	50
5000–9999	3	15
10000–14999	2	10
15000–19999	1	5
20000–24999	0	0
25000–29999	1	5
30000–34999	2	10
35000–39999	1	5
Total:	20	100

b.

Number of U.S. Locations

c. The distribution is skewed to the right; the majority of the franchises in this list have fewer than 20,000 locations (50% + 15% + 15% = 80%); McDonald's, Subway, and 7-Eleven have the highest number of locations

24. Starting Median Salary

```
4 | 6  8
5 | 1  2  3  3  5  6  8  8
6 | 0  1  1  1  2  2
7 | 1  2  5
```

Mid-Career Median Salary

```
 8 | 0  0  4
 9 | 3  3  5  6  7
10 | 5  6  6
11 | 0  1  4  4  4
12 | 2  3  6
```

There is a wider spread in the mid-career median salaries than in the starting median salaries. Also, as expected, the mid-career median salaries are higher that the starting median salaries. The mid-career median salaries were mostly in the $93,000 to $114,000 range while the starting median salaries were mostly in the $51,000 to $62,000 range.

26. a.

```
2 | 14
2 | 67
3 | 011123
3 | 5677
4 | 003333344
4 | 6679
5 | 00022
5 | 5679
6 | 14
6 | 6
7 | 2
```

b. 40–44 with 9
c. 43 with 5

27. a.

		y		
		1	**2**	**Total**
	A	5	0	5
x	**B**	11	2	13
	C	2	10	12
	Total	18	12	30

b.

		y		
		1	**2**	**Total**
	A	100.0	0.0	100.0
x	**B**	84.6	15.4	100.0
	C	16.7	83.3	100.0

c.

		y	
		1	**2**
	A	27.8	0.0
x	**B**	61.1	16.7
	C	11.1	83.3
	Total	100.0	100.0

d. *A* values are always in *y* = 1
B values are most often in *y* = 1
C values are most often in *y* = 2

28. a.

		y				Grand
		20–39	**40–59**	**60–79**	**80–100**	**Total**
	10–29			1	4	5
	30–49	2		4		6
x	**50–69**	1	3	1		5
	70–90	4				4
	Grand Total	7	3	6	4	20

b.

		y			
x	**20–39**	**40–59**	**60–79**	**80–100**	**Grand Total**
10–29			20.0	80.0	100
30–49	33.3		66.7		100
50–69	20.0	60.0	20.0		100
70–90	100.0				100

c.

		y		
x	**20–39**	**40–59**	**60–79**	**80–100**
10–29	0.0	0.0	16.7	100.0
30–49	28.6	0.0	66.7	0.0
50–69	14.3	100.0	16.7	0.0
70–90	57.1	0.0	0.0	0.0
Grand Total	100	100	100	100

d. Higher values of *x* are associated with lower values of *y* and vice versa

30. a.

			Year			
Average Speed	**1988–1992**	**1993–1997**	**1998–2002**	**2003–2007**	**2008–2012**	**Total**
130–139.9	16.7	0.0	0.0	33.3	50.0	100
140–149.9	25.0	25.0	12.5	25.0	12.5	100
150–159.9	0.0	50.0	16.7	16.7	16.7	100
160–169.9	50.0	0.0	50.0	0.0	0.0	100
170–179.9	0.0	0.0	100.0	0.0	0.0	100

b. It appears that most of the faster average winning times occur before 2003. This could be due to new regulations that take into account driver safety, fan safety, the environmental impact, and fuel consumption during races.

32. a. Row percentages are shown below.

Region	Under $15,000	$15,000 to $24,999	$25,000 to $34,999	$35,000 to $49,999	$50,000 to $74,999	$75,000 to $99,999	$100,000 and over	Total
Northeast	12.72	10.45	10.54	13.07	17.22	11.57	24.42	100.00
Midwest	12.40	12.60	11.58	14.27	19.11	12.06	17.97	100.00
South	14.30	12.97	11.55	14.85	17.73	11.04	17.57	100.00
West	11.84	10.73	10.15	13.65	18.44	11.77	23.43	100.00

b. The percent frequency distributions for each region now appear in each row of the table. For example, the

percent frequency distribution of the West region is as follows:

West: 18.44 + 11.77 + 23.43 = 53.64%

South: 17.73 + 11.04 + 17.57 = 46.34%

c.

West

The largest difference appears to be a higher percentage of household incomes of $100,000 and over for the Northeast and West regions.

d. Column percentages are shown below.

Region	Under $15,000	$15,000 to $24,999	$25,000 to $34,999	$35,000 to $49,999	$50,000 to $74,999	$75,000 to $99,999	$100,000 and over
Northeast	17.83	16.00	17.41	16.90	17.38	18.35	22.09
Midwest	21.35	23.72	23.50	22.68	23.71	23.49	19.96
South	40.68	40.34	38.75	39.00	36.33	35.53	32.25
West	20.13	19.94	20.34	21.42	22.58	22.63	25.70
Total	100.00	100.00	100.00	100.00	100.00	100.00	100.00

Each column is a percent frequency distribution of the region variable for one of the household income categories. For example, for an income level of $35,000 to $49,999 the percent frequency distribution for the region variable is as follows:
Northeast (16.9%), Midwest (22.68%), South (39.0%) and West (21.42%).

e. 32.25% of the houses with incomes $100,000 and over are from the South region. 17.57% of the houses form the South region have household incomes of $100,000 and over. These two percentage are different because they are calculated as percentages of different base. The first (row percentage) is based on income level and the second (column percentage) is based on region.

34. a.

Industry	Brand Revenue ($ billions)						
	0–25	25–50	50–75	75–100	100–125	125–150	Total
Automotive & Luxury	10	1	1		1	2	15
Consumer Packaged Goods	12						12
Financial Services	2	4	2	2	2	2	14
Other	13	5	3	2	2	1	26
Technology	4	4	4	1	2		15
Total	41	14	10	5	7	5	82

b.

Brand Revenue ($ billions)	Frequency
0–25	41
25–50	14
50–75	10
75–100	5
100–125	7
125–150	5
Total	82

c. Consumer packaged goods have the lowest brand revenues; each of the 12 consumer packaged goods brands in the sample data had a brand revenue of less than $25 billion. Approximately 57% of the financial services brands (8 out of 14) had a brand revenue of $50 billion or greater, and 47% of the technology brands (7 out of 15) had a brand revenue of at least $50 billion.

d.

Industry	1-Yr Value Change (%)						Total
	−60 - −41	−40 - −21	−20 - −1	0 - 19	20 - 39	40 - 60	
Automotive & Luxury				11	4		15
Consumer Packaged Goods			2	10			12
Financial Services		1	6	7			14
Other			2	20	4		26
Technology	1	3	4	4	2	1	15
Total	1	4	14	52	10	1	82

e.

1-Yr Value Change (%)	Frequency
−60 - −41	1
−40 - −21	4
−20 - −1	14
0 - 19	52
20 - 39	10
40 - 60	1
Total	82

f. The automotive & luxury brands all had a positive 1-year value change (%). The technology brands had the greatest variability.

36. a.

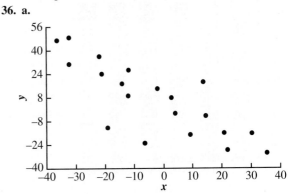

b. A negative relationship between x and y; y decreases as x increases

38. a.

		y		
		Yes	**No**	
	Low	66.667	33.333	100
x	**Medium**	30.000	70.000	100
	High	80.000	20.000	100

b.

40. a.

b. Colder average low temperature seems to lead to higher amounts of snowfall

c. Two cities have an average snowfall of nearly 100 inches of snowfall: Buffalo, New York and Rochester, New York; both are located near large lakes in New York

42. a.

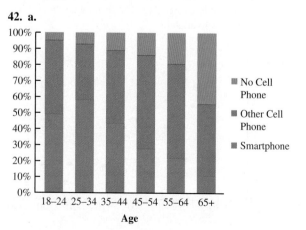

b. After an increase in age 25–34, smartphone ownership decreases as age increases; the percentage of people with no cell phone increases with age; there is less variation across age groups in the percentage who own other cell phones

c. Unless a newer device replaces the smartphone, we would expect smartphone ownership would become less sensitive to age; this would be true because current users will become older and because the device will become to be seen more as a necessity than a luxury

44. a.

SAT Score	Frequency
800–999	1
1000–1199	3
1200–1399	6
1400–1599	10
1600–1799	7
1800–1999	2
2000–2199	1
Total	30

b. Nearly symmetrical

c. 33% of the scores fall between 1400 and 1599
A score below 800 or above 2200 is unusual
The average is near or slightly above 1500

46. a.

Population in Millions	Frequency	Percent Frequency
0.0–2.4	15	30.0
2.5–4.9	13	26.0
5.0–7.4	10	20.0
7.5–9.9	5	10.0
10.0–12.4	1	2.0
12.5–14.9	2	4.0
15.0–17.4	0	0.0
17.5–19.9	2	4.0
20.0–22.4	0	0.0
22.5–24.9	0	0.0
25.0–27.4	1	2.0
27.5–29.9	0	0.0
30.0–32.4	0	0.0
32.5–34.9	0	0.0
35.0–37.4	1	2.0
37.5–39.9	0	0.0
More	0	0.0

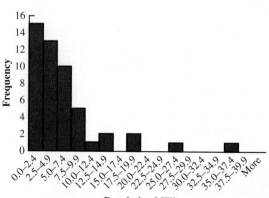

b. The distribution is skewed to the right

c. Fifteen states (30%) have a population less than 2.5 million; over half the states have population less than 5 million (28 states—56%); only seven states have a population greater than 10 million (California, Florida, Illinois, New York, Ohio, Pennsylvania, and Texas); the largest state is California (37.3 million) and the smallest states are Vermont and Wyoming (600 thousand)

48. a.

Industry	Frequency	Percent Frequency
Bank	26	13
Cable	44	22
Car	42	21
Cell	60	30
Collection	28	14
Total	200	100

b.

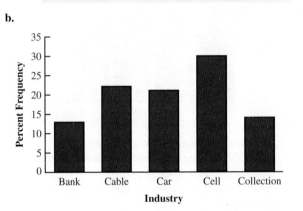

c. The cellular phone providers had the highest number of complaints

d. The percentage frequency distribution shows that the two financial industries (banks and collection agencies) had about the same number of complaints; new car dealers and cable and satellite television companies also had about the same number of complaints

50. a.

Level of Education	Percent Frequency
High School graduate	32,773/65,644(100) = 49.93
Bachelor's degree	22,131/65,644(100) = 33.71
Master's degree	9003/65,644(100) = 13.71
Doctoral degree	1737/65,644(100) = 2.65
Total	100.00

13.71 + 2.65 = 16.36% of heads of households have a master's or doctoral degree.

b.

Household Income	Percent Frequency
Under $25,000	13,128/65,644(100) = 20.00
$25,000 to $49,999	15,499/65,644(100) = 23.61
$50,000 to $99,999	20,548/65,644(100) = 31.30
$100,000 and over	16,469/65,644(100) = 25.09
Total	100.00

31.30 + 25.09 = 56.39% of households have an income of $50,000 or more.

c.

Level of Education	Household Income			
	Under $25,000	$25,000 to $49,999	$50,000 to $99,999	$100,000 and over
High School graduate	75.26	64.33	45.95	21.14
Bachelor's degree	18.92	26.87	37.31	47.46
Master's degree	5.22	7.77	14.69	24.86
Doctoral degree	0.60	1.03	2.05	6.53
Total	100.00	100.00	100.00	100.00

There is a large difference between the level of education for households with an income of under $25,000 and households with an income of $100,000 or more.

52 a.

Job Growth (%)	Size of Company			
	Small	Midsized	Large	Total
−10–0	4	6	2	12
0–10	18	13	29	60
10–20	7	2	4	13
20–30	3	3	2	8
30–40	0	3	1	4
60–70	0	1	0	1
Total	32	28	38	98

b. Frequency distribution for growth rate.

Job Growth (%)	Total
−10–0	12
0–10	60
10–20	13
20–30	8
30–40	4
60–70	1
Total	98

Frequency distribution for size of company.

Size	Total
Small	32
Medium	28
Large	38
Total	98

c. Crosstabulation showing column percentages.

Job Growth (%)	Small	Midsized	Large
	Size of Company		
−10–0	13	21	5
0–10	56	46	76
10–20	22	7	11
20–30	9	11	5
30–40	0	11	3
60–70	0	4	0
Total	100	100	100

d. Crosstabulation showing row percentages.

Job Growth (%)	Small	Midsized	Large	Total
	Size of Company			
−10–0	33	50	17	100
0–10	30	22	48	100
10–20	54	15	31	100
20–30	38	38	25	100
30–40	0	75	25	100
60–70	0	4	0	100

e. In terms of avoiding negative job growth, large companies were better off than small and midsized companies. In terms of better job growth rates, midsized companies performed better than either small or large companies.

54. c. Older colleges and universities tend to have higher graduation rates.

56. a.

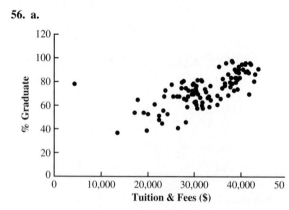

b. There appears to be a strong positive relationship between Tuition & Fees and % Graduation.

58. a.

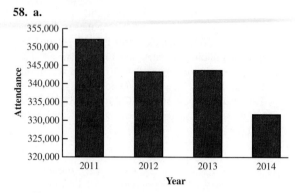

Zoo attendance appears to be dropping over time.

b.

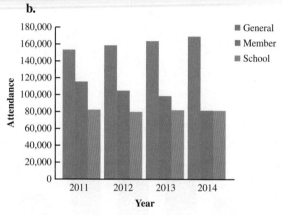

c. General attendance is increasing, but not enough to offset the decrease in member attendance. School membership appears fairly stable.

Chapter 3

2. 16, 16.5

4.

Period	Return (%)
1	−0.060
2	−0.080
3	−0.040
4	0.020
5	0.054

The mean growth factor over the five periods is

$$\bar{x}_g = \sqrt[n]{(x_1)(x_2)\cdots(x_5)}$$
$$= \sqrt[5]{(0.940)(0.920)(0.960)(1.020)(1.054)}$$
$$= \sqrt[5]{(0.8925)} = 0.9775$$

So the mean growth rate $(0.9775 - 1)100\% = -2.25\%$

5. 15, 20, 25, 25, 27, 28, 30, 34

$$L_{20} = \frac{p}{100}(n+1) = \frac{20}{100}(8+1) = 1.8$$

20th percentile $= 15 + .8(20 - 15) = 19$

$$L_{25} = \frac{p}{100}(n+1) = \frac{25}{100}(8+1) = 2.25$$

25th percentile $= 20 + .25(25 - 20) = 21.25$

$$L_{65} = \frac{p}{100}(n+1) = \frac{65}{100}(8+1) = 5.85$$

65th percentile $= 27 + .85(28 - 27) = 27.85$

$$L_{75} = \frac{p}{100}(n+1) = \frac{75}{100}(8+1) = 6.75$$

75th percentile $= 28 + .75(30 - 28) = 29.5$

6. 59.73, 57, 53

8. a. Median $= 80$ or $\$80,000$, slightly lower than the median salary reported by the Wall Street Journal.

b. $\bar{x} = 84$ Mean salary is $\$84,000$. The sample mean salary for the sample of 15 middle-level managers is greater than the median salary. This indicates that the distribution of salaries for middle-level managers working at firms in Atlanta is positively skewed.

c. The sorted data are as follows:

53 55 63 67 73 75 77 80
83 85 93 106 108 118 124

$$L_{25} = \frac{p}{100}(n+1) = \frac{25}{100}(16) = 4$$

First quartile or 25th percentile is the value in position 4 or 67.

$$L_{75} = \frac{p}{100}(n+1) = \frac{75}{100}(16) = 12$$

Third quartile or 75th percentile is the value in position 12 or 106.

10. a. $\bar{x} = 65.9$

Median or 50th percentile $= 66 + .5(67 - 66) = 66.5$

Mode is 61.

b. $L_{25} = \frac{p}{100}(n+1) = \frac{25}{100}(20+1) = 5.25$

First quartile or 25th percentile $= 61$

$$L_{75} = \frac{p}{100}(n+1) = \frac{75}{100}(20+1) = 15.75$$

Third quartile or 75th percentile $= 71$

c. $L_{90} = \frac{p}{100}(n+1) = \frac{90}{100}(20+1) = 18.9$

90th percentile $= 78 + .9(81 - 78) = 80.7$

90% of the ratings are 80.7 or less; 10% of the ratings are 80.7 or greater.

12. a. The minimum number of viewers who watched a new episode is 13.3 million, and the maximum number is 16.5 million

b. The mean number of viewers who watched a new episode is 15.04 million or approximately 15.0 million; the median is also 15.0 million; the data are multimodal (13.6, 14.0, 16.1, and 16.2 million); in such cases the mode is usually not reported

c. The data are first arranged in ascending order:

$$L_{25} = \frac{p}{100}(n+1) = \frac{25}{100}(21+1) = 5.50$$

First quartile or 25th percentile $= 14 + .50(14.1 - 14)$
$$= 14.05$$

$$L_{75} = \frac{p}{100}(n+1) = \frac{75}{100}(21+1) = 16.5$$

Third quartile or 75th percentile $= 16 + .5(16.1 - 16)$
$$= 16.05$$

d. A graph showing the viewership data over the air dates follows: Period 1 corresponds to the first episode of the season, period 2 corresponds to the second episode, and so on

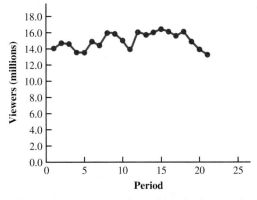

This graph shows that viewership of *The Big Bang Theory* has been relatively stable over the 2011–2012 television season

14. For March 2011:

$$L_{25} = \frac{p}{100}(n+1) = \frac{25}{100}(50+1) = 12.75$$

First quartile or 25th percentile $= 6.8 + .75(6.8 - 6.8)$
$$= 6.8$$

$$L_{50} = \frac{p}{100}(n+1) = \frac{50}{100}(50+1) = 25.5$$

Second quartile or median $= 8 + .5(8 - 8) = 8$

$$L_{75} = \frac{p}{100}(n+1) = \frac{75}{100}(50+1) = 38.25$$

Third quartile or 75th percentile $= 9.4 + .25(9.6 - 9.4)$
$$= 9.45$$

For March 2012:

$$L_{25} = \frac{p}{100}(n+1) = \frac{25}{100}(50+1) = 12.75$$

First quartile or 25th percentile $= 6.2 + .75(6.2 - 6.2)$
$$= 6.2$$

$$L_{50} = \frac{p}{100}(n+1) = \frac{50}{100}(50+1) = 25.5$$

Second quartile or median $= 7.3 + .5(7.4 - 7.3)$
$$= 7.35$$

$$L_{75} = \frac{p}{100}(n+1) = \frac{75}{100}(50+1) = 38.25$$

Third quartile or 75th percentile $= 8.6 + .25(8.6 - 8.6)$
$$= 8.6$$

It may be easier to compare these results if we place them in a table.

	March 2011	March 2012
First Quartile	6.80	6.20
Median	8.00	7.35
Third Quartile	9.45	8.60

The results show that in March 2012 approximately 25% of the states had an unemployment rate of 6.2% or less, lower than in March 2011; the median of 7.35% and the third quartile of 8.6% in March 2012 are both less than the corresponding values in March 2011, indicating that unemployment rates across the states are decreasing

16. a.

Grade x_i	Weight w_i
4 (A)	9
3 (B)	15
2 (C)	33
1 (D)	3
0 (F)	0
	60 credit hours

$$\bar{x} = \frac{\Sigma w_i x_i}{\Sigma w_i} = \frac{9(4) + 15(3) + 33(2) + 3(1)}{9 + 15 + 33 + 3}$$

$$= \frac{150}{60} = 2.5$$

b. Yes

18. 3.8, 3.7

20.

	Stivers		Trippi	
Year	End of Year Value ($)	Growth Factor	End of Year Value ($)	Growth Factor
2004	11,000	1.100	5,600	1.120
2005	12,000	1.091	6,300	1.125
2006	13,000	1.083	6,900	1.095
2007	14,000	1.077	7,600	1.101
2008	15,000	1.071	8,500	1.118
2009	16,000	1.067	9,200	1.082
2010	17,000	1.063	9,900	1.076
2011	18,000	1.059	10,600	1.071

For the Stivers mutual fund we have

$18000 = 10000[(x_1)(x_2) \cdots (x_8)]$, so $[(x_1)(x_2) \cdots (x_8)]$

$= 1.8$ and

$$\bar{x}_g = \sqrt[n]{(x_1)(x_2) \cdots (x_8)} = \sqrt[8]{1.80} = 1.07624$$

So the mean annual return for the Stivers mutual fund is $(1.07624 - 1)100 = 7.624\%$

For the Trippi mutual fund we have

$10600 = 5000 [(x_1)(x_2) \cdots (x_8)]$, so $[(x_1)(x_2) \cdots (x_8)]$

$= 2.12$ and

$$\bar{x}_g = \sqrt[n]{(x_1)(x_2) \cdots (x_8)} = \sqrt[8]{2.12} = 1.09848$$

So the mean annual return for the Trippi mutual fund is $(1.09848 - 1)100 = 9.848\%$

While the Stivers mutual fund has generated a nice annual return of 7.6%, the annual return of 9.8% earned by the Trippi mutual fund is far superior

22. $25,000,000 = 10,000,000[(x_1)(x_2) \cdots (x_6)]$,

so $[(x_1)(x_2) \cdots (x_6)] = 2.50$

so $\bar{x}_g = \sqrt[n]{(x_1)(x_2) \cdots (x_6)} = \sqrt[6]{2.50} = 1.165$

So the mean annual growth rate is $(1.165 - 1)100 = 16.5\%$

24. 16, 4

25. Range $= 34 - 15 = 19$

Arrange data in order: 15, 20, 25, 25, 27, 28, 30, 34

$$L_{25} = \frac{p}{100} (n + 1) = \frac{25}{100} (8 + 1) = 2.25$$

First quartile or 25th percentile $= 20 + .25(20 - 15) = 21.25$

$$L_{75} = \frac{p}{100} (n + 1) = \frac{75}{100} (8 + 1) = 6.75$$

Third quartile or 75th percentile $= 28 + .75(30 - 28) = 29.5$

IQR $= Q_3 - Q_1 = 29.5 - 21.25 = 8.25$

$$\bar{x} = \frac{\Sigma x_i}{n} = \frac{204}{8} = 25.5$$

$$s^2 = \frac{\Sigma (x_i - \bar{x})^2}{n - 1} = \frac{242}{7} = 34.57$$

$$s = \sqrt{34.57} = 5.88$$

x_i	$(x_i - \bar{x})$	$(x_i - \bar{x})^2$
27	1.5	2.25
25	−.5	.25
20	−5.5	30.25
15	−10.5	110.25
30	4.5	20.25
34	8.5	72.25
28	2.5	6.25
25	−.5	.25
		242.00

$$s^2 = \frac{\Sigma (x_i - \bar{x})^2}{n - 1} = \frac{242}{8 - 1} = 34.57$$

$$s = \sqrt{34.57} = 5.88$$

26. a. $\bar{x} = \dfrac{\Sigma_i x_i}{n} = \dfrac{74.4}{20} = 3.72$

b. $s = \sqrt{\dfrac{\Sigma_i (x_i - \bar{x})^2}{n - 1}} = \sqrt{\dfrac{1.6515}{20 - 1}} = \sqrt{.0869} = .2948$

c. The average price for a gallon of unleaded gasoline in San Francisco is much higher than the national average.

28. a. The mean serve speed is 180.95, the variance is 21.42, and the standard deviation is 4.63

b. Although the mean serve speed for the 20 Women's Singles serve speed leaders for the 2011 Wimbledon tournament is slightly higher, the difference is very small; furthermore, given the variation in the 20 Women's Singles serve speed leaders from the 2012 Australian Open and the 20 Women's Singles serve speed leaders from the 2011 Wimbledon tournament, the difference in the mean serve speeds is most likely due to random variation in the players' performances

30. *Dawson:* range $= 2$, $s = .67$
Clark: range $= 8$, $s = 2.58$

32. a. Automotive: 1960.05
Department store: 692.85

b. Automotive: 481.65
Department store: 155.06

c. Automotive: $2901 - 598 = 2303$
Department Store: $1011 - 448 = 563$

d. Automotive: First quartile or 25th percentile $= 1714 + .25(1720 - 1714) = 1715.5$
Department Store: First quartile or 25th percentile $= 589 + .25(597 - 589) = 591$
Automotive: Third quartile or 75th percentile $= 2202 + .75(2254 - 2202) = 2241$
Department Store: First quartile or 75th percentile $= 782 + .75(824 - 782) = 813.5$

e. Automotive spends more on average, has a larger standard deviation, larger max and min, and larger range than Department Store. Autos have all new model years and may spend more heavily on advertising.

34. *Quarter-milers: $s = .0564$, Coef. of Var. $= 5.8\%$*
Milers: $s = .1295$, Coef. of Var. $= 2.9\%$

36. $.20, 1.50, 0, -.50, -2.20$

37. a. $z = \dfrac{20 - 30}{5} = -2, z = \dfrac{40 - 30}{5} = 2 \quad 1 - \dfrac{1}{2^2} = .75$
At least 75%

b. $z = \dfrac{15 - 30}{5} = -3, z = \dfrac{45 - 30}{5} = 3 \quad 1 - \dfrac{1}{3^2} = .89$
At least 89%

c. $z = \dfrac{22 - 30}{5} = -1.6, z = \dfrac{38 - 30}{5} = 1.6 \quad 1 - \dfrac{1}{1.6^2} = .61$
At least 61%

d. $z = \dfrac{18 - 30}{5} = -2.4, z = \dfrac{42 - 30}{5} = 2.4 \quad 1 - \dfrac{1}{2.4^2} = .83$
At least 83%

e. $z = \dfrac{12 - 30}{5} = -3.6, z = \dfrac{48 - 30}{5} = 3.6 \quad 1 - \dfrac{1}{3.6^2} = .92$
At least 92%

38. a. 95%
b. Almost all
c. 68%

39. a. $z = 2$ standard deviations
$1 - \dfrac{1}{z^2} = 1 - \dfrac{1}{2^2} = \dfrac{3}{4}$; at least 75%

b. $z = 2.5$ standard deviations
$1 - \dfrac{1}{z^2} = 1 - \dfrac{1}{2.5^2} = .84$; at least 84%

c. $z = 2$ standard deviations
Empirical rule: 95%

40. a. 68%
b. 81.5%
c. 2.5%

42. a. $-.67$
b. 1.50
c. Neither is an outlier
d. Yes; $z = 8.25$

44. a. 76.5, 7
b. 16%, 2.5%
c. 12.2, 7.89; no outliers

46. 15, 21.25, 26, 29.5, 34

48. 5, 6, 8, 10, 10, 12, 15, 16, 18

Smallest $= 5$
$L_{25} = \dfrac{p}{100}(n + 1) = \dfrac{25}{100}(9 + 1) = 2.5$
First quartile or 25th percentile $= 6 + .5(8 - 6) = 7$
$L_{50} = \dfrac{p}{100}(n + 1) = \dfrac{50}{100}(9 + 1) = 5.0$

Second quartile or median $= 10$
$L_{75} = \dfrac{p}{100}(n + 1) = \dfrac{75}{100}(9 + 1) = 7.5$

Third quartile or 75th percentile $= 15 + .5(16 - 15) = 15.5$
Largest $= 18$

A box plot created using StatTools follows:

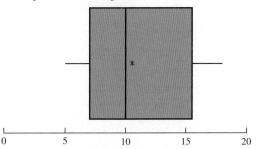

50. a. Men's 1st place 43.73 minutes faster
b. Medians: 109.64, 131.67
Men's median time 22.03 minutes faster
c. 65.30, 83.1025, 109.64, 129.025, 148.70
109.03, 122.08, 131.67, 147.18, 189.28
d. Men's Limits: 25.35 to 190.23; no outliers
Women's Limits: 84.43 to 184.83; 2 outliers
e. Women runners show less variation

51. a. Smallest $= 608$
$L_{25} = \dfrac{p}{100}(n + 1) = \dfrac{25}{100}(21 + 1) = 5.5$

First quartile or 25th percentile $= 1850 + .5(1872 - 1850) = 1861$

$L_{50} = \dfrac{p}{100}(n + 1) = \dfrac{50}{100}(21 + 1) = 11.0$

Second quartile or median $= 4019$
$L_{75} = \dfrac{p}{100}(n + 1) = \dfrac{75}{100}(21 + 1) = 16.5$

Third quartile or 75th percentile $= 8305 + .5(8408 - 8305) = 8356.5$

Largest $= 14138$
Five-number summary: 608, 1861, 4019, 8365.5, 14138
b. Limits:
$\text{IQR} = Q_3 - Q_1 = 8356.5 - 1861 = 6495.5$

Lower Limit: $Q_1 - 1.5(IQR) = 1861 - 1.5(6495.5) =$
$-7,882.25$
Upper Limit: $Q_3 + 1.5(IQR) = 8356.5 + 1.5(6495.5) =$
18,099.75

c. There are no outliers, all data are within the limits.

d. Yes, if the first two digits in Johnson and Johnson's sales were transposed to 41,138, sales would have shown up as an outlier. A review of the data would have enabled the correction of the data.

e. A box plot created using Minitab:

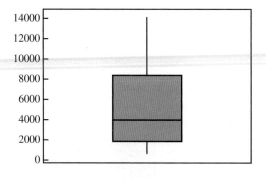

52. a. 73.5

b. 68, 71.25, 73.5, 74.75, 77

c. Limits: 66 and 80; no outliers

d. 66, 68, 71, 73, 75; 60.5 and 80.5
63, 65, 66, 67.75, 69; 60.875 and 71.875
75, 77, 78.5, 79.75, 81; 72.875 and 83.875
No outliers for any of the services

e. Verizon is highest rated
Sprint is lowest rated

54. a. Mean = 173.24 and median (second quartile) = 89.5

b. First quartile = 38.5 and the third quartile = 232

c. 21, 38.5, 89.5, 232, 995

d. A box plot created using Minitab follows.

Boxplot of Personal Vehicles (1000s)

There are three outliers:

NY: Buffalo-Niagra Falls	707
TX: El Paso	807
CA: San Ysidro	995

55. b. There appears to be a negative linear relationship between x and y

c.

x_i	y_i	$x_i - \bar{x}$	$y_i - \bar{y}$	$(x_i - \bar{x})(y_i - \bar{y})$
4	50	−4	4	−16
6	50	−2	4	−8
11	40	3	−6	−18
3	60	−5	14	−70
16	30	8	−16	−128
40	230	0	0	−240

$\bar{x} = 8; \bar{y} = 46$

$$s_{xy} = \frac{\Sigma(x_i - \bar{x})(y_i - \bar{y})}{n - 1} = \frac{-240}{4} = -60$$

The sample covariance indicates a negative linear association between x and y

d. $r_{xy} = \dfrac{s_{xy}}{s_x s_y} = \dfrac{-60}{(5.43)(11.40)} = -.969$

The sample correlation coefficient of $-.969$ is indicative of a strong negative linear relationship

56. b. There appears to be a positive linear relationship between x and y

c. $s_{xy} = 26.5$

d. $r_{xy} = .693$

58. $-.91$; negative relationship

60. a.

% Return of DJIA versus Russell 1000

b. DJIA: $\bar{x} = \dfrac{\Sigma x_i}{n} = \dfrac{227.57}{25} = 9.10$

$s = \sqrt{\dfrac{\Sigma(x_i - \bar{x})^2}{(n-1)}} = \sqrt{\dfrac{5672.61}{24}} = 15.37$

Russell 1000: $\bar{x} = \dfrac{\Sigma x_i}{n} = \dfrac{227.29}{25} = 9.09$

$s = \sqrt{\dfrac{\Sigma(x_i - \bar{x})^2}{(n-1)}} = \sqrt{\dfrac{7679.81}{24}} = 17.89$

c. $r_{xy} = \dfrac{s_{xy}}{s_x s_y} = \dfrac{263.611}{(15.37)(17.89)} = .959$

d. Based on this sample, the two indexes are very similar. They have a strong positive correlation. The variance of the Russell 1000 is slightly larger than that of the DJIA.

62. a. The mean is 2.95 and the median is 3.0
b. $L_{25} = 5.25$; first quartile = 1
$L_{75} = 15.75$; third quartile $= 4 + .75(1) = 4.75$
c. The range is 7 and the interquartile range is $4.75 - 1 = 3.75$
d. The variance is 4.37 and standard deviation is 2.09
e. Because most people dine out relatively few times per week and a few families dine out very frequently, we would expect the data to be positively skewed; the skewness measure of 0.34 indicates the data are somewhat skewed to the right
f. The lower limit is -4.625 and the upper limit is 10.375; no values in the data are less than the lower limit or greater than the upper limit, so there are no outliers

64. a. The mean and median patient wait times for offices with a wait-tracking system are 17.2 and 13.5, respectively; the mean and median patient wait times for offices without a wait-tracking system are 29.1 and 23.5, respectively
b. The variance and standard deviation of patient wait times for offices with a wait-tracking system are 86.2 and 9.3, respectively; the variance and standard deviation of patient wait times for offices without a wait-tracking system are 275.7 and 16.6, respectively
c. Offices with a wait-tracking system have substantially shorter patient wait times than offices without a wait-tracking system
d. $z = \dfrac{37 - 29.1}{16.6} = 0.48$
e. $z = \dfrac{37 - 17.2}{9.3} = 2.13$

As indicated by the positive z-scores, both patients had wait times that exceeded the means of their respective samples; even though the patients had the same wait time, the z-score for the sixth patient in the sample who visited an office with a wait-tracking system is much larger because that patient is part of a sample with a smaller mean and a smaller standard deviation

f. The z-scores for all patients follow

Without Wait-Tracking System	With Wait-Tracking System
-0.31	1.49
2.28	-0.67
-0.73	-0.34
-0.55	0.09
0.11	-0.56
0.90	2.13
-1.03	-0.88
-0.37	-0.45
-0.79	-0.56
0.48	-0.24

The z-scores do not indicate the existence of any outliers in either sample

66. a. $\bar{x} = \dfrac{\Sigma x_i}{n} = \dfrac{20665}{50} = 413.3$
This is slightly higher than the mean for the study.

b. $s = \sqrt{\dfrac{\Sigma(x_i - \bar{x})^2}{(n-1)}} = \sqrt{\dfrac{69424.5}{49}} = 37.64$

c. There are no outliers.

68. a. Median $= 52.1 + .5(52.1 - 52.1) = 52.1$
b. -6.1%
c. 25th percentile = 50.75
75th percentile = 52.6
d. 46.5   50.75   52.1   52.6   64.5
e. The last household income (64.5) has a z-score > 3 and is an outlier.
Using interquartile range as the approach, the first observation (46.5) and the last observation (64.5) would be considered outliers.

70. a. 364 rooms
b. \$457
c. $-.293$; slight negative correlation
Higher cost per night tends to be associated with smaller hotels

72. a. .268, low or weak positive correlation
b. Very poor predictor; spring training is practice and does not count toward standings or playoffs

74. a. 60.68
b. $s^2 = 31.23$; $s = 5.59$

Chapter 4

2. $\dbinom{6}{3} = \dfrac{6!}{3!3!} = \dfrac{6 \cdot 5 \cdot 4 \cdot 3 \cdot 2 \cdot 1}{(3 \cdot 2 \cdot 1)(3 \cdot 2 \cdot 1)} = 20$

ABC	ACE	BCD	BEF
ABD	ACF	BCE	CDE
ABE	ADE	BCF	CDF
ABF	ADF	BDE	CEF
ACD	AEF	BDF	DEF

4. b. (H,H,H), (H,H,T), (H,T,H), (H,T,T),
(T,H,H), (T,H,T), (T,T,H), (T,T,T)

 c. $\frac{1}{8}$

6. $P(E_1) = .40, P(E_2) = .26, P(E_3) = .34$
The relative frequency method was used

8. a. 4: Commission Positive—Council Approves
Commission Positive—Council Disapproves
Commission Negative—Council Approves
Commission Negative—Council Disapproves

9. $\binom{50}{4} = \frac{50!}{4!46!} = \frac{50 \cdot 49 \cdot 48 \cdot 47}{4 \cdot 3 \cdot 2 \cdot 1} = 230,300$

10. a. $P(\text{on-time arrival}) = .865$

 b. $P(\text{Less than 2}) = 3/10 = .30$

 c. $P(\text{more than 1}) = 5/10 = .50$

 d. $P(\text{not on time}) = 1 - P(\text{on time}) = 1 - .871 = .129$

12. a. Step 1: Use the counting rule for combinations:

$$\binom{59}{5} = \frac{59!}{5!(59-5)!} = \frac{(59)(58)(57)(56)(55)}{(5)(4)(3)(2)(1)} = 5,006,386$$

Step 2: There are 35 ways to select the red Powerball from digits 1 to 35
Total number of Powerball lottery outcomes:
$(5,006,386) \times (35) = 175,223,510$

 b. Probability of winning the lottery: 1 chance in 175,223,510
$= 1/(175,223,510) = .000000005707$

14. a. $\frac{1}{4}$

 b. $\frac{1}{2}$

 c. $\frac{3}{4}$

15. a. $S = \{$ace of clubs, ace of diamonds, ace of hearts, ace of spades$\}$

 b. $S = \{2$ of clubs, 3 of clubs, . . . , 10 of clubs, J of clubs, Q of clubs, K of clubs, A of clubs$\}$

 c. There are 12; jack, queen, or king in each of the four suits

 d. For (a): $4/52 = 1/13 = .08$
For (b): $13/52 = 1/4 = .25$
For (c): $12/52 = .23$

16. a. 36

 c. $\frac{1}{6}$

 d. $\frac{5}{18}$

 e. No; $P(\text{odd}) = P(\text{even}) = \frac{1}{2}$

 f. Classical

17. a. (4, 6), (4, 7), (4, 8)

 b. $.05 + .10 + .15 = .30$

 c. (2, 8), (3, 8), (4, 8)

 d. $.05 + .05 + .15 = .25$

 e. .15

18. a. Let C = corporate headquarters located in California.
$P(C) = 53/500 = .106$

 b. Let N = corporate headquarters located in New York
T = corporate headquarters located in Texas
$P(N) = 50/500 = .100$
$P(T) = 52/500 = .104$
$P(C) + P(N) + P(T) = .106 + .100 + .104 = .31$

 c. Let A = corporate headquarters located in one of the eight states. $P(A) = 283/500 = .566$

20. a.

Experimental Outcome	Age Financially Independent	Number of Responses	Probability
E_1	16 to 20	191	191/944 = 0.2023
E_2	21 to 24	467	467/944 = 0.4947
E_3	25 to 27	244	244/944 = 0.2585
E_4	28 or older	42	42/944 = 0.0445
		944	

 b. $P(\text{Age} < 25) = P(E_1) + P(E_2) = .2023 + .4947 = .6970$

 c. $P(\text{Age} > 24) = P(E_3) + P(E_4) = .2585 + .0445 = .3030$

 d. The probability of being financially independent before the age of 25, .6970, seems high given the general economic conditions. It appears that the teenagers who responded to this survey may have unrealistic expectations about becoming financially independent at a relatively young age.

22. a. .40, .40, .60

 b. .80, yes

 c. $A^c = \{E_3, E_4, E_5\}; C^c = \{E_1, E_4\};$
$P(A^c) = .60; P(C^c) = .40$

 d. $(E_1, E_2, E_5); .60$

 e. .80

23. a. $P(A) = P(E_1) + P(E_4) + P(E_6)$
$= .05 + .25 + .10 = .40$
$P(B) = P(E_2) + P(E_4) + P(E_7)$
$= .20 + .25 + .05 = .50$
$P(C) = P(E_2) + P(E_3) + P(E_5) + P(E_7)$
$= .20 + .20 + .15 + .05 = .60$

 b. $A \cup B = \{E_1, E_2, E_4, E_6, E_7\};$
$P(A \cup B) = P(E_1) + P(E_2) + P(E_4) + P(E_6) + P(E_7)$
$= .05 + .20 + .25 + .10 + .05$
$= .65$

 c. $A \cap B = \{E_4\}; P(A \cap B) = P(E_4) = .25$

 d. Yes, they are mutually exclusive

 e. $B^c = \{E_1, E_3, E_5, E_6\};$
$P(B^c) = P(E_1) + P(E_3) + P(E_5) + P(E_6)$
$= .05 + .20 + .15 + .10$
$= .50$

24. a. .05

   b. .70

26. a. Let D = Domestic Equity Fund. $P(D) = 16/25 = .64$

   b. Let A = 4- or 5-star rating. $P(A) = 12/25 = .48$

   c. 7 Domestic Equity funds were rated 4-star and 2 were rated 5-star. Thus, 9 funds were Domestic Equity funds and were rated 4-star or 5-star. $P(D \cap A) = 9/25 = .36$

   d. $P(D \cup A) = P(D) + P(A) - P(D \cap A) = .64 + .48 - .36 = .76$

28. Let B = rented a car for business reasons

      P = rented a car for personal reasons

   a. $P(B \cup P) = P(B) + P(P) - P(B \cap P)$

             $= .540 + .458 - .300$

             $= .698$

   b. $P(\text{Neither}) = 1 - .698 = .302$

30. a. $P(A \mid B) = \dfrac{P(A \cap B)}{P(B)} = \dfrac{.40}{.60} = .6667$

   b. $P(B \mid A) = \dfrac{P(A \cap B)}{P(A)} = \dfrac{.40}{.50} = .80$

   c. No, because $P(A \mid B) \neq P(A)$

32. a.

	Car	Light Truck	Total
U.S.	.1330	.2939	.4269
Non-U.S.	.3478	.2253	.5731
Total	.4808	.5192	1.0000

   b. .4269, .5731 Non-U.S. higher

      .4808, .5192 Light Truck slightly higher

   c. .3115, .6885 Light Truck higher

   d. .6909, .3931 Car higher

   e. .5661, U.S. higher for Light Trucks

33. a.

		Undergraduate Major			
		Business	**Engineering**	**Other**	**Totals**
Intended	**Full-Time**	0.270	0.151	0.192	0.613
Enrollment	**Part-Time**	0.115	0.123	0.149	0.387
Status	**Totals**	0.385	0.274	0.341	1.000

   b. $P(\text{Business}) = 0.385$, $P(\text{Engineering}) = 0.274$, and $P(\text{Other}) = 0.341$, so Business is the undergraduate major that produces the most potential MBA students

   c. $P(\text{Engineering} \mid \text{Full-Time})$

     $= \dfrac{P(\text{Engineering} \cap \text{Full-Time})}{P(\text{Full-Time})} = \dfrac{0.151}{0.613} = 0.246$

   d. $P(\text{Full-Time} \mid \text{Business})$

     $= \dfrac{P(\text{Full-Time} \cap \text{Business})}{P(\text{Business})} = \dfrac{0.270}{0.385} = 0.701$

   e. For independence, we must have that $P(A)P(B) = P(A \cap B)$; from the joint probability table in part (a) of this problem, we have

$P(A) = 0.613$

$P(B) = 0.385$

So $P(A)\, P(B) = (0.387)(0.385) = 0.236$

But

$P(A \cap B) = (0.270)$

Because $P(A)P(B) \neq P(A \cap B)$, the events are not independent

34. a. Let O = flight arrives on time

       L = flight arrives late

       J = Jet Blue flight

       N = United flight

       U = US Airways flight

   Given: $P(O \mid J) = .768$ $P(O \mid N) = .715$ $P(O \mid U) = .822$

   $P(J) = .30$ $P(N) = .32$ $P(U) = .38$

   Joint probabilities using the multiplication law

   $P(J \cap O) = P(J)P(O|J) = (.30)(.768) = .2304$

   $P(N \cap O) = P(N)P(O|N) = (.32)(.715) = .2288$

   $P(U \cap O) = P(U)P(O|U) = (.38)(.822) = .3124$

   With the marginal probabilities $P(J) = .30$, $P(N) = .32$, and $P(U) = .38$ given, the joint probability table can then be shown as follows.

	On time	Late	Total
Jet Blue	.2304	.0696	.30
United	.2288	.0912	.32
US Airways	.3124	.0676	.38
Total	.7716	.2284	1.00

   b. $P(O) = .2304 + .2288 + .3124 = .7716$

   c. Since US Airways has the highest percentage of flights into terminal C, US Airways with $P(U) = .38$ is the most likely airline for Flight 1382.

   d. From the joint probability table, $P(L) = .2284$

$$P(J|L) = \frac{P(J \cap L)}{P(L)} = \frac{.0696}{.2284} = .3047$$

$$P(N|L) = \frac{P(N \cap L)}{P(L)} = \frac{.0912}{.2284} = .3992$$

$$P(U|L) = \frac{P(U \cap L)}{P(L)} = \frac{.0676}{.2284} = .2961$$

   Most likely airline for Flight 1382 is now United with a probability of .3992. US Airways is now the least likely airline for this flight with a probability of .2961.

36. a. We have that $P(\text{Make the Shot}) = .93$ for each foul shot, so the probability that Jamal Crawford will make two consecutive foul shots is $P(\text{Make the Shot})$ $P(\text{Make the Shot}) = (.93)(.93) = .8649$

   b. There are three unique ways that Jamal Crawford can make at least one shot—he can make the first shot and miss the second shot, miss the first shot and make the second shot, or make both shots; since the event "Miss the Shot" is the complement of the event "Make the Shot," $P(\text{Miss the Shot}) = 1 - P(\text{Make the Shot}) = 1 - .93 = .07$; thus

$P(\text{Make the Shot}) \, P(\text{Miss the Shot}) = (.93)(.07) = .0651$

$P(\text{Miss the Shot}) \, P(\text{Make the Shot}) = (.07)(.93) = .0651$

$P(\text{Make the Shot}) \, P(\text{Make the Shot}) = (.93)(.93) = \underline{.8649}$

$.9951$

c. We can find this probability in two ways; we can calculate the probability directly

$P(\text{Miss the Shot}) \, P(\text{Miss the Shot}) = (.07)(.07) = .0049$

Or we can recognize that the event "Miss both Shots" is the complement of the event "Make at Least One of the Two Shots," so

$P(\text{Miss the Shot}) \, P(\text{Miss the Shot}) = 1 - .9951 = .0049$

d. For the Portland Trail Blazers' center, we have

$P(\text{Make the Shot}) = .58$ for each foul shot, so the probability that the Portland Trail Blazers' center will make two consecutive foul shots is $P(\text{Make the Shot}) \, P(\text{Make the Shot}) = (.58)(.58) = .3364$

Again, there are three unique ways that the Portland Trail Blazers' center can make at least one shot—he can make the first shot and miss the second shot, miss the first shot and make the second shot, or make both shots; since the event "Miss the Shot" is the complement of the event "Make the Shot," $P(\text{Miss the Shot}) = 1 - P(\text{Make the Shot}) = 1 - .58 = .42$; thus

$P(\text{Make the Shot}) \, P(\text{Miss the Shot}) = (.58)(.42) = .2436$

$P(\text{Miss the Shot}) \, P(\text{Make the Shot}) = (.42)(.58) = .2436$

$P(\text{Make the Shot}) \, P(\text{Make the Shot}) = (.58)(.58) = \underline{.3364}$

$.8236$

We can again find the probability the Portland Trail Blazers' center will miss both shots in two ways; we can calculate the probability directly

$P(\text{Miss the Shot}) \, P(\text{Miss the Shot}) = (.42)(.42) = .1764$

Or we can recognize that the event "Miss both Shots" is the complement of the event "Make at Least One of the Two Shots," so

$P(\text{Miss the Shot}) \, P(\text{Miss the Shot}) = 1 - .9951 = .1764$

Intentionally fouling the Portland Trail Blazers' center is a better strategy than intentionally fouling Jamal Crawford

38. Let Y = has a college degree
N = does not have a college degree
D = a delinquent student loan
a. From the table, $P(Y) = .42$
b. From the table, $P(N) = .58$
c. $P(D|Y) = \dfrac{P(D \cap Y)}{P(Y)} = \dfrac{.16}{.42} = .3810$
d. $P(D|N) = \dfrac{P(D \cap N)}{P(N)} = \dfrac{.34}{.58} = .5862$

e. Individuals who obtained a college degree have a .3810 probability of a delinquent student loan while individuals who dropped out without obtaining a college degree have a .5862 probability of a delinquent student loan. Not obtaining a college degree will lead to a greater probability of struggling to pay back the student loan and will likely lead to financial problems in the future.

39. a. Yes, because $P(A_1 \cap A_2) = 0$
b. $P(A_1 \cap B) = P(A_1)P(B \mid A_1) = .40(.20) = .08$
$P(A_2 \cap B) = P(A_2)P(B \mid A_2) = .60(.05) = .03$
c. $P(B) = P(A_1 \cap B) + P(A_2 \cap B) = .08 + .03 = .11$
d. $P(A_1 \mid B) = \dfrac{.08}{.11} = .7273$

$P(A_2 \mid B) = \dfrac{.03}{.11} = .2727$

40. a. .10, .20, .09
b. .51
c. .26, .51, .23

42. M = missed payment
D_1 = customer defaults
D_2 = customer does not default
$P(D_1) = .05, P(D_2) = .95, P(M \mid D_2) = .2, P(M \mid D_1) = 1$
a. $P(D_1 \mid M) = \dfrac{P(D_1)P(M \mid D_1)}{P(D_1)P(M \mid D_1) + P(D_2)P(M \mid D_2)}$

$= \dfrac{(.05)(1)}{(.05)(1) + (.95)(.2)}$

$= \dfrac{.05}{.24} = .21$

b. Yes, the probability of default is greater than .20

44. M = the current visitor to the ParFore website is a male
F = the current visitor to the Parfore website is a female
D = a visitor to the ParFore website previously visited the Dillard website
a. Using past history, $P(F) = .40$.
b. $P(M) = .60, P(D|F) = .30$, and $P(D|M) = .10$

$P(F|D) = \dfrac{P(F)P(D|F)}{P(F)P(D|F) + P(M)P(D|M)}$

$= \dfrac{(.40)(.30)}{(.40)(.30) + (.60)(.10)} = .6667$

46. a. $422 + 181 + 80 + 121 + 201 = 1005$ respondents
b. Most frequent response a day or less; Probability = $422/1005 = .4199$
c. $201/1005 = .20$
d. Responses of 2 days, 3 days, and 4 or more days = $181 + 80 + 121 = 382$.
Probability = $382/1005 = .3801$

48. a. 0.5029
b. 0.5758

c. No, from part (a) we have $P(F) = 0.5029$ and from part (b) we have $P(A \mid F) = 0.5758$; since $P(F) \neq P(A \mid F)$, events A and F are not independent

50. a. .76

b. .24

52. b. .2022

c. .4618

d. .4005

54. a. .7766

b. $P(\text{OKAY} \mid 30\text{--}49)$

$$= \frac{P(\text{OKAY} \cap 30\text{--}49)}{P(30\text{--}49)} = \frac{0.0907}{0.3180} = 0.2852$$

c. $P(50 + \mid \text{NOT OKAY})$

$$= \frac{P(50 + \cap \text{NOT OKAY})}{P(\text{NOT OKAY})} = \frac{0.4008}{0.7766} = 0.5161$$

d. The attitude about this practice is not independent of the age of the respondent; we can show this in several ways: One example is to use the result from part (b); We have

$$P(\text{OKAY} \mid 30\text{--}49) = 0.2852$$

and

$$P(\text{OKAY}) = 0.2234$$

If the attitude about this practice were independent of the age of the respondent, we would expect these probabilities to be equal; since these probabilities are not equal, the data suggest the attitude about this practice is not independent of the age of the respondent

e. Respondents in the 50+ age category are far more likely to say this practice is NOT OKAY than are respondents in the 18–29 age category:

$P(\text{NOT OKAY} \mid 50+)$

$$= \frac{P(\text{NOT OKAY} \cap 50+)}{P(50+)} = \frac{0.4008}{0.4731} = 0.8472$$

$P(\text{NOT OKAY} \mid 18\text{--}29)$

$$= \frac{P(\text{NOT OKAY} \cap 18 - 29)}{P(18 - 29)} = \frac{0.1485}{0.2089} = 0.7109$$

56. a. .25

b. .125

c. .0125

d. .10

e. No

58. a. Let A_1 = student studied abroad

A_2 = student did not study abroad

F = female student

M = male student

$P(A_1) = .095$

$P(A_2) = 1 - P(A_1) = 1 - .095 = .905$

$P(F \mid A_1) = .60$

$P(F \mid A_2) = .49$

Tabular computations

Events	$P(A_i)$	$P(F\mid A_i)$	$P(A_i \cap F)$	$P(A_i\mid F)$
A_1	.095	.60	.0570	.1139
A_2	.905	.49	.4435	.8861
			$P(F) = .5005$	

$P(A_1 \mid F) = .1139$

b.

Events	$P(A_i)$	$P(M\mid A_i)$	$P(A_i \cap M)$	$P(A_i\mid M)$
A_1	.095	.40	.0380	.0761
A_2	.905	.51	.4615	.9239
			$P(M) = .4995$	

$P(A_1 \mid M) = .0761$

c. From above, $P(F) = .5005$ and $P(M) = .4995$, so almost 50/50 female and male full-time students.

60. a. $P(\text{spam}\mid shipping!)$

$$= \frac{P(\text{spam})P(shipping!\mid\text{spam})}{P(\text{spam})P(shipping!\mid\text{spam}) + P(\text{ham})P(shipping!\mid\text{ham})}$$

$$= \frac{(0.10)(0.051)}{(0.10)(0.051) + (0.90)(0.0015)} = 0.791$$

$P(\text{ham}\mid shipping!)$

$$= \frac{P(\text{ham})P(shipping!\mid\text{ham})}{P(\text{ham})P(shipping!\mid\text{ham}) + P(\text{spam})P(shipping!\mid\text{spam})}$$

$$= \frac{(0.90)(0.0015)}{(0.90)(0.0015) + (0.10)(0.051)} = 0.209$$

If a message includes the word *shipping!*, the probability the message is spam is high (0.7910), and so the message should be flagged as spam

b. $P(\text{spam}\mid today!)$

$$= \frac{P(\text{spam})P(today!\mid\text{spam})}{P(\text{spam})P(today!\mid\text{spam}) + P(\text{ham})P(today!\mid\text{ham})}$$

$$= \frac{(0.10)(0.045)}{(0.10)(0.045) + (0.90)(0.0022)} = 0.694$$

$P(\text{spam}\mid here!)$

$$= \frac{P(\text{spam})P(here!\mid\text{spam})}{P(\text{spam})P(here!\mid\text{spam}) + P(\text{ham})P(here!\mid\text{ham})}$$

$$= \frac{(0.10)(0.034)}{(0.10)(0.034) + (0.90)(0.0022)} = 0.632$$

A message that includes the word *today!* is more likely to be spam because $P(today!\mid\text{spam})$ is larger than $P(here!\mid\text{spam})$; because *today!* occurs more often in unwanted messages (spam), it is easier to distinguish spam from ham in messages that include *today!*

c. $P(\text{spam}|available)$

$$= \frac{P(\text{spam})P(available|\text{spam})}{P(\text{spam})P(available|\text{spam}) + P(\text{ham})P(available|\text{ham})}$$

$$= \frac{(0.10)(0.014)}{(0.10)(0.014) + (0.90)(0.0041)} = 0.275$$

$P(\text{spam}|fingertips!)$

$$= \frac{P(\text{spam})P(fingertips!|\text{spam})|}{P(\text{spam})P(fingertips!|\text{spam}) + P(\text{ham})P(fingertips!|\text{ham})}$$

$$= \frac{(0.10)(0.014)}{(0.10)(0.014) + (0.90)(0.0011)} = 0.586$$

A message that includes the word *fingertips!* is more likely to be spam; because $P(fingertips!|\text{ham})$ is smaller than $P(available|\text{ham})$; because *available* occurs more often in legitimate messages (ham), it is more difficult to distinguish spam from ham in messages that include *available*

d. It is easier to distinguish spam from ham when a word occurs more often in unwanted messages (spam) and/ or less often in legitimate messages (ham)

Chapter 5

1. a. Head, Head (H, H)
Head, Tail (H, T)
Tail, Head (T, H)
Tail, Tail (T, T)

b. x = number of heads on two coin tosses

c.

Outcome	Values of x
(H, H)	2
(H, T)	1
(T, H)	1
(T, T)	0

d. Discrete; 0, 1, and 2

2. a. x = time in minutes to assemble product
b. Any positive value: $x > 0$
c. Continuous

3. Let Y = position is offered
N = position is not offered
a. $S = \{(Y, Y, Y), (Y, Y, N), (Y, N, Y), (Y, N, N), (N, Y, Y), (N, Y, N), (N, N, Y), (N, N, N)\}$
b. Let N = number of offers made; N is a discrete random variable

c.

Experimental Outcome	(Y, Y, Y)	(Y, Y, N)	(Y, N, Y)	(Y, N, N)	(N, Y, Y)	(N, Y, N)	(N, N, Y)	(N, N, N)
Value of N	3	2	2	1	2	1	1	0

4. $x = 0, 1, 2, \ldots, 9$

6. a. $0, 1, 2, \ldots, 20$; discrete
b. $0, 1, 2, \ldots$; discrete
c. $0, 1, 2, \ldots, 50$; discrete

d. $0 \le x \le 8$; continuous
e. $x > 0$; continuous

7. a. $f(x) \ge 0$ for all values of x
$\Sigma f(x) = 1$; therefore, it is a valid probability distribution
b. Probability $x = 30$ is $f(30) = .25$
c. Probability $x \le 25$ is $f(20) + f(25) = .20 + .15 = .35$
d. Probability $x > 30$ is $f(35) = .40$

8. a.

x	$f(x)$
1	$3/20 = .15$
2	$5/20 = .25$
3	$8/20 = .40$
4	$4/20 = .20$
	Total 1.00

b. $f(x)$

c. $f(x) \ge 0$ for $x = 1, 2, 3, 4$
$\Sigma f(x) = 1$

10. a.

x	1	2	3	4	5
$f(x)$	.05	.09	.03	.42	.41

b.

x	1	2	3	4	5
$f(x)$	.04	.10	.12	.46	.28

c. .83
d. .28
e. Senior executives are more satisfied

12. a. Yes; $f(x) \ge 0$. $\Sigma f(x) = 1$
b. $f(500{,}000) + f(600{,}000) = .10 + .05 = .15$
c. $f(100{,}000) = .10$

14. a. .05
b. .70
c. .40

16. a.

y	$f(y)$	$yf(y)$
2	.20	.4
4	.30	1.2
7	.40	2.8
8	.10	.8
Totals	1.00	5.2

$E(y) = \mu = 5.2$

b.

y	$y - \mu$	$(y - \mu)^2$	$f(y)$	$(y - \mu)^2 f(y)$
2	−3.20	10.24	.20	2.048
4	−1.20	1.44	.30	.432
7	1.80	3.24	.40	1.296
8	2.80	7.84	.10	.784
			Total	4.560

$$Var(y) = 4.56$$
$$\sigma = \sqrt{4.56} = 2.14$$

18. a/b.

x	$f(x)$	$xf(x)$	$x - \mu$	$(x - \mu)^2$	$(x - \mu)^2 f(x)$
0	.2188	.0000	−1.1825	1.3982	.3060
1	.5484	.5484	−.1825	.0333	.0183
2	.1241	.2483	.8175	.6684	.0830
3	.0489	.1466	1.8175	3.3035	.1614
4	.0598	.2393	2.8175	7.9386	.4749
Total	1.0000	1.1825			1.0435
		↑			↑
		$E(x)$			$Var(x)$

c/d.

y	$f(y)$	$yf(y)$	$y - \mu$	$(y - \mu)^2$	$(y - \mu)^2 f(y)$
0	.2497	.0000	-1.2180	1.4835	.3704
1	.4816	.4816	-.2180	.0475	.0229
2	.1401	.2801	.7820	.6115	.0856
3	.0583	.1749	1.7820	3.1755	.1851
4	.0703	.2814	2.7820	7.7395	.5444
Total	1.0000	1.2180			1.2085
		↑			↑
		$E(y)$			$Var(y)$

e. The expected number of times that owner-occupied units have a water supply stoppage lasting 6 or more hours in the past 3 months is 1.1825, slightly less than the expected value of 1.2180 for renter-occupied units. And, the variability is somewhat less for owner-occupied units (1.0435) as compared to renter-occupied units (1.2085).

20. a. 430

   b. −90; concern is to protect against the expense of a large loss

22. a. 445

   b. $1250 loss

24. a. Medium: 145; large: 140

   b. Medium: 2725; large: 12,400

25. a.

$$E(x) = .2(50) + .5(30) + .3(40) = 37$$
$$E(y) = .2(80) + .5(50) + .3(60) = 59$$
$$Var(x) = .2(50-37)^2 + .5(30-37)^2 + .3(40-37)^2 = 61$$
$$Var(y) = .2(80-59)^2 + .5(50-59)^2 + .3(60-59)^2 = 129$$

b.

$x + y$	$f(x + y)$
130	.2
80	.5
100	.3

c.

$x + y$	$f(x + y)$	$(x + y)f(x + y)$	$x + y - E(x + y)$
130	.2	26	34
80	.5	40	−16
100	.3	30	4
		$E(x + y) = 96$	

$[x + y - E(x + y)]^2$	$[x + y - E(x + y)]^2 f(x + y)$
1156	231.2
256	128.0
16	4.8
	$Var(x + y) = 364$

d.
$$\sigma_{xy} = [Var(x + y) - Var(x) - Var(y)]/2 = (364-61-129)/2 = 87$$
$Var(x) = 61$ and $Var(y) = 129$ were computed in part (a), so

$$\sigma_x = \sqrt{61} = 7.8102 \qquad \sigma_y = \sqrt{129} = 11.3578$$

$$\rho_{xy} = \frac{\sigma_{xy}}{\sigma_x \sigma_y} = \frac{87}{(7.8102)(11.3578)} = .98$$

The random variables x and y are positively related; both the covariance and correlation coefficient are positive; indeed, they are very highly correlated; the correlation coefficient is almost equal to 1

e. $Var(x + y) = Var(x) + Var(y) + 2\sigma_{xy}$
$$= 61 + 129 + 2(87) = 364$$
$Var(x) + Var(y) = 61 + 129 = 190$
The variance of the sum of x and y is greater than the sum of the variances by two times the covariance: 2(87) = 174; the reason it is positive is that, in this case, the variables are positively related; whenever two random variables are positively related, the variance of the sum of the random variables will be greater than the sum of the variances of the individual random variables

26. a. 5%, 1%, stock 1 is riskier

   b. $42.25, $25.00

   c. 5.825, 2.236

   d. 6.875%, 3.329%

   e. −.6, strong negative relationship

27. a. Dividing each of the frequencies in the table by the total number of restaurants provides the joint probability table below; the bivariate probability for each pair of quality and meal price is shown in the body of the table; this is the bivariate probability distribution; for instance, the probability of a rating of 2 on quality and a rating of 3 on meal price is given by $f(2, 3) = .18$; the marginal probability distribution for quality, x, is in the rightmost column; the marginal probability for meal price, y, is in the bottom row

| | Meal Price y | | | |
Quality x	1	2	3	Total
1	0.14	0.13	0.01	0.28
2	0.11	0.21	0.18	0.50
3	0.01	0.05	0.16	0.22
Total	0.26	0.39	0.35	1

b. $E(x) = 1(.28) + 2(.50) + 3(.22) = 1.94$
$Var(x) = .28(1 - 1.94)^2 + .50(2 - 1.94)^2$
$\quad\quad + .22(3 - 1.94)^2 = .4964$

c. $E(y) = 1(.26) + 2(.39) + 3(.35) = 2.09$
$Var(y) = .26(1 - 2.09)^2 + .39(2 - 2.09)^2$
$\quad\quad + .35(3 - 2.09)^2 = .6019$

d. $\sigma_{xy} = [Var(x + y) = Var(x) - Var(y)]/2$
$\quad\quad = [1.6691 - .4964 - .6019]/2 = .2854$
Since the covariance $\sigma_{xy} = .2854$ is positive, we can conclude that as the quality rating goes up, the meal price goes up; this is as we would expect

e. $\rho_{xy} = \dfrac{\sigma_{xy}}{\sigma_x \sigma_y} = \dfrac{.2854}{\sqrt{.4964}\sqrt{.6019}} = .5221$

With a correlation coefficient of .5221, we would call this a moderately positive relationship; it is not likely to find a low-cost restaurant that is also high quality, but, it is possible; there are 3 of them leading to $f(3,1) = .01$

28. a. $E(y) = \$45.30$, $Var(y) = 3.81$, $\sigma_y = \$1.95$
b. $E(x) = \$90.50$, $Var(x) = 24.75$, $\sigma_x = \$4.97$
c.

z	f(z)
128	.05
130	.20
133	.20
138	.25
140	.20
143	.10
	1.00

d. $135.8, 21.26, \$4.61$
e. No, $\sigma_{xy} = -3.65$
f. No, they are less

30. a. $333.486, -1.974$
b. $9.055\%, 19.89\%$
c. $9.425\%, 11.63\%$
d. $7.238\%, 4.94\%$
e. Aggresive: 50% Core Bonds, 50% REITS
Conservative: 80% Core Bonds, 20% REITS

31. a.

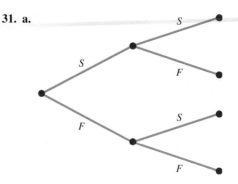

b. $f(1) = \binom{2}{1}(.4)^1(.6)^1 = \dfrac{2!}{1!1!}(.4)(.6) = .48$

c. $f(0) = \binom{2}{0}(.4)^0(.6)^2 = \dfrac{2!}{0!2!}(1)(.36) = .36$

d. $f(2) = \binom{2}{2}(.4)^2(.6)^0 = \dfrac{2!}{2!0!}(.16)(.1) = .16$

e. $P(x \geq 1) = f(1) + f(2) = .48 + .16 = .64$
f. $E(x) = np = 2(.4) = .8$
$Var(x) = np(1 - p) = 2(.4)(.6) = .48$
$\sigma = \sqrt{.48} = .6928$

32. a. .3487
b. .1937
c. .9298
d. .6513
e. 1
f. .9, .95

34. a. Yes. Since the teenagers are selected randomly, p is the same from trial to trial and the trials are independent. The two outcomes per trial are use Pandora Media Inc.'s online radio service or do not use Pandora Media Inc.'s online radio service.

Binomial $n = 10$ and $p = .35$
$f(x) = \dfrac{10!}{x!(10 - x)!}(.35)^x(1 - .35)^{10-x}$

b. $f(0) = \dfrac{10!}{x!(10 - 0)!}(.35)^0(.65)^{10-0} = .0135$

c. $f(4) = \dfrac{10!}{4!(10 - 4)!}(.35)^4(.65)^{10-4} = .2377$

d. Probability $(x \geq 2) = 1 - f(0) - f(1)$
From part (b), $f(0) = .0135$
$f(1) = \dfrac{10!}{1!(10 - 1)!}(.35)^1(.65)^{10-1} = .0725$

36. a. Probability of a defective part being produced must be .03 for each part selected; parts must be selected independently
b. Let D = defective
$\quad\quad G$ = not defective

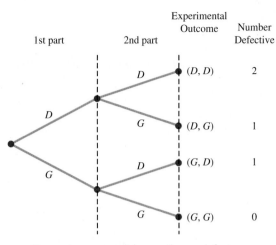

Experimental
Outcome   Number
Defective

1st part   2nd part

D • (D, D) 2

D

G • (D, G) 1

D • (G, D) 1

G

G • (G, G) 0

c. Two outcomes result in exactly one defect
d. P(no defects) $= (.97)(.97) = .9409$
P(1 defect) $= 2(.03)(.97) = .0582$
P(2 defects) $= (.03)(.03) = .0009$

38. a. .90
b. .99
c. .999
d. Yes

40. a. Yes. Since the 18- to 34-year olds living with their parents are selected randomly, p is the same from trial to trial and the trials are independent. The two outcomes per trial are contribute to household expenses or do not contribute to household expenses.

Binomial $n = 15$ and $p = .75$

$$f(x) = \frac{15!}{x!(15 - x)!}(.75)^x(1 - .75)^{15-x}$$

b. The probability that none of the fifteen contribute to household expenses $= .0000$
c. Probability $= .1651 + .2252 + .2252 + .1559 + .0668 + .0134 = .8516$

42. a. $f(4) = \dfrac{20!}{4!(20 - 4)!}(.30)^4(.70)^{20-4} = .1304$

b. Probability $(x \geq 2) = 1 - f(0) - f(1)$

$$f(0) = \frac{20!}{0!(20 - 0)!}(.30)^0(.70)^{20-0} = .0008$$

$$f(1) = \frac{20!}{1!(20 - 1)!}(.30)^1(.70)^{20-1} = .0068$$

Probability $(x \geq 2) = 1 - f(0) - f(1) = 1 - (.0008 + .0068) = .9924$
c. $E(x) = np = 20(.30) = 6$
d. $Var(x) = np(1 - p) = 20(.30)(1 - .30) = 4.2$
$\sigma = \sqrt{4.2} = 2.0499$

44. a. $f(x) = \dfrac{3^x e^{-3}}{x!}$

b. .2241

c. .1494
d. .8008

45. a. $f(x) = \dfrac{2^x e^{-2}}{x!}$

b. $\mu = 6$ for 3 time periods

c. $f(x) = \dfrac{6^x e^{-6}}{x!}$

d. $f(2) = \dfrac{2^2 e^{-2}}{2!} = \dfrac{4(.1353)}{2} = .2706$

e. $f(6) = \dfrac{6^6 e^{-6}}{6!} = .1606$

f. $f(5) = \dfrac{4^5 e^{-4}}{5!} = .1563$

46. a. .1952
b. .1048
c. .0183
d. .0907

48. a. For a 15-minute period the mean is $14.4/4 = 3.6$

$$f(0) = \frac{3.6^0 e^{-3.6}}{0!} = e^{-3.6} = .0273$$

b. probability $= 1 - f(0) = 1 - .2073 = .9727$
c. probability $= 1 - [f(0) + f(1) + f(2) + f(3)] = 1 - [.0273 + .0984 + .1771 + .2125] = .4847$

50. a. $\mu = 18/30 = .6$ per day during June

b. $f(0) = \dfrac{.6^0 e^{-.6}}{0!} = .5488$

c. $f(1) = \dfrac{.6^1 e^{-.6}}{1!} = .3293$

d. P(More than 1) $= 1 - f(0) - f(1) = 1 - .5488 - .3293 = .1219$

52. a. $f(1) = \dfrac{\binom{3}{1}\binom{10-3}{4-1}}{\binom{10}{4}} = \dfrac{\left(\dfrac{3!}{1!2!}\right)\left(\dfrac{7!}{3!4!}\right)}{\dfrac{10!}{4!6!}}$

$= \dfrac{(3)(35)}{210} = .50$

b. $f(2) = \dfrac{\binom{3}{2}\binom{10-3}{2-2}}{\binom{10}{2}} = \dfrac{(3)(1)}{45} = .067$

c. $f(0) = \dfrac{\binom{3}{0}\binom{10-3}{2-0}}{\binom{10}{2}} = \dfrac{(1)(21)}{45} = .4667$

d. $f(2) = \dfrac{\binom{3}{2}\binom{10-3}{4-2}}{\binom{10}{4}} = \dfrac{(3)(21)}{210} = .30$

e. $x = 4$ is *greater than* $r = 3$; thus, $f(4) = 0$

54. a. .5250

    b. .8167

56. $N = 60$, $n = 10$

    a. $r = 20$, $x = 0$

$$f(0) = \frac{\binom{20}{0}\binom{40}{10}}{\binom{60}{10}} = \frac{(1)\left(\frac{40!}{10!30!}\right)}{\frac{60!}{10!50!}}$$

$$= \left(\frac{40!}{10!30!}\right)\left(\frac{10!50!}{60!}\right)$$

$$= \frac{40 \cdot 39 \cdot 38 \cdot 37 \cdot 36 \cdot 35 \cdot 34 \cdot 33 \cdot 32 \cdot 31}{60 \cdot 59 \cdot 58 \cdot 57 \cdot 56 \cdot 55 \cdot 54 \cdot 53 \cdot 52 \cdot 51}$$

$$= .0112$$

    b. $r = 20$, $x = 1$

$$f(1) = \frac{\binom{20}{1}\binom{40}{9}}{\binom{60}{10}} = 20\left(\frac{40!}{9!31!}\right)\left(\frac{10!50!}{60!}\right)$$

$$= .0725$$

    c. $1 - f(0) - f(1) = 1 - .0112 - .0725 = .9163$

    d. Same as the probability one will be from Hawaii; .0725

58. a. .2917

    b. .0083

    c. .5250, .1750; 1 bank

    d. .7083

    e. .90, .49, .70

60. a.

x	$f(x)$
1	.150
2	.050
3	.075
4	.050
5	.125
6	.050
7	.100
8	.125
9	.125
10	.150
Total	1.000

    b. Probability of outstanding service is $.125 + .150$
       $= .275$

    c. $E(x) = 5.925$ and $Var(x) = 9.6694$

    d. The probability of a new car dealership receiving an outstanding wait-time rating is $2/7 = .2857$. For the remaining $40 - 7 = 33$ service providers, 9 received an outstanding rating; this corresponds to a probability of $9/33 = .2727$.

62. a. .05, .40, 0 terminal only used when a purchase is made

    b.

x	$f(x)$	$E(x) = 1.14$	$Var(x) = .3804$
0	.13		
1	.60		
2	.27		
	1.00		

    c. .5, .45

    d.

t	$f(t)$	$E(t)$ 1.64	$Var(t)$ .5504
1	.50		
2	.38		
3	.10		
4	.02		
	1.00		

    e. $\sigma_{xy} = -.14$, $\rho_{xy} = -.3384$, negative relationship

64. a. $f(3) = \binom{20}{3}(.53)^3(.47)^{17} = .0005$

    b. $n = 20$ and $x = 0$
      $P(x \leq 5) = f(0) + f(1) + f(2) + f(3) + f(4) + f(5)$
      $= .4952$

    c. $E(x) = np = 2000(.49) = 980$

    d. $E(x) = np = 2000(.36) = 720$. $\sigma^2 = np(1 - p)$
      $= 2000(.36)(.64) = 460.8$
      $\sigma = \sqrt{460.8} = 21.4663$

66. a. .9510

    b. .0480

    c. .0490

68. a. $E(x) = 200(.235) = 47$

    b. $\sigma = \sqrt{np(1 - p)} = \sqrt{200(.235)(.765)} = 5.9962$

    c. 5.9962

70. .1912

72. a. .2240

    b. .5767

74. a. .4667

    b. .4667

    c. .0667

Chapter 6

1. a.

b. $P(x = 1.25) = 0$; the probability of any single point is zero because the area under the curve above any single point is zero

c. $P(1.0 \leq x \leq 1.25) = 2(.25) = .50$

d. $P(1.20 < x < 1.5) = 2(.30) = .60$

2. b. .50

c. .60

d. 15

e. 8.33

4. a.

$f(x)$

1.5

1.0

.5

0   1   2   3 x

b. $P(.25 < x < .75) = 1(.50) = .50$

c. $P(x \leq .30) = 1(.30) = .30$

d. $P(x > .60) = 1(.40) = .40$

6. a. Uniform probability density function. $a = 136 - \frac{1}{2}(160) = 56$ and $b = 136 + \frac{1}{2}(160) = 216$

b. $P(100 \leq x \leq 200) = (200 - 100)(.00625) = .6250$

c. $P(x \geq 150) = (216 - 150)(.00625) = .4125$

d. $P(x \leq 80) = (80 - 56)(.00625) = .1500$

10. a. .9332

b. .8413

c. .0919

d. .4938

12. a. .2967

b. .4418

c. .3300

d. .5910

e. .8849

f. .2389

13. a. $P(-1.98 \leq z \leq .49) = P(z \leq .49) - P(z < -1.98)$
$= .6879 - .0239 = .6640$

b. $P(.52 \leq z \leq 1.22) = P(z \leq 1.22) - P(z < .52)$
$= .8888 - .6985 = .1903$

c. $P(-1.75 \leq z \leq -1.04) = P(z \leq -1.04) - P(z < -1.75) = .1492 - .0401 = .1091$

14. a. $z = 1.96$

b. $z = 1.96$

c. $z = .61$

d. $z = 1.12$

e. $z = .44$

f. $z = .44$

15. a. The z value corresponding to a cumulative probability of .2119 is $z = -.80$

b. Compute $.9030/2 = .4515$; the cumulative probability of $.5000 + .4515 = .9515$ corresponds to $z = 1.66$

c. Compute $.2052/2 = .1026$; z corresponds to a cumulative probability of $.5000 + .1026 = .6026$, so $z = .26$

d. The z value corresponding to a cumulative probability of .9948 is $z = 2.56$

e. The area to the left of z is $1 - .6915 = .3085$, so $z = -.50$

16. a. $z = 2.33$

b. $z = 1.96$

c. $z = 1.645$

d. $z = 1.28$

18. $\mu = 14.4$ and $\sigma = 4.4$

a. At $x = 20$, $z = \dfrac{20 - 14.4}{4.4} = 1.27$

$P(z \leq 1.27) = .8980$
$P(x \geq 20) = 1 - .8980 = .1020$

b. At $x = 10$, $z = \dfrac{10 - 14.4}{4.4} = -1.00$

$P(z \leq -1.00) = .1587$
So, $P(x \leq 10) = .1587$

c. A z-value of 1.28 cuts off an area of approximately 10% in the upper tail

$x = 14.4 + 4.4(1.28) = 20.03$

A return of 20.03% or higher will put a domestic stock fund in the top 10%

20. a. .1788

b. 69.15%

c. .0495

22. a. .6553

b. 13.05 hours

c. .9838

24. a. $z = \dfrac{x - \mu}{\sigma} = \dfrac{400 - 749}{225} = -1.55$

$P(x < 400) = P(z < -1.55) = .0606$

b. $z = \dfrac{x - \mu}{\sigma} = \dfrac{800 - 749}{225} = .23$

$P(x \geq 800) = P(z \geq .23) = 1 - P(z \leq .23) = 1 - .5910 = .4090$

c. For $x = 1000$, $z = \dfrac{x - \mu}{\sigma} = \dfrac{1000 - 749}{225} = 1.12$

For $x = 500$, $z = \dfrac{x - \mu}{\sigma} = \dfrac{500 - 749}{225} = -1.11$

$P(500 \leq x \leq 1000) = P(z \leq 1.12) - P(z \leq -1.11) = .8686 - .1335 = .7351$

d. The upper 5%, or area $= 1 - .05 = .95$ occurs for $z = 1.645$

$x = \mu + z\sigma = 749 + 1.645(225) = \$1119$

26. a. $\mu = np = 100(.20) = 20$

$\sigma^2 = np(1 - p) = 100(.20)(.80) = 16$

$\sigma = \sqrt{16} = 4$

b. Yes, because $np = 20$ and $n(1 - p) = 80$

c. $P(23.5 \leq x \leq 24.5)$

$z = \dfrac{24.5 - 20}{4} = 1.13 \qquad P(z \leq 1.13) = .8708$

$z = \dfrac{23.5 - 20}{4} = .88 \qquad P(z \leq .88) = .8106$

$P(23.5 \leq x \leq 24.5) = P(.88 \leq z \leq 1.13)$
$$= .8708 - .8106 = .0602$$

d. $P(17.5 \leq x \leq 22.5)$

$z = \dfrac{22.5 - 20}{4} = .63 \qquad P(z \leq .63) = .7357$

$z = \dfrac{17.5 - 20}{4} = -.63 \qquad P(z \leq -.63) = .2643$

$P(17.5 \leq x \leq 22.5) = P(-.63 \leq z \leq .63)$
$$= .7357 - .2643 = .4714$$

e. $P(x \leq 15.5)$

$z = \dfrac{15.5 - 20}{4} = -1.13 \qquad P(z \leq -1.13) = .1292$

$P(x \leq 15.5) = P(z \leq -1.13) = .1292$

28. a. $\mu = np = 250(.20) = 50$

b. $\sigma^2 = np(1 - p) = 250(.20)(1 - 20) = 40$

$\sigma = \sqrt{40} = 6.3246$

$P(x < 40) = P(x \leq 39.5)$

$z = \dfrac{x - \mu}{\sigma} = \dfrac{39.5 - 50}{6.3246} = -1.66 \quad \text{Area} = .0485$

$P(x \leq 39.5) = .0485$

c. $P(55 \leq x \leq 60) = P(54.5 \leq x \leq 60.5)$

$z = \dfrac{x - \mu}{\sigma} = \dfrac{54.5 - 50}{6.3246} = .71 \quad \text{Area} = .7611$

$z = \dfrac{x - \mu}{\sigma} = \dfrac{60.5 - 50}{6.3246} = 1.66 \quad \text{Area} = .9515$

$P(54.5 \leq x \leq 60.5) = .9515 - .7611 = .1904$

d. $P(x \geq 70) = P(x \geq 69.5)$

$z = \dfrac{x - \mu}{\sigma} = \dfrac{69.5 - 50}{6.3246} = 3.08 \quad \text{Area} = .9990$

$P(x \geq 69.5) = 1 - .9990 = .0010$

30. a. 144

b. .1841

c. .9943

32. a. .5276

b. .3935

c. .4724

d. .1341

33. a. $P(x \leq x_0) = 1 - e^{-x_0/3}$

b. $P(x \leq 2) = 1 - e^{-2/3} = 1 - .5134 = .4866$

c. $P(x \geq 3) = 1 - P(x \leq 3) = 1 - (1 - e^{-3/3})$
$$= e^{-1} = .3679$$

d. $P(x \leq 5) = 1 - e^{-5/3} = 1 - .1889 = .8111$

e. $P(2 \leq x \leq 5) = P(x \leq 5) - P(x \leq 2)$
$$= .8111 - .4866 = .3245$$

34. a. $f(x) = \dfrac{1}{20} e^{-x/20}$

b. .5276

c. .3679

d. .5105

35. a.

b. $P(x \leq 12) = 1 - e^{-12/12} = 1 - .3679 = .6321$

c. $P(x \leq 6) = 1 - e^{-6/12} = 1 - .6065 = .3935$

d. $P(x \geq 30) = 1 - P(x < 30)$
$$= 1 - (1 - e^{-30/12})$$
$$= .0821$$

36. a. $P(x \leq 1) = 1 - e^{-1/2} = 1 - e^{-.5} = 1 - .6065 = .3935$

b. $P(x \leq 2) = 1 - e^{-2/2} = 1 - e^{-1.0} = 1 - .3679 = .6321$

$P(1 \leq x \leq 2) = P(x \leq 2) - P(x \leq 1) = .6321 - .3935$
$$= .2386$$

c. For this customer, the cable service repair would have to take longer than 4 hours.

$P(x > 4) = 1 - P(x \leq 4) = 1 - (1 - e^{-4/2}) = e^{-2.0}$
$$= .1353$$

38. a. Time between calls follows an exponential distribution.

$\mu = \dfrac{60 \text{ minutes/hour}}{1.6 \text{ calls/hour}} = 37.5 \text{ minutes per call}$

b. The exponential probability density function is $f(x) =$

$\left(\dfrac{1}{37.5}\right) e^{-x/37.5}$ for $x \geq 0$

where x is the minutes between 911 calls.

c. $P(x < 60) = 1 - e^{-60/37.5} = 1 - .2019 = .7981$

d. $P(x \geq 30) = 1 - P(x \leq 30) = 1 - (1 - e^{-30/37.5})$
$$= 1 - .5507 = .4493$$

e. $P(5 \leq x \leq 20) = (1 - e^{-20/37.5}) - (1 - e^{-5/37.5})$
$$= .4134 - .1248 = .2886$$

40. a. \$16,312

b. 7.64%

c. \$22,948

42. a. $\sigma = 25.5319$

b. .9401

c. 706 or more

44. a. .0228

b. \$50

46. a. 38.3%

b. 3.59% better, 96.41% worse

c. 38.21%

48. $\mu = 19.23$ ounces

50. a. Lose $240
b. .1788
c. .3557
d. .0594

52. a. $\frac{1}{7}$ minute
b. $7e^{-7x}$
c. .0009
d. .2466

54. a. 2 minutes
b. .2212
c. .3935
d. .0821

Chapter 7

1. a. AB, AC, AD, AE, BC, BD, BE, CD, CE, DE
b. With 10 samples, each has a $\frac{1}{10}$ probability
c. E and C because 8 and 0 do not apply; 5 identifies E; 7 does not apply; 5 is skipped because E is already in the sample; 3 identifies C; 2 is not needed because the sample of size 2 is complete

2. 22, 147, 229, 289

3. 459, 147, 385, 113, 340, 401, 215, 2, 33, 348

4. a. Bell South, LSI Logic, General Electric
b. 120

6. 2782, 493, 825, 1807, 289

8. ExxonMobil, Chevron, Travelers, Microsoft, Pfizer, and Intel

10. a. finite; **b.** infinite; **c.** infinite; **d.** finite; **e.** infinite

11. a. $\bar{x} = \dfrac{\Sigma x_i}{n} = \dfrac{54}{6} = 9$

b. $s = \sqrt{\dfrac{\Sigma(x_i - \bar{x})^2}{n - 1}}$

$\Sigma(x_i - \bar{x})^2 = (-4)^2 + (-1)^2 + 1^2 + (-2)^2 + 1^2 + 5^2$
$= 48$

$s = \sqrt{\dfrac{48}{6 - 1}} = 3.1$

12. a. .50
b. .3667

13. a. $\bar{x} = \dfrac{\Sigma x_i}{n} = \dfrac{465}{5} = 93$

b.

x_i	$(x_i - \bar{x})$	$(x_i - \bar{x})^2$
94	+1	1
100	+7	49
85	−8	64
94	+1	1
92	−1	1
Totals 465	0	116

$s = \sqrt{\dfrac{\Sigma(x_i - \bar{x})^2}{n - 1}} = \sqrt{\dfrac{116}{4}} = 5.39$

14. a. .05
b. .425
c. .20

16. a. All U.S. adults age 50 and older
b. .8216
c. 315
d. .8310
e. Target population is same as sampled population; if restricted to AARP members, inferences are questionable

18. a. 200
b. 5
c. Normal with $E(\bar{x}) = 200$ and $\sigma_{\bar{x}} = 5$
d. The probability distribution of $\bar{x}$

19. a. The sampling distribution is normal with
$E(\bar{x}) = \mu = 200$
$\sigma_{\bar{x}} = \sigma/\sqrt{n} = 50/\sqrt{100} = 5$
For ±5, $195 \le \bar{x} \le 205$
Using the standard normal probability table:
At $\bar{x} = 205$, $z = \dfrac{\bar{x} - \mu}{\sigma_{\bar{x}}} = \dfrac{5}{5} = 1$

$P(z \le 1) = .8413$

At $\bar{x} = 195$, $z = \dfrac{\bar{x} - \mu}{\sigma_{\bar{x}}} = \dfrac{-5}{5} = -1$

$P(z < -1) = .1587$
$P(195 \le \bar{x} \le 205) = .8413 - .1587 = .6826$

b. For ±10, $190 \le \bar{x} \le 210$
Using the standard normal probability table:
At $\bar{x} = 210$, $z = \dfrac{\bar{x} - \mu}{\sigma_{\bar{x}}} = \dfrac{10}{5} = 2$

$P(z \le 2) = .9772$

At $\bar{x} = 190$, $z = \dfrac{\bar{x} - \mu}{\sigma_{\bar{x}}} = \dfrac{-10}{5} = -2$

$P(z < -2) = .0228$
$P(190 \le \bar{x} \le 210) = .9772 - .0228 = .9544$

20. 3.54, 2.50, 2.04, 1.77
$\sigma_{\bar{x}}$ decreases as n increases

22. a. Normal with $E(\bar{x}) = 51,800$ and $\sigma_{\bar{x}} = 516.40$
b. $\sigma_{\bar{x}}$ decreases to 365.15
c. $\sigma_{\bar{x}}$ decreases as n increases

23. a.

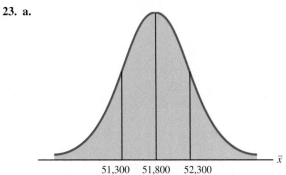

51,300   51,800   52,300

$$\sigma_{\bar{x}} = \frac{\sigma}{\sqrt{n}} = \frac{4000}{\sqrt{60}} = 516.40$$

At $\bar{x} = 52{,}300$, $z = \dfrac{52{,}300 - 51{,}800}{516.40} = .97$

$$P(\bar{x} \le 52{,}300) = P(z \le .97) = .8340$$

At $\bar{x} = 51{,}300$, $z = \dfrac{51{,}300 - 51{,}800}{516.40} = -.97$

$$P(\bar{x} < 51{,}300) = P(z < -.97) = .1660$$
$$P(51{,}300 \le \bar{x} \le 52{,}300) = .8340 - .1660 = .6680$$

b. $\sigma_{\bar{x}} = \dfrac{\sigma}{\sqrt{n}} = \dfrac{4000}{\sqrt{120}} = 365.15$

At $\bar{x} = 52{,}300$, $z = \dfrac{52{,}300 - 51{,}800}{365.15} = 1.37$
$$P(\bar{x} \le 52{,}300) = P(z \le 1.37) = .9147$$

At $\bar{x} = 51{,}300$, $z = \dfrac{51{,}300 - 51{,}800}{365.15} = -1.37$
$$P(\bar{x} < 51{,}300) = P(z < -1.37) = .0853$$
$$P(51{,}300 \le \bar{x} \le 52{,}300) = .9147 - .0853 = .8294$$

24. a. Normal with $E(\bar{x}) = 17.5$ and $\sigma_{\bar{x}} = .57$
    b. .9198
    c. .6212

26. a. .3544, .4448, .5934, .9044
    b. Higher probability the sample mean will be close to the population mean.

28. a. Normal with $E(\bar{x}) = 22$ and $\sigma_{\bar{x}} = .7303$
    b. .8294
    c. .9070
    d. New York in part (c) because the sample size is larger

30. a. $n/N = .01$; no
    b. 1.29, 1.30; little difference
    c. .8764

32. a. $E(\bar{p}) = .40$

$$\sigma_{\bar{p}} = \sqrt{\frac{p(1-p)}{n}} = \sqrt{\frac{(.40)(.60)}{200}} = .0346$$

Within $\pm.03$ means $.37 \le \bar{p} \le .43$

$$z = \frac{\bar{p} - p}{\sigma_{\bar{p}}} = \frac{.03}{.0346} = .87$$

$$P(.37 \le \bar{p} \le .43) = P(-.87 \le z \le .87)$$
$$= .8078 - .1922$$
$$= .6156$$

b. $z = \dfrac{\bar{p} - p}{\sigma_{\bar{p}}} = \dfrac{.05}{.0346} = 1.44$

$$P(.35 \le \bar{p} \le .45) = P(-1.44 \le z \le 1.44)$$
$$= .9251 - .0749$$
$$= .8502$$

34. a. .6156
    b. .7814
    c. .9488
    d. .9942
    e. Higher probability with larger n

35. a.

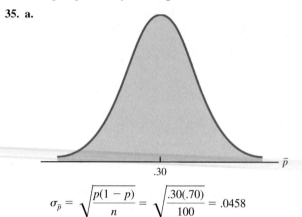

$$\sigma_{\bar{p}} = \sqrt{\frac{p(1-p)}{n}} = \sqrt{\frac{.30(.70)}{100}} = .0458$$

The normal distribution is appropriate because $np = 100(.30) = 30$ and $n(1 - p) = 100(.70) = 70$ are both greater than 5

b. $P(.20 \le \bar{p} \le .40) = ?$

$$z = \frac{.40 - .30}{.0458} = 2.18$$

$$P(.20 \le \bar{p} \le .40) = P(-2.18 \le z \le 2.18)$$
$$= .9854 - .0146$$
$$= .9708$$

c. $P(.25 \le \bar{p} \le .35) = ?$

$$z = \frac{.35 - .30}{.0458} = 1.09$$

$$P(.25 \le \bar{p} \le .35) = P(-1.09 \le z \le 1.09)$$
$$= .8621 - .1379$$
$$= .7242$$

36. a. Normal with $E(\bar{p}) = .55$ and $\sigma_{\bar{p}} = .0352$
    b. .8444
    c. Normal with $E(\bar{p}) = .45$ and $\sigma_{\bar{p}} = .0352$
    d. .8444
    e. No, standard error is the same in both parts
    f. .9556, the probability is larger because the increased sample size reduces the standard error

38. a. Normal with $E(\bar{p}) = .42$ and $\sigma_{\bar{p}} = .0285$
    b. .7062
    c. .9198
    d. Probabilities would increase

40. a. Normal with $E(\bar{p}) = .76$ and $\sigma_{\bar{p}} = .0214$
    b. .8384
    c. .9452

42. a. LMI Aerospace, Alpha & Omega Semiconductor, Olympic Steel, Kimball International, International Shipholding

b. It is extremely unlikely that you will get the same companies as in part (a).

44. a. Normal with $E(\bar{x}) = 406$ and $\sigma_{\bar{x}} = 10$

b. .8664

c. $z = -2.60, .0047$, Yes

46. a. 955

b. .50

c. .7062

d. .8230

48. a. 625

b. .7888

50. a. Normal with $E(\bar{p}) = .15$ and $\sigma_{\bar{p}} = .0230$

b. .9182

c. .6156

52. a. .8882

b. .0233

54. a. 48

b. Normal, $E(\bar{p}) = .25, \sigma_{\bar{p}} = .0625$

c. .2119

Chapter 8

2. Use $\bar{x} \pm z_{\alpha/2}(\sigma/\sqrt{n})$

a. $32 \pm 1.645(6/\sqrt{50})$

32 ± 1.4; 30.6 to 33.4

b. $32 \pm 1.96(6/\sqrt{50})$

32 ± 1.66; 30.34 to 33.66

c. $32 \pm 2.576(6/\sqrt{50})$

32 ± 2.19; 29.81 to 34.19

4. 54

5. a. With 99% confidence $z_{\alpha/2} = z_{.005} = 2.576$

Margin of Error $= 2.576\, \sigma/\sqrt{n} = 2.576\,(6/\sqrt{64}) = 1.93$

b. Confidence Interval: 21.52 ± 1.93 or 19.59 to 23.45

6. 39.13 to 41.49

8. a. Population is at least approximately normal

b. 3.41

c. 4.48

10. a. $3388 to $3584

b. $3370 to $3602

c. $3333 to $3639

d. Width increases as confidence level increases

12. a. 2.179

b. -1.676

c. 2.457

d. -1.708 and 1.708

e. -2.014 and 2.014

13. a. $\bar{x} = \dfrac{\Sigma x_i}{n} = \dfrac{80}{8} = 10$

b. $s = \sqrt{\dfrac{\Sigma(x_i - \bar{x})^2}{n - 1}} = \sqrt{\dfrac{84}{7}} = 3.464$

c. $t_{.025}\left(\dfrac{s}{\sqrt{n}}\right) = 2.365\left(\dfrac{3.46}{\sqrt{8}}\right) = 2.9$

d. $\bar{x} \pm t_{.025}\left(\dfrac{s}{\sqrt{n}}\right)$

10 ± 2.9 (7.1 to 12.9)

14. a. 21.5 to 23.5

b. 21.3 to 23.7

c. 20.9 to 24.1

d. A larger margin of error and a wider interval

15. $\bar{x} \pm t_{\alpha/2}(s/\sqrt{n})$

90% confidence: $df = 64$ and $t_{.05} = 1.669$

$19.5 \pm 1.669\left(\dfrac{5.2}{\sqrt{65}}\right)$

19.5 ± 1.08 or (18.42 to 20.58)

95% confidence: $df = 64$ and $t_{.025} = 1.998$

$19.5 \pm 1.998\left(\dfrac{5.2}{\sqrt{65}}\right)$

19.5 ± 1.29 or (18.21 to 20.79)

16. a. 9.7063, 7.9805

b. 7.1536 to 12.2590

c. 3.8854, 1.6194

d. 3.3674 to 4.4034

18. a. 22 weeks

b. 3.8020

c. 18.20 to 25.80

d. Larger n next time

20. a. $\bar{x} = 2551$

b. $2409.99 to $2692.01

c. We would be 95% confident that auto insurance premiums in Michigan are above the national average.

22. a. $21,613 to $24,587.

b. 2,848

c. Total number of customers $= 11,619,840$, Total box office ticket sales $= \$94,248,000$

24. a. Planning value of $\sigma = \dfrac{\text{Range}}{4} = \dfrac{36}{4} = 9$

b. $n = \dfrac{z_{.025}^2 \sigma^2}{E^2} = \dfrac{(1.96)^2(9)^2}{(3)^2} = 34.57$; use $n = 35$

c. $n = \dfrac{(1.96)^2(9)^2}{(2)^2} = 77.79$; use $n = 78$

25. a. Use $n = \dfrac{z_{\alpha/2}^2 \sigma^2}{E^2}$

$n = \dfrac{(1.96)^2(6.84)^2}{(1.5)^2} = 79.88$; use $n = 80$

b. $n = \dfrac{(1.645)^2(6.84)^2}{(2)^2} = 31.65$; use $n = 32$

26. a. 25

     b. 49

     c. 97

28. a. 188

     b. 267

     c. 461

     d. The sample size gets larger as the confidence level is increased. We would not recommend 99% confidence.

30. 1537

31. a. $\bar{p} = \dfrac{100}{400} = .25$

     b. $\sqrt{\dfrac{\bar{p}(1-\bar{p})}{n}} = \sqrt{\dfrac{.25(.75)}{400}} = .0217$

     c. $\bar{p} \pm z_{.025} \sqrt{\dfrac{\bar{p}(1-\bar{p})}{n}}$

        $.25 \pm 1.96(.0217)$

        $.25 \pm .0424$; .2076 to .2924

32. a. .6733 to .7267

     b. .6682 to .7318

34. 1068

35. a. $\bar{p} = \dfrac{1760}{2000} = .88$

     b. Margin of error

        $z_{.05} = \sqrt{\dfrac{\bar{p}(1-\bar{p})}{n}}$

        $= 1.645 \sqrt{\dfrac{.88(1-.88)}{2000}} = .0120$

     c. Confidence interval

        $.88 \pm .0120$ or .868 to .892

     d. Margin of error

        $z_{.05} = \sqrt{\dfrac{\bar{p}(1-\bar{p})}{n}} = 1.96 \sqrt{\dfrac{.88(1-.88)}{2000}} = .0142$

        95% confidence interval

        $.88 \pm .0142$ or .8658 to .8942

36. a. .23

     b. .1716 to .2884

38. a. .5704

     b. .0814, .4890 to .6518

     c. 1046

39. a. $n = \dfrac{z_{.025}^2 \, p^*(1-p^*)}{E^2} = \dfrac{(1.96)^2(.156)(1-.156)}{(.03)^2}$

        $= 562$

b. $n = \dfrac{z_{.005}^2 \, p^*(1-p^*)}{E^2} = \dfrac{(2.576)^2(.156)(1-.156)}{(.03)^2}$

        $= 970.77$; use 971

40. .0346 (.4854 to .5546)

42. a. .0442

     b. 601, 1068, 2401, 9604

44. a. 4.00

     b. $29.77 to $37.77

46. a. 122

     b. $1751 to $1995

     c. $172, 316 million

     d. Less than $1873

48. a. $712.27 to $833.73

     b. $172.31 to $201.69

     c. .34

     d. Part (a) is 60.73; the margin of error in part (a) is larger because the sample standard deviation in part (a) is larger.

50. 37

52. 176

54. a. .5420

     b. .0508

     c. .4912 to .5928

56. a. .22

     b. .1904 to .2496

     c. .3847 to .4553

     d. The confidence interval in part (c) is wider. The sample proportion is closer to .5 in part (c).

58. a. 1267

     b. 1509

60. a. .3101

     b. .2898 to .3304

     c. 8219; no, this sample size is unnecessarily large

Chapter 9

2. a. $H_0: \mu \le 14$

       $H_a: \mu > 14$

     b. No evidence that the new plan increases sales

     c. The research hypothesis $\mu > 14$ is supported; the new plan increases sales

4. a. $H_0: \mu \ge 220$

       $H_a: \mu < 220$

     b. Cannot conclude proposed method reduces cost.

     c. Can conclude proposed method reduces cost.

5. a. Conclude that the population mean monthly cost of electricity in the Chicago neighborhood is greater than $104 and hence higher than in the comparable neighborhood in Cincinnati

     b. The Type I error is rejecting H_0 when it is true; this error occurs if the researcher concludes that the population mean monthly cost of electricity is greater than $104 in the Chicago neighborhood when the population mean cost is actually less than or equal to $104

c. The Type II error is accepting H_0 when it is false; this error occurs if the researcher concludes that the population mean monthly cost for the Chicago neighborhood is less than or equal to $104 when it is not

6. a. $H_0: \mu \leq 1$
$H_a: \mu > 1$
b. Claiming $\mu > 1$ when it is not true
c. Claiming $\mu \leq 1$ when it is not true

8. a. $H_0: \mu \geq 220$
$H_a: \mu < 220$
b. Claiming $\mu < 220$ when it is not true
c. Claiming $\mu \geq 220$ when it is not true

10. a. $z = \dfrac{\bar{x} - \mu_0}{\sigma/\sqrt{n}} = \dfrac{26.4 - 25}{6/\sqrt{40}} = 1.48$

b. Using normal table with $z = 1.48$: p-value $=$ $1.0000 - .9306 = .0694$
c. p-value $> .01$, do not reject H_0
d. Reject H_0 if $z \geq 2.33$
$1.48 < 2.33$, do not reject H_0

11. a. $z = \dfrac{\bar{x} - \mu_0}{\sigma/\sqrt{n}} = \dfrac{14.15 - 15}{3/\sqrt{50}} = -2.00$

b. p-value $= 2(.0228) = .0456$
c. p-value $\leq .05$, reject H_0
d. Reject H_0 if $z \leq -1.96$ or $z \geq 1.96$
$-2.00 \leq -1.96$, reject H_0

12. a. .1056; do not reject H_0
b. .0062; reject H_0
c. ≈ 0; reject H_0
d. .7967; do not reject H_0

14. a. .3844; do not reject H_0
b. .0074; reject H_0
c. .0836; do not reject H_0

15. a. $H_0: \mu \geq 1056$
$H_a: \mu < 1056$
b. $z = \dfrac{\bar{x} - \mu_0}{\sigma/\sqrt{n}} = \dfrac{910 - 1056}{1600/\sqrt{400}} = -1.83$

p-value $= .0336$
c. p-value $\leq .05$, reject H_0; the mean refund of "last-minute" filers is less than $1056
d. Reject H_0 if $z \leq -1.645$
$-1.83 \leq -1.645$; reject H_0

16. a. $H_0: \mu \leq 3173$
$H_a: \mu > 3173$
b. .0207
c. Reject H_0, conclude mean credit card balance for undergraduate student has increased

18. a. $H_0: \mu = 192$
$H_a: \mu \neq 192$
b. -2.23, .0258
c. Reject H_0; mean number of restaurant meals eaten by young millennials has changed in 2012.

20. a. $H_0: \mu \geq 838$
$H_a: \mu < 838$
b. -2.40
c. .0082
d. Reject H_0; conclude that the annual expenditure per person on prescription drugs is less in the Midwest than in the Northeast.

22. a. $H_0: \mu = 8$
$H_a: \mu \neq 8$
b. .1706
c. Do not reject H_0; we cannot conclude the mean waiting time differs from 8 minutes
d. 7.83 to 8.97; yes

24. a. $t = \dfrac{\bar{x} - \mu_0}{s/\sqrt{n}} = \dfrac{17 - 18}{4.5/\sqrt{48}} = -1.54$

b. Degrees of freedom $= n - 1 = 47$
Area in lower tail is between .05 and .10
p-value (two-tail) is between .10 and .20
Exact p-value $= .1303$
c. p-value $> .05$; do not reject H_0
d. With $df = 47$, $t_{.025} = 2.012$
Reject H_0 if $t \leq -2.012$ or $t \geq 2.012$
$t = -1.54$; do not reject H_0

26. a. Between .02 and .05; exact p-value $= .0397$; reject H_0
b. Between .01 and .02; exact p-value $= .0125$; reject H_0
c. Between .10 and .20; exact p-value $= .1285$; do not reject H_0

27. a. $H_0: \mu \geq 13.04$
$H_a: \mu < 13.04$
b. p-value is between .05 and .10
Exact p-value is .0751
c. Do not reject H_0; do not conclude that the cost of a restaurant meal is significantly cheaper than a comparable meal fixed at home.
d. $df = 99$ $t_{.05} = -1.66$
Reject H_0 if $t \leq -1.66$
$-1.45 > -1.66$; do not reject H_0

28. a. $H_0: \mu \geq 9$
$H_a: \mu < 9$
b. Between .005 and .01
Exact p-value $= .0072$
c. Reject H_0; mean tenure of a CEO is less than 9 years

30. a. $H_0: \mu = 6.4$
$H_a: \mu \neq 6.4$
b. Between .10 and .20
Exact p-value $= .1268$
c. Do not reject H_0; cannot conclude that the group consensus is wrong

32. a. $H_0: \mu = 10,192$
$H_a: \mu \neq 10,192$
b. Between .02 and .05
Exact p-value $= .0304$
c. Reject H_0; mean price at dealership differs from national mean price

34. a. H_0: $\mu = 2$
H_a: $\mu \neq 2$
b. 2.2
c. .516
d. Between .20 and .40
Exact p-value = .2535
e. Do not reject H_0; no reason to change from 2 hours for cost estimating

36. a. $z = \dfrac{\bar{p} - p_0}{\sqrt{\dfrac{p_0(1 - p_0)}{n}}} = \dfrac{.68 - .75}{\sqrt{\dfrac{.75(1 - .75)}{300}}} = -2.80$

p-value = .0026
p-value $\leq$ .05; reject H_0

b. $z = \dfrac{.72 - .75}{\sqrt{\dfrac{.75(1 - .75)}{300}}} = -1.20$

p-value = .1151
p-value > .05; do not reject H_0

c. $z = \dfrac{.70 - .75}{\sqrt{\dfrac{.75(1 - .75)}{300}}} = -2.00$

p-value = .0228
p-value $\leq$ .05; reject H_0

d. $z = \dfrac{.77 - .75}{\sqrt{\dfrac{.75(1 - .75)}{300}}} = .80$

p-value = .7881
p-value > .05; do not reject H_0

38. a. H_0: $p = .64$
H_a: $p \neq .64$
b. $\bar{p} = 52/100 = .52$

$z = \dfrac{\bar{p} - p_0}{\sqrt{\dfrac{p_0(1 - p_0)}{n}}} = \dfrac{.52 - .64}{\sqrt{\dfrac{.64(1 - .64)}{100}}} = -2.50$

p-value = 2(.0062) = .0124
c. p-value $\leq$ .05; reject H_0
Proportion differs from the reported .64
d. Yes, because $\bar{p} = .52$ indicates that fewer believe the supermarket brand is as good as the name brand

40. a. 21
b. H_0: $p \geq .46$
H_a: $p < .46$
p-value $\approx$ .0436
c. Yes, .0436

42. a. $\bar{p} = .15$
b. .0718 to .2282

c. The return rate for the Houston store is different than the national average
44. a. H_0: $p \leq .50$
H_a: $p > .50$
b. $\bar{p} = .6133$, p-value = .0027
c. Reject H_0; conclude that the proportion of physicians over the age of 55 who have been sued at least once is greater than .50.

46.

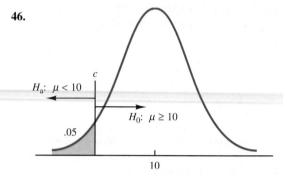

$c = 10 - 1.645(5/\sqrt{120}) = 9.25$
Reject H_0 if $\bar{x} \leq 9.25$
a. When $\mu = 9$,

$$z = \dfrac{9.25 - 9}{5/\sqrt{120}} = .55$$

$P(\text{Reject } H_0) = (1.0000 - .7088) = .2912$
b. Type II error
c. When $\mu = 8$,

$$z = \dfrac{9.25 - 8}{5/\sqrt{120}} = 2.74$$

$\beta = (1.0000 - .9969) = .0031$
48. a. Concluding $\mu \leq 15$ when it is not true
b. .2676
c. .0179
49. a. H_0: $\mu \geq 25$
H_a: $\mu < 25$
Reject H_0 if $z \leq -2.05$

$$z = \dfrac{\bar{x} - \mu_0}{\sigma/\sqrt{n}} = \dfrac{\bar{x} - 25}{3/\sqrt{30}} = -2.05$$

Solve for $\bar{x} = 23.88$
Decision Rule: Accept H_0 if $\bar{x} > 23.88$
Reject H_0 if $\bar{x} \leq 23.88$
b. For $\mu = 23$,

$$z = \dfrac{23.88 - 23}{3/\sqrt{30}} = 1.61$$

$\beta = 1.0000 - .9463 = .0537$
c. For $\mu = 24$,

$$z = \dfrac{23.88 - 24}{3/\sqrt{30}} = -.22$$

$\beta = 1.0000 - .4129 = .5871$

d. The Type II error cannot be made in this case; note that when $\mu = 25.5$, H_0 is true; the Type II error can only be made when H_0 is false

50. a. Concluding $\mu = 28$ when it is not true

b. .0853, .6179, .6179, .0853

c. .9147

52. .1151, .0015

Increasing n reduces β

54. $n = \dfrac{(z_\alpha + z_\beta)^2 \sigma^2}{(\mu_0 - \mu_a)^2} = \dfrac{(1.645 + 1.28)^2(5)^2}{(10 - 9)^2} = 214$

56. 109

57. At $\mu_0 = 400$, $\alpha = .02$; $z_{.02} = 2.05$

At $\mu_a = 385$, $\beta = .10$; $z_{.10} = 1.28$

With $\sigma = 30$,

$n = \dfrac{(z_\alpha + z_\beta)^2 \sigma^2}{(\mu_0 - \mu_a)^2} = \dfrac{(2.05 + 1.28)^2(30)^2}{(400 - 385)^2} = 44.4$ or 45

58. 324

60. a. H_0: $\mu = 16$

H_a: $\mu \neq 16$

b. .0286; reject H_0

Readjust line

c. .2186; do not reject H_0

Continue operation

d. $z = 2.19$; reject H_0

$z = -1.23$; do not reject H_0

Yes, same conclusion

62. a. H_0: $\mu \leq 4$

H_a: $\mu > 4$

b. p-value $= .0049$

c. Reject H_0; conclude that the mean daily background television that children from low-income families are exposed to is greater than four hours.

64. H_0: $\mu \leq 30.8$

H_a: $\mu > 30.8$

$t = 1.0894$

p-value is between .10 and .20.

Exact p-value is .1408

Do not reject H_0; there is no evidence to conclude that the mean age of recently wed British men exceeds the mean age for those wed in 2013.

66. $t = 2.26$

p-value between .01 and .025

Exact p-value $= .0155$

Reject H_0; mean cost is greater than $125,000

68. a. H_0: $p \leq .80$

H_a: $p > .80$

Conclude that airline travelers feel security will be improved

b. Cannot reject H_0; mandatory use is not recommended

70. a. H_0: $p \leq .30$

H_a: $p > .30$

b. .34

c. p-value $= .0401$

d. Reject H_0; conclude that more than 30% of the millennials either live at home with their parents or are otherwise dependent on their parents.

72. H_0: $p \geq .90$

H_a: $p < .90$

p-value $= .0808$

Do not reject H_0; claim of at least 90% cannot be rejected

74. a. H_0: $\mu \leq 72$

H_a: $\mu > 72$

b. .2912

c. .7939

d. 0, because H_0 is true

76. a. 45

b. .0192, .2358, .7291, .7291, .2358, .0192

Chapter 10

1. a. $\bar{x}_1 - \bar{x}_2 = 13.6 - 11.6 = 2$

b. $z_{\alpha/2} = z_{.05} = 1.645$

$$\bar{x}_1 - \bar{x}_2 \pm 1.645 \sqrt{\dfrac{\sigma_1^2}{n_1} + \dfrac{\sigma_2^2}{n_2}}$$

$$2 \pm 1.645 \sqrt{\dfrac{(2.2)^2}{50} + \dfrac{(3)^2}{35}}$$

$2 \pm .98 \qquad (1.02 \text{ to } 2.98)$

c. $z_{\alpha/2} = z_{.05} = 1.96$

$$2 \pm 1.96 \sqrt{\dfrac{(2.2)^2}{50} + \dfrac{(3)^2}{35}}$$

$2 \pm 1.17 \ (.83 \text{ to } 3.17)$

2. a. $z = \dfrac{(\bar{x}_1 - \bar{x}_2) - D_0}{\sqrt{\dfrac{\sigma_1^2}{n_1} + \dfrac{\sigma_2^2}{n_2}}} = \dfrac{(25.2 - 22.8) - 0}{\sqrt{\dfrac{(5.2)^2}{40} + \dfrac{(6)^2}{50}}} = 2.03$

b. p-value $= 1.0000 - .9788 = .0212$

c. p-value $\leq .05$; reject H_0

4. a. $\bar{x}_1 - \bar{x}_2 = 85.36 - 81.40 = 3.96$

b. $z_{.025} \sqrt{\dfrac{\sigma_1^2}{n_1} + \dfrac{\sigma_2^2}{n_2}} = 1.96 \sqrt{\dfrac{(4.55)^2}{37} + \dfrac{(3.97)^2}{44}} = 1.88$

c. $3.96 \pm 1.88 \ (2.08 \text{ to } 5.84)$

6. p-value $= .0351$

Reject H_0; mean price in Atlanta lower than mean price in Houston

8. a. Reject H_0; customer service has improved for Rite Aid

b. Do not reject H_0; the difference is not statistically significant

c. p-value $= .0336$; reject H_0; customer service has improved for Expedia

d. 1.80

e. The increase for J.C. Penney is not statistically significant

9. a. $\bar{x}_1 - \bar{x}_2 = 22.5 - 20.1 = 2.4$

b. $df = \dfrac{\left(\dfrac{s_1^2}{n_1} + \dfrac{s_2^2}{n_2}\right)^2}{\dfrac{1}{n_1 - 1}\left(\dfrac{s_1^2}{n_1}\right)^2 + \dfrac{1}{n_2 - 1}\left(\dfrac{s_2^2}{n_2}\right)^2}$

$= \dfrac{\left(\dfrac{2.5^2}{20} + \dfrac{4.8^2}{30}\right)^2}{\dfrac{1}{19}\left(\dfrac{2.5^2}{20}\right)^2 + \dfrac{1}{29}\left(\dfrac{4.8^2}{30}\right)^2} = 45.8$

c. $df = 45$, $t_{.025} = 2.014$

$t_{.025}\sqrt{\dfrac{s_1^2}{n_1} + \dfrac{s_2^2}{n_2}} = 2.014\sqrt{\dfrac{2.5^2}{20} + \dfrac{4.8^2}{30}} = 2.1$

d. 2.4 ± 2.1 (.3 to 4.5)

10. a. $t = \dfrac{(\bar{x}_1 - \bar{x}_2) - 0}{\sqrt{\dfrac{s_1^2}{n_1} + \dfrac{s_2^2}{n_2}}} = \dfrac{(13.6 - 10.1) - 0}{\sqrt{\dfrac{5.2^2}{35} + \dfrac{8.5^2}{40}}} = 2.18$

b. $df = \dfrac{\left(\dfrac{s_1^2}{n_1} + \dfrac{s_2^2}{n_2}\right)^2}{\dfrac{1}{n_1 - 1}\left(\dfrac{s_1^2}{n_1}\right)^2 + \dfrac{1}{n_2 - 1}\left(\dfrac{s_2^2}{n_2}\right)^2}$

$= \dfrac{\left(\dfrac{5.2^2}{35} + \dfrac{8.5^2}{40}\right)^2}{\dfrac{1}{34}\left(\dfrac{5.2^2}{35}\right)^2 + \dfrac{1}{39}\left(\dfrac{8.5^2}{40}\right)^2} = 65.7$

Use $df = 65$

c. $df = 65$, area in tail is between .01 and .025; two-tailed p-value is between .02 and .05
Exact p-value $= .0329$

d. p-value $\leq .05$; reject H_0

12. a. $\bar{x}_1 - \bar{x}_2 = 22.5 - 18.6 = 3.9$ miles

b. $df = \dfrac{\left(\dfrac{s_1^2}{n_1} + \dfrac{s_2^2}{n_2}\right)^2}{\dfrac{1}{n_1 - 1}\left(\dfrac{s_1^2}{n_1}\right)^2 + \dfrac{1}{n_2 - 1}\left(\dfrac{s_2^2}{n_2}\right)^2}$

$= \dfrac{\left(\dfrac{8.4^2}{50} + \dfrac{7.4^2}{40}\right)^2}{\dfrac{1}{49}\left(\dfrac{8.4^2}{50}\right)^2 + \dfrac{1}{39}\left(\dfrac{7.4^2}{40}\right)^2} = 87.1$

Use $df = 87$, $t_{.025} = 1.988$

$3.9 \pm 1.988\sqrt{\dfrac{8.4^2}{50} + \dfrac{7.4^2}{40}}$

3.9 ± 3.3 (.6 to 7.2)

14. a. $H_0: \mu_1 - \mu_2 \geq 0$
$H_a: \mu_1 - \mu_2 < 0$

b. -2.41

c. Using t table, p-value is between .005 and .01
Exact p-value $= .009$

d. Reject H_0; nursing salaries are lower in Tampa

16. a. $H_0: \mu_1 - \mu_2 \leq 0$
$H_a: \mu_1 - \mu_2 > 0$

b. 38

c. $t = 1.80$, $df = 25$
Using t table, p-value is between .025 and .05
Exact p-value $= .0420$

d. Reject H_0; conclude higher mean score if college grad

18. a. $H_0: \mu_1 - \mu_2 = 0$
$H_a: \mu_1 - \mu_2 \neq 0$

b. 50.6 and 52.8 minutes

c. p-value greater than .40
Do not reject H_0; cannot conclude population mean delay times differ

19. a. 1, 2, 0, 0, 2

b. $\bar{d} = \Sigma d_i/n = 5/5 = 1$

c. $s_d = \sqrt{\dfrac{\Sigma(d_i - \bar{d})^2}{n - 1}} = \sqrt{\dfrac{4}{5 - 1}} = 1$

d. $t = \dfrac{\bar{d} - \mu}{s_d/\sqrt{n}} = \dfrac{1 - 0}{1/\sqrt{5}} = 2.24$

$df = n - 1 = 4$
Using t table, p-value is between .025 and .05
Exact p-value $= .0443$
p-value $\leq .05$; reject H_0

20. a. 3, -1, 3, 5, 3, 0, 1

b. 2

c. 2.08

d. 2

e. .07 to 3.93

21. $H_0: \mu_d \leq 0$
$H_a: \mu_d > 0$
$\bar{d} = .625$
$s_d = 1.30$

$t = \dfrac{\bar{d} - \mu_d}{s_d/\sqrt{n}} = \dfrac{.625 - 0}{1.30/\sqrt{8}} = 1.36$

$df = n - 1 = 7$
Using t table, p-value is between .10 and .20
Exact p-value $= .1080$
p-value $> .05$; do not reject H_0; cannot conclude commercial improves mean potential to purchase

22. a. $3.41

b. $1.67 to $5.15
Very nice increase

24. a. $H_0: \mu_d \leq 0$
$H_a: \mu_d > 0$

$\bar{d} = 23, t = 2.05$

p-value between .05 and .025

Reject H_0; conclude airfares have increased

b. $487, $464

c. 5% increase in airfares

26. a. $t = -1.42$

Using t table, p-value is between .10 and .20

Exact p-value = .1718

Do not reject H_0; no difference in mean scores

b. -1.05

c. 1.28; yes

28. a. $\bar{p}_1 - \bar{p}_2 = .48 - .36 = .12$

b. $\bar{p}_1 - \bar{p}_2 \pm z_{.05} \sqrt{\dfrac{\bar{p}_1(1 - \bar{p}_1)}{n_1} + \dfrac{\bar{p}_2(1 - \bar{p}_2)}{n_2}}$

$.12 \pm 1.645 \sqrt{\dfrac{.48(1 - .48)}{400} + \dfrac{.36(1 - .36)}{300}}$

$.12 \pm .0614 \ (.0586 \text{ to } .1814)$

c. $.12 \pm 1.96 \sqrt{\dfrac{.48(1 - .48)}{400} + \dfrac{.36(1 - .36)}{300}}$

$.12 \pm .0731 \ (.0469 \text{ to } .1931)$

29. a. $\bar{p} = \dfrac{n_1 \bar{p}_1 + n_2 \bar{p}_2}{n_1 + n_2} = \dfrac{200(.22) + 300(.16)}{200 + 300} = .1840$

$z = \dfrac{\bar{p}_1 - \bar{p}_2}{\sqrt{\bar{p}(1 - \bar{p})\left(\dfrac{1}{n_1} + \dfrac{1}{n_2}\right)}}$

$= \dfrac{.22 - .16}{\sqrt{.1840(1 - .1840)\left(\dfrac{1}{200} + \dfrac{1}{300}\right)}} = 1.70$

p-value $= 1.0000 - .9554 = .0446$

b. p-value $\leq .05$; reject H_0

30. $\bar{p}_1 = 220/400 = .55 \qquad \bar{p}_2 = 192/400 = .48$

$\bar{p}_1 - \bar{p}_2 \pm z_{.025} \sqrt{\dfrac{\bar{p}_1(1 - \bar{p}_1)}{n_1} + \dfrac{\bar{p}_2(1 - \bar{p}_2)}{n_2}}$

$.55 - .48 \pm 1.96 \sqrt{\dfrac{.55(1 - .55)}{400} + \dfrac{.48(1 - .48)}{400}}$

$.07 \pm .0691 \ (.0009 \text{ to } .1391)$

32. a. $\bar{p}_1 = .45$

b. $\bar{p}_2 = .35$

c. .0011 to .1989

34. a. $H_0: p_1 - p_2 \leq 0$

$H_a: p_1 - p_2 > 0$

b. $\bar{p}_1 = .2017$

c. $\bar{p}_2 = .1111$

d. p-value = .0179

Reject H_0; conclude that wells drilled in 2005 were dry more frequently than wells drilled in 2012.

36. a. $H_0: p_1 - p_2 \leq 0$

$H_a: p_1 - p_2 > 0$

b. .84, .81

c. p-value = .0094

Reject H_0; conclude an increase

d. .005 to .055; yes due to increase

38. a. $H_0: \mu_1 - \mu_2 = 0$

$H_a: \mu_1 - \mu_2 \neq 0$

$z = 2.79$

p-value = .0052

Reject H_0; a significant difference between systems exists

40. a. $H_0: \mu_1 - \mu_2 \leq 0$

$H_a: \mu_1 - \mu_2 > 0$

b. $t = .60, df = 57$

Using t table, p-value is greater than .20

Exact p-value = .2754

Do not reject H_0; cannot conclude that funds with loads have a higher mean rate of return

42. a. $\bar{d} = 14$

b. -6.78 to 34.78

c. $H_0: \mu_d = 0$

$H_a: \mu_d \neq 0$

$t = \dfrac{\bar{d} - \mu_d}{s_d / \sqrt{n}} = \dfrac{14 - 0}{53.744 / \sqrt{20}} = 1.165$

The p-value is between .20 and .40

The exact p-value is .2584

Do not reject H_0; do not conclude that there is a difference between the mean scores for the no sibling and with sibling groups.

44. a. p-value ≈ 0, reject H_0

b. .0468 to .1332

46. a. .35 and .47

b. $.12 \pm .1037 \ (.0163 \text{ to } .2237)$

c. Yes, we would expect occupancy rates to be higher

Chapter 11

2. $s^2 = 25$

a. With 19 degrees of freedom, $\chi^2_{.05} = 30.144$ and $\chi^2_{.95} = 10.117$

$\dfrac{19(25)}{30.144} \leq \sigma^2 \leq \dfrac{19(25)}{10.117}$

$15.76 \leq \sigma^2 \leq 46.95$

b. With 19 degrees of freedom, $\chi^2_{.025} = 32.852$ and $\chi^2_{.975} = 8.907$

$\dfrac{19(25)}{32.852} \leq \sigma^2 \leq \dfrac{19(25)}{8.907}$

$14.46 \leq \sigma^2 \leq 53.33$

c. $3.8 \leq \sigma \leq 7.3$

4. a. .22 to .71

b. .47 to .84

6. a. $41

  b. 23.52

  c. 17.37 to 36.40

8. a. .4748

  b. .6891

  c. .2383 to 1.3687

  .4882 to 1.1699

9. $H_0: \sigma^2 \leq .0004$

  $H_a: \sigma^2 > .0004$

  $\chi^2 = \dfrac{(n-1)s^2}{\sigma_0^2} = \dfrac{(30-1)(.0005)}{.0004} = 36.25$

  From table with 29 degrees of freedom, p-value is greater than .10

  p-value $> .05$; do not reject H_0

  The product specification does not appear to be violated

10. a. 84

  b. 118.71

  c. 10.90

  d. $\chi^2 = 11.54$; p-value $> .20$

  Do not reject hypothesis $\sigma = 12$

12. a. .8106

  b. $\chi^2 = 9.49$

  p-value greater than .20

  Do not reject H_0; cannot conclude the variance for the other magazine is different

14. a. $F = 2.4$

  p-value between .025 and .05

  Reject H_0

  b. $F_{.05} = 2.2$; reject H_0

15. a. Larger sample variance is s_1^2

  $F = \dfrac{s_1^2}{s_2^2} = \dfrac{8.2}{4} = 2.05$

  Degrees of freedom: 20, 25

  From table, area in tail is between .025 and .05

  p-value for two-tailed test is between .05 and .10

  p-value $> .05$; do not reject H_0

  b. For a two-tailed test:

  $F_{\alpha/2} = F_{.025} = 2.30$

  Reject H_0 if $F \geq 2.30$

  $2.05 < 2.30$; do not reject H_0

16. $F = 1.59$

  p-value is between .05 and .025

  Reject H_0; the Fidelity Fund has greater variance

17. a. Population 1 is 4-year-old automobiles

  $H_0: \sigma_1^2 \leq \sigma_2^2$

  $H_a: \sigma_1^2 > \sigma_2^2$

  b. $F = \dfrac{s_1^2}{s_2^2} = \dfrac{170^2}{100^2} = 2.89$

  Degrees of freedom: 25, 24

  From tables, p-value is less than .01

  p-value $\leq .01$; reject H_0

  Conclude that 4-year-old automobiles have a larger variance in annual repair costs compared to 2-year-old automobiles, which is expected because older automobiles are more likely to have more expensive repairs that lead to greater variance in the annual repair costs

18. $F = 1.44$

  p-value greater than .20

  Do not reject H_0; the difference between the variances is not statistically significant

20. $F = 5.29$

  p-value ≈ 0

  Reject H_0; population variances are not equal for seniors and managers

22. a. $F = 4$

  p-value less than .01

  Reject H_0; greater variability in stopping distance on wet pavement

24. 10.72 to 24.68

26. a. $\chi^2 = 27.44$

  p-value between .01 and .025

  Reject H_0; variance exceeds maximum requirements

  b. .00012 to .00042

28. $\chi^2 = 31.50$

  p-value between .05 and .10

  Reject H_0; conclude that population variance is greater than 1

30. a. $n = 15$

  b. 6.25 to 11.13

32. $F = 1.39$

  Do not reject H_0; cannot conclude the variances of grade point averages are different

34. $F = 2.08$

  p-value between .05 and .10

  Reject H_0; conclude the population variances are not equal

Chapter 12

1. $H_0: p_1 = p_2 = p_3$

  $H_a:$ Not all population proportions are equal

  Expected frequencies (e_{ij}):

	1	2	3	Total
Yes	132.0	158.4	105.6	396
No	118.0	141.6	94.4	354
Total	250	300	200	750

Chi-square calculations $(f_{ij} - e_{ij})^2/e_{ij}$:

	1	2	3	Total
Yes	2.45	.45	.87	3.77
No	2.75	.50	.98	4.22
				$\chi^2 = 7.99$

$df = k - 1 = (3 - 1) = 2$

χ^2 table with $\chi^2 = 7.99$ shows p-value between .025 and .01

p-value $\leq .05$, reject H_0; not all population proportions are equal

2. a. $\bar{p}_1 = 150/250 = .60$

$\bar{p}_2 = 150/300 = .50$

$\bar{p}_3 = 96/200 = .48$

b. For 1 vs. 2

$$CV_{12} = \sqrt{\chi^2_{\alpha; k-1}} \sqrt{\frac{\bar{p}_1(1 - \bar{p}_1)}{n_1} + \frac{\bar{p}_2(1 - \bar{p}_2)}{n_2}}$$

$$= \sqrt{5.991} \sqrt{\frac{.60(1 - .60)}{250} + \frac{.50(1 - .50)}{300}} = .1037$$

p_i	p_j	Difference	n_i	n_j	Critical Value	Significant Diff > CV
.60	.50	.10	250	300	.1037	
.60	.48	.12	250	200	.1150	Yes
.50	.48	.02	300	200	.1117	

One comparison is significant, 1 vs. 3

4. a. $H_0: p_1 = p_2 = p_3$

H_a: Not all population proportions are equal

b. Expected frequencies (e_{ij}):

Component	A	B	C	Total
Defective	25	25	25	75
Good	475	475	475	1425
Total	500	500	500	1500

Chi-square calculations $(f_{ij} - e_{ij})^2/e_{ij}$:

Component	A	B	C	Total
Defective	4.00	1.00	9.00	14.00
Good	.21	.05	.47	0.74
				$\chi^2 = 14.74$

$df = k - 1 = (3 - 1) = 2$

χ^2 table, $\chi^2 = 14.74$, p-value is less than .01

p-value $\leq .05$, reject H_0; three suppliers do not provide equal proportions of defective components

c. $\bar{p}_1 = 15/500 = .03$

$\bar{p}_2 = 20/500 = .04$

$\bar{p}_3 = 40/500 = .08$

For supplier A vs. supplier B

$$CV_{ij} = \sqrt{\chi^2_{\alpha; k-1}} \sqrt{\frac{\bar{p}_i(1 - \bar{p}_i)}{n_i} + \frac{\bar{p}_j(1 - \bar{p}_j)}{n_j}}$$

$$= \sqrt{5.991} \sqrt{\frac{.03(1 - .03)}{500} + \frac{.04(1 - .04)}{500}} = .0284$$

Comparison	p_i	p_j	Difference	n_i	n_j	Critical Value	Significant Diff > CV
A vs. B	.03	.04	.01	500	500	.0284	
A vs. C	.03	.08	.05	500	500	.0351	Yes
B vs. C	.04	.08	.04	500	500	.0366	Yes

Supplier A and supplier B are both significantly different from supplier C

6. a. .14, .09

b. $\chi^2 = 3.41$, $df = 1$

p-value between .10 and .05

Reject H_0; conclude two offices do not have equal error rates

c. z provides options for one-tailed tests

8. $\chi^2 = 5.70$, $df = 4$

p-value greater than .10

Do no reject H_0; no evidence suppliers differ in quality

9. H_0: The column variable is independent of the row variable

H_a: The column variable is not independent of the row variable

Expected frequencies (e_{ij}):

	A	B	C	Total
P	28.5	39.9	45.6	114
Q	21.5	30.1	34.4	86
Total	50	70	80	200

Chi-square calculations $(f_{ij} - e_{ij})^2/e_{ij}$:

	A	B	C	Total
P	2.54	.42	.42	3.38
Q	3.36	.56	.56	4.48
				$\chi^2 = 7.86$

$df = (2 - 1)(3 - 1) = 2$

Using the χ^2 table, p-value between .01 and .025

p-value $\leq .05$, reject H_0; conclude variables are not independent

10. $\chi^2 = 19.77$, $df = 4$

p-value less than .005

Reject H_0; conclude variables are not independent

11. a. H_0: Ticket purchased is independent of flight

H_a: Ticket purchased is not independent of flight

Expected frequencies:

$e_{11} = 35.59$ $e_{12} = 15.41$
$e_{21} = 150.73$ $e_{22} = 65.27$
$e_{31} = 455.68$ $e_{32} = 197.32$

Observed Frequency (f_i)	Expected Frequency (e_i)	Chi-square $(f_i - e_i)^2 / e_i$
29	35.59	1.22
22	15.41	2.82
95	150.73	20.61
121	65.27	47.59
518	455.68	8.52
135	197.32	19.68
920		$\chi^2 = 100.43$

$df = (r - 1)(c - 1) = (3 - 1)(2 - 1) = 2$
Using the χ^2 table, p-value is less than .005
p-value $\le$ .05, reject H_0; conclude ticket purchased is not independent of the type of flight

b. Column Percentages

Type of Ticket	Type of Flight	
	Domestic	International
First Class	4.5%	7.9%
Business Class	14.8%	43.5%
Economy Class	80.7%	48.6%

A higher percentage of first-class and business-class tickets are purchased for international flights

12. a. $\chi^2 = 9.44$, $df = 2$
   p-value is less than .01
   Reject H_0; plan not independent of type of company
b.

Employment Plan	Private	Public
Add Employees	.5139	.2963
No Change	.2639	.3148
Lay Off Employees	.2222	.3889

Employment opportunities better for private companies

14. a. $\chi^2 = 6.57$, $df = 6$
   p-value greater than .10
   Do not reject H_0; cannot reject assumption of independence
b. 29%, 46%, and 25%
   Outstanding is most frequent owner rating
16. a. 900
b. The movie fans favored Jennifer Lawrence ($\bar{p} = .2278$), but three other nominees (Jessica Chastain, Emmanuelle Riva, and Naomi Watts) each were favored by almost as many of the fans.
c. $\chi^2 = 77.74$

p-value is approximately 0.
Reject H_0; conclude that attitude toward the actress who was most deserving of the 2013 Academy Award for actress in a leading role is not independent of age.

18. $\chi^2 = 45.36$, $df = 4$
   p-value less than .005
   Reject H_0; conclude that the ratings of the hosts are not independent

19. a. Expected frequencies:
   $e_1 = 200(.40) = 80$, $e_2 = 200(.40) = 80$
   $e_3 = 200(.20) = 40$
   Observed frequencies: $f_1 = 60, f_2 = 120, f_3 = 20$
   $$\chi^2 = \frac{(60 - 80)^2}{80} + \frac{(120 - 80)^2}{80} + \frac{(20 - 40)^2}{40}$$
   $$= \frac{400}{80} + \frac{1600}{80} + \frac{400}{40} = 35$$
   $df = k - 1 = 3 - 1 = 2$
   $\chi^2 = 35$ shows p-value less than .005
   p-value $\le$ .01; reject H_0
   Conclude proportions differ from .40, .40, and .20
b. Reject H_0 if $\chi^2 \ge 9.210$; reject H_0

20. With $n = 30$, use six classes, each probability $= .1667$
   $\bar{x} = 22.8$, $s = 6.27$

z	Cutoff value of x
$-.98$	$22.8 - .98 (6.27) = 16.66$
$-.43$	$22.8 - .43 (6.27) = 20.11$
0	$22.8 + 0 (6.27) = 22.80$
$.43$	$22.8 + .43 (6.27) = 25.49$
$.98$	$22.8 + .98 (6.27) = 28.94$

Interval	Observed Frequency	Expected Frequency	Difference
less than 16.66	3	5	-2
16.66–20.11	7	5	2
20.11–22.80	5	5	0
22.80–25.49	7	5	2
25.49–28.94	3	5	-2
28.94 and up	5	5	0

$$\chi^2 = \frac{(-2)^2}{5} + \frac{(2)^2}{5} + \frac{(0)^2}{5} + \frac{(2)^2}{5} + \frac{(-2)^2}{5} + \frac{(0)^2}{5} + \frac{16}{5}$$

$= 3.20$

$df = k - 2 - 1 = 6 - 2 - 1 = 3$
$\chi^2 = 3.20$ shows p-value greater than .10
p-value $>$ .05; do not reject H_0; normal distribution cannot be rejected

21. H_0: The population proportions are .29, .28, .25, and .18
   H_a: The proportions are not as shown above
   Expected frequencies: $300(.29) = 87$, $300(.28) = 84$
   $300(.25) = 75$, $300(.18) = 54$
   Observed frequencies: $f_1 = 95, f_2 = 70, f_3 = 89, f_4 = 46$
   $$\chi^2 = \frac{(95 - 87)^2}{87} + \frac{(70 - 84)^2}{84} + \frac{(89 - 75)^2}{75}$$

$$+ \frac{(46 - 54)^2}{54} = 6.87$$

$df = k - 1 = 4 - 1 = 3$

$\chi^2 = 6.87$ shows p-value between .05 and .10

p-value $> .05$; do not reject H_0; no significant change in viewing audience proportions

22. $\chi^2 = 5.85$, $df = 5$

p-value greater than .10

Do not reject H_0; cannot reject the hypothesis that percentages are as stated

24. a. $\chi^2 = 14.33$, $df = 6$

p-value between .05 and .025

Reject H_0; conclude proportion not the same for each day of the week

b. 15.17, 11.90, 12.62, 11.19, 13.10, 16.43, 19.05

Saturday and Friday have the highest percentage

26. $\chi^2 = 2.8$, $df = 3$

p-value greater than .10

Do not reject H_0; assumption of a normal distribution cannot be rejected

28. a. 8.8%, 11.7%, 9.0%, 8.5%

b. $\chi^2 = 2.48$, $df = 3$

p-value greater than .10

Do not reject H_0; cannot reject assumption that the population proportions are equal

30. a. $\chi^2 = 9.56$, $df = 2$

p-value is less than .01

Reject H_0; conclude preferred pace is not independent of gender

b. Women slower 75.17% to 67.65%

Men faster 26.47% to 16.55%

32. $\chi^2 = 6.17$, $df = 6$

p-value greater than .10

Do not reject H_0; assumption county and day of week are independent is not rejected

34. $\chi^2 = 2.00$, $df = 5$

p-value greater than .10

Do not reject H_0; assumption of normal distribution cannot be rejected

Chapter 13

1. a. $\bar{\bar{x}} = (156 + 142 + 134)/3 = 144$

$$\text{SSTR} = \sum_{j=1}^{k} n_j(\bar{x}_j - \bar{\bar{x}})^2$$

$$= 6(156 - 144)^2 + 6(142 - 144)^2 + 6(134 - 144)^2$$

$$= 1488$$

b. $\text{MSTR} = \dfrac{\text{SSTR}}{k - 1} = \dfrac{1488}{2} = 744$

c. $s_1^2 = 164.4$, $s_2^2 = 131.2$, $s_3^2 = 110.4$

$$\text{SSE} = \sum_{j=1}^{k} (n_j - 1)s_j^2$$

$$= 5(164.4) + 5(131.2) + 5(110.4)$$

$$= 2030$$

d. $\text{MSE} = \dfrac{\text{SSE}}{n_T - k} = \dfrac{2030}{18 - 3} = 135.3$

e.

Source of Variation	Sum of Squares	Degrees of Freedom	Mean Square	F	p-value
Treatments	1488	2	744	5.50	.0162
Error	2030	15	135.3		
Total	3518	17			

f. $F = \dfrac{\text{MSTR}}{\text{MSE}} = \dfrac{744}{135.3} = 5.50$

From the F table (2 numerator degrees of freedom and 15 denominator), p-value is between .01 and .025

Using Excel or Minitab, the p-value corresponding to $F = 5.50$ is .0162

Because p-value $\leq \alpha = .05$, we reject the hypothesis that the means for the three treatments are equal

2.

Source of Variation	Sum of Squares	Degrees of Freedom	Mean Square	F	p-value
Treatments	300	4	75	14.07	.0000
Error	160	30	5.33		
Total	460	34			

4.

Source of Variation	Sum of Squares	Degrees of Freedom	Mean Square	F	p-value
Treatments	150	2	75	4.80	.0233
Error	250	16	15.63		
Total	400	18			

Reject H_0 because p-value $\leq \alpha = .05$

6. Because p-value $= .0082$ is less than $\alpha = .05$, we reject the null hypothesis that the means of the three treatments are equal

8. $\bar{\bar{x}} = (79 + 74 + 66)/3 = 73$

$$\text{SSTR} = \sum_{j=1}^{k} n_j(\bar{x}_j - \bar{\bar{x}})^2 = 6(79 - 73)^2 + 6(74 - 73)^2$$
$$+ 6(66 - 73)^2 = 516$$

$$\text{MSTR} = \frac{\text{SSTR}}{k - 1} = \frac{516}{2} = 258$$

$s_1^2 = 34$ $s_2^2 = 20$ $s_3^2 = 32$

$$\text{SSE} = \sum_{j=1}^{k} (n_j - 1)s_j^2 = 5(34) + 5(20) + 5(32) = 430$$

$$\text{MSE} = \frac{\text{SSE}}{n_T - k} = \frac{430}{18 - 3} = 28.67$$

$$F = \frac{\text{MSTR}}{\text{MSE}} = \frac{258}{28.67} = 9.00$$

Source of Variation	Sum of Squares	Degrees of Freedom	Mean Square	F	p-value
Treatments	516	2	258	9.00	.003
Error	430	15	28.67		
Total	946	17			

Using F table (2 numerator degrees of freedom and 15 denominator), p-value is less than .01

Using Excel or Minitab, the p-value corresponding to $F = 9.00$ is .003

Because p-value $\leq \alpha = .05$, we reject the null hypothesis that the means for the three plants are equal; in other words, analysis of variance supports the conclusion that the population mean examination scores at the three NCP plants are not equal

10. p-value = .0000

Because p-value $\leq \alpha = .05$, we reject the null hypothesis that the means for the three groups are equal

12. p-value = .0038

Because p-value $\leq \alpha = .05$, we reject the null hypothesis that the mean meal prices are the same for the three types of restaurants

13. a. $\bar{\bar{x}} = (30 + 45 + 36)/3 = 37$

$$\text{SSTR} = \sum_{j=1}^{k} n_j(\bar{x}_j - \bar{\bar{x}})^2 = 5(30 - 37)^2 + 5(45 - 37)^2$$
$$+ 5(36 - 37)^2 = 570$$

$$\text{MSTR} = \frac{\text{SSTR}}{k - 1} = \frac{570}{2} = 285$$

$$\text{SSE} = \sum_{j=1}^{k} (n_j - 1)s_j^2 = 4(6) + 4(4) + 4(6.5) = 66$$

$$\text{MSE} = \frac{\text{SSE}}{n_T - k} = \frac{66}{15 - 3} = 5.5$$

$$F = \frac{\text{MSTR}}{\text{MSE}} = \frac{285}{5.5} = 51.82$$

Using F table (2 numerator degrees of freedom and 12 denominator), p-value is less than .01

Using Excel or Minitab, the p-value corresponding to $F = 51.82$ is .0000

Because p-value $\leq \alpha = .05$, we reject the null hypothesis that the means of the three populations are equal

b. $\text{LSD} = t_{\alpha/2} \sqrt{\text{MSE}\left(\frac{1}{n_i} + \frac{1}{n_j}\right)}$

$$= t_{.025} \sqrt{5.5\left(\frac{1}{5} + \frac{1}{5}\right)}$$

$$= 2.179\sqrt{2.2} = 3.23$$

$|\bar{x}_1 - \bar{x}_2| = |30 - 45| = 15 > \text{LSD}$; significant difference
$|\bar{x}_1 - \bar{x}_3| = |30 - 36| = 6 > \text{LSD}$; significant difference
$|\bar{x}_2 - \bar{x}_3| = |45 - 36| = 9 > \text{LSD}$; significant difference

c. $\bar{x}_1 - \bar{x}_2 \pm t_{\alpha/2} \sqrt{\text{MSE}\left(\frac{1}{n_1} + \frac{1}{n_2}\right)}$

$$(30 - 45) \pm 2.179 \sqrt{5.5\left(\frac{1}{5} + \frac{1}{5}\right)}$$

$$-15 \pm 3.23 = -18.23 \text{ to } -11.77$$

14. a. Significant; p-value = .0106

b. LSD = 15.34
1 and 2; significant
1 and 3; not significant
2 and 3; significant

15. a.

	Manufacturer 1	Manufacturer 2	Manufacturer 3
Sample Mean	23	28	21
Sample Variance	6.67	4.67	3.33

$$\bar{\bar{x}} = (23 + 28 + 21)/3 = 24$$

$$\text{SSTR} = \sum_{j=1}^{k} n_j(\bar{x}_j - \bar{\bar{x}})^2$$
$$= 4(23 - 24)^2 + 4(28 - 24)^2 + 4(21 - 24)^2$$
$$= 104$$

$$\text{MSTR} = \frac{\text{SSTR}}{k - 1} = \frac{104}{2} = 52$$

$$\text{SSE} = \sum_{j=1}^{k} (n_j - 1)s_j^2$$
$$= 3(6.67) + 3(4.67) + 3(3.33) = 44.01$$

$$\text{MSE} = \frac{\text{SSE}}{n_T - k} = \frac{44.01}{12 - 3} = 4.89$$

$$F = \frac{\text{MSTR}}{\text{MSE}} = \frac{52}{4.89} = 10.63$$

Using F table (2 numerator degrees of freedom and 9 denominator), p-value is less than .01

Using Excel or Minitab, the p-value corresponding to $F = 10.63$ is .0043

Because p-value $\leq \alpha = .05$, we reject the null hypothesis that the mean time needed to mix a batch of material is the same for each manufacturer

b. $\text{LSD} = t_{\alpha/2} \sqrt{\text{MSE}\left(\frac{1}{n_1} + \frac{1}{n_3}\right)}$

$$= t_{.025} \sqrt{4.89\left(\frac{1}{4} + \frac{1}{4}\right)}$$

$$= 2.262\sqrt{2.45} = 3.54$$

Since $|\bar{x}_1 - \bar{x}_3| = |23 - 21| = 2 < 3.54$, there does not appear to be any significant difference between the means for manufacturer 1 and manufacturer 3

16. $\bar{x}_1 - \bar{x}_2 \pm \text{LSD}$
$23 - 28 \pm 3.54$
$\quad -5 \pm 3.54 = -8.54$ to -1.46

18. a. Significant; p-value $= .0000$
  b. Significant; $2.3 > \text{LSD} = 1.19$

20. a. Significant; p-value $= .011$
  b. Comparing North and South
  $|7702 - 5566| = 2136 > \text{LSD} = 1620.76$
  significant difference
  Comparing North and West
  $|7702 - 8430| = 728 > \text{LSD} = 1620.76$
  no significant difference
  Comparing South and West
  $|5566 - 8430| = 2864 > \text{LSD} = 1775.45$
  significant difference

21. *Treatment Means*
$\bar{x}_{.1} = 13.6, \quad \bar{x}_{.2} = 11.0, \quad \bar{x}_{.3} = 10.6$

Block Means
$\bar{x}_{1.} = 9, \; \bar{x}_{2.} = 7.67, \; \bar{x}_{3.} = 15.67, \; \bar{x}_{4.} = 18.67, \; \bar{x}_{5.} = 7.67$

Overall Mean
$\bar{\bar{x}} = 176/15 = 11.73$

Step 1
$\text{SST} = \sum_i \sum_j (x_{ij} - \bar{\bar{x}})^2$
$\quad = (10 - 11.73)^2 + (9 - 11.73)^2 + \cdots + (8 - 11.73)^2$
$\quad = 354.93$

Step 2
$\text{SSTR} = b \sum_j (\bar{x}_{.j} - \bar{\bar{x}})^2$
$\quad = 5[(13.6 - 11.73)^2 + (11.0 - 11.73)^2$
$\qquad + (10.6 - 11.73)^2] = 26.53$

Step 3
$\text{SSBL} = k \sum_j (\bar{x}_{i.} - \bar{\bar{x}})^2$
$\quad = 3[(9 - 11.73)^2 + (7.67 - 11.73)^2$
$\qquad + (15.67 - 11.73)^2 + (18.67 - 11.73)^2$
$\qquad + (7.67 - 11.73)^2] = 312.32$

Step 4
$\text{SSE} = \text{SST} - \text{SSTR} - \text{SSBL}$
$\quad = 354.93 - 26.53 - 312.32 = 16.08$

Source of Variation	Sum of Squares	Degrees of Freedom	Mean Square	F	p-value
Treatments	26.53	2	13.27	6.60	.0203
Blocks	312.32	4	78.08		
Error	16.08	8	2.01		
Total	354.93	14			

From the F table (2 numerator degrees of freedom and 8 denominator), p-value is between .01 and .025
Actual p-value $= .0203$
Because p-value $\leq \alpha = .05$, we reject the null hypothesis that the means of the three treatments are equal

22.

Source of Variation	Sum of Squares	Degrees of Freedom	Mean Square	F	p-value
Treatments	310	4	77.5	17.69	.0005
Blocks	85	2	42.5		
Error	35	8	4.38		
Total	430	14			

Significant; p-value $\leq \alpha = .05$

24. p-value $= .0453$
Because p-value $\leq \alpha = .05$, we reject the null hypothesis that the mean tune-up times are the same for both analyzers

26. a. Significant; p-value $= .0231$
  b. Writing section

28. *Step 1*
$\text{SST} = \sum_i \sum_j \sum_k (x_{ijk} - \bar{\bar{x}})^2$
$\quad = (135 - 111)^2 + (165 - 111)^2$
$\qquad + \cdots + (136 - 111)^2 = 9028$

Step 2
$\text{SSA} = br \sum_i (\bar{x}_{i.} - \bar{\bar{x}})^2$
$\quad = 3(2)[(104 - 111)^2 + (118 - 111)^2] = 588$

Step 3
$\text{SSB} = ar \sum_j (\bar{x}_{.j} - \bar{\bar{x}})^2$
$\quad = 2(2)[(130 - 111)^2 + (97 - 111)^2 + (106 - 111)^2]$
$\quad = 2328$

Step 4
$\text{SSAB} = r \sum_i \sum_j (\bar{x}_{ij} - \bar{x}_{i.} - \bar{x}_{.j} + \bar{\bar{x}})^2$
$\quad = 2[(150 - 104 - 130 + 111)^2$
$\qquad + (78 - 104 - 97 + 111)^2$
$\qquad + \cdots + (128 - 118 - 106 + 111)^2] = 4392$

Step 5
$\text{SSE} = \text{SST} - \text{SSA} - \text{SSB} - \text{SSAB}$
$\quad = 9028 - 588 - 2328 - 4392 = 1720$

Source of Variation	Sum of Squares	Degrees of Freedom	Mean Square	F	p-value
Factor A	588	1	588	2.05	.2022
Factor B	2328	2	1164	4.06	.0767
Interaction	4392	2	2196	7.66	.0223
Error	1720	6	286.67		
Total	9028	11			

Factor A: $F = 2.05$

Using F table (1 numerator degree of freedom and 6 denominator), p-value is greater than .10

Using Excel or Minitab, the p-value corresponding to $F = 2.05$ is .2022

Because p-value $> \alpha = .05$, Factor A is not significant

Factor B: $F = 4.06$

Using F table (2 numerator degrees of freedom and 6 denominator), p-value is between .05 and .10

Using Excel or Minitab, the p-value corresponding to $F = 4.06$ is .0767

Because p-value $> \alpha = .05$, Factor B is not significant

Interaction: $F = 7.66$

Using F table (2 numerator degrees of freedom and 6 denominator), p-value is between .01 and .025

Using Excel or Minitab, the p-value corresponding to $F = 7.66$ is .0223

Because p-value $\leq \alpha = .05$, interaction is significant

30. Design: p-value $= .0104$; significant
Size: p-value $= .1340$; not significant
Interaction: p-value $= .2519$; not significant

32. Class: p-value $= .0002$; significant
Type: p-value $= .0006$; significant
Interaction: p-value $= .4229$; not significant

34. Significant; p-value $= .0134$

36. Not significant; p-value $= .088$

38. Not significant; p-value $= .2455$

40. a. Significant; p-value $= .0175$

42. The blocks correspond to the 12 golfers (Golfer) and the treatments correspond to the three designs (Design).

The Minitab ANOVA output is

Source	DF	SS	MS	F	P
Design	2	3032.0	1516.0	12.89	0.000
Golfer	11	5003.3	454.8	3.87	0.003
Error	22	2586.7	117.6		
Total	35	10622.0			

Because the p-value for Design (.000) is less than $\alpha = .05$, there is a significant difference in the mean driving distance for the three designs.

44. Type of machine (p-value $= .0226$) is significant; type of loading system (p-value $= .7913$) and interaction (p-value $= .0671$) are not significant

Chapter 14

1. a.

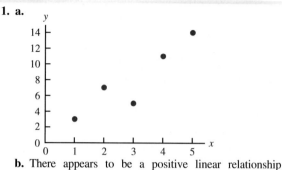

b. There appears to be a positive linear relationship between x and y

c. Many different straight lines can be drawn to provide a linear approximation of the relationship between x and y; in part (d) we will determine the equation of a straight line that "best" represents the relationship according to the least squares criterion

d. Summations needed to compute the slope and y-intercept:

$$\bar{x} = \frac{\Sigma x_i}{n} = \frac{15}{5} = 3, \quad \bar{y} = \frac{\Sigma y_i}{n} = \frac{40}{5} = 8,$$

$$\Sigma(x_i - \bar{x})(y_i - \bar{y}) = 26, \quad \Sigma(x_i - \bar{x})^2 = 10$$

$$b_1 = \frac{\Sigma(x_i - \bar{x})(y_i - \bar{y})}{\Sigma(x_i - \bar{x})^2} = \frac{26}{10} = 2.6$$

$$b_0 = \bar{y} - b_1\bar{x} = 8 - (2.6)(3) = 0.2$$

$$\hat{y} = 0.2 - 2.6x$$

e. $\hat{y} = .2 + 2.6x = .2 + 2.6(4) = 10.6$

2. b. There appears to be a negative linear relationship between x and y

d. $\hat{y} = 68 - 3x$

e. 38

4. a.

b. There appears to be a positive linear relationship between the percentage of women working in the five companies (x) and the percentage of management jobs held by women in that company (y)

c. Many different straight lines can be drawn to provide a linear approximation of the relationship between x and y; in part (d) we will determine the equation of a straight line that "best" represents the relationship according to the least squares criterion

d. $\bar{x} = \dfrac{\Sigma x_i}{n} = \dfrac{300}{5} = 60$ $\bar{y} = \dfrac{\Sigma y_i}{n} = \dfrac{215}{5} = 43$

$\Sigma(x_i - \bar{x})(y_i - \bar{y}) = 624$ $\Sigma(x_i - \bar{x})^2 = 480$

$b_1 = \dfrac{\Sigma(x_i - \bar{x})(y_i - \bar{y})}{\Sigma(x_i - \bar{x})^2} = \dfrac{624}{480} = 1.3$

$b_0 = \bar{y} - b_1\bar{x} = 43 - 1.3(60) = -35$

$\hat{y} = -35 + 1.3x$

e. $\hat{y} = -35 + 1.3x = -35 + 1.3(60) = 43\%$

6. c. $\hat{y} = -70.391 + 17.175x$
   e. 43.8 or approximately 44%

8. c. $\hat{y} = .2046 + .9077x$
   e. 3.29 or approximately 3.3

10. c. $\hat{y} = -167.81 + 2.7149x$
    e. Yes

12. c. $\hat{y} = 17.49 + 1.0334x$
    d. \$150

14. a. The scatter diagram indicates a negative linear relationship between $x = $ distance to work and $y = $ number of days absent.
    b. $\hat{y} = 8.0978 - .3442x$
    c. $\hat{y} = 8.0978 - .3442(5) = 6.4$ or approximately 6 days.

15. a. $\hat{y}_i = .2 + 2.6x_i$ and $\bar{y} = 8$

x_i	y_i	$\hat{y}_i$	$y_i - \hat{y}_i$	$(y_i - \hat{y}_i)^2$	$y_i - \bar{y}$	$(y_i - \bar{y})^2$
1	3	2.8	.2	.04	-5	25
2	7	5.4	1.6	2.56	-1	1
3	5	8.0	-3.0	9.00	-3	9
4	11	10.6	.4	.16	3	9
5	14	13.2	.8	.64	6	36
				SSE = 12.40		SST = 80

$\text{SSR} = \text{SST} - \text{SSE} = 80 - 12.4 = 67.6$

b. $r^2 = \dfrac{\text{SSR}}{\text{SST}} = \dfrac{67.6}{80} = .845$

The least squares line provided a good fit; 84.5% of the variability in y has been explained by the least squares line

c. $r_{xy} = \sqrt{.845} = +.9192$

16. a. SSE = 230, SST = 1850, SSR = 1620
    b. $r^2 = .876$
    c. $r_{xy} = -.936$

18. a. $\bar{x} = \Sigma x_i/n = 600/6 = 100$ $y = \Sigma y_i/n = 330/6 = 55$
$\text{SST} = \Sigma(y_i - \bar{y})^2 = 1800$ $\text{SSE} = \Sigma(y_i - \hat{y}_i)^2 = 287.624$
$\text{SSR} = \text{SST} - \text{SSR} = 1800 - 287.624 = 1512.376$

b. $r^2 = \dfrac{\text{SSR}}{\text{SST}} = \dfrac{1512.376}{1800} = .84$

c. $r = \sqrt{r^2} = \sqrt{.84} = .917$

20. a. $\hat{y} = 28,574 - 1439x$
    b. $r^2 = .864$
    c. \$6989

22. a. $r^2 = \dfrac{\text{SSR}}{\text{SST}} = \dfrac{9524.97}{10,568} = .9013$
    b. The estimated regression equation provided a very good fit; approximately 90% of the variability in the dependent variable was explained by the linear relationship between the two variables.
    c. $r = \sqrt{r^2} = \sqrt{.9013} = .95$ This reflects a strong linear relationship between the two variables.

23. a. $s^2 = \text{MSE} = \dfrac{\text{SSE}}{n-2} = \dfrac{12.4}{3} = 4.133$

    b. $s = \sqrt{\text{MSE}} = \sqrt{4.133} = 2.033$

    c. $\Sigma(x_i - \bar{x})^2 = 10$

$$s_{b_1} = \dfrac{s}{\sqrt{\Sigma(x_i - \bar{x})^2}} = \dfrac{2.033}{\sqrt{10}} = .643$$

    d. $t = \dfrac{b_1 - \beta_1}{s_{b_1}} = \dfrac{2.6 - 0}{.643} = 4.044$

From the t table (3 degrees of freedom), area in tail is between .01 and .025

p-value is between .02 and .05

Using Excel or Minitab, the p-value corresponding to $t = 4.04$ is .0272

Because p-value $\le \alpha$, we reject $H_0: \beta_1 = 0$

    e. $\text{MSR} = \dfrac{\text{SSR}}{1} = 67.6$

$$F = \dfrac{\text{MSR}}{\text{MSE}} = \dfrac{67.6}{4.133} = 16.36$$

From the F table (1 numerator degree of freedom and 3 denominator), p-value is between .025 and .05

Using Excel or Minitab, the p-value corresponding to $F = 16.36$ is .0272

Because p-value $\le \alpha$, we reject $H_0: \beta_1 = 0$

Source of Variation	Sum of Squares	Degrees of Freedom	Mean Square	F	p-value
Regression	67.6	1	67.6	16.36	.0272
Error	12.4	3	4.133		
Total	80	4			

24. a. 76.6667
    b. 8.7560
    c. .6526
    d. Significant; p-value = .0193
    e. Significant; p-value = .0193

26. a. In the statement of exercise 18, $\hat{y} = 23.194 + .318x$

In solving exercise 18, we found SSE = 287.624

$s^2 = \text{MSE} = \text{SSE}/(n-2) = 287.624/4 = 71.906$

$s = \sqrt{\text{MSE}} = \sqrt{71.906} = 8.4797$

$\Sigma(x - \bar{x})^2 = 14{,}950$

$s_{b_1} = \dfrac{s}{\sqrt{\Sigma(x-\bar{x})^2}} = \dfrac{8.4797}{\sqrt{14{,}950}} = .0694$

$t = \dfrac{b_1}{s_{b_1}} = \dfrac{.318}{.0694} = 4.58$

Using t table (4 degrees of freedom), area in tail is between .005 and .01

p-value is between .01 and .02

Using Excel, the p-value corresponding to $t = 4.58$ is .010

Because p-value $\leq \alpha$, we reject $H_0: \beta_1 = 0$; there is a significant relationship between price and overall score

b. In exercise 18 we found SSR = 1512.376

MSR = SSR/1 = 1512.376/1 = 1512.376

$F = \text{MSR}/\text{MSE} = 1512.376/71.906 = 21.03$

Using F table (1 degree of freedom numerator and 4 denominator), p-value is between .025 and .01

Using Excel, the p-value corresponding to $F = 11.74$ is .010

Because p-value $\leq \alpha$, we reject $H_0: \beta_1 = 0$

c.

Source of Variation	Sum of Squares	Degrees of Freedom	Mean Square	F	p-value
Regression	1512.376	1	1512.376	21.03	.010
Error	287.624	4	71.906		
Total	1800	5			

28. They are related; p-value = .000

30. Using t table (4 degrees of freedom), area in tail is less than .005 p-value is less than .01. There is a significant relationship between cars in service and annual revenue.

32. a. $s = 2.033$

$\bar{x} = 3, \Sigma(x_i - \bar{x})^2 = 10$

$s_{\hat{y}*} = s\sqrt{\dfrac{1}{n} + \dfrac{(x^* - \bar{x})^2}{\Sigma(x_i - \bar{x})^2}}$

$= 2.033\sqrt{\dfrac{1}{5} + \dfrac{(4-3)^2}{10}} = 1.11$

b. $\hat{y}* = .2 + 2.6x* = .2 + 2.6(4) = 10.6$

$\hat{y}* \pm t_{\alpha/2}s_{\hat{y}*}$

$10.6 \pm 3.182(1.11)$

10.6 ± 3.53, or 7.07 to 14.13

c. $s_{\text{pred}} = s\sqrt{1 + \dfrac{1}{n} + \dfrac{(x^*-\bar{x})^2}{\Sigma(x_i-\bar{x})^2}}$

$= 2.033\sqrt{1 + \dfrac{1}{5} + \dfrac{(4-3)^2}{10}} = 2.32$

d. $\hat{y}* \pm t_{\alpha/2}s_{\text{pred}}$

$10.6 \pm 3.182(2.32)$

10.6 ± 7.38, or 3.22 to 17.98

34. Confidence interval: 8.65 to 21.15

Prediction interval: -4.50 to 41.30

35. a. $\hat{y}* = 2090.5 + 581.1x* = 2090.5 + 581.1(3) = 3833.8$

b. $s = \sqrt{\text{MSE}} = \sqrt{21{,}284} = 145.89$

$\bar{x} = 3.2, \Sigma(x_i - \bar{x})^2 = 0.74$

$s_{\hat{y}*} = s\sqrt{\dfrac{1}{n} + \dfrac{(x^*-\bar{x})^2}{\Sigma(x_i-\bar{x})^2}}$

$= 145.89\sqrt{\dfrac{1}{6} + \dfrac{(3-3.2)^2}{0.74}} = 68.54$

$\hat{y}* \pm t_{\alpha/2}s_{\hat{y}*}$

$3833.8 \pm 2.776(68.54) = 3833.8 \pm 190.27$

or \$3643.53 to \$4024.07

c. $s_{\text{pred}} = s\sqrt{1 + \dfrac{1}{n} + \dfrac{(x^*-\bar{x})^2}{\Sigma(x_i-\bar{x})^2}}$

$= 145.89\sqrt{1 + \dfrac{1}{6} + \dfrac{(3-3.2)^2}{0.74}} = 161.19$

$\hat{y}* \pm t_{\alpha/2}s_{\text{pred}}$

$3833.8 \pm 2.776(161.19) = 3833.8 \pm 447.46$

or \$3386.34 to \$4281.26

d. As expected, the prediction interval is much wider than the confidence interval. This is due to the fact that it is more difficult to predict the starting salary for one new student with a GPA of 3.0 than it is to estimate the mean for all students with a GPA of 3.0.

36. a. \$112,190 to \$119,810

b. \$104,710 to \$127,290

38. a. \$5046.67

b. \$3815.10 to \$6278.24

c. Not out of line

40. a. 9

b. $\hat{y} = 20.0 + 7.21x$

c. 1.3626

d. SSE = SST − SSR = 51,984.1 − 41,587.3 = 10,396.8

MSE = 10,396.8/7 = 1485.3

$F = \dfrac{\text{MSR}}{\text{MSE}} = \dfrac{41{,}587.3}{1485.3} = 28.0$

From the F table (1 numerator degree of freedom and 7 denominator), p-value is less than .01

Using Excel or Minitab, the p-value corresponding to $F = 28.0$ is .0011

Because p-value $\leq \alpha = .05$, we reject H_0: $\beta_1 = 0$

e. $\hat{y} = 20.0 + 7.21(50) = 380.5$, or \$380,500

42. a. $\hat{y} = 80.0 + 50.0x$

   b. 30

   c. Significant; p-value = .000

   d. \$680,000

44. b. Yes

   c. $\hat{y} = 2044.38 - 28.35$ weight

   d. Significant; p-value = .000

   e. .774; a good fit

45. a. $\bar{x} = \dfrac{\Sigma x_i}{n} = \dfrac{70}{5} = 14, \quad \bar{y} = \dfrac{\Sigma y_i}{n} = \dfrac{76}{5} = 15.2,$

$\Sigma(x_i - \bar{x})(y_i - \bar{y}) = 200, \quad \Sigma(x_i - \bar{x})^2 = 126$

$b_1 = \dfrac{\Sigma(x_i - \bar{x})(y_i - \bar{y})}{\Sigma(x_i - \bar{x})^2} = \dfrac{200}{126} = 1.5873$

$b_0 = \bar{y} - b_1\bar{x} = 15.2 - (1.5873)(14) = -7.0222$

$\hat{y} = -7.02 + 1.59x$

b.

x_i	y_i	$\hat{y}_i$	$y_i - \hat{y}_i$
6	6	2.52	3.48
11	8	10.47	-2.47
15	12	16.83	-4.83
18	20	21.60	-1.60
20	30	24.78	5.22

c.

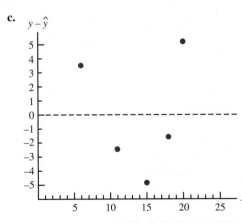

With only five observations, it is difficult to determine whether the assumptions are satisfied; however, the plot does suggest curvature in the residuals, which would indicate that the error term assumptions are not satisfied; the scatter diagram for these data also indicates

that the underlying relationship between x and y may be curvilinear

d. $s^2 = 23.78$

$h_i = \dfrac{1}{n} + \dfrac{(x_i - \bar{x})^2}{\Sigma(x_i - \bar{x})^2} = \dfrac{1}{5} + \dfrac{(x_i - 14)^2}{126}$

x_i	h_i	$s_{y_i - \hat{y}_i}$	$y_i - \hat{y}_i$	Standardized Residuals
6	.7079	2.64	3.48	1.32
11	.2714	4.16	-2.47	-.59
15	.2079	4.34	-4.83	-1.11
18	.3270	4.00	-1.60	-.40
20	.4857	3.50	5.22	1.49

e. The plot of the standardized residuals against $\hat{y}$ has the same shape as the original residual plot; as stated in part (c), the curvature observed indicates that the assumptions regarding the error term may not be satisfied

46. a. $\hat{y} = 2.32 + .64x$

   b. No; the variance appears to increase for larger values of x

47. a. Let x = advertising expenditures and y = revenue

$\hat{y} = 29.4 + 1.55x$

   b. SST = 1002, SSE = 310.28, SSR = 691.72

$MSR = \dfrac{SSR}{1} = 691.72$

$MSE = \dfrac{SSE}{n - 2} = \dfrac{310.28}{5} = 62.0554$

$F = \dfrac{MSR}{MSE} = \dfrac{691.72}{62.0554} = 11.15$

From the F table (1 numerator degree of freedom and 5 denominator), p-value is between .01 and .025

Using Excel or Minitab, p-value = .0206

Because p-value $\leq \alpha = .05$, we conclude that the two variables are related

   c.

x_i	y_i	$\hat{y}_i = 29.40 + 1.55x_i$	$y_i - \hat{y}_i$
1	19	30.95	-11.95
2	32	32.50	-.50
4	44	35.60	8.40
6	40	38.70	1.30
10	52	44.90	7.10
14	53	51.10	1.90
20	54	60.40	-6.40

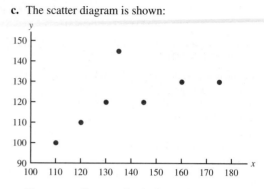

c. The scatter diagram is shown:

d. The residual plot leads us to question the assumption of a linear relationship between x and y; even though the relationship is significant at the $\alpha = .05$ level, it would be extremely dangerous to extrapolate beyond the range of the data

48. b. Yes

50. a. Using Minitab, we obtained the estimated regression equation $\hat{y} = 66.1 + .402x$; a portion of the Minitab output is shown in Figure D14.50; the fitted values and standardized residuals are shown:

x_i	y_i	$\hat{y}_i$	Standardized Residuals
135	145	120.41	2.11
110	100	110.35	−1.08
130	120	118.40	.14
145	120	124.43	−.38
175	130	136.50	−.78
160	130	130.47	−.04
120	110	114.38	−.41

b.

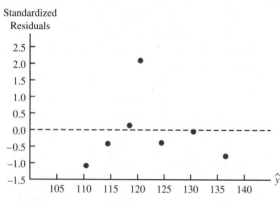

The standardized residual plot indicates that the observation $x = 135$, $y = 145$ may be an outlier; note that this observation has a standardized residual of 2.11

The scatter diagram also indicates that the observation $x = 135$, $y = 145$ may be an outlier; the implication is that for simple linear regression outliers can be identified by looking at the scatter diagram

52. b. $\hat{y} = 91.0 - 0.917x$
b. Smithsonian Institution: outlier
American Cancer Society: influential observation

54. a. The scatter diagram does indicate potential outliers and/or influential observations. For example, the New York Yankees have both the highest revenue and value, and appears to be an influential observation. The Los Angeles Dodgers have the second highest value and appears to be an outlier.
b. $\hat{y} = -601.4814 + 5.9271$ Revenue.
c. The Standard Residual value for the Los Angeles Dodgers is 4.7 and should be treated as an outlier.

58. b. $\hat{y} = -669 + .157$ DJIA
c. Significant; p-value $= .001$
d. $r^2 = .949$; excellent fit

60. b. GR(%) = 25.4 + .285 RR(%)
c. Significant; p-value $= .000$
d. No; $r^2 = .449$
e. Yes
f. Yes

62. a. $\hat{y} = 22.2 - .148x$
b. Significant relationship; p-value $= .028$
c. Good fit; $r^2 = .739$
d. 12.294 to 17.271

64. a. $\hat{y} = 220 + 132x$
b. Significant; p-value $= .000$
c. $r^2 = .873$; very good fit
d. $559.50 to $933.90

66. a. Market beta $= .95$
b. Significant; p-value $= .029$
c. $r^2 = .470$; not a good fit
d. Xerox has a higher risk

68. b. There appears to be a negative linear relationship between the two variables
c. $\hat{y} = 16.5 - .0588$ Miles
d. Significant; p-value $= .000$
e. $r^2 = .539$; reasonably good fit
g. approximately $13,000; no

FIGURE D14.50

```
The regression equation is
Y = 66.1 + 0.402 X

Predictor        Coef      SE Coef         T          p
Constant        66.10        32.06      2.06      0.094
X              0.4023       0.2276      1.77      0.137

S = 12.62      R-sq = 38.5%      R-sq(adj) = 26.1%

Analysis of Variance

SOURCE              DF          SS         MS         F          p
Regression           1       497.2      497.2      3.12      0.137
Residual Error       5       795.7      159.1
Total                6      1292.9

Unusual Observations
Obs      X          Y         Fit      SE Fit    Residual    St Resid
  1    135     145.00      120.42        4.87       24.58       2.11R
```

R denotes an observation with a large standardized residual

Chapter 15

2. a. The estimated regression equation is
$\hat{y} = 45.06 + 1.94x_1$
An estimate of y when $x_1 = 45$ is
$\hat{y} = 45.06 + 1.94(45) = 132.36$
b. The estimated regression equation is
$\hat{y} = 85.22 + 4.32x_2$
An estimate of y when $x_2 = 15$ is
$\hat{y} = 85.22 + 4.32(15) = 150.02$
c. The estimated regression equation is
$\hat{y} = -18.37 + 2.01x_1 + 4.74x_2$
An estimate of y when $x_1 = 45$ and $x_2 = 15$ is
$\hat{y} = -18.37 + 2.01(45) + 4.74(15) = 143.18$

4. a. $255,000

5. a. The Minitab output is shown in Figure D15.5a
b. The Minitab output is shown in Figure D15.5b
c. It is 1.60 in part (a) and 2.29 in part (b); in part (a) the coefficient is an estimate of the change in revenue due to a one-unit change in television advertising expenditures; in part (b) it represents an estimate of the change in revenue due to a one-unit change in television advertising expenditures when the amount of newspaper advertising is held constant
d. Revenue = 83.2 + 2.29(3.5) + 1.30(1.8) = 93.56 or $93,560

FIGURE D15.5a

```
The regression equation is
Revenue = 88.6 + 1.60 TVAdv

Predictor        Coef      SE Coef         T          p
Constant       88.638        1.582     56.02      0.000
TVAdv          1.6039       0.4778      3.36      0.015

S = 1.215      R-sq = 65.3%      R-sq(adj) = 59.5%

Analysis of Variance

SOURCE              DF          SS         MS         F          p
Regression           1      16.640     16.640     11.27      0.015
Residual Error       6       8.860      1.477
Total                7      25.500
```

FIGURE D15.5b

```
The regression equation is
Revenue = 83.2 + 2.29 TVAdv + 1.30 NewsAdv

Predictor        Coef      SE Coef        T          p
Constant       83.230        1.574      52.88      0.000
TVAdv           2.2902       0.3041       7.53      0.001
NewsAdv         1.3010       0.3207       4.06      0.010


S = 0.6426        R-sq = 91.9%      R-sq(adj) = 88.7%

Analysis of Variance

SOURCE              DF        SS         MS        F         p
Regression           2     23.435     11.718     28.38     0.002
Residual Error       5      2.065      0.413
Total                7     25.500
```

6. a. Win% = −58.8 + 16.4 Yds/Att
   b. Win% = 97.5 − 1600 Int/Att
   c. Win% = −5.8 + 12.9 Yds/Att − 1084 Int/Att
   d. 35%

8. a. Overall = 69.3 + .235 Shore Excursions
   b. Overall = 45.2 + .253 Shore Excursions
        + .248 Food/Dining
   c. 87.76 or approximately 88.

10. a. R/IP = .676 − .284 SO/IP
   b. R/IP = .308 + 1.35 HR/IP
   c. R/IP = .537 − .248 SO/IP + 1.03 HR/IP
   d. .48
   e. Suggestion does not make sense

12. a. $R^2 = \dfrac{\text{SSR}}{\text{SST}} = \dfrac{14{,}052.2}{15{,}182.9} = .926$

   b. $R_a^2 = 1 - (1 - R^2)\dfrac{n-1}{n-p-1}$

   $= 1 - (1 - .926)\dfrac{10-1}{10-2-1} = .905$

   c. Yes; after adjusting for the number of independent variables in the model, we see that 90.5% of the variability in y has been accounted for

14. a. .75
   b. .68

15. a. $R^2 = \dfrac{\text{SSR}}{\text{SST}} = \dfrac{23.435}{25.5} = .919$

   $R_a^2 = 1 - (1 - R^2)\dfrac{n-1}{n-p-1}$

   $= 1 - (1 - .919)\dfrac{8-1}{8-2-1} = .887$

   b. Multiple regression analysis is preferred because both R^2 and R_a^2 show an increased percentage of the variability of y explained when both independent variables are used

16. a. No, $R^2 = .577$
   b. Better fit with multiple regression

18. a. $R^2 = .563$, $R_a^2 = .512$
   b. The fit is not very good

19. a. $\text{MSR} = \dfrac{\text{SSR}}{p} = \dfrac{6216.375}{2} = 3108.188$

   $\text{MSE} = \dfrac{\text{SSE}}{n-p-1} = \dfrac{507.75}{10-2-1} = 72.536$

   b. $F = \dfrac{\text{MSR}}{\text{MSE}} = \dfrac{3108.188}{72.536} = 42.85$

   From the F table (2 numerator degrees of freedom and 7 denominator), p-value is less than .01

   Using Excel or Minitab the p-value corresponding to $F = 42.85$ is .0001

   Because p-value $\le \alpha$, the overall model is significant

   c. $t = \dfrac{b_1}{s_{b_1}} = \dfrac{.5906}{.0813} = 7.26$

   p-value = .0002

   Because p-value $\le \alpha$, β_1 is significant

   d. $t = \dfrac{b_2}{s_{b_2}} = \dfrac{.4980}{.0567} = 8.78$

   p-value = .0001

   Because p-value $\le \alpha$, β_2 is significant

20. a. Significant; p-value = .000
   b. Significant; p-value = .000
   c. Significant; p-value = .002

22. a. SSE $= 4000$, $s^2 = 571.43$,
MSR $= 6000$
b. Significant; p-value $= .008$

23. a. $F = 28.38$
p-value $= .002$
Because p-value $\leq \alpha$, there is a significant relationship
b. $t = 7.53$
p-value $= .001$
Because p-value $\leq \alpha$, β_1 is significant and x_1 should not be dropped from the model
c. $t = 4.06$
p-value $= .010$
Because p-value $\leq \alpha$, β_2 is significant and x_2 should not be dropped from the model

24. a. $\hat{y} = 60.5 + 0.3186$ OffPassYds/G $- 0.2413$ DefYds/G
b. Significant;, p-value $= .000$
c. OffPassYds/G is significant; p-value $= .000$
DefYds/G is significant; p-value $= .011$

26. a. Significant; p-value $= .001$
b. All significant; p-values are all $< \alpha = .05$

28. a. Using Minitab, the 95% confidence interval is 132.16 to 154.16
b. Using Minitab, the 95% prediction interval is 111.13 at 175.18

29. a. See Minitab output in Figure D15.5b.
$\hat{y} = 83.23 + 2.29(3.5) + 1.30(1.8) = 93.555$ or $\$93,555$
b. Minitab results: 92.840 to 94.335, or $\$92,840$ to $\$94,335$
c. Minitab results: 91.774 to 95.401, or $\$91,774$ to $\$95,401$

30. a. $\hat{y} = 60.5 + 0.3186(223) - 0.2413(300) = 59.1578$
b. Partial Minitab output follows

```
Regression Equation
Win% = 60.5 + 0.3186 OffPassYds/G - 0.2413 DefYds/G


Variable      Setting
OffPassYds/G     225
DefYds/G         300


   Fit    SE Fit       95% CI             95% PI
59.8270  4.88676  (49.8325, 69.8216)  (26.9589, 92.6952)
```

The 95% prediction interval is 26.9589 to 92.6952.

32. a. $E(y) = \beta_0 + \beta_1 x_1 + \beta_2 x_2$

where $x_2 = \begin{cases} 0 \text{ if level 1} \\ 1 \text{ if level 2} \end{cases}$

b. $E(y) = \beta_0 + \beta_1 x_1 + \beta_2(0) = \beta_0 + \beta_1 x_1$
c. $E(y) = \beta_0 + \beta_1 x_1 + \beta_2(1) = \beta_0 + \beta_1 x_1 + \beta_2$
d. $\beta_2 = E(y \mid \text{level 2}) - E(y \mid \text{level 1})$
β_1 is the change in $E(y)$ for a 1-unit change in x_1 holding x_2 constant

34. a. $\$15,300$
b. $\hat{y} = 10.1 - 4.2(2) + 6.8(8) + 15.3(0) = 56.1$
Sales prediction: $\$56,100$
c. $\hat{y} = 10.1 - 4.2(1) + 6.8(3) + 15.3(1) = 41.6$
Sales prediction: $\$41,600$

36. a. $\hat{y} = 1.86 + 0.291$ Months $+ 1.10$ Type $- 0.609$ Person
b. Significant; p-value $= .002$
c. Person is not significant; p-value $= .167$

38. a. $\hat{y} = -91.8 + 1.08$ Age $+ .252$ Pressure $+ 8.74$ Smoker
b. Significant; p-value $= .01$
c. 95% prediction interval is 21.35 to 47.18 or a probability of .2135 to .4718; quit smoking and begin some type of treatment to reduce his blood pressure

39. a. The Minitab output is shown in Figure D15.39
b. Minitab provides the following values:

x_i	y_i	$\hat{y}_i$	Standardized Residual
1	3	2.8	.16
2	7	5.4	.94
3	5	8.0	-1.65
4	11	10.6	.24
5	14	13.2	.62

FIGURE D15.39

```
The regression equation is
Y = 0.20 + 2.60 X

Predictor       Coef    SE Coef        T          p
Constant       0.200     2.132      0.09      0.931
X             2.6000     0.6429     4.04      0.027

S = 2.033     R-sq = 84.5%      R-sq(adj) = 79.3%

Analysis of Variance
SOURCE              DF        SS         MS        F         p
Regression           1    67.600     67.600    16.35     0.027
Residual Error       3    12.400      4.133
Total                4    80.000
```

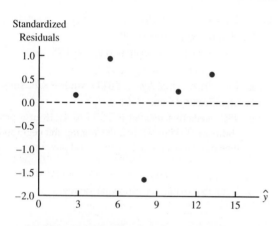

The point (3, 5) does not appear to follow the trend of the remaining data; however, the value of the standardized residual for this point, -1.65, is not large enough for us to conclude that (3, 5) is an outlier

c. Minitab provides the following values:

x_i	y_i	Studentized Deleted Residual
1	3	.13
2	7	.91
3	5	−4.42
4	11	.19
5	14	.54

$t_{.025} = 4.303$ ($n - p - 2 = 5 - 1 - 2 = 2$ degrees of freedom)

Because the studentized deleted residual for (3, 5) is $-4.42 < -4.303$, we conclude that the 3rd observation is an outlier

40. a. $\hat{y} = -53.3 + 3.11x$

   b. $-1.94, -.12, 1.79, .40, -1.90$; no

   c. .38, .28, .22, .20, .92; no

   d. .60, .00, .26, .03, 11.09; yes, the fifth observation

41. a. The Minitab output appears in Figure D15.5b; the estimated regression equation is

$$\text{Revenue} = 83.2 + 2.29\, \text{TVAdv} + 1.30\, \text{NewsAdv}$$

   b. Minitab provides the following values:

$\hat{y}_i$	Standardized Residual	$\hat{y}_i$	Standardized Residual
96.63	−1.62	94.39	1.10
90.41	−1.08	94.24	−.40
94.34	1.22	94.42	−1.12
92.21	−.37	93.35	1.08

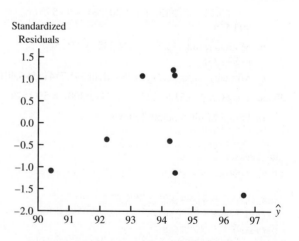

With relatively few observations, it is difficult to determine whether any of the assumptions regarding ϵ have been violated; for instance, an argument could be made that there does not appear to be any pattern in the plot; alternatively, an argument could be made that there is a curvilinear pattern in the plot

   c. The values of the standardized residuals are greater than -2 and less than $+2$; thus, using this test, there are no outliers

As a further check for outliers, we used Minitab to compute the following studentized deleted residuals:

Observation	Studentized Deleted Residual	Observation	Studentized Deleted Residual
1	−2.11	5	1.13
2	−1.10	6	−.36
3	1.31	7	−1.16
4	−.33	8	1.10

$t_{.025} = 2.776 \; (n - p - 2 = 8 - 2 - 2 = 4$ degrees of freedom)

Because none of the studentized deleted residuals are less than −2.776 or greater than 2.776, we conclude that there are no outliers in the data

d. Minitab provides the following values:

Observation	h_i	D_i
1	.63	1.52
2	.65	.70
3	.30	.22
4	.23	.01
5	.26	.14
6	.14	.01
7	.66	.81
8	.13	.06

The critical leverage value is

$$\frac{3(p + 1)}{n} = \frac{3(2 + 1)}{8} = 1.125$$

Because none of the values exceed 1.125, we conclude that there are no influential observations; however, using Cook's distance measure, we see that $D_1 > 1$ (rule of thumb critical value); thus, we conclude that the first observation is influential

Final conclusion: observation 1 is an influential observation

42. b. Unusual trend
c. No outliers
d. Observation 2 is an influential observation

44. a. $E(y) = \dfrac{e^{\beta_0 + \beta_1 x}}{1 + e^{\beta_0 + \beta_1 x}}$

b. Estimate of the probability that a customer who does not have a Simmons credit card will make a purchase
c. $\hat{g}(x) = -0.9445 + 1.0245x$
d. .28 for customers who do not have a Simmons credit card
.52 for customers who have a Simmons credit card
e. Estimated odds ratio = 2.79

46. a. $E(y) = \dfrac{e^{\beta_0 + \beta_1 x}}{1 + e^{\beta_0 + \beta_1 x}}$

b. $E(y) = \dfrac{e^{-2.6355 + 0.22018x}}{1 + e^{-2.6355 + 0.22018x}}$

c. Significant; p-value = .0002
d. .39

e. $1200
f. Estimated odds ratio = 1.25

48. a. $E(y) = \dfrac{e^{\beta_0 + \beta_1 x_1 + \beta_2 x_2}}{1 + e^{\beta_0 + \beta_1 x_1 + \beta_2 x_2}}$

b. $\hat{g}(x) = -39.4982 + 3.37449$ Wet + 1.81628 Noise
c. .88
d. Probability is .04

50. b. 155.14

52. a. $\hat{y} = -1.41 + .0235x_1 + .00486x_2$
b. Significant; p-value = .0001
c. Both significant
d. $R^2 = .937$; $R_a^2 = 9.19$; good fit

54. a. Buy Again = −7.522 + 1.8151 Steering
b. Yes
c. Buy Again = −5.388 + .6899 Steering + .9113 Treadwear
d. Significant; p-value = .001

56. a. $\hat{y} = 4.9090 + 10.4658$ FundDE + 21.6823 FundIE
b. $R^2 = .6144$; reasonably good fit
c. $\hat{y} = 1.1899 + 6.8969$ FundDE + 17.6800 FundIE
$+ 0.0265$ Net Asset Value ($)
$+ 6.4564$ Expense Ratio (%)
Net Asset Value ($) is not significant and can be deleted
d. $\hat{y} = -4.6074 + 8.1713$ FundDE + 19.5194 FundIE
$+ 5.5197$ Expense Ratio (%) + 5.9237 3StarRank
$+ 8.2367$ 4StarRank + 6.6241 5StarRank
e. 15.28%

Chapter 16

1. a. The Minitab output is shown in Figure D16.1a
b. Because the p-value corresponding to $F = 6.85$ is $.059 > \alpha = .05$, the relationship is not significant
c.

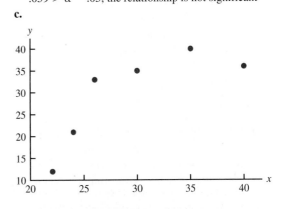

The scatter diagram suggests that a curvilinear relationship may be appropriate
d. The Minitab output is shown in Figure D16.1d
e. Because the p-value corresponding to $F = 25.68$ is $.013 < \alpha = .05$, the relationship is significant
f. $\hat{y} = -168.88 + 12.187(25) - .17704(25)^2 = 25.145$

FIGURE D16.1a

```
The regression equation is
Y = - 6.8 + 1.23 X

Predictor        Coef     SE Coef        T          p
Constant        -6.77       14.17     -0.48      0.658
X              1.2296      0.4697      2.62      0.059

S = 7.269     R-sq = 63.1%      R-sq(adj) = 53.9%

Analysis of Variance

SOURCE             DF        SS          MS       F         p
Regression          1    362.13      362.13    6.85     0.059
Residual Error      4    211.37       52.84
Total               5    573.50
```

FIGURE D16.1d

```
The regression equation is
Y = - 169 + 12.2 X - 0.177 XSQ

Predictor        Coef     SE Coef        T          p
Constant      -168.88       39.79     -4.74      0.024
X              12.187        2.663      4.58      0.020
XSQ          -0.17704      0.04290     -4.13      0.026

S = 3.248     R-sq = 94.5%      R-sq(adj) = 90.8%

Analysis of Variance

SOURCE             DF        SS          MS       F         p
Regression          2    541.85      270.92    25.68    0.013
Residual Error      3     31.65       10.55
Total               5    573.50
```

2. a. $\hat{y} = 9.32 + .424x$; p-value $= .117$ indicates a weak relationship between x and y
   b. $\hat{y} = -8.10 + 2.41x - .0480x^2$
   $R_a^2 = .932$; a good fit
   c. 20.965

4. a. $\hat{y} = 943 + 8.71x$
   b. Significant; p-value $= .005 < \alpha = .01$

5. a. The Minitab output is shown in Figure D16.5a
   b. Because the p-value corresponding to $F = 73.15$ is $.003 < \alpha = .01$, the relationship is significant; we would reject $H_0: \beta_1 = \beta_2 = 0$
   c. See Figure D16.5c

6. b. No, the relationship appears to be curvilinear
   c. Several possible models; e.g.,
   $\hat{y} = 2.90 - .185x + .00351x^2$

8. a. It appears that a simple linear regression model is not appropriate

b. Price $= 33829 - 4571$ Rating $+ 154$ RatingSq
c. logPrice $= -10.2 + 10.4$ logRating
d. Part (c); higher percentage of variability is explained

10. a. Significant; p-value $= .000$
   b. Significant; p-value $= .000$

11. a. SSE $= 1805 - 1760 = 45$

$$F = \frac{MSR}{MSE} = \left(\frac{1760/4}{45/25}\right) = 244.44$$

Because p-value $= .000$, the relationship is significant

   b. SSE$(x_1, x_2, x_3, x_4) = 45$
   c. SSE$(x_2, x_3) = 1805 - 1705 = 100$

   d. $F = \dfrac{(100 - 45)/2}{1.8} = 15.28$

Because p-value $= .000$, x_1 and x_2 are significant

FIGURE D16.5a

```
The regression equation is
Y = 433 + 37.4 X -0.383 XSQ

Predictor        Coef     SE Coef         T         p
Constant        432.6       141.2      3.06     0.055
X              37.429       7.807      4.79     0.017
XSQ           -0.3829      0.1036     -3.70     0.034


S = 15.83     R-sq = 98.0%     R-sq(adj) = 96.7%

Analysis of Variance

SOURCE             DF         SS        MS         F        p
Regression          2      36643     18322     73.15    0.003
Residual Error      3        751       250
Total               5      37395
```

FIGURE D16.5c

```
   Fit   Stdev.Fit               95% C.I.                   95% P.I.
1302.01   9.93        (1270.41, 1333.61)         (1242.55, 1361.47)
```

12. a. The Minitab output is shown in Figure D16.12a
   b. The Minitab output is shown in Figure D16.12b
   c.

$$F = \frac{\dfrac{\text{SSE(reduced)} - \text{SSE(full)}}{\text{number of extra terms}}}{\text{MSE(full)}} = \frac{\dfrac{166.95 - 15.521}{2}}{.119} = 634.19$$

The p-value associated with $F = 634.19$ (2 degrees of freedom numerator and 130 denominator) is 0.00. With a p-value $< \alpha = .05$, the addition of the two independent variables is statistically significant.

FIGURE D16.12a

```
Analysis of Variance
Source           DF   Adj SS    Adj MS   F-Value   P-Value
Regression         1    78.25   78.2452     61.86     0.000
  Putting Ave.     1    78.25   78.2452     61.86     0.000
Error            132   166.95    1.2648
  Lack-of-Fit     98   137.21    1.4001      1.60     0.060
  Pure Error      34    29.74    0.8747
Total            133   245.20


      S   R-sq  R-sq(adj)  R-sq(pred)
1.12463  31.91%    31.40%      29.66%


Term            Coef  SE Coef  T-Value  P-Value   VIF
Constant       47.95     3.12    15.36    0.000
Putting Ave.   0.806    0.102     7.87    0.000  1.00

Scoring Ave. = 47.95 + 0.806 Putting Ave.
```

FIGURE D16.12b

```
Analysis of Variance
Source              DF    Adj SS    Adj MS   F-Value   P-Value
Regression           3   229.677    76.559    641.25    0.000
  Putting Ave.       1   122.801   122.801   1028.58    0.000
  Greens in Reg.     1   149.336   149.336   1250.83    0.000
  Drive Accuracy     1     0.000     0.000      0.00    0.964
Error              130    15.521     0.119
Total              133   245.197


        S    R-sq   R-sq(adj)   R-sq(pred)
 0.345528   93.67%    93.52%       93.08%


Term                 Coef   SE Coef   T-Value   P-Value    VIF
Constant            57.16      1.06     53.95     0.000
Putting Ave.       1.0319    0.0322     32.07     0.000    1.04
Greens in Reg.    -23.102     0.653    -35.37     0.000    1.05
Drive Accuracy     -0.022     0.481     -0.05     0.964    1.02


Regression Equation
Scoring Ave. = 57.16 + 1.0319 Putting Ave. - 23.102
Greens in Reg. - 0.022 Drive Accuracy
```

14. a. $\hat{y} = -111 + 1.32$ Age $+ .296$ Pressure

b. $\hat{y} = -123 + 1.51$ Age $+ .448$ Pressure $+ 8.87$ Smoker $- .00276$ AgePress

c. Significant; p-value $= .000$

16. a. Weeks $= -8.9 + 1.51$ Age

b. Weeks $= -.07 + 1.73$ Age $- 2.7$ Manager $- 15.1$ Head $- 17.4$ Sales

c. Same as part (b)

d. Same as part (b)

e. Weeks $= 13.1 + 1.64$ Age $- 9.76$ Married $- 19.4$ Head $- 29.0$ Manager $- 19.0$ Sales

18. a. RPG $= -4.05 + 27.6$ OBP

b. A variety of models will provide a good fit; the five-variable model identified using Minitab's Stepwise Regression procedure with Alpha-to-Enter $= .10$ and Alpha-to-Remove $= .10$ follows:

RPG $= -.0909 + 32.2$ OBP $+ .109$ HR $- 21.5$ AVG $+ .244$ 3B $- .0223$ BB

20.

x_1	x_2	x_3	Treatment
0	0	0	A
1	0	0	B
0	1	0	C
0	0	1	D

$E(y) = \beta_0 + \beta_1 x_1 + \beta_2 x_2 + \beta_3 x_3$

22. Factor A: $x_1 = 0$ if level 1 and 1 if level 2

Factor B:

x_2	x_3	Level
0	0	1
1	0	2
0	1	3

$E(y) = \beta_0 + \beta_1 x_1 + \beta_2 x_2 + \beta_3 x_1 x_2 + \beta_4 x_1 x_3$

23. a. The dummy variables are defined as follows:

D1	D2	Mfg.
0	0	1
1	0	2
0	1	3

$E(y) = \beta_0 + \beta_1 D1 + \beta_2 D2$

```
The regression equation is
TIME = 23.0 + 5.00 D1 - 2.00 D2

Predictor           Coef    SE Coef         T        p
Constant          23.000      1.106     20.80    0.000
D1                 5.000      1.563      3.20    0.011
D2                -2.000      1.563     -1.28    0.233


S = 2.211           R-Sq = 70.3%    R-Sq(adj) = 63.7%


Analysis of Variance

SOURCE              DF         SS        MS        F        p
Regression           2    104.000    52.000     1064    0.004
Residual Error       9     44.000     4.889
Total               11    148.000
```

b. The Minitab output is shown above:

c. H_0: $\beta_1 = \beta_2 = 0$

d. The *p*-value of .004 is less than $\alpha = .05$; therefore, we can reject H_0 and conclude that the mean time to mix a batch of material is not the same for each manufacturer

24. a. Not significant at the .05 level of significance; *p*-value = .093

b. 139

26. Overall significant; *p*-value = .029

Individually, none of the variables are significant at the .05 level of significance; a larger sample size would be helpful

28. $d = 1.60$; test is inconclusive

30. a.

There appears to be a curvilinear relationship between weight and price

b. A portion of the Minitab output follows:

```
The regression equation is
Price = 11376 - 728 Weight + 12.0 WeightSq

Predictor     Coef    SE Coef        T        p
Constant     11376       2565     4.43    0.000
Weight      -728.3      193.7    -3.76    0.002
WeightSq    11.974      3.539     3.38    0.004


S = 242.804    R-Sq = 77.0%     R-Sq(adj) = 74.1%


Analysis of Variance

SOURCE              DF         SS         MS        F        p
Regression           2    3161747    1580874    26.82    0.000
Residual Error      16     943263      58954
Total               18    4105011
```

The results obtained support the conclusion that there is a curvilinear relationship between weight and price

c. A portion of the Minitab output follows:

```
The regression equation is
Price = 1284 - 572 Type_Fitness - 907 Type_Comfort

Predictor          Coef    SE Coef       T       p
Constant        1283.75      95.22   13.48   0.000
Type_Fitness     -571.8      153.5   -3.72   0.002
Type_Comfort     -907.1      145.5   -6.24   0.000


S = 269.328    R-Sq = 71.7%    R-Sq(adj) = 68.2%

Analysis of Variance

SOURCE            DF         SS        MS       F       p
Regression         2    2944410   1472205   20.30   0.000
Residual Error    16    1160601     72538
Total             18    4105011
```

Type of bike appears to be a significant factor in predicting price, but the estimated regression equation developed in part (b) appears to provide a slightly better fit

d. A portion of the Minitab output follows; in this output WxF denotes the interaction between the weight of the bike and the dummy variable Type_Fitness and WxC denotes the interaction between the weight of the bike and the dummy variable Type_Comfort

```
The regression equation is
Price = 5924 - 215 Weight - 6343 Type_Fitness - 7232
        Type_Comfort + 261 WxF + 266 WxC

Predictor          Coef    SE Coef       T       p
Constant          5924       1547    3.83   0.002
Weight         -214.56      71.42   -3.00   0.010
Type_Fitness     -6343       2596   -2.44   0.030
Type_Comfort     -7232       2518   -2.87   0.013
WxF              261.3      111.8    2.34   0.036
WxC             266.41      93.98    2.83   0.014


S = 224.438    R-Sq = 84.0%    R-Sq(adj) = 77.9%

Analysis of Variance

SOURCE            DF         SS        MS       F       p
Regression         5    3450170    690034   13.70   0.000
Residual Error    13     654841     50372
Total             18    4105011
```

By taking into account the type of bike, the weight, and the interaction between these two factors, this estimated regression equation provides an excellent fit

32. a. Delay = 63.0 + 11.1 Industry; no significant positive autocorrelation

34. Significant differences between comfort levels for the three types of browsers; p-value = .034

Chapter 17

1. The following table shows the calculations for parts (a), (b), and (c):

Week	Time Series Value	Forecast	Forecast Error	Absolute Value of Forecast Error	Squared Forecast Error	Percentage Error	Absolute Value of Percentage Error
1	18						
2	13	18	−5	5	25	−38.46	38.46
3	16	13	3	3	9	18.75	18.75
4	11	16	−5	5	25	−45.45	45.45
5	17	11	6	6	36	35.29	35.29
6	14	17	−3	3	9	−21.43	21.43
			Totals	22	104	−51.30	159.38

a. $\text{MAE} = \dfrac{22}{5} = 4.4$

b. $\text{MSE} = \dfrac{104}{5} = 20.8$

c. $\text{MAPE} = \dfrac{159.38}{5} = 31.88$

d. Forecast for week 7 is 14

2. The following table shows the calculations for parts (a), (b), and (c):

Week	Time Series Value	Forecast	Forecast Error	Absolute Value of Forecast Error	Squared Forecast Error	Percentage Error	Absolute Value of Percentage Error
1	18						
2	13	18.00	−5.00	5.00	25.00	−38.46	38.46
3	16	15.50	0.50	0.50	0.25	3.13	3.13
4	11	15.67	−4.67	4.67	21.81	−42.45	42.45
5	17	14.50	2.50	2.50	6.25	14.71	14.71
6	14	15.00	−1.00	1.00	1.00	−7.14	7.14
			Totals	13.67	54.31	−70.21	105.86

a. $\text{MAE} = \dfrac{13.67}{5} = 2.73$

b. $\text{MSE} = \dfrac{54.31}{5} = 10.86$

c. $\text{MAPE} = \dfrac{105.89}{5} = 21.18$

d. Forecast for week 7 is

$\dfrac{18 + 13 + 16 + 11 + 17 + 14}{6} = 14.83$

4. a. $\text{MSE} = \dfrac{363}{6} = 60.5$

Forecast for month 8 is 15

b. $\text{MSE} = \dfrac{216.72}{6} = 36.12$

Forecast for month 8 is 18

c. The average of all the previous values is better because MSE is smaller

5. a. The data appear to follow a horizontal pattern

b. Three-week moving average

Week	Time Series Value	Forecast	Forecast Error	Squared Forecast Error
1	18			
2	13			
3	16			
4	11	15.67	−4.67	21.78
5	17	13.33	3.67	13.44
6	14	14.67	−0.67	0.44
			Total	35.67

$$MSE = \frac{35.67}{3} = 11.89$$

The forecast for week 7 $= \dfrac{(11 + 17 + 14)}{3} = 14$

c. Smoothing constant = .2

Week	Time Series Value	Forecast	Forecast Error	Squared Forecast Error
1	18			
2	13	18.00	−5.00	25.00
3	16	17.00	−1.00	1.00
4	11	16.80	−5.80	33.64
5	17	15.64	1.36	1.85
6	14	15.91	−1.91	3.66
			Total	65.15

$$MSE = \frac{65.15}{5} = 13.03$$

The forecast for week 7 is $.2(14) + (1 − .2)15.91 = 15.53$

d. The three-week moving average provides a better forecast since it has a smaller MSE

e. Smoothing constant = .4

Week	Time Series Value	Forecast	Forecast Error	Squared Forecast Error
1	18			
2	13	18.00	−5.00	25.00
3	16	16.00	0.00	0.00
4	11	16.00	−5.00	25.00
5	17	14.00	3.00	9.00
6	14	15.20	−1.20	1.44
			Total	60.44

$$MSE = \frac{60.44}{5} = 12.09$$

The exponential smoothing forecast using $\alpha = .4$ provides a better forecast than the exponential smoothing forecast using $\alpha = .2$ since it has a smaller MSE

6. a. The data appear to follow a horizontal pattern

b. $MSE = \dfrac{110}{4} = 27.5$

The forecast for week 8 is 19

c. $MSE = \dfrac{252.87}{6} = 42.15$

The forecast for week 7 is 19.12

d. The three-week moving average provides a better forecast since it has a smaller MSE

e. $MSE = 39.79$

The exponential smoothing forecast using $\alpha = .4$ provides a better forecast than the exponential smoothing forecast using $\alpha = .2$ since it has a smaller MSE

8. a.

Week	4	5	6	7	8	9	10	11	12
Forecast	19.33	21.33	19.83	17.83	18.33	18.33	20.33	20.33	17.83

b. $MSE = 11.49$

Prefer the unweighted moving average here; it has a smaller MSE

c. You could always find a weighted moving average at least as good as the unweighted one; actually the unweighted moving average is a special case of the weighted ones where the weights are equal

10. b. The more recent data receive the greater weight or importance in determining the forecast; the moving averages method weights the last n data values equally in determining the forecast

12. a. The data appear to follow a horizontal pattern

b. MSE(3-Month) = .12
MSE(4-Month) = .14
Use 3-Month moving averages

c. 9.63

13. a. The data appear to follow a horizontal pattern

b.

Month	Time-Series Value	3-Month Moving Average Forecast	(Error)²	$\alpha = .2$ Forecast	(Error)²
1	240				
2	350			240.00	12100.00
3	230			262.00	1024.00
4	260	273.33	177.69	255.60	19.36
5	280	280.00	0.00	256.48	553.19
6	320	256.67	4010.69	261.18	3459.79
7	220	286.67	4444.89	272.95	2803.70
8	310	273.33	1344.69	262.36	2269.57
9	240	283.33	1877.49	271.89	1016.97
10	310	256.67	2844.09	265.51	1979.36
11	240	286.67	2178.09	274.41	1184.05
12	230	263.33	1110.89	267.53	1408.50
		Totals	17,988.52		27,818.49

MSE (3-Month) = 17,988.52/9 = 1998.72
MSE ($\alpha = .2$) = 27,818.49/11 = 2528.95

Based on the preceding MSE values, the 3-Month moving averages appear better; however, exponential smoothing was penalized by including month 2, which was difficult for any method to forecast; using only the errors for months 4 to 12, the MSE for exponential smoothing is

$$MSE(\alpha = .2) = 14{,}694.49/9 = 1632.72$$

Thus, exponential smoothing was better considering months 4 to 12

c. Using exponential smoothing,

$$F_{13} = \alpha Y_{12} + (1 - \alpha)F_{12}$$
$$= .20(230) + .80(267.53) = 260$$

14. a. The data appear to follow a horizontal pattern

b. Values for months 2–12 are as follows:

| 105.00 | 114.00 | 115.80 | 112.56 | 105.79 | 110.05 |
| 120.54 | 126.38 | 118.46 | 106.92 | 104.85 | |

$$MSE = 510.29$$

c. Values for months 2–12 are as follows:

| 105.00 | 120.00 | 120.00 | 112.50 | 101.25 | 110.63 |
| 127.81 | 133.91 | 116.95 | 98.48 | 99.24 | |

$$MSE = 540.55$$

Conclusion: A smoothing constant of .3 is better than a smoothing constant of .5 since the MSE is less for 0.3

16. a.

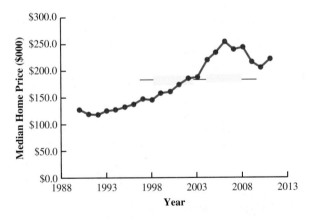

The time series plot exhibits a trend pattern; although the recession of 2008 led to a downturn in prices, the median price rose from 2010 to 2011

b. The methods discussed in this section are only applicable for a time series that has a horizontal pattern; because the time series plot exhibits a trend pattern, the methods discussed in this section are not appropriate

c. In 2003 the median price was $189,500, and in 2004 the median price was $222,300, so, it appears that the time series shifted to a new level in 2004; the time series plot using just the data for 2004 and later follows

This time series plot exhibits a horizontal pattern; therefore, the methods discussed in this section are appropriate

17. a. The time series plot shows a linear trend

b. $\bar{t} = \dfrac{\sum\limits_{t=1}^{n} t}{n} = \dfrac{15}{5} = 3$ $\bar{Y} = \dfrac{\sum\limits_{t=1}^{n} Y_t}{n} = \dfrac{55}{5} = 11$

$$\Sigma(t - \bar{t})(Y_t - \bar{Y}) = 21 \quad \Sigma(t - \bar{t})^2 = 10$$

$$b_1 = \frac{\sum\limits_{t=1}^{n}(t - \bar{t})(Y_t - \bar{Y})}{\sum\limits_{t=1}^{n}(t - \bar{t})^2} = \frac{21}{10} = 2.1$$

$$b_0 = \bar{Y} - b_1\bar{t} = 11 - (2.1)(3) = 4.7$$

$$T_t = 4.7 + 2.1t$$

c. $T_6 = 4.7 + 2.1(6) = 17.3$

18. a. The time series plot shows a downward linear trend.

b. $T_t = 11 - 1.0357(t)$

c. $T_8 = 11 - 1.0357(8) = 2.7$

20. a. The time series plot exhibits a curvilinear trend

b. $T_t = 107.857 - 28.9881t + 2.65476t^2$

c. 45.86

21. a.

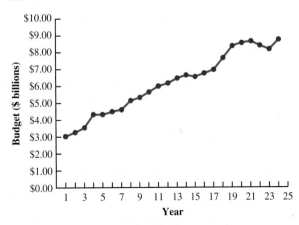

b. $\bar{t} = \dfrac{\sum\limits_{t=1}^{n} t}{n} = \dfrac{300}{24} = 12.5$ $\bar{Y} = \dfrac{\sum\limits_{t=1}^{n} Y_t}{n} = \dfrac{148.2}{24} = 6.175$

$\Sigma(t - \bar{t})(Y_t - \bar{Y}) = 290.86 \quad \Sigma(t - \bar{t})^2 = 1150$

$b_1 = \dfrac{\sum\limits_{t=1}^{n}(t - \bar{t})(Y_t - \bar{Y})}{\sum\limits_{t=1}^{n}(t - \bar{t})^2} = \dfrac{290.86}{1150} = .25292$

$b_0 = \bar{Y} - b_1\bar{x} = 6.175 - (.25292)(12.5) = 3.0135$

c. $\hat{y} = 3.0135 + .25292(25) = 9.34$

Forecast for 2012 is $9.34 billion

22. a.

The time series plot shows a downward linear trend

b. $\bar{t} = \dfrac{\sum\limits_{t=1}^{n} t}{n} = \dfrac{28}{7} = 4$ $\bar{Y} = \dfrac{\sum\limits_{t=1}^{n} Y_t}{n} = \dfrac{77}{7} = 11$

$\Sigma(t - \bar{t})(Y_t - \bar{Y}) = -19.6 \quad \Sigma(t - \bar{t})^2 = 28$

$b_1 = \dfrac{\sum\limits_{t=1}^{n}(t - \bar{t})(Y_t - \bar{Y})}{\sum\limits_{t=1}^{n}(t - \bar{t})^2} = \dfrac{-19.6}{28} = -.7$

$b_0 = \bar{Y} - b_1\bar{t} = 11 - (-.7)(4) = 13.8$

$T_t = 13.8 - .7t$

c. 2013 corresponds to time period $t = 8$, $T_8 = 13.8 - .7(8) = 8.2$

d. If SCF can continue to decrease the percentage of funds spent on administrative and fundraising by .7% per year, the forecast of expenses for 2018 is 4.70%

24. a. The time series plot shows a linear trend

b. $T_t = 7.5623 - .07541t$

c. 6.7328

d. Given the uncertainty in global market conditions, making a prediction for December using only time is not recommended

26. a. A linear trend is not appropriate

b. $T_t = 5.702 + 2.889t - 1618t^2$

c. 17.90

28. a. The time series plot shows a horizontal pattern, but there is a seasonal pattern in the data; for instance, in each year the lowest value occurs in quarter 2 and the highest value occurs in quarter 4

b. A portion of the Minitab regression output is shown;

```
The regression equation is
Value = 77.0 - 10.0 Qtr1 - 30.0
        Qtr2 - 20.0 Qtr3
```

c. The quarterly forecasts for next year are as follows:

Quarter 1 forecast $= 77.0 - 10.0(1) - 30.0(0)$
$- 20.0(0) = 67$

Quarter 2 forecast $= 77.0 - 10.0(0) - 30.0(1)$
$- 20.0(0) = 47$

Quarter 3 forecast $= 77.0 - 10.0(0) - 30.0(0)$
$- 20.0(1) = 57$

Quarter 4 forecast $= 77.0 - 10.0(0) - 30.0(0)$
$- 20.0(0) = 77$

30. a. There appears to be a seasonal pattern in the data and perhaps a moderate upward linear trend

b. A portion of the Minitab regression output follows:

```
The regression equation is
Value = 2492 - 712 Qtr1 - 1512
        Qtr2 + 327 Qtr3
```

c. The quarterly forecasts for next year are as follows:

Quarter 1 forecast is 1780
Quarter 2 forecast is 980
Quarter 3 forecast is 2819
Quarter 4 forecast is 2492

d. A portion of the Minitab regression output follows:

```
The regression equation is
Value = 2307 - 642 Qtr1 - 1465
        Qtr2 + 350 Qtr3 + 23.1 t
```

The quarterly forecasts for next year are as follows:

Quarter 1 forecast is 2058
Quarter 2 forecast is 1258
Quarter 3 forecast is 3096
Quarter 4 forecast is 2769

32. a. The time series plot shows both a linear trend and seasonal effects

b. A portion of the Minitab regression output follows:

```
The regression equation is
Revenue = 70.0 + 10.0 Qtr1 + 105
          Qtr2 + 245 Qtr3
```

Quarter 1 forecast is 80
Quarter 2 forecast is 175

Quarter 3 forecast is 315

Quarter 4 forecast is 70

c. A portion of the Minitab regression output follows

```
The regression equation is
Revenue = -70.1 + 45.0 Qtr1 + 128
          Qtr2 + 257 Qtr3 + 11.7 Period
```

Quarter 1 forecast = is 221

Quarter 2 forecast = is 315

Quarter 3 forecast = is 456

Quarter 4 forecast = is 211

34. a. The time series plot shows seasonal and linear trend effects

b. *Note:* Jan = 1 if January, 0 otherwise; Feb = 1 if February, 0 otherwise; and so on

A portion of the Minitab regression output follows:

```
The regression equation is
Expense = 175 - 18.4 Jan - 3.72 Feb +
          12.7 Mar + 45.7 Apr + 57.1
          May + 135 Jun + 181 Jul + 105
          Aug + 47.6 Sep + 50.6 Oct +
          35.3 Nov + 1.96 Period
```

c. *Note:* The next time period in the time series is Period = 37 (January of Year 4); the forecasts for January–December are 229; 246; 264; 299; 312; 392; 440; 366; 311; 316; 302; 269

35. a. The time series plot indicates a linear trend and a seasonal pattern

b.

Year	Quarter	Time Series Value	Four-Quarter Moving Average	Centered Moving Average
1	1	4		
	2	2		
			3.50	
	3	3		3.750
			4.00	
	4	5		4.125
			4.25	
2	1	6		4.500
			4.75	
	2	3		5.000
			5.25	
	3	5		5.375
			5.50	
	4	7		5.875
			6.25	
3	1	7		6.375
			6.50	
	2	6		6.625
			6.75	
	3	6		
	4	8		

c.

Year	Quarter	Time Series Value	Centered Moving Average	Seasonal-Irregular Component
1	1	4		
	2	2		
	3	3	3.750	0.800
	4	5	4.125	1.212
2	1	6	4.500	1.333
	2	3	5.000	0.600
	3	5	5.375	0.930
	4	7	5.875	1.191
3	1	7	6.375	1.098
	2	6	6.625	0.906
	3	6		
	4	8		

Quarter	Seasonal-Irregular Values		Seasonal Index	Adjusted Seasonal Index
1	1.333	1.098	1.216	1.205
2	0.600	0.906	0.752	0.746
3	0.800	0.930	0.865	0.857
4	1.212	1.191	1.201	1.191
		Total	4.036	

$$\text{Adjustment for seasonal index} = \frac{4.000}{4.036} = 0.991$$

36. a.

Year	Quarter	Deseasonalized Value
1	1	3.320
	2	2.681
	3	3.501
	4	4.198
2	1	4.979
	2	4.021
	3	5.834
	4	5.877
3	1	5.809
	2	8.043
	3	7.001
	4	6.717

b. Let Period = 1 denote the time series value in Year 1—Quarter 1; Period = 2 denote the time series value in Year 1—Quarter 2; and so on; a portion of the Minitab regression output treating Period as the independent variable and the Deseasonlized Values as the values of the dependent variable follows:

```
The regression equation is
Deseasonalized Value = 2.42 + 0.422
                       Period
```

c. The quarterly deseasonalized trend forecasts for Year 4 (Periods 13, 14, 15, and 16) are as follows:

Forecast for quarter 1 is 7.906
Forecast for quarter 2 is 8.328
Forecast for quarter 3 is 8.750
Forecast for quarter 4 is 9.172

d. Adjusting the quarterly deseasonalized trend forecasts provides the following quarterly estimates:

Forecast for quarter 1 is 9.527
Forecast for quarter 2 is 6.213
Forecast for quarter 3 is 7.499
Forecast for quarter 4 is 10.924

38. a. The time series plot shows a linear trend and seasonal effects

b. 0.71   0.78   0.83   0.97   1.02   1.30   1.50
   1.23   0.98   0.99   0.93   0.79

c.

Month	Deseasonalized Expense
1	239.44
2	230.77
3	246.99
4	237.11
5	235.29
6	242.31
7	240.00
8	235.77
9	244.90
10	242.42
11	247.31
12	246.84
13	253.52
14	262.82
15	259.04
16	252.58
17	259.80
18	253.85
19	266.67
20	272.36
21	265.31
22	272.73
23	274.19
24	278.48
25	274.65
26	269.23
27	277.11
28	288.66
29	284.31
30	300.00
31	280.00
32	268.29
33	295.92
34	297.98
35	301.08
36	316.46

d. Let Period = 1 denote the time series value in January —Year 1; Period = 2 denote the time series value in February—Year 2; and so on; a portion of the Minitab regression output treating Period as the independent variable and the Deseasonlized Values as the values of the dependent variable follows:

```
The regression equation is
Deseasonalized Expense = 228 + 1.96
                            Period
```

e.

Month	Monthly Forecast
January	213.37
February	235.93
March	252.69
April	297.21
May	314.53
June	403.42
July	486.42
August	386.52
September	309.88
October	314.98
November	297.71
December	254.44

40. a. The time series plot indicates a seasonal effect; power consumption is lowest in the time period 12–4 A.M., steadily increases to the highest value in the 12–4 P.M. time period, and then decreases again. There may also be some linear trend in the data

b.

Time Period	Adjusted Seasonal Index
12–4 A.M.	0.3256
4–8 A.M.	0.4476
8–12 noon	1.3622
12–4 P.M.	1.6959
4–8 P.M.	1.4578
8–12 midnight	0.7109

c. The following Minitab output shows the results of fitting a linear trend equation to the deseasonalized time series:

```
The regression equation is
Deseasonalized Power = 63108 + 1854 t
```

Deaseasonalized Power (t = 19) = 63,108 + 1854(19) = 98,334

Forecast for 12–4 P.M. = 1.6959(98,334) = 166,764.63 or approximately 166,765 kWh

Deaseasonalized Power (t = 20) = 63,108 + 1854(20)
= 100,188

Forecast for 4–8 P.M. = 1.4578(100,188) = 146,054.07
or approximately 146,054 kWh

Thus, the forecast of power consumption from noon to
8 P.M. is 166,765 + 146,054 = 312,819 kWh

42. a. The time series plot indicates a horizontal pattern
   b.
$$MSE(\alpha = .2) = 1.40$$
$$MSE(\alpha = .3) = 1.27$$
$$MSE(\alpha = .4) = 1.23$$

A smoothing constant of $\alpha = .4$ provides the best forecast because it has a smaller MSE

   c. 31.00

44. a. There appears to be an increasing trend in the data
   through April 2011 followed by periods of decreasing
   and increasing cost.
   b. Cost = 81.29 + .58t, t = 1 corresponds to January 2010,
   t = 2 corresponds to February 2010, and so on. The
   forecast for January 2014 (t = 49) is Cost = 81.29 +
   .58(49) = $109.71
   c. Cost = 68.82 + 2.08t − .03t^2. The forecast for January
   2014 (t = 49) is Cost = 68.82 + 2.08(49) − .03(49)^2
   = $98.71.
   d. Linear trend equation: MSE = 69.6 Quadratic trend
   equation: MSE = 41.9

46. a. The forecast for July is 236.97
   Forecast for August, using forecast for July as the
   actual sales in July, is 236.97
   Exponential smoothing provides the same forecast for
   every period in the future; this is why it is not usually
   recommended for long-term forecasting
   b. Using Minitab's regression procedure we obtained the
   linear trend equation
$$T_t = 149.72 + 18.451t$$
   Forecast for July is 278.88
   Forecast for August is 297.33
   c. The proposed settlement is not fair since it does not
   account for the upward trend in sales; based upon trend
   projection, the settlement should be based on forecasted
   lost sales of $278,880 in July and $297,330 in August

48. a. The time series plot shows a linear trend
   b. $T_t = -5 + 15t$
   The slope of 15 indicates that the average increase in
   sales is 15 pianos per year
   c. 85, 100

50. a.

Quarter	Adjusted Seasonal Index
1	1.2717
2	0.6120
3	0.4978
4	1.6185

Note: Adjustment for seasonal index $= \dfrac{4}{3.8985} = 1.0260$

   b. The largest effect is in quarter 4; this seems reasonable
   since retail sales are generally higher during October,
   November, and December

52. a. Yes, a linear trend pattern appears to be present
   b. A portion of the Minitiab regression output follows:

```
The regression equation is
Number Sold = 22.9 + 15.5 Year
```

   c. Forecast in year 8 is or approximately 147 units

54. b. The centered moving average values smooth out the
   time series by removing seasonal effects and some of
   the random variability; the centered moving average
   time series shows the trend in the data
   c.

Quarter	Adjusted Seasonal Index
1	0.899
2	1.362
3	1.118
4	0.621

   d. Hudson Marine experiences the largest seasonal increase in quarter 2; since this quarter occurs prior to
   the peak summer boating season, this result seems reasonable, but the largest seasonal effect is the seasonal
   decrease in quarter 4; this is also reasonable because of
   decreased boating in the fall and winter

Chapter 18

1. $n = 27$ cases with a value different than 150
   Normal approximation $\mu = .5n = .5(27) = 13.5$
$$\sigma = \sqrt{.25\,n} = \sqrt{.25(27)} = 2.5981$$
   With the number of plus signs = 22 in the upper tail,
   use continuity correction factor as follows
$$P(x \geq 21.5) = P\left(z \geq \frac{21.5 - 13.5}{2.5981}\right) = P(z \geq 3.08)$$
   p-value = (1.0000 − .9990) = .0010
   p-value ≤ .01; reject H_0; conclude population median > 150

2. Dropping the no preference, the binomial probabilities
   for $n = 9$ and $p = .50$ are as follows

x	Probability	x	Probability
0	0.0020	5	0.2461
1	0.0176	6	0.1641
2	0.0703	7	0.0703
3	0.1641	8	0.0176
4	0.2461	9	0.0020

Number of plus signs = 7

$P(x \geq 7) = P(7) + P(8) + P(9)$

$\qquad = .0703 + .0176 + .0020$

$\qquad = .0899$

Two-tailed p-value = $2(.0899) = .1798$

p-value $> .05$, do not reject H_0; conclude no indication that a difference exists

4. a. H_0: Median ≥ 15

$\quad\ H_a$: Median < 15

b. $n = 9$; number of plus signs = 1

p-value = .0196

Reject H_0; bond mutual funds have lower median

6. $n = 18$; $z = 1.88$

p-value = .0301

Reject H_0; conclude median $> \$56.2$ thousand

8. a. $n = 15$

p-value = .1186

Do not reject H_0; no significant difference for the pace

b. 25%, 68.8%; recommend larger sample

10. $n = 600$; $z = 2.41$

p-value = .0160

Reject H_0; *Empire* is preferred

12. H_0: Median for Additive 1 − Median for Additive 2 = 0

$\quad\ H_a$: Median for Additive 1 − Median for Additive 2 ≠ 0

	Absolute		Signed Ranks	
Difference	Difference	Rank	Negative	Positive
2.07	2.07	9		9
1.79	1.79	7		7
−0.54	0.54	3	−3	
2.09	2.09	10		10
0.01	0.01	1		1
0.97	0.97	4		4
−1.04	1.04	5	−5	
3.57	3.57	12		12
1.84	1.84	8		8
3.08	3.08	11		11
0.43	0.43	2		2
1.32	1.32	6		6
		Sum of Positive Signed Ranks	$T^+ = 70$	

$$\mu_{T^+} = \frac{n(n+1)}{4} = \frac{12(13)}{4} = 39$$

$$\sigma_{T^+} = \sqrt{\frac{n(n+1)(2n+1)}{24}} = \sqrt{\frac{12(13)(25)}{24}} = 12.7475$$

$$P(T^+ \geq 70) = P\left(z \geq \frac{69.5 - 39}{12.7475}\right) = P(z \geq 2.39)$$

p-value = $2(1.0000 - .9916) = .0168$

p-value $\leq .05$, reject H_0; conclude significant difference between additives

13. H_0: Median time without Relaxant 1 − Median time with Relaxant ≤ 0

$\quad\ H_a$: Median time without Relaxant 1 − Median time with Relaxant > 0

	Absolute		Signed Ranks	
Difference	Difference	Rank	Negative	Positive
5	5	9		9
2	2	3		3
10	10	10		10
−3	3	6.5	−6.5	
1	1	1		1
2	2	3		3
−2	2	3	−3	
3	3	6.5		6.5
3	3	6.5		6.5
3	3	6.5		6.5
		Sum of Positive Signed Ranks	$T^+ = 45.5$	

$$\mu_{T^+} = \frac{n(n+1)}{4} = \frac{10(11)}{4} = 27.5$$

$$\sigma_{T^+} = \sqrt{\frac{n(n+1)(2n+1)}{24}} = \sqrt{\frac{10(11)(12)}{24}} = 9.8107$$

$$P(T^+ \geq 45.5) = P\left(z \geq \frac{45 - 27.5}{12.7475}\right) = P(z \geq 1.78)$$

p-value = $(1.0000 - .9925) = .0375$

p-value $\leq .05$; reject H_0; conclude without the relaxant has a greater median time

14. $n = 11$; $T^+ = 61$; $z = 2.45$

p-value = .0142

Reject H_0; conclude significant difference; on-time % better in 2006

16. $n = 12$; $T^+ = 49.5$; $z = .78$

p-value = .4354

Do not reject H_0; conclude no difference between the median scores

18. H_0: The two populations of additives are identical

$\quad\ H_a$: The two populations of additives are not identical

Additive 1	Rank	Additive 2	Rank
17.3	2	18.7	8.5
18.4	6	17.8	4
19.1	10	21.3	15
16.7	1	21.0	14
18.2	5	22.1	16
18.6	7	18.7	8.5
17.5	3	19.8	11
		20.7	13
		20.2	12
	$W = 34$		

$$\mu_W = \frac{1}{2}n_1(n_1 + n_2 + 1) = \frac{1}{2}7(7 + 9 + 1) = 59.5$$

$$\sigma_W = \sqrt{\frac{1}{12}n_1 n_2(n_1 + n_2 + 1)} = \sqrt{\frac{1}{12}7(9)(7 + 9 + 1)}$$

$$= 9.4472$$

With $W = 34$ in lower tail, use the continuity correction

$$P(W \le 34) = P\left(z \le \frac{34.5 - 595}{9.4472}\right) = P(z \le -2.65)$$

p-value $= 2(.0040) = .0080$

p-value $< .05$; reject H_0; conclude additives are not identical

Additive 2 tends to provide higher miles per gallon

19. a. H_0: The two populations of salaries are identical

H_a: The two populations of salaries are not identical

Public Accountant	Rank	Financial Planner	Rank
50.2	5	49.0	2
58.8	19	49.2	3
56.3	16	53.1	10
58.2	18	55.9	15
54.2	13	51.9	8.5
55.0	14	53.6	11
50.9	6	49.7	4
59.5	20	53.9	12
57.0	17	51.8	7
51.9	8.5	48.9	1
	$W = 136.5$		

$$\mu_w = \frac{1}{2}n_1(n_1 + n_2 + 1) = \frac{1}{2}10(10 + 10 + 1) = 105$$

$$\sigma_w = \sqrt{\frac{1}{12}n_1 n_2(n_1 + n_2 + 1)} = \sqrt{\frac{1}{12}10(10)(10 + 10 + 1)}$$

$$= 13.2288$$

With $W = 136.5$ in upper tail, use the continuity correction

$$P(W \ge 136.5) = P\left(z \ge \frac{136 - 105}{13.2288}\right) = P(z \ge 2.34)$$

p-value $= 2(1.0000 - .9904) = .0192$

p-value $\le .05$; reject H_0; conclude populations are not identical

Public accountants tend to have higher salaries

b. Public Accountant $\dfrac{(55.0 + 56.3)}{2} = \$55.65$ thousand

Financial Planner $\dfrac{(51.8 + 51.9)}{2} = \$51.85$ thousand

20. a. $\$54,900, \$40,400$

b. $W = 69$; $z = 2.04$

p-value $= .0414$

Reject H_0; conclude a difference between salaries; men higher

22. $W = 157$; $z = 2.74$

p-value $= .0062$

Reject H_0; conclude a difference between ratios; Japan tends to be higher

24. $W = 116$; $z = -.22$

p-value $= .8258$

Do not reject H_0; conclude no evidence prices differ

26. H_0: All populations of product ratings are identical

H_a: Not all populations of product ratings are identical

	A	B	C
	4	11	7
	8	14	2
	10	15	1
	3	12	6
	9	13	5
Sum of Ranks	34	65	21

$$H = \left[\frac{12}{15(16)}\left(\frac{34^2}{5} + \frac{65^2}{5} + \frac{21^2}{5}\right)\right] - 3(16) = 10.22$$

χ^2 table with $df = 2$, $\chi^2 = 10.22$; the p-value is between .005 and .01

p-value $\le .01$; reject H_0; conclude the populations of ratings are not identical

28. H_0: All populations of calories burned are identical

H_a: Not all populations calories burned are identical

	Swimming	Tennis	Cycling
	8	9	5
	4	14	1
	11	13	3
	6	10	7
	12	15	2
Sum of Ranks	41	61	18

$$H = \left[\frac{12}{15(16)}\left(\frac{41^2}{5} + \frac{61^2}{5} + \frac{18^2}{5}\right)\right] - 3(16) = 9.26$$

χ^2 table with $df = 2$, $\chi^2 = 9.26$; the p-value is between .005 and .01

p-value $\le .05$ reject H_0; conclude that the populations of calories burned are not identical

30. $H = 8.03$ with $df = 3$

p-value is between .025 and .05

Reject H_0; conclude a difference between quality of courses

32. a. $\Sigma d_i^2 = 52$

$$r_s = 1 - \frac{6\Sigma d_i^2}{n(n^2 - 1)} = 1 - \frac{6(52)}{10(99)} = .685$$

b. $\sigma_{r_s} = \sqrt{\frac{1}{n - 1}} = \sqrt{\frac{1}{9}} = .3333$

$$z = \frac{r_s - 0}{\sigma_{r_s}} = \frac{.685}{.3333} = 2.05$$

p-value $= 2(1.0000 - .9798) = .0404$

p-value $\leq .05$, reject H_0; conclude significant positive rank correlation

34. $\Sigma d_i^2 = 250$

$$r_s = 1 - \frac{6\Sigma d_i^2}{n(n^2 - 1)} = 1 - \frac{6(250)}{11(120)} = -.136$$

$$\sigma_{r_s} = \sqrt{\frac{1}{n-1}} = \sqrt{\frac{1}{10}} = .3162$$

$$z = \frac{r_s - 0}{\sigma_{r_s}} = \frac{-.136}{.3162} = -.43$$

p-value $= 2(.3336) = .6672$

p-value $> .05$, do not reject H_0; we cannot conclude that there is a significant relationship

36. $r_s = -.709, z = -2.13$

p-value $= .0332$

Reject H_0; conclude a significant rank correlation

38. Number of plus signs $= 905, z = -3.15$

p-value less than .0020

Reject H_0; conclude a significant difference between the preferences

40. $n = 12; T^+ = 6; z = -2.55$

p-value $= .0108$

Reject H_0; conclude significant difference between prices

42. $W = 70; z = -2.93$

p-value $= .0034$

Reject H_0; conclude populations of weights are not identical

44. $H = 12.61$ with $df = 2$

p-value is less than .005

Reject H_0; conclude the populations of ratings are not identical

46. $r_s = .757, z = 2.83$

p-value $= .0046$

Reject H_0; conclude a significant positive rank correlation

Chapter 19

2. a. 5.42

b. UCL $= 6.09$, LCL $= 4.75$

4. *R* chart:

UCL $= \bar{R}D_4 = 1.6(1.864) = 2.98$

LCL $= \bar{R}D_3 = 1.6(.136) = .22$

$\bar{x}$ chart:

UCL $= \bar{\bar{x}} + A_2\bar{R} = 28.5 + .373(1.6) = 29.10$

LCL $= \bar{\bar{x}} - A_2\bar{R} = 28.5 - .373(1.6) = 27.90$

6. 20.01, .082

8. a. .0470

b. UCL $= .0989$, LCL $= -0.0049$ (use LCL $= 0$)

c. $\bar{p} = .08$; in control

d. UCL $= 14.826$, LCL $= -0.726$ (use LCL $= 0$)

Process is out of control if more than 14 defective

e. In control with 12 defective

f. *np* chart

10. $f(x) = \dfrac{n!}{x!(n-x)!} p^x(1-p)^{n-x}$

When $p = .02$, the probability of accepting the lot is

$$f(0) = \frac{25!}{0!(25-0)!}(.02)^0(1 - .02)^{25} = .6035$$

When $p = .06$, the probability of accepting the lot is

$$f(0) = \frac{25!}{0!(25-0)!}(.06)^0(1 - .06)^{25} = .2129$$

12. $p_0 = .02$; producer's risk $= .0599$

$p_0 = .06$; producer's risk $= .3396$

Producer's risk decreases as the acceptance number c is increased

14. $n = 20, c = 3$

16. a. 95.4

b. UCL $= 96.07$, LCL $= 94.73$

c. No

18.

	R Chart	$\bar{x}$ Chart
UCL	4.23	6.57
LCL	0	4.27

Estimate of standard deviation $= .86$

20.

	R Chart	$\bar{x}$ Chart
UCL	.1121	3.112
LCL	0	3.051

22. a. UCL $= .0817$, LCL $= -.0017$ (use LCL $= 0$)

24. a. .03

b. $\beta = .0802$

Chapter 20

1. a.

Item	Price Relative
A	$103 = (7.75/7.50)(100)$
B	$238 = (1500/630)(100)$

b. $I_{2011} = \dfrac{7.75 + 1500.00}{7.50 + 630.00}(100) = \dfrac{1507.75}{637.50}(100) = 237$

c. $I_{2011} = \dfrac{7.75(1500) + 1500.00(2)}{7.50(1500) + 630.00(2)}(100)$

$\qquad = \dfrac{14,625.00}{12,510.00}(100) = 117$

d. $I_{2011} = \dfrac{7.75(1800) + 1500.00(1)}{7.50(1800) + 630.00(1)}(100)$

$= \dfrac{15,450.00}{14,130.00}(100) = 109$

2. a. 32%

   b. \$8.14

3. a. Price relatives for A = (6.00/5.45)100 = 110

                                          B = (5.95/5.60)100 = 106

                                          C = (6.20/5.50)100 = 113

   b. $I_{2011} = \dfrac{6.00 + 5.95 + 6.20}{5.45 + 5.60 + 5.50}(100) = 110$

   c. $I_{2011} = \dfrac{6.00(150) + 5.95(200) + 6.20(120)}{5.45(150) + 5.60(200) + 5.50(120)}(100)$

         = 109

         9% increase over the two-year period

4. I_{2011} = 114

6.

Item	Price Relative	Base Period Price	Usage	Weight	Weighted Price Relative
A	150	22.00	20	440	66,000
B	90	5.00	50	250	22,500
C	120	14.00	40	560	67,200
			Totals	1250	155,700

$$I = \dfrac{155,700}{1250} = 125$$

7. a. Price relatives for A = (3.95/2.50)100 = 158

                                          B = (9.90/8.75)100 = 113

                                          C = (.95/.99)100 = 96

   b.

Item	Price Relative	Base Price	Quantity	Weight $P_{i0}Q_i$	Weighted Price Relative
A	158	2.50	25	62.5	9,875
B	113	8.75	15	131.3	14,837
C	96	.99	60	59.4	5,702
			Totals	253.2	30,414

$$I = \dfrac{30,414}{253.2} = 120$$

        Cost of raw materials is up 20% for the chemical

8. I = 105; portfolio is up 5%

10. a. Deflated 2007 wages: $\dfrac{\$30.04}{207.3}(100) = \$14.49$

        Deflated 2011 wages: $\dfrac{\$33.23}{224.9}(100) = \$14.78$

   b. $\dfrac{33.23}{30.04}(100) = 1.11$; the percentange increase in actual wages is 11%

   c. $\dfrac{14.78}{14.49}(100) = 1.02$; the percentage increase in real wages is 2%

12. a. 2009: $\dfrac{\$29.1}{216.0}(100) = \$13.47$

       2010: $\dfrac{\$33.3}{218.4}(100) = \$15.25$

       2011: $\dfrac{\$32.9}{226.9}(100) = \$14.50$

   b. 2009: $\dfrac{\$29.1}{173.4}(100) = \$16.78$

       2010: $\dfrac{\$33.3}{180.2}(100) = \$18.48$

       2011: $\dfrac{\$32.9}{192.5}(100) = \$17.09$

   c. PPI is more appropriate than CPI because these figures reflect prices paid by retailers (rather than by consumers)

14. $I = \dfrac{300(18.00) + 400(4.90) + 850(15.00)}{350(18.00) + 220(4.90) + 730(15.00)}(100)$

$= \dfrac{20,110}{18,328}(100) = 110$

15. $I = \dfrac{95(1200) + 75(1800) + 50(2000) + 70(1500)}{120(1200) + 86(1800) + 35(2000) + 60(1500)}(100)$

$= 99$

Quantities are down slightly

16. I = 83

18. a. 151, 197, 143, 178

   b. I = 170

20. I_{Jan} = 73.5, I_{Mar} = 70.1

22.

Item	Price Relatives $(P_{it}/P_{i0})100$	Base Price P_{i0}	Quantity Q_i	Weight $W_i = P_{i0}Q_i$	Weighted Price Relatives $(P_{it}/P_{i0})100\,W_i$
Handle	126.9	7.46	1	7.46	946.67
Blades	153.7	1.9	17	32.30	4964.51
			Totals	39.76	5911.18

$I_{2011} = (5911.18/39.76) = 148.7$

24. 2008   (84810/215.3)100 = \$39,392

      2009   (87210/214.5)100 = \$40,657

      2010   (87650/218.1)100 = \$40,188

      2011   (91060/224.9)100 = \$40,489

      (40489/39392) = 1.028

The median salary increased 2.8% over the period

26. I = 143; quantity is up 43%

Microsoft Excel 2013, part of the Microsoft Office 2013 system, is a spreadsheet program that can be used to organize and analyze data, perform complex calculations, and create a wide variety of graphical displays. We assume that readers are familiar with basic Excel operations such as selecting cells, entering formulas, copying, and so on. But we do not assume readers are familiar with Excel 2013 or the use of Excel for statistical analysis.

The purpose of this appendix is twofold. First, we provide an overview of Excel 2013 and discuss the basic operations needed to work with Excel 2013 workbooks and work sheets. Second, we provide an overview of the tools that are available for conducting statistical analysis with Excel. These include Excel functions and formulas which allow users to conduct their own analyses and add-ins that provide more comprehensive analysis tools.

Excel's Data Analysis add-in, included with the basic Excel system, is a valuable tool for conducting statistical analysis. In the last section of this appendix we provide instruction for installing the Data Analysis add-in. Other add-ins have been developed by outside suppliers to supplement the basic statistical capabilities provided by Excel. In the last section we also discuss StatTools, a commercially available add-in developed by Palisade Corporation.

Overview of Microsoft Excel 2013

A workbook is a file containing one or more worksheets.

When using Excel for statistical analysis, data is displayed in workbooks, each of which contains a series of worksheets that typically include the original data as well as any resulting analysis, including charts. Figure E.1 shows the layout of a blank workbook created each time Excel is opened. The workbook is named Book1, and contains one worksheet named Sheet1. Excel highlights the worksheet currently displayed (Sheet1) by setting the name on the worksheet tab in bold. Note that cell A1 is initially selected.

The wide bar located across the top of the workbook is referred to as the Ribbon. Tabs, located at the top of the Ribbon, provide quick access to groups of related commands. There are eight tabs shown on the workbook in Figure E.1: FILE; HOME; INSERT; PAGE LAYOUT; FORMULAS; DATA; REVIEW; and VIEW. Each tab contains a series of groups of related commands. Note that the HOME tab is selected when Excel is opened. Figure E.2 displays the groups available when the HOME tab is selected. Under the HOME tab there are seven groups: Clipboard; Font; Alignment; Number; Styles; Cells; and Editing. Commands are arranged within each group. For example, to change selected text to boldface, click the HOME tab and click the Bold B button in the Font group.

Figure E.3 illustrates the location of the Quick Access Toolbar and the Formula Bar. The Quick Access Toolbar allows you to quickly access workbook options. To add or remove features on the Quick Access Toolbar, click the Customize Quick Access Toolbar button ▾ at the end of the Quick Access Toolbar.

The Formula Bar (see Figure E.3) contains a Name box, the Insert Function button *fx*, and a Formula box. In Figure E.3, "A1" appears in the name box because cell A1 is selected. You can select any other cell in the worksheet by using the mouse to move the cursor to another cell and clicking or by typing the new cell location in the Name box. The Formula box is used to display the formula in the currently selected cell. For instance, if you enter $=A1+A2$ into cell A3, whenever you select cell A3 the formula $=A1+A2$ will be shown in the Formula box. This feature makes it very easy to see and edit a formula in

FIGURE E.1   BLANK WORKBOOK CREATED WHEN EXCEL IS OPENED

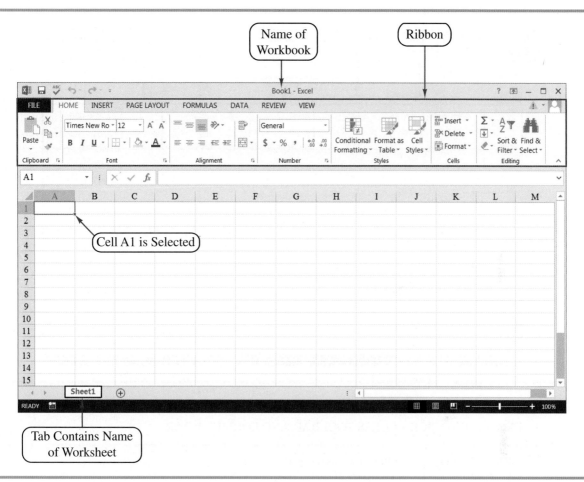

a particular cell. The Insert Function button allows you to quickly access all the functions available in Excel. Later we show how to find and use a particular function.

Basic Workbook Operations

Figure E.4 illustrates the worksheet options that can be performed after right-clicking on a worksheet tab. For instance, to change the name of the current worksheet from "Sheet1" to "Data," right-click the worksheet tab named "Sheet1" and select the Rename option. The current worksheet name (Sheet1) will be highlighted. Then, simply type the new name (Data) and press the Enter key to rename the worksheet.

Suppose that you wanted to create a copy of "Sheet1." After right-clicking the tab named "Sheet1," select the Move or Copy option. When the Move or Copy dialog box appears, select Create a Copy and click OK. The name of the copied worksheet will appear as "Sheet1 (2)." You can then rename it, if desired.

To add a new worksheet to the workbook, right-click any worksheet tab and select the Insert option; when the Insert dialog box appears, select Worksheet and click OK. An additional blank worksheet will appear in the workbook. You can also insert a new worksheet by clicking the New sheet button ⊞ that appears to the right of the last worksheet tab displayed. Worksheets can be deleted by right-clicking the worksheet tab and choosing

FIGURE E.2   PORTION OF THE HOME TAB

FIGURE E.3   EXCEL 2013 QUICK ACCESS TOOLBAR AND FORMULA BAR

FIGURE E.4   WORKSHEET OPTIONS OBTAINED AFTER RIGHT-CLICKING
ON A WORKSHEET TAB

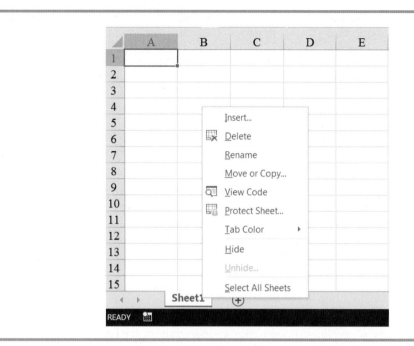

Delete. Worksheets can also be moved to other workbooks or a different position in the current workbook by using the Move or Copy option.

Creating, Saving, and Opening Files

Data can be entered into an Excel worksheet by manually entering the data into the worksheet or by opening another workbook that already contains the data. As an illustration of manually entering, saving, and opening a file we will use the example from Chapter 2 involving data for a sample of 50 soft drink purchases. The original data are shown in Table E.1.

Suppose we want to enter the data for the sample of 50 soft drink purchases into Sheet1 of the new workbook. First we enter the label "Brand Purchased" into cell A1; then we enter the data for the 50 soft drink purchases into cells A2:A51. As a reminder that this worksheet contains the data, we will change the name of the worksheet from "Sheet1" to "Data" using the procedure described previously. Figure E.5 shows the data worksheet that we just developed.

Before doing any analysis with these data, we recommend that you first save the file; this will prevent you from having to reenter the data in case something happens that causes Excel to close. To save the file as an Excel 2013 workbook using the filename SoftDrink we perform the following steps:

Step 1: Click the **FILE** tab
Step 2: Click **Save** in the list of options
Step 3: When the **Save As** window appears:
　　　　　　Select the location where you want to save the file
　　　　　　Type the filename **SoftDrink** in the **File name** box
　　　　　　Click **Save**

TABLE E.1   DATA FROM A SAMPLE OF 50 SOFT DRINK PURCHASES

Coca-Cola	Sprite	Pepsi
Diet Coke	Coca-Cola	Coca-Cola
Pepsi	Diet Coke	Coca-Cola
Diet Coke	Coca-Cola	Coca-Cola
Coca-Cola	Diet Coke	Pepsi
Coca-Cola	Coca-Cola	Dr. Pepper
Dr. Pepper	Sprite	Coca-Cola
Diet Coke	Pepsi	Diet Coke
Pepsi	Coca-Cola	Pepsi
Pepsi	Coca-Cola	Pepsi
Coca-Cola	Coca-Cola	Pepsi
Dr. Pepper	Pepsi	Pepsi
Sprite	Coca-Cola	Coca-Cola
Coca-Cola	Sprite	Dr. Pepper
Diet Coke	Dr. Pepper	Pepsi
Coca-Cola	Pepsi	Sprite
Coca-Cola	Diet Coke	

FIGURE E.5   WORKSHEET CONTAINING THE SOFT DRINK DATA

Note: Rows 11–49 are hidden.

Keyboard shortcut: To save the file, press CTRL+S.

Excel's Save command is designed to save the file as an Excel 2013 workbook. As you work with the file to do statistical analysis you should follow the practice of periodically saving the file so you will not lose any statistical analysis you may have performed. Simply click the File tab and select Save in the list of options.

Sometimes you may want to create a copy of an existing file. For instance, suppose you would like to save the soft drink data and any resulting statistical analysis in a new file named "SoftDrink Analysis." The following steps show how to create a copy of the SoftDrink workbook and analysis with the new filename, "SoftDrink Analysis."

Step 1: Click the **FILE** tab
Step 2: Click **Save As**
Step 3: When the Save As window appears:
  Select the location where you want to save the file
  Type the filename **SoftDrink Analysis** in the **File name** box
  Click **Save**

Once the workbook has been saved, you can continue to work with the data to perform whatever type of statistical analysis is appropriate. When you are finished working with the file simply click the FILE tab and then click close in the list of options. To access the SoftDrink Analysis file at another point in time you can open the file by performing the following steps:

Step 1: Click the **FILE** tab
Step 2: Click **Open**
Step 3: When the Open window appears:
  Select the location where you previously saved the file
  Enter the filename **SoftDrink Analysis** in the **File name** box
  Click **Open**

The procedures we showed for saving or opening a workbook begin by clicking the File tab to access the Save and Open commands. Once you have used Excel for a while you will probably find it more convenient to add these commands to the Quick Access Toolbar.

Using Excel Functions

Excel 2013 provides a wealth of functions for data management and statistical analysis. If we know what function is needed, and how to use it, we can simply enter the function into the appropriate worksheet cell. However, if we are not sure what functions are available to accomplish a task, or are not sure how to use a particular function, Excel can provide assistance. Many new functions for statistical analysis have been added with Excel 2013. To illustrate we will use the SoftDrink Analysis workbook created in the previous subsection.

Finding the Right Excel Function

To identify the functions available in Excel, select the cell where you want to insert the function; we have selected cell D2. Click the **FORMULAS** tab on the Ribbon and then click the **Insert Function** button in the **Function Library** group. Alternatively, click the *ƒx* button on the formula bar. Either approach provides the **Insert Function** dialog box shown in Figure E.6.

The **Search for a function** box at the top of the Insert Function dialog box enables us to type a brief description of what we want to do. After doing so and clicking **Go**, Excel will search for and display, in the **Select a function** box, the functions that may accomplish our task. In many situations, however, we may want to browse through an entire category of functions to see what is available. For this task, the **Or select a category** box is helpful.

FIGURE E.6   INSERT FUNCTION DIALOG BOX

It contains a drop-down list of several categories of functions provided by Excel. Figure E.6 shows that we selected the **Statistical** category. As a result, Excel's statistical functions appear in alphabetic order in the Select a function box. We see the AVEDEV function listed first, followed by the AVERAGE function, and so on.

The AVEDEV function is highlighted in Figure E.6, indicating it is the function currently selected. The proper syntax for the function and a brief description of the function appear below the Select a function box. We can scroll through the list in the Select a function box to display the syntax and a brief description for each of the statistical functions that are available. For instance, scrolling down farther, we select the COUNTIF function as shown in Figure E.7. Note that COUNTIF is now highlighted, and that immediately below the Select a function box we see **COUNTIF(range,criteria)**, which indicates that the COUNTIF function contains two inputs, range and criteria. In addition, we see that the description of the COUNTIF function is "Counts the number of cells within a range that meet the given condition."

If the function selected (highlighted) is the one we want to use, we click **OK**; the **Function Arguments** dialog box then appears. The Function Arguments dialog box for the COUNTIF function is shown in Figure E.8. This dialog box assists in creating the appropriate arguments (inputs) for the function selected. When finished entering the arguments, we click OK; Excel then inserts the function into a worksheet cell.

Using Excel Add-Ins

Excel's Data Analysis Add-In

Excel's Data Analysis add-in, included with the basic Excel package, is a valuable tool for conducting statistical analysis. Before you can use the Data Analysis add-in it must be installed. To see if the Data Analysis add-in has already been installed, click the DATA tab on the Ribbon. In the Analysis group you should see the Data Analysis command. If you

FIGURE E.7   DESCRIPTION OF THE COUNTIF FUNCTION IN THE INSERT FUNCTION
DIALOG BOX

do not have an Analysis group and/or the Data Analysis command does not appear in the Analysis group, you will need to install the Data Analysis add-in. The steps needed to install the Data Analysis add-in are as follows:

Step 1. Click the **FILE** tab
Step 2. Click **Options**
Step 3. When the Excel Options dialog box appears:
Select **Add-Ins** from the list of options (on the pane on the left)
In the **Manage** box, select **Excel Add-Ins**
Click **Go**
Step 4. When the Add-Ins dialog box appears:
Select **Analysis ToolPak**
Click **OK**

FIGURE E.8   FUNCTION ARGUMENTS DIALOG BOX FOR THE COUNTIF FUNCTION

Here we describe how Minitab and Excel can be used to compute *p*-values for the z, t, χ^2, and F statistics that are used in hypothesis tests. As discussed in the text, only approximate *p*-values for the t, χ^2, and F statistics can be obtained by using tables. This appendix is helpful to a person who has computed the test statistic by hand, or by other means, and wishes to use computer software to compute the exact *p*-value.

Using Minitab

Minitab can be used to provide the cumulative probability associated with the z, t, χ^2, and F test statistics. So the lower tail *p*-value is obtained directly. The upper tail *p*-value is computed by subtracting the lower tail *p*-value from 1. The two-tailed *p*-value is obtained by doubling the smaller of the lower and upper tail *p*-values.

The z test statistic We use the Hilltop Coffee lower tail hypothesis test in Section 9.3 as an illustration; the value of the test statistic is $z = -2.67$. The Minitab steps used to compute the cumulative probability corresponding to $z = -2.67$ follow.

> **Step 1.** Select the **Calc** menu
> **Step 2.** Choose **Probability Distributions**
> **Step 3.** Choose **Normal**
> **Step 4.** When the Normal Distribution dialog box appears:
> > Select **Cumulative probability**
> > Enter 0 in the **Mean** box
> > Enter 1 in the **Standard deviation** box
> > Select **Input Constant**
> > Enter -2.67 in the **Input Constant** box
> > Click **OK**

Minitab provides the cumulative probability of .0037926. This cumulative probability is the lower tail *p*-value used for the Hilltop Coffee hypothesis test.

For an upper tail test, the *p*-value is computed from the cumulative probability provided by Minitab as follows:

$$p\text{-value} = 1 - \text{cumulative probability}$$

For instance, the upper tail *p*-value corresponding to a test statistic of $z = -2.67$ is $1 - .0037926 = .996207$. The two-tailed *p*-value corresponding to a test statistic of $z = -2.67$ is 2 times the minimum of the upper and lower tail *p*-values; that is, the two-tailed *p*-value corresponding to $z = -2.67$ is $2(.0037926) = .007585$.

The t test statistic We use the Heathrow Airport example from Section 9.4 as an illustration; the value of the test statistic is $t = 1.84$ with 59 degrees of freedom. The Minitab steps used to compute the cumulative probability corresponding to $t = 1.84$ follow.

> **Step 1.** Select the **Calc** menu
> **Step 2.** Choose **Probability Distributions**

Step 3. Choose **t**
Step 4. When the t Distribution dialog box appears:
> Select **Cumulative probability**
> Enter 59 in the **Degrees of freedom** box
> Select **Input Constant**
> Enter 1.84 in the **Input Constant** box
> Click **OK**

Minitab provides a cumulative probability of .9646, and hence the lower tail *p*-value = .9646. The Heathrow Airport example is an upper tail test; the upper tail *p*-value is 1 − .9646 = .0354. In the case of a two-tailed test, we would use the minimum of .9646 and .0354 to compute *p*-value = 2(.0354) = .0708.

The χ^2 test statistic We use the St. Louis Metro Bus example from Section 11.1 as an illustration; the value of the test statistic is $\chi^2 = 28.18$ with 23 degrees of freedom. The Minitab steps used to compute the cumulative probability corresponding to $\chi^2 = 28.18$ follow.

Step 1. Select the **Calc** menu
Step 2. Choose **Probability Distributions**
Step 3. Choose **Chi-Square**
Step 4. When the Chi-Square Distribution dialog box appears:
> Select **Cumulative probability**
> Enter 23 in the **Degrees of freedom** box
> Select **Input Constant**
> Enter 28.18 in the **Input Constant** box
> Click **OK**

Minitab provides a cumulative probability of .790949, which is the lower tail *p*-value. The upper tail *p*-value = 1 − the cumulative probability, or 1 − .790949 = .209051. The two-tailed *p*-value is 2 times the minimum of the lower and upper tail *p*-values. Thus, the two-tailed *p*-value is 2(.209051) = .418102. The St. Louis Metro Bus example involved an upper tail test, so we use *p*-value = .209051.

The F test statistic We use the Dullus County Schools example from Section 11.2 as an illustration; the test statistic is $F = 2.40$ with 25 numerator degrees of freedom and 15 denominator degrees of freedom. The Minitab steps to compute the cumulative probability corresponding to $F = 2.40$ follow.

Step 1. Select the **Calc** menu
Step 2. Choose **Probability Distributions**
Step 3. Choose **F**
Step 4. When the F Distribution dialog box appears:
> Select **Cumulative probability**
> Enter 25 in the **Numerator degrees of freedom** box
> Enter 15 in the **Denominator degrees of freedom** box
> Select **Input Constant**
> Enter 2.40 in the **Input Constant** box
> Click **OK**

Minitab provides the cumulative probability and hence a lower tail *p*-value = .959401. The upper tail *p*-value is 1 − .959401 = .040599. Because the Dullus County Schools example is a two-tailed test, the minimum of .959401 and .040599 is used to compute *p*-value = 2(.040599) = .0811198.

Using Excel

DATA *file*

p-Value

Excel functions and formulas can be used to compute p-values associated with the z, t, χ^2, and F test statistics. We provide a template in the data file entitled p-Value for use in computing these p-values. Using the template, it is only necessary to enter the value of the test statistic and, if necessary, the appropriate degrees of freedom. Refer to Figure F.1 as we describe how the template is used. For users interested in the Excel functions and formulas being used, just click on the appropriate cell in the template.

The z test statistic We use the Hilltop Coffee lower tail hypothesis test in Section 9.3 as an illustration; the value of the test statistic is $z = -2.67$. To use the p-value template for this hypothesis test, simply enter -2.67 into cell B6 (see Figure F.1). After doing so, p-values for all three types of hypothesis tests will appear. For Hilltop Coffee, we would use the lower tail p-value $= .0038$ in cell B9. For an upper tail test, we would use the p-value in cell B10, and for a two-tailed test we would use the p-value in cell B11.

The t test statistic We use the Heathrow Airport example from Section 9.4 as an illustration; the value of the test statistic is $t = 1.84$ with 59 degrees of freedom. To use the p-value template for this hypothesis test, enter 1.84 into cell E6 and enter 59 into cell E7 (see Figure F.1). After doing so, p-values for all three types of hypothesis tests will appear.

FIGURE F.1   EXCEL WORKSHEET FOR COMPUTING p-VALUES

	A	B	C	D	E	F
1	**Computing p-Values**					
2						
3						
4	**Using the Test Statistic z**			**Using the Test Statistic t**		
5						
6	**Enter z -->**	-2.67		**Enter t -->**	1.84	
7				**df -->**	59	
8						
9	**p-value (Lower Tail)**	0.0038		**p-value (Lower Tail)**	0.9646	
10	**p-value (Upper Tail)**	0.9962		**p-value (Upper Tail)**	0.0354	
11	**p-value (Two Tail)**	0.0076		**p-value (Two Tail)**	0.0708	
12						
13						
14						
15						
16	**Using the Test Statistic Chi Square**			**Using the Test Statistic F**		
17						
18	**Enter Chi Square -->**	28.18		**Enter F -->**	2.40	
19	**df -->**	23		**Numerator df-->**	25	
20				**Denominator df -->**	15	
21						
22	**p-value (Lower Tail)**	0.7909		**p-value (Lower Tail)**	0.9594	
23	**p-value (Upper Tail)**	0.2091		**p-value (Upper Tail)**	0.0406	
24	**p-value (Two Tail)**	0.4181		**p-value (Two Tail)**	0.0812	
25						

The Heathrow Airport example involves an upper tail test, so we would use the upper tail *p*-value = .0354 provided in cell E10 for the hypothesis test.

The χ^2 test statistic We use the St. Louis Metro Bus example from Section 11.1 as an illustration; the value of the test statistic is $\chi^2 = 28.18$ with 23 degrees of freedom. To use the *p*-value template for this hypothesis test, enter 28.18 into cell B18 and enter 23 into cell B19 (see Figure F.1). After doing so, *p*-values for all three types of hypothesis tests will appear. The St. Louis Metro Bus example involves an upper tail test, so we would use the upper tail *p*-value = .2091 provided in cell B23 for the hypothesis test.

The F test statistic We use the Dullus County Schools example from Section 11.2 as an illustration; the test statistic is $F = 2.40$ with 25 numerator degrees of freedom and 15 denominator degrees of freedom. To use the *p*-value template for this hypothesis test, enter 2.40 into cell E18, enter 25 into cell E19, and enter 15 into cell E20 (see Figure F.1). After doing so, *p*-values for all three types of hypothesis tests will appear. The Dullus County Schools example involves a two-tailed test, so we would use the two-tailed *p*-value = .0812 provided in cell E24 for the hypothesis test.

Statistics for Business and Economics 13e DATAfiles

Chapter 1

Nations	Table 1.1
Norris	Table 1.5
Shadow02	Exercise 25

Chapter 2

2011Movies	Case Problem 2
2012Names	Exercise 5
2012Networks	Exercise 6
2012Population	Exercise 46
AirSurvey	Exercise 7
ApTest	Table 2.8
Audit	Table 2.4
BaseballHall	Exercise 8
BBB	Exercise 48
BestPayingDegrees	Exercise 25
BrandValue	Exercises 32, 33, & 34
CEOTime	Exercise 20
Colleges	Exercises 53, 54, 55, & 56
Crosstab	Exercise 27
Crosstab2	Exercise 28
DJIABeta	Exercise 49
EngineeringSalary	Exercise 24
FortuneBest100	Exercise 52
Franchise	Exercise 22
Frequency	Exercise 11
FuelData2012	Exercise 35
HotelRatings	Exercise 10
Hypertension	Exercise 41
LargeCorp	Exercise 21
Majors	Exercise 9
ManagerTime	Exercise 43
Marathon	Exercise 26
MarketIndexes	Exercise 23
MedianHousehold	Exercise 45
MPG	Exercise 39
NBAPlayerPts	Exercise 18
NewSAT	Exercise 44
PelicanStores	Case Problem 1
Ports	Exercise 19
QueenCity	Case 3
Restaurant	Table 2.9
Scatter	Exercise 36
SmartPhones	Exercise 42
Snow	Exercise 40
SoftDrink	Table 2.1
StartUps	Exercise 47
Stereo	Table 2.14
Syndicated	Exercise 4
Zoo	Exercise 58

Chapter 3

2011Movies	Case Problem 2
2012MajorSalary	Figure 3.8
2012Start Salary	Table 3.1
AdmiredCompanies	Exercise 53
Advertising	Exercise 32
AdvertisingSpend	Exercise 9
AfricanElephants	Case Problem 5
Asian	Case Problem 3
AustralianOpen	Exercise 28
BestPrivateColleges	Exercise 61
BigBangTheory	Exercise 12
BorderCrossings	Exercise 54

BowlGames	Exercise 57
CellService	Exercise 52
Coaches	Exercise 63
Coffee	Exercise 31
CommuteTime	Exercise 7
Flights	Exercise 27
FoodIndustry	Exercise 69
JacketRatings	Exercise 10
NCAA	Exercise 44
NFLTeamValue	Exercise 71
PanamaRailroad	Exercise 75
PelicanStores	Case Problem 1
Runners	Exercise 50
Russell	Exercise 60
SFGasPrices	Exercise 26
Shoppers	Case Problem 4
Sleep	Exercise 65
Smartphone	Exercise 66
SmokeDetectors	Exercise 59
SpringTraining	Exercise 72
StateUnemp	Exercise 14
Stereo	Table 3.6
Travel	Exercise 70
WaitTracking	Exercise 64

Chapter 4

Judge	Case Problem

Chapter 5

Coldstream12	Exercise 17

Chapter 7

EAI	Section 7.1
MetAreas	Appendix 7.2
Morningstar	Exercise 14
ShadowStocks	Exercise 42

Chapter 8

Auto	Case Problem 3
AutoInsurance	Exercise 20
CasualDining	Exercise 38
ChildOutlook	Exercise 37
CorporateBonds	Exercise 16
DrugCost	Exercise 48
Guardians	Exercise 22
GulfProp	Case Problem 2
HongKongMeals	Exercise 19
Houston	Exercise 5
Interval p	Appendix 8.2
JobSearch	Exercise 18
Lloyd's	Section 8.1
Miami	Exercise 17
NewBalance	Table 8.3
Professional	Case Problem 1
Russia	Exercise 47
Scheer	Table 8.4
Setters	Exercise 7
Standing	Exercise 49
TeeTimes	Section 8.4
TeleHealth	Exercise 21
TobaccoFires	Exercise 9
TravelTax	Exercise 6

Chapter 9

Administrator	Exercise 29
AirRating	Section 9.4

Bayview	Case Problem 2
BritainMarriages	Exercise 64
ChildCare	Exercise 30
Coffee	Section 9.3
Eagle	Exercise 43
Fowle	Exercise 21
GolfTest	Section 9.3
HomeState	Exercise 39
Hyp Sigma Known	Appendix 9.2
Hyp Sigma Unknown	Appendix 9.2
Hypothesis p	Appendix 9.2
LawSuit	Exercise 44
Orders	Section 9.4
Quality	Case Problem 1
UsedCars	Exercise 32
WeeklyPay	Exercise 65
WomenGolf	Section 9.5

Chapter 10

AirDelay	Exercise 18
BusinessTravel	Exercise 24
CheckAcct	Section 10.2
CollegeCosts	Exercise 13
ExamScores	Section 10.1
Golf	Case Problem
GolfScores	Exercise 26
HomePrices	Exercise 39
Hotel	Exercise 6
Matched	Table 10.2
Mutual	Exercise 40
Occupancy	Exercise 46
SATMath	Exercise 16
SoftwareTest	Table 10.1
StockPrices	Exercise 22
TaxPrep	Section 10.4
TestScores	Exercise 25
Twins	Exercise 42

Chapter 11

Bags	Exercise 19
BatteryTime	Exercise 21
BusTimes	Section 11.1
Costco	Exercise 10
Halloween	Exercise 6
PriceChange	Exercise 8
SchoolBus	Section 11.2
Training	Case Problem
Travel	Exercise 25
Yields	Exercise 11

Chapter 12

Ambulance	Exercise 32
AutoLoyalty	Table 12.1
AutoQuality	Exercise 14
BeerPreference	Table 12.6
Chemline	Table 12.10
ChiSquare	Appendix 12.2
Demand	Exercise 26
Grades	Exercise 34
M&M	Exercise 22
NYReform	Case Problem
WorkforcePlan	Exercise 12